Residential Building Systems

Portland Community College - Architectural Design & Drafting

Alan Jefferis / Janice Jefferis

CENGAGE
Learning·

Australia • Brazil • Japan • Korea • Mexico • Singapore • Spain • United Kingdom • United States

CENGAGE
Learning

Residential Building Systems
Portland Community College - Architectural
Design & Drafting

Residential- Design, Drafting, and Detailing, Second Edition
Jefferis / Jefferis
© 2014 Cengage Learning. All rights reserved.

Senior Project Development Manager:
Linda deStefano

Market Development Manager:
Heather Kramer

Senior Production/Manufacturing Manager:
Donna M. Brown

Production Editorial Manager:
Kim Fry

Sr. Rights Acquisition Account Manager:
Todd Osborne

This book contains select works from existing Cengage Learning resources and was produced by Cengage Learning Custom Solutions for collegiate use. As such, those adopting and/or contributing to this work are responsible for editorial content accuracy, continuity and completeness.

Compilation © 2013 Cengage Learning
ISBN-13: 978-1-305-00271-5

ISBN-10: 1-305-00271-7

Cengage Learning
5191 Natorp Boulevard
Mason, Ohio 45040
USA

Cengage Learning is a leading provider of customized learning solutions with office locations around the globe, including Singapore, the United Kingdom, Australia, Mexico, Brazil, and Japan. Locate your local office at:
international.cengage.com/region.

Cengage Learning products are represented in Canada by Nelson Education, Ltd.
For your lifelong learning solutions, visit **www.cengage.com/custom.**
Visit our corporate website at **www.cengage.com.**

Printed in the United States of America

Custom Contents

(* Note – this is a "custom" textbook that has been designed specifically for this course in a joint effort between you instructor and the publisher. Please note that some chapters have been removed intentionally.)

Chapter 5
Guidelines and Codes That Affect Design

Architects and designers must deal with a multitude of guidelines and required codes that affect home design. Guidelines traditionally have come from homeowners' associations, but many designers and builders are now attempting to follow green building guidelines established by the LEED **(Leadership in Energy and Environmental Design)** or the National Green Building Standard (NGBS) provided by the National Association of Home Builders (NAHB). For most municipalities, these guidelines are just that, but some areas have adopted the core of these guidelines into law. Building codes are laws intended to protect the public by establishing minimum standards of safety for the design and construction of most types of buildings. Although landowners in some municipalities assume they can build whatever they want because they own the property, building codes are intended to protect everyone, including neighbors, visitors, and potential future owners.

Consider the stories you have seen in the national news media about structures that have been damaged by high winds, raging floodwaters, hurricanes, tornadoes, mudslides, earthquakes, and fire. Although they do not make the national news, hundreds of other structures become uninhabitable due to inadequate foundation design, failed members from poor design, mold, rot, or termite infestation. Building codes are designed to protect consumers by providing minimum guidelines for construction and inspection of a structure to prevent fire, structural collapse, and general deterioration. Many other aspects of building construction, such as electrical wiring, heating equipment, and sanitary facilities, represent potential hazards to occupants if not designed and constructed or installed properly. Building codes are enforced as a safeguard against these risks.

In addition to the LEED guidelines, the 2012 family of codes published by the **International Code Council** (ICC) now includes the International Green Construction Code™ (IgCC™).

Key Terms

Accessible route	Fenestration	Handrail	LEED
Basic wind speed	Ground snow load	Insulation	Mass walls
Egress	Guardrail	International Green Construction Code	Nonhabitable
Exterior envelope	Habitable		

R-value	Solar heat gain coefficient	Water closet	Window well
Seismic design zone		Weathering	Winter design temperature
Solar heat gain	Thermal resistance	Wet-bulb temperature	

CAD Commands and Tools

This chapter does not introduce any new CAD commands. Check with your local building department about the availability of electronic copies of governing codes and ordinances that will affect your projects.

NOTE:

Beginning in the spring of 2012, many municipalities have moved from green guidelines to green codes. Before you begin any design project, it is imperative that you verify which city, county, state, and federal regulations control the project, and what codes will govern your project. Although the ICC has published the 2012 family of codes, the governing bodies that will oversee your project may be working with an older edition of the code. Another common alternative is a state adoption of a modified code based on the ICC codes.

NOTE:

Although both LEED and NGBS have produced "guidelines," many municipalities are moving beyond the recommendation stage and are incorporating portions of these guidelines into their own design and building requirements. The International Green Construction Code (IgCC) is a new edition to the 2012 ICC codes, and moves guidelines to law. Currently the IgCC applies to all types of structures EXCEPT those covered by the International Residential Code (IRC). Check with the municipality that will govern each specific building project to determine if compliance with specific aspects of the IgBC is required.

GREEN BUILDING GUIDELINES

Green building incorporates environmental considerations and resources into every step of the construction process. A green or environmentally friendly building is a structure that is designed, built, operated, renovated, and recycled in an ecological and resource-efficient manner. Green buildings similar to the home in Figure 5.1 are designed to meet objectives such as protecting the health of the occupants; using energy, water, and other resources more efficiently; and reducing the overall impact to the environment. The biggest leaders in residential green building are LEED and the NGBS-ICC 700™-2008 (National Green Building Standards).

LEED Green Building Guidelines

The **U.S. Green Building Council (USGBC)** developed the Leadership in Energy and Environmental Design (*LEED*) rating system to help improve the quality of buildings and to minimize the impact of these buildings on the environment. The rating system is intended to blend the structure with the environment, reduce operating costs, and aid in marketing the structure for resale. LEED certification for green buildings requires that the project

meet the fundamentals of green construction established by the USGBC, and score a minimum number of points in a LEED rating system. LEED acknowledges four levels of certification, including:

- Certified: 26–32 points.
- Silver: 33–38 points.
- Gold: 39–51 points.
- Platinum: 52 points or more.

Key areas of the construction process covered by the LEED rating system include: Integrative process, location and transportation, sustainable sites, water efficiency, energy

NOTE:

Key portions of each section of the construction process that the LEED rating system covers appear below. Be sure to reference the complete standard at the USGBC website to find complete requirements to earn each credit.

FIGURE 5.1 An environmentally friendly home is designed to blend with its environment; protect the health of the occupants; use energy, water, and other resources efficiently; and reduce the overall impact to the environment. This sunroom provides a comfortable living area while serving as a passive solar collector.

and atmosphere, materials and resources, indoor environmental quality, performance, innovation, and regional priority.

Integrative Process

This portion of the LEED rating system aims to maximize opportunities for cost-effective adoption of green design and construction strategies. One point is awarded for conducting a preliminary LEED for Homes meeting early in the design process with key members of the verification and project team. Key goals of this meeting include an action plan that identifies:

- Targeted LEED award level (Certified, Silver, Gold, or Platinum) to be obtained.
- The LEED credits selected to meet targeted award levels.
- The party accountable for meeting the LEED requirements for each selected credit.

Additional points are earned by conducting a minimum of eight hours of training meetings prior to construction that include key members of the design team, the general contractor, and representatives of framing, plumbing, HVAC, insulation, and air sealing crews. Meetings focus on the green aspects of the project, each LEED prerequisite, and the expectations for ensuring certification.

Location and Transportation

The goal of this portion of the rating system is to reduce the environmental impact of land development practices by building homes in LEED certified developments. Up to 15 points are awarded for things that are done and not

done at the construction site. On the positive side, points are awarded to encourage development within existing cities and suburbs, to reduce adverse environmental effects associated with urban sprawl, by design features such as:

- Selecting a lot where at least 75 percent of the perimeter immediately borders previously developed land.
- Selecting a lot where at least 75 percent of the total buildable land is previously developed.
- Locating the project on a site, part or all of which was documented as contaminated but has been certified to be a clean site, free of contamination, by the controlling public authority and approved as effective, safe, and appropriate for the future use of the site.
- Using compact development patterns to conserve land and promote community livability, transportation efficiency, and pedestrian traffic.

Figure 5.2 is an example of how creative design can be used to incorporate dynamic homes in a small site in

FIGURE 5.2 LEED credits can be awarded for reducing the environmental impact of land development by building within existing cities to reduce adverse environmental effects associated with sprawl. This creative design incorporates a dynamic home in a small site in a developed neighborhood.

a developed neighborhood. Points are also awarded for things not done at a job site, such as:

- Not developing buildings, roads, or parking areas on portions of sites where the elevation is at or below the 100-year flood elevation as defined by the **Federal Emergency Management Agency (FEMA)**.

- Not building on land that prior, to acquisition for the project was public parkland, unless land of equal or greater value as parkland is accepted in trade by the public landowner.

- Not building on land within 50 feet of any wetlands as defined by the U.S. Code of Federal Regulations.

- Not building on previously undeveloped land that is within 100 feet of a river, lake, or ocean.

FIGURE 5.3 LEED credits can be awarded for designs that incorporate planting that will provide shade to hardscape areas to reduce heat islands.

Sustainable Sites

This area of the credits is applied to efficient design and construction as it relates to the construction site in order to reduce pollution from construction activities by controlling soil erosion, waterway sedimentation, and airborne dust generation. A total of eight points can be awarded for:

- A design that includes appropriate erosion control measures prior to construction, and the implementation of these measures during construction.

- Designing landscapes to avoid invasive species.

- Conserving existing natural areas and restoring damaged areas to provide habitat and promote biodiversity.

- Reducing heat islands to minimize impacts on microclimates and human and wildlife habitats. This can be done by ensuring that at least 50 percent of sidewalks, patios, driveways, and roofs on the site receive shade from trees or from installing light-colored, vegetation covered hardscapes.

- Designs that restore or maintain the natural hydrology and water balance of the site based on historical conditions and undeveloped ecosystems in the region.

- Design of home features to minimize the need for poisons for control of insects, rodents, and other pests.

Figure 5.3 shows a home that qualifies for LEED sustainable site credits. Section 2 of this text will further explore environmental considerations of site design.

Water Efficiency

Credits for water efficiency relate to the reduction of water usage in the structure and at the building site through the use of high-efficiency fixtures and efficient landscaping practices. Four of the twelve available credits for this

section must be earned. Chapter 14 explores the use of water in a residence. LEED credits for water efficiency include:

- Installing water-efficient landscaping.

- Using innovative wastewater technologies that reduce total indoor and outdoor water consumption by at least 15 percent over standard practices.

- Maintaining water pressure in the building at less than 60 psi with no detectable water leaks.

- Using plumbing fixtures that meet specific flow levels or a design that shows a total calculated water use reduction of up to at least five gallons per day relative to the baseline for all indoor water fixtures and fittings.

Energy and Atmosphere

This section of the LEED standard is intended to improve the overall energy performance of a home and to lower the building's greenhouse gas emissions. Twenty-nine credits are available related to the use of energy to control the atmosphere within a residence. Chapters 8 and 15 address this area of home design. Credits for energy and atmosphere are awarded for:

- Reducing energy consumption associated with the domestic hot water system by designing and installing an energy-efficient hot water distribution system or by providing a central manifold distribution system.

- Reducing energy consumption and greenhouse gas emissions by designing the structure to maximize opportunities for solar design.

- Reducing energy consumption by ensuring that the heating and cooling systems are operating at peak efficiency by having a qualified third party commission all heating, cooling, and heat or energy recovery ventilation equipment, and certifying their compliance.

- Minimizing energy consumption caused by uncontrolled air leakage into and out of conditioned spaces.

- Designing and installing insulation to minimize heat transfer and thermal bridging by installing insulation that exceeds the R-value requirements listed in Chapter 4 of the 2012 International Energy Conservation Code or local code, whichever is more stringent.

- Maximizing the energy performance of windows by specifying windows, skylights, and glass doors that have **National Fenestration Rating Council® (NFRC®)** ratings that exceed the window requirements in the ENERGY STAR for Homes National Builder Option Package.

- Designing and installing HVAC equipment that is substantially better than the equipment required by the ENERGY STAR v3 Prescriptive Pathway.

- Installing ENERGY STAR qualified water heaters, or a solar water heater that meets at least 40 percent of the annual domestic hot water (DHW) load in combination with an ENERGY STAR qualified water heater.

- Reducing energy consumption associated with interior and exterior lighting by installing LEDs in at least 80 percent of high-use rooms including the kitchen, dining room, living room, family room, and hallways.

- Installing appliances that meet the applicable ENERGY STAR requirement.

- Reducing consumption of nonrenewable energy sources by encouraging the installation and operation of renewable electric generation systems.

Materials and Resources

Eleven credits are available that are related to the materials and products used to build and sustain a structure. Ten percent of the available credits must be earned. Sections 4, 5, 6, 7, and 8 address these areas of home design. LEED credits are awarded for homes that:

- Promote durability and high performance of the building enclosure and its components and systems through appropriate design, materials selection, and construction practices similar to those shown in Figure 5.4.

- Use only **Forest Stewardship Council® (FSC®)** certified tropical wood products if tropical wood is specified.

- Optimize the use of framing materials by using advanced framing techniques (AFT) for 90 percent of each component.

- Increase demand for products or building components that minimize material consumption through recycled and recyclable content, reclamation, or overall reduced life-cycle impacts.

- Reduce or divert waste generated from new construction activities from landfills and incinerators to a level below the industry norm.

- Reduce the materials needed for, and waste produced from future maintenance, repair, renovation, and rehabilitation through structural, mechanical, and user-induced design.

Indoor Environmental Quality

Fifteen credits are available related to the interior air quality of the structure. Twenty percent of the credits in this section must be earned. Chapter 8 and Chapter 15 address these areas of home design. LEED credits for indoor environmental quality include:

- Reducing moisture and exposure to indoor pollutants from kitchens and bathrooms and other sources by exhausting pollutants to the outside and ventilating with outdoor air.

- Reducing occupant exposure to indoor pollutants originating from an adjacent garage.

- Reducing moisture and exposure to indoor pollutants from kitchens and bathrooms and other sources by exhausting pollutants to the outside and ventilating with outdoor air.

Courtesy Reward Wall Systems®

FIGURE 5.4 LEED credits in the Materials and Resources category can be awarded for designs that promote durability and high performance of the building enclosure.

- Reducing occupant exposure to radon gas and other soil gas contaminants.
- Reducing particulate matter from the air supply system.
- Reducing occupants' exposure to indoor airborne contaminants through source control and removal.
- Reducing occupant exposure to chemical contaminants in air through product selection.
- Preventing or minimizing exposure of building occupants, indoor surfaces, and ventilation air distribution systems to tobacco smoke.
- Providing appropriate distribution of space heating and cooling in the home to improve thermal comfort and energy performance.
- Controlling indoor moisture levels to provide comfort, reduce the risk of mold, and increase the durability of the home.
- Providing acoustic comfort by minimizing intruding noise into and within buildings.
- Minimizing the leakage of combustion gases into the occupied space of the home.

Performance

The goal of this section is to provide monitoring and reconciliation of energy and water use at the whole building level and provide for the ongoing accountability of building utility consumption over time. Two LEED credits for indoor environmental quality are available and include:

- Maintaining the performance of the home by educating the occupants about the operations and maintenance of the home's LEED features and equipment.
- Providing advanced monitoring and reconciliation of energy and water use at the whole building and end-use levels.
- Providing for the ongoing accountability of building utility consumption over time.

Innovation

Six credits are available that are related to providing projects the opportunity to achieve exceptional performance above the requirements set by the LEED Green Building Rating System. Points can also be achieved for innovative performance in categories not specifically addressed by the LEED Green Building Rating System. Section 1 addresses these areas of home design. LEED credits for innovation and design include:

- Achieving significant, measurable environmental performance using a strategy not addressed in the LEED Green Building Rating System.

Regional Priorities

Four credits are available to provide an incentive for the achievement of credits that address geographically specific environmental, social equity, and public health priorities. USGBC regional councils identify credits that have regional importance for the project. A database of Regional Priority credits and their geographic applicability is available on the USGBC website. One credit is awarded for each Regional Priority credit achieved up to a maximum of four credits.

National Green Building Code Standard

In collaboration with the NAHB, the ICC has developed the National Green Building Standard ICC 700-2008. The guidelines allow the designer to use a whole-house systems approach throughout the design process to increase the home's performance and efficiency. Seven key sections are included in the NGBS-ICC 700 guidelines: site design and development; lot design, preparation, and development; resource efficiency; energy efficiency; water efficiency; indoor environmental quality; and operation, maintenance, and building owner education.

Site Design and Development

This area of the guidelines describes considerations for resource efficient site design and development practices for improving the energy efficiency of a structure. Section 2 of this textbook will further explore environmental considerations of site design.

Site Design, Preparation, and Development

This area of the standards describes considerations for site selection, site design, and site construction, as well as innovative practices that can be incorporated in the design of the driveway and parking areas, and heat island mitigation. Section 2 of this text further explores environmental considerations of lot design.

Resource Efficiency

Creating resource efficiency includes the consideration of materials for building and furnishing the home to maximize the function and optimize the use of natural resources. Areas covered include quality of construction materials and waste, enhanced durability and reduced maintenance, reduced and salvaged materials, recycled-content building materials, recycled construction waste, renewable materials, resource-efficient materials, indigenous materials, life-cycle analysis, and innovative practices. Sections 4, 5, 6, 7, and 8 of this text further address the use of energy-efficient materials like those shown in Figure 5.5 for residential projects.

Courtesy PolySteel® Insulating Concrete Forms

FIGURE 5.5 The use of energy-efficient materials such as insulated concrete forms, structurally insulated panels (SIPs), and engineered products can increase the energy efficiency of a home.

Energy Efficiency

This area of the standard describes considerations for helping the residents of the home reduce their dependence on fossil-fuel energy sources. Attention is given to the operation of the home, throughout the construction of the home, and for the materials that are used to construct the home. Major elements of the standard include minimum energy efficiency requirements, performance path, prescriptive path, additional practices, and innovative practices. Sections 3, 4, 5, 6, 7, and 8 of this text will further address the use of energy-efficient materials.

Water Efficiency

This portion of the standard is aimed at reducing water consumption both inside and outside the home as well as the incorporation of innovative practices. The plumbing products and appliances that are specified can help reduce water use inside the home. The selection of native and drought-resistant landscaping, the collection of rainwater for irrigation, as well as the reuse of gray water from the house can reduce or eliminate water use outside the home. Chapter 14 of this text will explore the use of water in a residence.

Indoor Environmental Quality

According to NAHB research, the indoor air quality of a home is often the number one green consideration of homebuyers. Inside air quality is affected by the mechanical equipment used to heat and cool the home and by the materials used to construct and furnish it. The NGBS-ICC 700 awards points for the categories of pollutant source control, pollutant control, moisture management, and innovative practices. Chapters 8 and 15 of this text address these areas of home design.

Operation, Maintenance, and Building Owner Education

Designing or building an energy-efficient home is futile if you can't convince the homeowner to invest in it, or to maintain key features of the home once it is constructed. This credit is earned by providing the building owners with the operation and maintenance manuals to operate their homes properly.

Levels of Certification

Similar to the LEED system that allows credits to be accumulated based on the areas of the guidelines that are used, the NGBS-ICC 700 provides for four levels of performance to be achieved, based on how green building categories are incorporated into the plan. The basic level of achievement is the Bronze level. A Bronze designation indicates that the home features items that demonstrate that the design pays attention to a project's environmental impact. The Silver, Gold, and Emerald levels of certification include additional criteria that place increasingly greater emphasis on green practices.

NATIONAL BUILDING CODES

The LEED standards and National Green Building Standards are guidelines for energy-efficient construction. The building codes adopted by each municipality provide mandatory requirements for construction. The regulation of buildings can be traced through recorded history for more than 4000 years. In early America, George Washington and Thomas Jefferson encouraged building regulations as minimum standards for health and safety. Building codes are now used throughout most of the United States to regulate issues related to fire, structural ability, health, security, and energy conservation. Architects, engineers, interior designers, and contractors also rely on building codes to help regulate the use of new materials and technology.

Model Code Organizations oversee accredited laboratories and testing facilities to develop safe, cost-effective, timely construction methods. In addition to the testing facilities of each major code, several major material suppliers have their own testing facilities. A list of websites for several major testing labs, quality assurance, and inspection agencies is available at the end of this chapter in the Additional Resources section.

Although most areas of the country understand the benefits of regulating construction, and each city, county, or state has the authority to adopt building codes in accordance with their state laws, some areas have not adopted codes. Figure 5.6 shows a home built in an area that had

Going Green

Passivhaus Standards

Environmentally friendly building methods had a resurgence in the United States during the gas crisis in the mid-seventies. Designers and contractors today use guidelines from groups such as ENERGY STAR and LEED standards to decrease the energy demands of a home. A newer standard that originated in Europe and is slowly making its way to the United States is called Passivhaus (Passive House). The term passive house (see Chapters 8 and 15) describes homes that reduce heating and cooling cost by non-mechanical means. Using the home orientation, glass placement, insulation, and storage mass, passive solar methods have been incorporated in homes for centuries. The energy-use standards of Passivhaus are more stringent than those of the U.S. Green Building Council that issues certifications for LEED, or the federal government's ENERGY STAR for Homes program. The Passivhaus Standard has a goal of using zero energy to maintain a comfortable interior climate without active heating and cooling systems. Developed by the Passive House Institute (Passivhaus Institut), this goal is achieved through a system of interior and exterior air exchange, an airtight building envelope, and energy-saving appliances.

Rather than having a heating or cooling system, houses designed to meet the Passive House Standard have a ventilation system called an energy recovery ventilator (ERV). The ventilator pulls inside air through a ventilator, transferring heat from the air and allowing cooled air to exit as exhaust. At the same time, fresh outside air is pulled in and is heated by the ERV using a principle referred to as counterflow. Triple-pane windows and two-foot thick walls create an airtight home to enhance the efficiency of the system. Although similar to a heat pump, by filtering the air, the ventilator offers an asset unavailable through traditional technology by keeping carbon dioxide levels low. Renewable sources generate any additional energy that is required. Although it's estimated that the Passivhaus standards add 10 to 15 percent to the cost of construction, the higher construction costs are offset by the resulting low energy costs from using less than a quarter of the energy of a traditionally powered home.

not adopted a building code and allowed the owners to build to their own standard. Many jurisdictions that have building codes adopt them with local amendments. As a result, even though the majority of the United States uses a base model building code developed by the ICC, users should be aware of local amendments to the basic code.

National Code Options

Most states have adopted the building codes published by the International Code Council (ICC), but a small number of jurisdictions are still using one of the legacy codes of the ICC. The current ICC codes are the 2012 editions that incorporate 30 percent more energy efficiency than the 2009 editions. The ICC legacy codes consist of:

- **Building Officials and Code Administrators International, Inc.** The 1999 BOCA National Building Code (NBC) was the last edition published.

- **Southern Building Code Congress International, Inc.** The 1999 SBC (Standard Building Code) was the last edition published.

- **International Conference of Building Officials.** The 1997 Uniform Building Code (UBC) was the last edition published.

Courtesy APA - The Engineered Wood Association®

FIGURE 5.6 Some areas of the country have not adopted a building code and allow owners to build to their own standard. Most wise homeowners understand the need for codes such as the I-codes to ensure a safe structure that will protect their family.

International Model Codes

In 1972, in order to serve designers better, BOCA, SBCCI, and ICBO joined forces to form the **Council of American Building Officials (CABO)** to create a national residential code. While some jurisdictions adopted the One- and Two-Family Dwelling Code®, most others chose to continue using the NBC, SBC, and UBC codes. In 1994, in another attempt to create a national code, the International Code Council (ICC) was formed. Its goal was to develop a single set of comprehensive, coordinated national codes that would eliminate disparities among the previous three major legacy codes. The ICC has published the 2012 editions of the International Building Code® (IBC®) and the International Residential Code (IRC). These codes are referred to as model codes. The IBC in general covers all buildings except detached single-family, two-family, and townhouses three stories or less in height. The IRC covers detached single-family, two-family, and townhouses that are three stories or less in height to ensure quality residential construction. Each of these codes combines certain features of the BOCA, NBC, SBC, and the UBC into one base code. Most municipalities now use these codes, or

> **NOTE:**
>
> *It is important to remember that each municipality and state has the right to adopt all, or a portion, of the indicated code. Although all of the legacy code organizations of BOCA, ICBO, and SBCCI have merged to form the ICC and the IRC (for residential construction) and 14 other codes (for other types of construction). The legacy codes, NBC, SBC, and UBC are still available and are in use in some municipalities.*

> **NOTE:**
>
> *Information in this text is based on the 2012 International Residential Code for One- and Two-Family Dwellings published by the ICC. Listings of metric sizes in this chapter are shown as hard metric conversions to be consistent with the IRC listings. Visit the International Code Council website to verify the release of the codes that govern your area. You will need to verify with your local building department to determine if the new edition has been adopted.*

their amended versions, to govern construction. The ICC also published the International Energy Conservation Code with portions that apply to both residential and commercial construction. Verify the building code that governs your area with your local building department prior to starting construction drawings.

In addition to these national codes, the **Department of Housing and Urban Development (HUD)**, the **Federal Housing Authority (FHA)**, and the Americans with Disabilities Act (ADA) each publish guidelines for minimum property standards for accessibility for the disabled. Some provisions may apply to certain residential construction.

Choosing the Right Code

The project manager is responsible for checking with the local jurisdictions to determine the codes that will be used during the design process and to ensure that the structure complies with all required codes. Although CAD technicians are not expected to make decisions regarding the codes as they affect the design, they are expected to know the content of the codes and how they affect construction.

Each of the major codes is divided into similar sections that specify regulations covering these areas:

- Fire and Life Safety
- Structural
- Mechanical
- Electrical
- Plumbing

The Fire and Life Safety and Structural codes have the largest effect on the design and construction of a residence. The effect of the codes on residential construction will be discussed throughout this textbook.

Basic Tools of the Model Codes

Building codes influence both the design and construction methods. Areas of the code such as climatic and geographical design criteria affect the materials used to resist forces such as wind, snow, and earthquakes. Chapter 23 covers these forces and how they affect a residence. The influence of codes on construction methods is covered later in this chapter and throughout Sections 3, 4, 6, 7, and 8 of this text. CAD technicians need to be familiar with several areas in order to meet minimum design standards, including basic design criteria. Keep in mind that the following discussion is only an introduction to building codes. As a professional CAD technician or designer, you will need to become familiar with, and constantly use, the building code that governs your area. It's also important as you start to explore building codes that you understand the common markings that are used to identify items in the text of the code including:

- Black text represents information that has not changed from the previous edition of the code.
- Black text with a bold vertical line in the margin beside the text represents information that is new or has been revised from the last edition.
- A bold black arrow placed in the margin between lines of text or between paragraphs represents where information has been deleted from the current code.

NOTE:

A key element to remember as you start exploring building codes is that this text is based on the International Residential Code. Many municipalities will take a base code such as the 2012 IRC, amend it to meet specific local issues, and then publish the state version of the code in the following year. Although the ICC is making efforts to include more options in the base codes, read the title of your code carefully to verify you're working with the correct code.

CLIMATE AND GEOGRAPHIC DESIGN CRITERIA

Chapter 3 of the model codes establishes the guidelines for determining the climatic and geographic factors that influence each construction site. Key values that must be determined based on Table R301.2(1) of the IRC to design a safe structure include:

- Air freezing index.
- Flood hazard.
- Ground snow load.
- Mean annual temperature.

- Ice barrier underlayment.
- Seismic design zone.
- Susceptibility to damage by frost line depth.
- Susceptibility to damage by termites.
- Susceptibility to damage by weathering.
- Wind design—speed.
- Wind design—topographic effects.
- Winter design—temperature.

Values for each category will consist of a YES, NO, or a design value. Information for many of these categories can be obtained from tables contained in the IRC. Other factors need to be determined from the website of the governing building department. Building codes specify how a building can be constructed to resist the forces from wind pressure, seismic activity, freezing, decay, and insects. Each of these areas will be discussed in detail in later chapters.

NOTE:

Because of wide variation in the weather patterns and the seismic risk across the country, most municipalities have altered the national code to address local considerations. A key role of the designer is to verify local requirements and ensure that projects exceed those standards. In exploring the variables, some can be taken directly from a table in the code or provided by the building department. Other factors require information from the local jurisdiction.

Ground Snow Load

The **ground snow load** factor will affect the sizes of structural materials and the plans for accessing the structure when the maximum amount of snow is on the ground. Maps provided by the IRC will aid in determining the ground snow load factor. Figure 5.7 shows the ground snow loads for the western portion of the United States. Zones of the map are designated by the maximum ground elevation of the zone, and the snow load to be used in the design for that area. For instance, in the southeastern corner of California, the maximum elevation is 1000', and the snow load is zero. In the southwestern corner of California, the maximum elevation ranges from 2000' to 1800', and the snow load ranges from five to zero. In the northeastern corner of Washington, the snow load is listed as CS, indicating the need to perform a site-specific case study. The local building department will be able to provide the snow loads that should be used to determine the sizes of building materials as well as the ground snow that should be planned

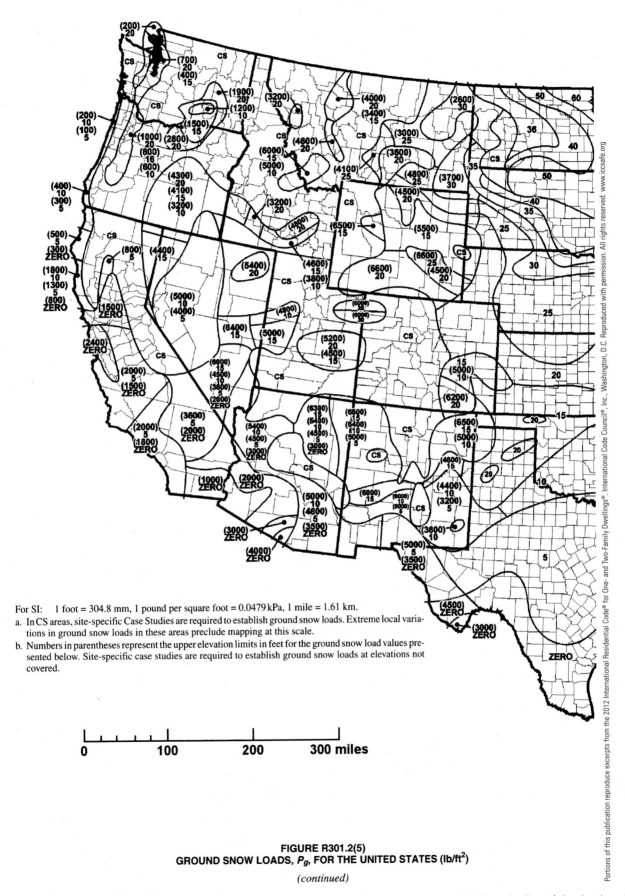

For SI: 1 foot = 304.8 mm, 1 pound per square foot = 0.0479 kPa, 1 mile = 1.61 km.

a. In CS areas, site-specific Case Studies are required to establish ground snow loads. Extreme local variations in ground snow loads in these areas preclude mapping at this scale.

b. Numbers in parentheses represent the upper elevation limits in feet for the ground snow load values presented below. Site-specific case studies are required to establish ground snow loads at elevations not covered.

FIGURE R301.2(5)
GROUND SNOW LOADS, P_g, FOR THE UNITED STATES (lb/ft^2)

(continued)

FIGURE 5.7 Maps similar to Figure R301.2.(5) can be used to determine the snow loads to be used in the selection of structural members.

for as access to the structure is planned. The IRC allows construction of buildings designed in areas with a snow load of 70 pounds per square foot (3.35 kPa) or less. In areas that exceed this, a licensed engineer using accepted engineering practice must determine this value.

Winter Design Temperature

The outdoor design temperature can be determined from Appendix D of the International Plumbing Code® (IPC®) or from the websites of the local jurisdiction. The *winter design temperature* is important as the heating loads of the home are considered; see Chapter 15.

Flood Hazard

It's not just homes and other structures that are built on a riverbank, oceanfront property, or the banks of a lake that must be designed to withstand floodwaters. The risk of flood damage will vary for each region based on several factors. In areas that are prone to hurricanes, low-lying land several miles from the shoreline can often be flooded by the storm surge. The amount of expected rain is also a major consideration in flood risk. Areas of the country such as the Pacific Northwest and the Gulf states that receive large amounts of rain typically have drainage systems to handle the runoff. Arid areas of the country often have poor facilities for coping with excess runoff. Designers should verify with local municipalities which specific areas of their jurisdiction are prone to flooding, and design the foundation accordingly. The building department can provide a date that the area was placed into the National Floor Insurance Program and the adoption of the code or ordinance of management of flood hazard area. This information helps in determining the design flood elevation height of the floor. Section 7 explores precautions for strengthening the foundation based on the risk of flooding.

Mean Annual Temperature

Based on the mean annual temperature from the **National Climate Data Center**, the governing jurisdiction will determine the mean annual temperature. This information will be used for planning the heating system as well as calculating the insulation requirements for the building envelope.

Ice Barrier Underlayment

The governing jurisdiction determines the value of the ice barrier underlayment based on local history of damage from the effects of ice damming. For areas that have a YES value, an ice barrier must be provided that meets the requirements of Section R905.2.7.1 of the IRC. These guidelines will be covered in Chapter 16 of this textbook as roof construction is explored.

Seismic Design Zone

The governing jurisdiction determines the *seismic design zone* value based on one of seven categories, including zones A, B, C, D_0, D_1, D_2, and E. The IRC specifically addresses construction methods for use in zones C, D_0, D_1, and D_2. Zones A and B require no special provision, and Zone E requires construction per the International Building Code or design by an engineer. Construction in zones C through D_2 requires designing for increasing seismic risk as the risk zone progresses. The effects of these zones in construction of the roof, wall, floor, and foundation assemblies are addressed in Chapters 16, 21, 22, and 26.

Susceptibility to Damage by Frost Line Depth

Depending on the frost line depth, the governing jurisdiction requires a minimum depth of footings below the finish grade. Chapter 26 includes information regarding the frost line depth and how it affects the design and construction of the foundation.

Susceptibility to Damage by Termites

The governing jurisdiction determines the need for protection from termites based on the history of subterranean termite damage. In areas of potential damage, one of the alternatives from Section R318 must be provided to control damage. Chapter 26 includes information regarding each method as it relates to foundation construction.

Susceptibility to Damage by Weathering

The general risk of damage due to *weathering* can be determined from using the map shown in Figure 5.8. In areas of the country with wide variances in weather conditions, the governing jurisdiction determines the need for weathering protection to the foundation based on local conditions. Possible weathering zones include negligible, moderate, or severe. As the risk of weathering increases, a higher strength of concrete or grade of masonry is necessary to reduce the chance of damage. Chapter 26 of this text covers concrete weathering.

Wind Design

The effects of wind on a structure must be considered in terms of the wind speed, how the topography affects the wind, and how to protect openings from windborne debris.

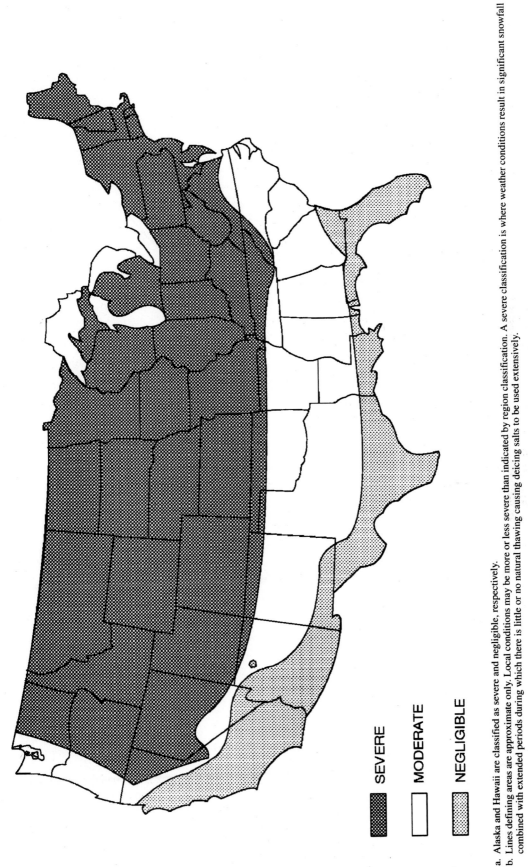

FIGURE R301.2(3)
WEATHERING PROBABILITY MAP FOR CONCRETE

SEVERE

MODERATE

NEGLIGIBLE

a. Alaska and Hawaii are classified as severe and negligible, respectively.
b. Lines defining areas are approximate only. Local conditions may be more or less severe than indicated by region classification. A severe classification is where weather conditions result in significant snowfall combined with extended periods during which there is little or no natural thawing causing deicing salts to be used extensively.

FIGURE 5.8 Maps similar to Figure R301.2(3) can be used to determine the risk of damage to the foundation from weathering. Based on the risk, precautions will need to be taken as the foundation is designed.

Wind Speed

The general risk of wind damage can be determined using a map similar to Figure 5.9 that shows *basic wind speeds*. The wind speed values are 3-second gust speeds listed in miles per hour. Although this map provides general design guidelines, the governing jurisdiction determines the actual wind speed based on local ground conditions referred to as exposures. The IRC defines four basic exposures including:

- Exposure A—Large city centers where at least 50 percent of the buildings have a height in excess of 70' (21 336 mm).

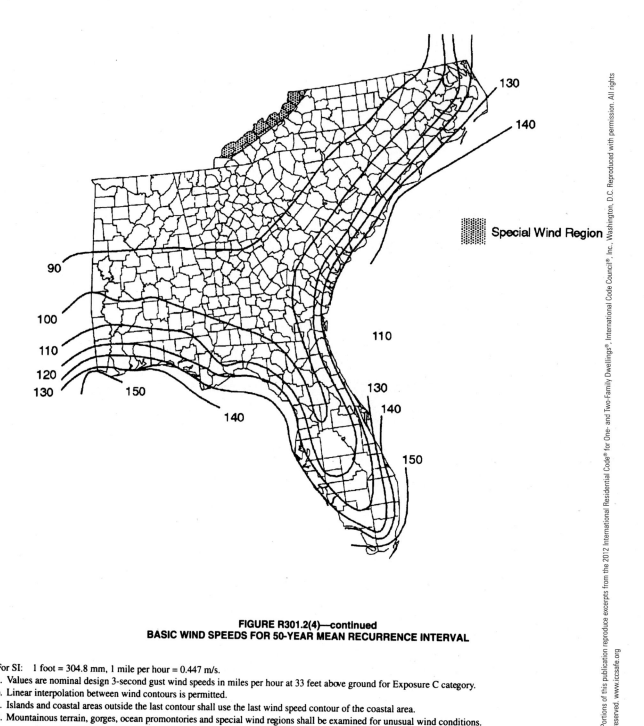

FIGURE R301.2(4)—continued
BASIC WIND SPEEDS FOR 50-YEAR MEAN RECURRENCE INTERVAL

For SI: 1 foot = 304.8 mm, 1 mile per hour = 0.447 m/s.
a. Values are nominal design 3-second gust wind speeds in miles per hour at 33 feet above ground for Exposure C category.
b. Linear interpolation between wind contours is permitted.
c. Islands and coastal areas outside the last contour shall use the last wind speed contour of the coastal area.
d. Mountainous terrain, gorges, ocean promontories and special wind regions shall be examined for unusual wind conditions.

FIGURE 5.9 Several maps are provided in the IRC to represent wind speeds in various portions of the country. Figure R301.2(4) can be used to determine the anticipated wind speed in the southern portion of the United States. Speeds are listed as 3-second gust speeds in miles per hour, assumed at 33' above the ground for exposure C. Based on the speed, precautions will need to be taken as the roof, wall, and foundation assemblies are designed.

- Exposure B—Urban and suburban areas, wooded areas, or other terrain where numerous, closely spaced obstructions the size of single-family dwellings or larger with heights generally less than 30' (9144 mm), extending more than 600' (183 m) from the building site in any quadrant.

- Exposure C—Open terrain with scattered obstructions including surface undulations or other irregularities, with heights generally less than 30' (9144 mm), extending more than 1500' (457 m) from the building site in any quadrant.

- Exposure D—Flat, unobstructed areas exposed to wind flowing over open water (excluding shorelines in hurricane-prone regions) for a distance of at least one mile (1.61 km).

Once the speed and exposure zone are known, the structure can be designed to resist the lateral stress resulting from the wind. Methods of protecting the structure from windborne debris must also be considered. Chapter 25 and Chapter 26 explore ways to resist the wind loads and protect the structure.

> ## NOTE:
>
> *In regions where wind design is required based on the maps included in Chapter 3 of the IRC, or where basic wind speeds equal or exceed 110 mph (49 m/s), the structure must be built to meet the standards in the Wood Frame Construction Manual published by the **American Wood Council,** or ICC Standards for Residential Construction in High Wind Regions ICC®-600.*

Topographic Effects

The governing jurisdiction determines the risk of wind damage based on local historical data documenting structural damage caused by topographic wind speed-up effects at isolated hills, ridges, and escarpments that are abrupt changes from the general topography of the area. If a structure is in the top half of one of the designated areas, the basic wind speed must be adjusted upward based on the values in Figure 5.10.

TABLE R301.2.1.5.1
BASIC WIND MODIFICATION FOR TOPOGRAPHIC WIND EFFECT

BASIC WIND SPEED FROM FIGURE R301.2(4) (mph)	AVERAGE SLOPE OF THE TOP HALF OF HILL, RIDGE OR ESCARPMENT (percent)						
	0.10	0.125	0.15	0.175	0.20	0.23	0.25 or greater
	Required basic wind speed-up, modified for topographic wind speed up (mph)						
85	100	100	100	110	110	110	120
90	100	100	110	110	120	120	120
100	110	120	120	130	130	130	140
110	120	130	130	140	140	150	150
120	140	140	150	150	N/A	N/A	N/A
130	150	N/A	N/A	N/A	N/A	N/A	N/A

For SI: 1 mile per hour = 0.447 m/s.

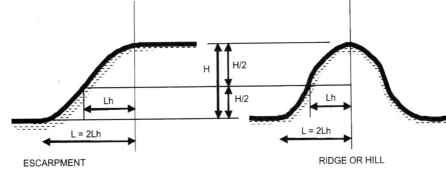

ESCARPMENT

RIDGE OR HILL

Note: H/2 determines the measurement point for Lh. L is twice Lh.

FIGURE R301.2.1.5.1(1)
TOPOGRAPHIC FEATURES FOR WIND SPEED-UP EFFECT

FIGURE 5.10 When a structure is built on the upper half of a hill, the assumed wind speed must be increased.

Protection of Openings from Windborne Debris

All exterior glazing of a structure must be protected from the risk of damage from windborne debris. The risk of damage is defined by a map contained in the IRC Figure R301.2(4)C. Major areas of risk extend from the southeastern tip of Texas along the states bordering the Gulf of Mexico, around the tip of Florida, and up the Atlantic coast to Massachusetts. Exterior glazed must be protected from windborne debris and must meet or exceed the requirements of the Large Missile Test defined in ASTM© E1996-12©. Exterior glazing protected by plywood with a minimum thickness of 7/16" (11 mm) and a maximum width of 8' (2438 mm) is allowed for residential construction that is two stories or less in height if the following conditions are met:

- Panels are precut and attached to the framing surrounding the glazed product.
- Panels are predrilled to meet the requirements of the fastener method specified in Table R301.2(2) of the IRC.

CODE REQUIREMENTS AFFECTING BUILDING DESIGN

The major influence of the model codes on a structure has to do with structural components. Chapters covering foundations, wall construction, wall coverings, floors, roof-ceiling construction, roof coverings, and chimney and fireplace construction are provided to specify minimum construction standards. Minimum code requirements affecting the design and construction of a structure include regulations related to the following major design categories:

- Habitable and nonhabitable space.
- The location of the project on the property.
- Egress and accessibility requirements.
- Minimum room size requirements.
- Light, ventilation, and heating requirements.
- Safety equipment.

Habitable and Nonhabitable Space

The space within a home or dwelling unit is divided into habitable and nonhabitable spaces. A room is considered *habitable* space when it is used for sleeping, living, cooking, or dining. *Nonhabitable* spaces include closets, pantries, bath or toilet rooms, hallways, utility rooms, storage spaces, garages, darkrooms, and other similar spaces.

Location on the Property

For building code purposes, the exterior walls of a residential building cannot be within 5' (1524 mm) of the property lines unless special provisions are met. Zoning regulations may further restrict the location of the structure to the property lines. Typically, an exterior wall built within 5' (1524 mm) of the property line must be made from materials tested and evaluated in accordance with ASTM E119© or UL 263™ to resist a fire for one hour. This is known as a one-hour fire rating. Although only 1/2" (12.7 mm) gypsum board is required on each side of the wall in certain wall assemblies, using 5/8" (16 mm) type X gypsum board on each side of the wall is a common method of achieving a one-hour wall. Many municipalities require any walls built into the minimum side yard to be of one-hour construction. Openings such as doors or windows are not allowed in a wall with a fire separation distance less than 36" (914 mm). Projections such as a roof or chimney cannot project more than 24" (610 mm) from the line used to determine the fire separation distance, with one exception: a detached garage located within 24" (610 mm) of the property line may have a 4" (102 mm) eave projection.

Egress and Accessibility Requirements for a Residence

The major subjects to be considered in this area of the code are means of egress, emergency egress (exits), and stairs.

Means of Egress

Residential projects must provide a continuous and unobstructed path of vertical and horizontal egress travel from all portions of the dwelling to the exterior at the required egress door without requiring travel through a garage. The IRC uses the term *egress* to specify areas of access or exits provided by doors, windows, and hallways.

Access Doors. Each dwelling unit, as a residence is referred to in the codes, must have a minimum of one door that can be opened from the interior side without the use of a key. The egress door must have a minimum clear opening of 32" (813 mm) wide measured between the face of the door when open 90° (1.57 rad) and the stop. The minimum clear height of the door opening must be 78" (1981 mm) from the top of the threshold to the bottom of the stop. The designer can determine all other door sizes based on personal preferences or the client's needs.

A floor or landing must be provided on each side of an exterior door. The IRC requires the landing to be a maximum distance of 1 1/2" (38 mm) from the top of

> ### ➤ NOTE:
>
> The IRC may allow the main entry door to be 32" clear opening (813 mm) wide, but common practice is to provide a 36" (900 mm) or larger door to provide an inviting entrance. Remember building codes dictate minimum sizes, not desirable or practical sizes. Chapter 11 provides guidelines for determining door sizes throughout a residence.

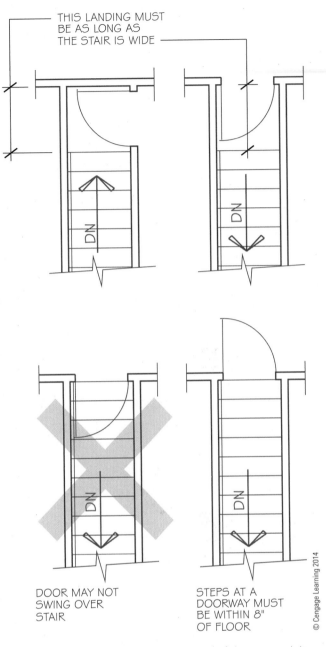

DOOR MAY NOT SWING OVER STAIR

STEPS AT A DOORWAY MUST BE WITHIN 8" OF FLOOR

© Cengage Learning 2014

FIGURE 5.11 The IRC regulates placement of doors near stairs. Landings by doors must be within 1 1/2" (38 mm) of the door threshold. When the door does not swing over the landing, the landing can be a maximum of 7 3/4" (197 mm) below the threshold.

door threshold for required egress doors. The landing for an exterior door can be within 7 3/4" (196 mm) from the top of the door threshold provided that the door does not swing over the landing. The minimum landing width must be equal to or greater than the width of the door at the landing, and the landing length must be a minimum of 36" (914 mm) measured in the direction of travel. The landing is required on each side of the required egress door. While interior landings must be level, exterior landings may have a maximum slope of 1/4" / 12" (2% slope). This often becomes a design problem when trying to place a door near a stairway. Figure 5.11 shows some common door and landing problems and their solutions.

Emergency Egress Openings. The size and location of windows is a major consideration in designing exits. Basements, habitable attics, and every sleeping room require emergency egress. For basements that contain more than one sleeping room, emergency egress and rescue openings must be in each sleeping room. Escape may be made through a door or window that opens directly onto a public street, alley, yard, or exit court. The emergency escape must be operable from the inside without the use of any keys or tools. The sill of all emergency escape bedroom windows must be within 44" (1118 mm) of the floor. Windows used for emergency egress must have a minimum net clear area of 5.7 sq ft (0.530 m²). Grade floor opening size can be reduced to 5.0 sq ft (0.465 m²). The net clear opening area must have a minimum width of 20" (508 mm) and a minimum height of 24" (610 mm). All net clear openings must be obtainable during normal operation of the window. This opening gives occupants in each sleeping area a method of escape in case of a fire (see Figure 5.12).

Emergency escape windows with a finished sill height below the surrounding ground elevation must have a **window well** that allows the window to be fully opened. The window well is required to have a clear opening of 9 sq ft (0.9 m²) with a minimum horizontal projection and width of 36" (914 mm) when the window is fully open. Emergency escape windows are permissible under decks provided the emergency escape window can be fully opened and provides a path not less than 36" (914 mm) in height to a yard or court.

If the window well has a depth of more than 44" (1118 mm), the well must have an approved, permanently fixed ladder or stair that can be accessed when the window is fully opened. The ladder or stair cannot encroach more than 6" (152 mm) into the required well dimensions and must have rungs with a minimum inside width of 12" (305 mm). The rungs must be a minimum of 3" (76 mm) from the wall and must be spaced at a maximum distance

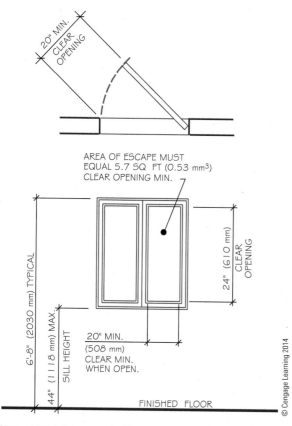

FIGURE 5.12 Minimum window opening sizes for emergency escape. A means of escape is required for all sleeping units, including those in basements or habitable attic space.

TABLE 5.1 IRC Minimum Stair Guidelines

Width (minimum)	36"*	914 mm*
Individual riser height (maximum)	7 3/4"**	196 mm**
Individual tread depth (minimum)	10	254 mm
Headroom (minimum)	6'-8"	2032 mm

* Minimum clear width above the permitted handrail and below the required headroom height. Below the handrail, 31.5" (787 mm) minimum width with handrail on one side, 27" (698 mm) minimum width with handrail on each side.
** The opening between open treads shall not permit the passage of a 4" (102 mm) diameter sphere.

Portions of this publication reproduce excerpts from the 2012 International Residential Code® for One- and Two-Family Dwellings®, International Code Council®, Inc., Washington, D.C. Reproduced with permission. All rights reserved. www.iccsafe.org

of 18" (457 mm) o.c. vertically for the full height of the window well. Unless the window well is located in well-drained soil or gravel, a drain connected to the foundation drainage system must be provided.

Halls

Hallways must be a minimum of 36" (914 mm) wide. This is rarely a design consideration because the layout of hallways is often 42" (1067 mm) or wider at the main and service entries to create an open feeling and to enhance accessibility from room to room.

Stairs

Stairs often dictate the layout of an entire structure. Because of their importance, they must be considered early in the design process. For a complete description of stair construction, see Chapter 31. Minimum code requirements for stairs are listed in Table 5.1. Following the minimum standards results in stairs that are extremely steep, very narrow, and have very little room for foot placement. Good design practice allows for stairs with a width of 36" to 42" (914 to 1067 mm) for ease of movement. A common tread depth

is 10" to 10 1/2" (254 to 267 mm) with a rise of about 7 1/2" (191 mm). Figure 5.13 shows the difference between the minimum stair layout and some common alternatives. Within any flight of stairs, there cannot be more than 12' (3658 mm) between floor levels or landings and the largest step run must not exceed the smallest step by 3/8" (9.5 mm). The difference between the largest and smallest rise must not exceed 3/8" (9.5 mm). Headroom above stairs must also be a consideration during the design phase. Stairs must have 6'–8" (2032 mm) minimum headroom. Spiral stairs may have headroom of 6'–6" (1981 mm). The headroom requirements can greatly affect wall placement on the upper floor above the stairwell. Figure 5.14 shows some alternatives in wall placement around stairs.

Winding Stairs. Winding stairs may be used if a minimum width of 10" (254 mm) is provided at a point not more than 12" (305 mm) from the side of the treads. The narrowest portion of a winding stairway may not be less than

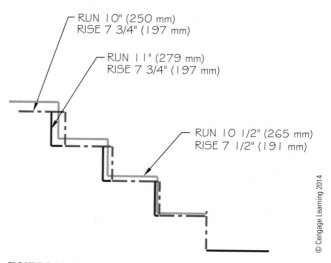

FIGURE 5.13 Stair layout comparing minimum run and maximum rise based on common practice.

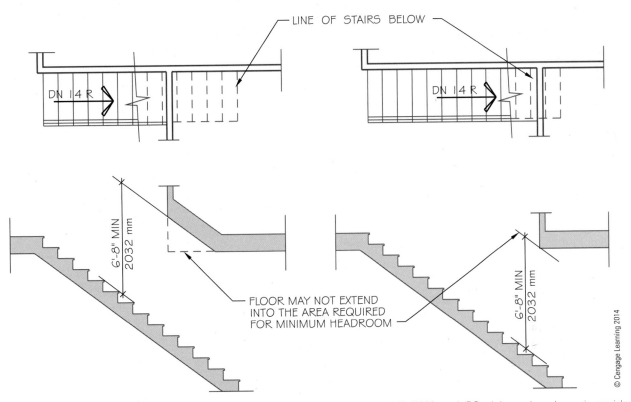

FIGURE 5.14 Wall placement over stairs. Walls must be placed so that the required 6'-8" (2032 mm) IRC minimum headroom is provided. The "inclined floor" is usually only acceptable if it can be hidden in a closet or a cabinet.

6" (152 mm) wide at any point. When a spiral stair is the only stair serving an upper floor area, it can be difficult to move furniture from one floor to another. Spiral stair treads must provide a clear walking width of 26" (660 mm) measured from the outer edge of the support column to the inner edge of the handrail. A tread depth of 7 1/2" (190 mm) must be provided within 12" (305 mm) of the narrowest part of the tread. The rise for a spiral stair must be sufficient to provide 6'–6" (1981 mm) headroom, but no riser may exceed 9 1/2" (241 mm), and all risers must be equal. Circular stairways must have a minimum tread run of 11" (279 mm) measured at a point not more than 12" (305 mm) from the narrow edge. At no point can the run be less than 6" (152 mm).

Landings. Regardless of the type of stair, a floor or landing must be provided at the top and bottom of the stair run. The landing must have a minimum depth equal to the width of the stairs, but may not be less than 36" (914 mm). Although landings are usually square or rectangular, the landing may have an irregular shape as long as the area of the landing is not less than the area of a quarter circle with a radius equal to the required landing width. The landing and treads are generally level, but the IRC does allow each to have a maximum slope of one vertical unit per 48 horizontal units (2% slope).

Handrails. All stairways with four or more risers must have at least one smooth *handrail* that extends the entire length of the stair. The rail must be placed on the open side of the stairs and must be between 34" to 38" (864 to 965 mm) above the front edge of the stair. The height may exceed the maximum height as the handrail transitions into the guardrail. The IRC allows the following types of handrails:

Type I—Circular. Handrails with a circular cross section must have a minimum outside diameter of 1 1/4" (32 mm) and not exceed 2" (51 mm).

Type I—Noncircular. The rail must have a minimum perimeter dimension of 4" (102 mm) and not exceed 6 1/4" (160 mm) with a maximum cross section of 2 1/4" (57 mm).

Type II. Rails with a perimeter greater than 6 1/4" (160 mm) must have a graspable finger recess area on both sides of the profile.

Handrails must be 1 1/2" (38 mm) from the wall but may not extend into the required stair width by more than 4 1/2" (114 mm). For a single handrail, the IRC requires a clear width at or below the handrail to be 31 1/2" (787 mm). A clear width of 27" (698 mm) is necessary if there is a handrail on each side of the stair.

Guardrails. A *guardrail* must be provided at changes in floor or ground elevation that exceed 30" (762 mm). Guardrails must be 36" (914 mm) high except on the open side of the stairs where the railing can be reduced to 34" (864 mm) when measured vertically from a line extending from the leading edges of the treads. Railings must be constructed so that a 4" (102 mm) diameter sphere cannot pass through the opening in the rail. Guardrails on the open side of a stair must be constructed so that a 4 3/8" (111 mm) diameter sphere cannot pass through the opening in the rail. The triangular opening formed by the bottom of the rail and the stairs must be constructed so that a 6" (152 mm) sphere cannot pass through the opening. Horizontal rails or other ornamental designs that form a ladder effect must not be used.

Minimum Room Size Requirements

Room dimension requirements affect the size and ceiling height of rooms. Every dwelling unit must have at least one room with a minimum of 120 sq ft (11.2 m²) of total floor area. Other habitable rooms except kitchens must have a minimum of 70 sq ft (6.5 m²) and shall not be less than 7' (2134 mm) in any horizontal direction. These code requirements rarely affect home design.

Kitchens

The influence of the IRC will generally never affect the design of a kitchen. The code requires every dwelling unit to have a kitchen area with a sink that must be connected to an approved water supply and to a sanitary sewer or approved private sewage disposal system.

Toilet Facilities

One major code requirement affecting room size governs the space allowed for a toilet, which is typically referred to as a *water closet*. There must be a space 30" (762 mm) wide for water closets. A distance of 21" (533 mm) is required in front of a toilet to any obstruction such as a counter or other plumbing feature. A minimum clearance of 21" (533 mm) is also required in front of a bathroom sink to any obstruction, and a minimum distance of 24" (610 mm) is required in front of a shower. These sizes can often affect the layout of a small bathroom, but they are rarely a problem in a custom home. Additional requirements will be explored later in this chapter. Chapter 11 provides additional information related to the layout of the plumbing fixtures.

Sanitation

Code requirements for sanitation rarely affect the design of a structure. In addition to the kitchen sink, each residence must have a toilet, sink, and tub or shower. All plumbing fixtures must be connected to an approved water supply, and kitchen sinks, lavatories, bathtubs, showers, bidets, laundry sinks, and washing machines all must have hot and cold water. Each plumbing fixture must also be connected to a sanitary sewer or an approved private sewage disposal system. The room containing the toilet must be separated from the food preparation area by a tight-fitting door. Chapter 11 provides further information regarding the layout of each fixture, and Chapter 14 provides information regarding plumbing plans.

Ceiling Heights

Habitable rooms, hallways, corridors, bathrooms, toilet rooms, laundry rooms, and habitable space in basements must all have a minimum ceiling height of 7'-0" (2134 mm). The bathroom ceiling may be reduced above a counter or plumbing fixture to 6'-8" (2032 mm). This lowered ceiling can often be used for lighting or for heating ducts. Beams spaced at a maximum distance of 48" (1219 mm) O.C. may extend 6" (152 mm) below the required ceiling height. A shower or tub equipped with a showerhead must also have a minimum ceiling height of 6'-8" (2032 mm) above a minimum area of 30" × 30" (762 × 762 mm) at the showerhead. In a room with a sloping ceiling, the minimum ceiling height must be maintained in at least half of the room. The balance of the room height may slope to 5' (1524 mm) minimum. Any part of a room with a sloping ceiling less than 5' (1524 mm) high, or 7'-0" (2134 mm) for furred ceilings, may not be included as habitable square footage (see Figure 5.15). Portions of basements without habitable space, and bathrooms, toilet rooms, and laundry rooms located in a basement must have a minimum ceiling height of 6'-8" (2032 mm). Beams, ducts, or other obstructions in the basement may project to within 6'-4" (1931 mm) of the finished floor.

Light, Ventilation, and Heating Requirements

The light and ventilation requirements of building codes have a major effect on window size and placement. The codes covering light, ventilation, and heating have a broad impact on the design of the house. Many preliminary designs often show entire walls of glass that take advantage of beautiful surroundings. At the other extreme, some houses have very little glass and thus have no view but very little heat loss. Building codes affect both types of designs.

Providing Natural Light

The IRC requires that all habitable rooms have natural light provided through windows or skylights. Kitchens are

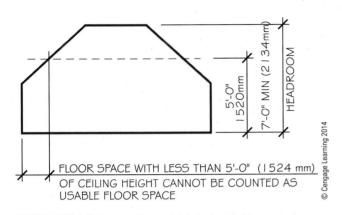

FLOOR SPACE WITH LESS THAN 5'-0" (1524 mm) OF CEILING HEIGHT CANNOT BE COUNTED AS USABLE FLOOR SPACE

© Cengage Learning 2014

FIGURE 5.15 Minimum ceiling heights for habitable rooms. In habitable rooms that have a sloping ceiling, the minimum ceiling must be maintained in at least half of the room. The balance of the room height may slope to 5' (1524 mm) minimum.

habitable rooms but are not required to meet the light and ventilation requirements. Windows for other habitable rooms must open directly into a street, public alley, or yard on the same building site. Windows may open into an enclosed structure such as a porch as long as the area is at least 65 percent open. Required glazed openings may face into the area under a balcony, bay, deck, or floor cantilever provided there is a clear vertical space at least 36" (914 mm) in height. Required glazing is also permitted to open into a sunroom or covered patio that abuts a street, yard, or court if more than 40 percent of the exterior sunroom walls are open, or enclosed only by insect screening and the ceiling height of the sunroom is not less than 7'-0" (2134 mm).

Unless there is a whole-house mechanical ventilation system, all habitable rooms must have a glazing area equal to 8 percent of the room's floor area, and one-half of the area used to provide light must also be openable to provide ventilation. Remember that bedrooms have additional requirements based on emergency egress. A room that is 9' × 10' (2743 × 3048 mm) must have a window with a glass area of 7.2 sq ft (0.66 m²) to meet minimum standards. Another limit to the amount of glass area is in locations that are subject to strong winds or earthquakes. These restrictions will be explored later in this chapter as climatic and geographic design criteria are discussed.

Alternative Methods of Providing Light and Ventilation

Two alternatives to the light and ventilation requirements are allowed in all habitable rooms. Mechanical ventilation and lighting equipment can be used in place of openable windows in habitable rooms except bedrooms. Glazing may

be eliminated except when required for emergency egress when artificial light capable of producing six-footcandles (6.46 lux) over the area of the room at a height of 30" (762 mm) above the floor is provided.

Ventilation may be eliminated when there is an approved mechanical ventilation system capable of producing 0.35 air changes per hour for the room. Ventilation may also be waived if a whole-house mechanical ventilation system capable of producing 15 cfm (7.08 L/s) per occupant is provided. Occupancy is based on two for the first bedroom and one for each additional bedroom.

The second method of providing lighting and ventilation allows floor areas of two adjoining rooms to be considered as one if 50 percent of the area of the common wall is open and unobstructed. The opening must also be equal to 10 percent of the floor area of the interior room, or 25 sq ft (2.3 m²), whichever is greater. Openings required for light and ventilation may open into a thermally isolated sunroom or covered patio. To use this ventilation option, the openable area between the adjoining rooms must be equal to 10 percent of the floor area of the interior room, but must not be less than 20 sq ft (2 m²).

Bathroom and Laundry Room Venting. Although considered nonhabitable, bathrooms and laundry rooms must also be provided with an openable window. The window must be a minimum of 3 sq ft (0.3 m²), of which one-half must open. A fan that provides 50 cfm (24 L/s) for intermittent ventilation or 10 cfm (10 L/s) for continuous ventilation is allowable instead of a window. These fans must be vented directly to outside air. For mechanical ventilation, careful consideration must be given to the type and placement of the intake and exhaust vents. Exterior vents must be protected from local weather conditions and covered with corrosion-resistant grills, louvers, or screens that have 1/4" (6.4 mm) minimum and a 1/2" (12.7 mm) maximum opening. Intake openings must be located a minimum of 10' (3048 mm) from hazardous or noxious contaminants, and from any plumbing vents, chimneys, alleys, parking lots, or loading docks. The minimum distance may be reduced if the intake vent is 2' (610 mm) minimum below the contaminant source.

Heating

Heating requirements for a residence are very minimal. The IRC requires the installation of a heating unit in any residence built in an area where the winter design temperature is below 60°F (16°C). So unless you're building in Hawaii, plan for a heating unit capable of producing and maintaining a room temperature of 68°F, or 20°C at a point 3' (914 mm) above the floor and 2' (610 mm) from exterior walls for all habitable rooms. Portable space heaters no longer meet compliance with the current codes. Chapter 15 provides additional information regarding heating and cooling.

Safety Equipment

Major considerations of required safety equipment include automatic fire sprinkler systems, smoke detectors, and carbon monoxide alarms.

Automatic Fire Sprinkler Systems

A stand-alone or multipurpose automatic fire sprinkler system that meets Section P2904 of the International Plumbing Code (IPC) or **National Fire Protection Association® (NFPA®)** 13D is required for all new construction covered by the IRC. A stand-alone system depends on water independent from a home's water distribution system. Multipurpose systems use the same water distribution system as the home. Sprinkler heads similar to the head shown in Figure 5.16 should be installed in all areas of the home except the attic, crawl space, and normally unoccupied concealed spaces that do not contain fuel-fired appliances. If there is a fuel-fired appliance in an attic or basement, there must be a sprinkler above the appliance, but not in the balance of the attic or basement space. The IRC allows additional exceptions, including:

- Closets having walls and ceilings covered with gypsum board not exceeding 24 sq ft (2.2 m²) in area with the smallest dimension not greater than 3' (915 mm).
- Bathrooms totaling not more than 55 sq ft (5.1 m²) in area.
- Garages, carports, exterior porches, unheated entry areas, and mudrooms that are adjacent to exterior doors.

FIGURE 5.16 An automatic fire sprinkler system is required for all new construction covered by the 2012 edition of the IRC.

Courtesy Uponor Wirsbo

Sprinkler Head Requirements. The area of coverage for a single sprinkler head shall not exceed 400 sq ft (37 m²). The discharge from each head shall not be blocked by obstructions unless additional heads are provided. The actual sprinkler head must have a temperature rating of not less than 135°F (57°C) and not more than 170°F (77°C). When a sprinkler head is installed under a skylight, in an attic, or in a concealed space directly beneath a roof, it must have an intermediate temperature rating of not less than 175°F (79°C) and not more than 225°F (77°C). In areas where freezing is required, piping that supplies each head must also be protected from freezing. Chapter 14 provides additional information related to sprinklers.

Smoke Detectors and Alarms

Smoke detectors and alarms allow for safe exit through early detection of fire and smoke. A smoke alarm that meets the requirements of UL 217™ must be installed per NFPA-72® in each sleeping room, as well as at a point centrally located in a corridor that provides access to the bedrooms. For a one-level residence, a smoke detector must be located:

- At the start of every hall that serves a bedroom.
- In each sleeping room.

For multilevel homes, a smoke alarm is required on every floor, including the basement. The smoke alarm should be located over the stair leading to the upper level. In split-level homes, the smoke alarm is only required on the upper level if the lower level is less than one full story below the upper level. If a door separates the levels of a split-level home, there must be a smoke alarm on each level. A smoke alarm must be on the lower level if there is a sleeping unit on that level. Smoke alarms should not be placed in or near kitchens or fireplaces because a small amount of smoke can set them off, resulting in a false alarm.

Smoke alarms must be within 12" (305 mm) of the ceiling or mounted on the ceiling. Alarms must receive their primary power from the building wiring when the power is served from a commercial source. When the primary power is interrupted, the alarm system must be connected to electrical wiring with a battery-powered backup system. Smoke alarms must be interconnected so that if one alarm is activated, all will sound.

Carbon Monoxide Detection System and Alarms

A carbon monoxide alarm or detection system is required in all new residential construction that contains fuel-fired appliances or has an attached garage. Alarms that meet UL 2034™ must be placed outside of each separate sleeping area in the immediate vicinity of the bedrooms in dwelling units. Detection systems that include carbon monoxide detectors and audible notification appliances may be used in place of an alarm if the system is a permanent fixture of the home and is monitored by an approved supervising station.

INTERNATIONAL ENERGY CONSERVATION CODE

The 2012 International Energy Conservation Code (IECC) is published by the International Code Council and is updated every three years to conform to the other I-codes. The purpose of the IECC is to regulate the design and construction of homes for the effective use and conservation of energy over the useful life of the building. The main focus of the code is the exterior envelope and selection of HVAC, water heating, electrical distribution and illuminating systems, and equipment required for effective use of energy in buildings. The *exterior envelope* is made up of the elements of a building that enclose conditioned (heated and cooled) spaces through which thermal energy transfers to or from the exterior. This chapter addresses the basic IECC requirements for the building envelope. Section 3 of this text addresses methods for improving the environment inside the building envelope.

Determining the Required Building Envelope

The exterior envelope of a residence comprises the exterior walls, the ceiling, the openings in the walls and ceiling, and the floor. The IECC refers to the openings in the envelope as *fenestration*. The construction of the envelope depends on the climate zone where the home is to be located.

The IECC divides the United States into three major regions and eight climate zones as seen in Figure 5.17. The climate zones are based on the wet-bulb temperature of the area. The *wet-bulb temperature* is a measurement of the environment that reflects the physical properties of the surrounding air. Taking the measurement requires a thermometer with its bulb wrapped in cloth that draws moisture from the surrounding air. These zones are further divided by the expected humidity in each zone and include A—moist; B—dry; and C—marine. Zones without moisture designations are areas where moisture is deemed irrelevant.

Although this map provides guidelines for the designer, it's also important to consult Table 301.1 of the IECC for a lengthy list of zones by state and by county or to contact the governing building department to verify specific climate requirements.

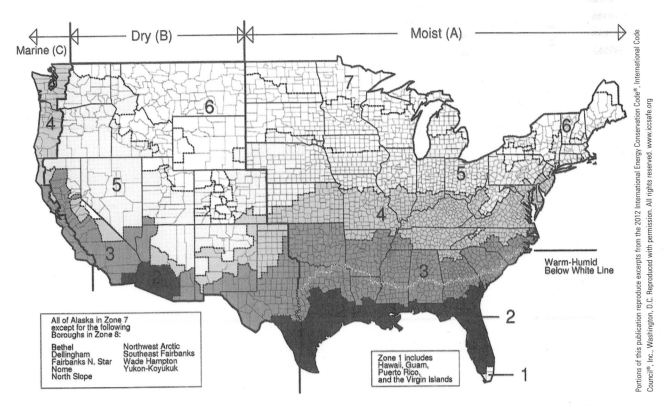

FIGURE 5.17 The International Energy Conservation Code divides the United States into three major regions and eight climate zones. These zones are further divided by the expected humidity to be encountered in each zone. Once the climate zone of the building site is determined, the required insulation and fenestration efficiency can be determined.

TABLE R402.1.1
INSULATION AND FENESTRATION REQUIREMENTS BY COMPONENT [a]

CLIMATE ZONE	FENESTRATION U-FACTOR [b]	SKYLIGHT [b] U-FACTOR	GLAZED FENESTRATION SHGC [b, e]	CEILING R-VALUE	WOOD FRAME WALL R-VALUE	MASS WALL R-VALUE [i]	FLOOR R-VALUE	BASEMENT [c] WALL R-VALUE	SLAB [d] R-VALUE & DEPTH	CRAWL SPACE [c] WALL R-VALUE
1	NR	0.75	0.25	30	13	3/4	13	0	0	0
2	0.40	0.65	0.25	38	13	4/6	13	0	0	0
3	0.35	0.55	0.25	38	20 or 13 + 5 [h]	8/13	19	5/13 [f]	0	5/13
4 except Marine	0.35	0.55	0.40	49	20 or 13 + 5 [h]	8/13	19	10 /13	10, 2 ft	10/13
5 and Marine 4	0.32	0.55	NR	49	20 or 13 + 5 [h]	13/17	30 [g]	15/19	10, 2 ft	15/19
6	0.32	0.55	NR	49	20 + 5 or 13 + 10 [h]	15/20	30 [g]	15/19	10, 4 ft	15/19
7 and 8	0.32	0.55	NR	49	20 + 5 or 13 + 10 [h]	19/21	38 [g]	15/19	10, 4 ft	15/19

For SI: 1 foot = 304.8 mm.

a. *R*-values are minimums. *U*-factors and SHGC are maximums. When insulation is installed in a cavity which is less than the label or design thickness of the insulation, the installed *R*-value of the insulation shall not be less than the *R*-value specified in the table.

b. The fenestration *U*-factor column excludes skylights. The SHGC column applies to all glazed fenestration.
   Exception: Skylights may be excluded from glazed fenestration SHGC requirements in Climate Zones 1 through 3 where the SHGC for such skylights does not exceed 0.30.

c. "15/19" means R-15 continuous insulation on the interior or exterior of the home or R-19 cavity insulation at the interior of the basement wall. "15/19" shall be permitted to be met with R-13 cavity insulation on the interior of the basement wall plus R-5 continuous insulation on the interior or exterior of the home. "10/13" means R-10 continuous insulation on the interior or exterior of the home or R-13 cavity insulation at the interior of the basement wall.

d. R-5 shall be added to the required slab edge *R*-values for heated slabs. Insulation depth shall be the depth of the footing or 2 feet, whichever is less in Climate Zones 1 through 3 for heated slabs.

e. There are no SHGC requirements in the Marine Zone.

f. Basement wall insulation is not required in warm-humid locations as defined by Figure R301.1 and Table R301.1.

g. Or insulation sufficient to fill the framing cavity, R-19 minimum.

h. First value is cavity insulation, second is continuous insulation or insulated siding, so "13 + 5" means R-13 cavity insulation plus R-5 continuous insulation or insulated siding. If structural sheathing covers 40 percent or less of the exterior, continuous insulation *R*-value shall be permitted to be reduced by no more than R-3 in the locations where structural sheathing is used – to maintain a consistent total sheathing thickness.

i. The second *R*-value applies when more than half the insulation is on the interior of the mass wall.

FIGURE 5.18 Table 402.1.1 of the IECC defines the minimum insulation and fenestration requirements.

General Requirements for the Building Envelope

The IRC governs the actual construction of the walls, floor, and ceiling assemblies that form the building envelope. The IECC governs the insulation and fenestration for use in completing the envelope. IECC Table 402.1.1 shown in Figure 5.18 specifies general requirements for these two areas of construction.

Table 5.2 offers a comparison of envelope components for a home built in Houston, Texas, in a warm, humid area in climate zone 2A; a home in Walla Walla, Washington, in a marine zone 5B; and a home in Grand Forks, North Dakota, in a moist zone 7.

TABLE 5.2 Comparison of Envelope Components Based on the 2012 IECC

ENVELOPE COMPONENT	HOUSTON	WALLA WALLA	GRAND FORKS
Fenestration U-factor	0.40	0.32	0.32
Skylight U-factor	0.65	0.55	0.55
Glazed fenestration	0.25	NR	NR
Ceiling R-value	38	49	49
Wood-framed wall R-value	13	20 or 13+5	20+5 or 13+10
Mass wall R-value	4/6	13/17	19/21
Floor R-value	13	30	38
Basement wall R-value	0	15/19	15/19
Slab R-value and depth	0	10, 2'	10, 4'
Crawl space wall R-value	0	15/19	15/19

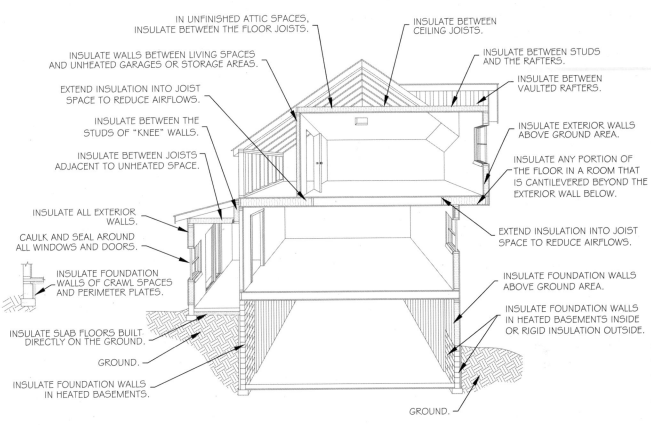

FIGURE 5.19 Locations where insulation must be installed based on the IECC.

© Cengage Learning 2014

The IECC allows the envelope to be described in U-factor in lieu of using R-values. U-values can be determined in the IECC and are not addressed in this chapter.

Insulation

Insulation is material used to restrict the flow of heat, cold, or sound in the building envelope, keeping the home warm in winter and cool in summer. It saves energy costs, and when properly installed it helps maintain a uniform temperature throughout the house. Various types of insulation are available and are discussed in Chapter 15. Figure 5.19 shows the locations where insulation is required.

Insulation reduces the amount of heat lost through walls, ceilings, and floors during the winter and helps keep heat from entering the residence during the summer. The ability of materials to slow heat transfer is called *thermal resistance*. The *R-value* of a material is a measure of thermal resistance to heat flow. The higher the R-value assigned to a material, the greater the material's insulating ability. Insulation is critical in helping reduce heat loss, but it must be combined with proper caulking and construction methods.

The amount of insulation a home should have depends on local and national codes, climate, energy costs, budget, and personal preference. The IECC provides minimum required insulation levels and the **U.S. Department of Energy (DOE)** recommends insulation levels by zip codes for walls, ceilings, floors, and foundations. Recommended

R-values for a wood-frame residence in the ceiling range from R-30 to R-60 depending on the type of heating to be provided and the climate zone of the home. Vaulted ceilings can vary from R-22 to R-60. R-13 to R-30 insulation is recommended for use in floors, although homes built in some warm climates do not require floor insulation. Wall insulation levels vary from R-13 to R-21 depending on the climate. Insulation values for steel-frame structures can be determined using Table R402.2.6 in the IECC. Always confirm the minimum insulation required by the codes governing your area. In general, more insulation means better energy efficiency.

Fenestration

The listing for glazed fenestration in Figure 5.18 show the letters SHGC in the column heading and footnotes. These letters represent the *solar heat gain coefficient*. SHGC is a ratio of the solar heat gain entering the space inside the envelope through the fenestration to the incident solar radiation. *Solar heat gain* includes solar heat that is transmitted through the fenestration and energy that is absorbed radiation.

Specific Requirements for the Building Envelope

The IECC provides specific criteria to supplement the general information provided in Figure 5.18. The specific requirements are divided by ceilings with attics, ceilings without attics, walls, floors, and fenestration.

Ceilings with Attic Storage

The prescriptive method of installing insulation according to IECC section 402.1.1 allows for the reduction of some some ceiling values. Ceilings requiring insulation values of R-38 can be reduced to R-30 if the uncompressed height of the insulation extends over the top plate of the exterior walls. If the same conditions are met, R-49 insulation can be replaced by R-38 insulation.

Ceilings with No Attic Storage

When section 402.1.1 of the IECC requires insulation values greater than R-30, the value of insulation can be reduced to R-30 if the roof/ceiling assembly does not allow for the required insulation height. This reduction in insulation R-value is limited to 500 sq ft (46 m²) or 20 percent of the total insulated ceiling area, whichever is less.

Mass Walls

The listing for **mass walls** in IECC Table 402.1.1 refers to concrete block, poured concrete, insulated concrete form (ICF), masonry cavity, brick, adobe, earth block, rammed earth, and solid timber logs. This category excludes masonry veneer. The requirements for mass walls apply if at least 50 percent of the required insulation R-value is part of the wall or on the exterior side of the wall. Walls that do not meet this requirement may be insulated to meet the standards for wood frame walls.

Floor/Crawl Space Walls

Typical floor insulation methods place the insulation so that it will be in permanent contact with the underside of the floor decking. The IECC also allows the floor to be uninsulated, and the walls of the crawl space to be insulated. To use this insulation method, the crawl space can't be vented to outside air, and the insulation is required to meet the following placement guidelines:

- Insulation must be permanently attached to the stem wall.

- Insulation must extend from the floor to the line of the finish grade. From the grade, the insulation must extend an additional 24" (610 mm) vertically along the wall, or along the grade in the crawl space. When placed horizontally along the soil in the crawl space, the insulation must be laid over a continuous vapor retarder. Chapters 23 and 26 cover other requirements for placing the vapor retarder.

Basement Walls

The walls of basements that are part of the building envelope must be insulated from the top of the wall down to 10' (3048 mm) below grade or to the basement floor. Basement walls that surround unconditioned air do not need to be insulated if the floor supported by the wall is insulated. If the floor is uninsulated, the basement wall must be insulated to the same standards as walls surrounding rooms with conditioned air.

Slab-on-Grade Floors

The edge of concrete slabs that are at or within 12" (305 mm) of the grade must be insulated. The insulation can be on the inside or outside face of the concrete wall. Insulation extending away from the slab must be protected by a minimum of 10" (254 mm) of soil similar to the footing in Figure 5.20a and Figure 5.20b.

MULTIFAMILY BUILDING AND UNIT ASSEMBLY

The IRC regulates the design and construction of single-family residencies, duplexes, and buildings containing three or more dwelling units (townhouses). Each type of construction must be limited to three stories above the grade line. A single-family residence, duplex, or townhouse that consists of four or more levels above grade must be built to comply with the restrictions of the International Building Code (IBC).

The IBC divides residential structures into different categories or occupancies that are represented by the letter R, including:

R-1: Residential occupancies consisting of structures containing ten or more sleeping units where the

> **NOTE:**
>
> *Although the following material is not required for one- and two-family residential dwellings covered by the IRC, it is important to have a basic understanding on the accessibility requirements for other types of residential units. Since very few design firms work strictly on single-family homes, in your career you're bound to work on other types of residential units. It's also important because of the aging of the American population; many owners choose to have their homes designed to allow for comfortable living should a member lose mobility.*

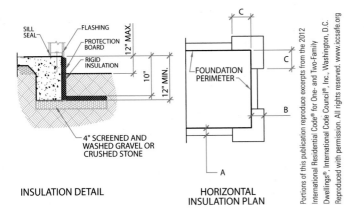

INSULATION DETAIL   HORIZONTAL
                           INSULATION PLAN

FIGURE 5.20a Insulation placement for frost-protected footings based on Figure R403.3(1) of the IRC.

occupants are primarily transient in nature such as boarding houses, hotels, and motels.

R-2: Residential occupancies containing sleeping units or more than two dwelling units where the occupants are primarily permanent in nature including apartment houses, boarding houses, dormitories, fraternity and sorority houses, hotels, motels, and vacation property.

R-3: Residential occupancies where the occupants are primarily permanent in nature, and are

not classified as R-1, R-2, R-4, or I (Institutional) including:

- Buildings that do not contain more than two dwelling units.
- Adult-care facilities that provide accommodations for five or fewer persons of any age for less than 24 hours.
- Child-care facilities that provide accommodations for five or fewer persons of any age for less than 24 hours.
- Building or parts of buildings that contain sleeping units where residents share bathrooms and/or kitchen facilities with 16 or fewer persons.

R-4: Residential occupancies that meet the requirements for construction as defined in R-3 except as otherwise provided in the IRC and are equipped with an automatic sprinkler system installed in accordance with Section 903.2.7 of the IBC.

One of the key considerations of group R occupancies is the type of living unit based on its level of accessibility. The IBC divides R-1 units into type A and type B units, both of which are designed and constructed to meet ICC A117.1®–2009 standards published by the ICC. Major sections of this standard include accessible routes, general site and building elements, plumbing elements and

MINIMUM INSULATION REQUIREMENTS FOR FROST-PROTECTED FOOTINGS IN HEATED BUILDINGS[a]

AIR FREEZING INDEX (°F-DAYS)[b]	VERTICAL INSULATION R-VALUE[c,d]	HORIZONTAL INSULATION R-VALUE[c,e]		HORIZONTAL INSULATION DIMENSIONS PER FIGURE R403.3(1) (INCHES)		
		ALONG WALLS	AT CORNERS	A	B	C
1500 or less	4.5	NR	NR	NR	NR	NR
2000	5.6	NR	NR	NR	NR	NR
2500	6.7	1.7	4.9	12	24	40
3000	7.8	6.5	8.6	12	24	40
3500	9.0	8.0	11.2	24	30	60
4000	10.1	10.5	13.1	24	36	60

For SI: 1 inch = 25.4 mm, °C = [(°F) – 32]/1.8.

a. Insulation requirements are for protection against frost damage in heated buildings. Greater values may be required to meet energy conservation standards. Interpolation between values is permissible.

b. See Figure R403.3(2) for Air Freezing Index values.

c. Insulation materials shall provide the stated minimum R-values under long-term exposure to moist, below-ground conditions in freezing climates. The following R-values shall be used to determine insulation thicknesses required for this application: Type II expanded polystyrene—2.4R per inch; Type IV extruded polystyrene—4.5R per inch; Type VI extruded polystyrene—4.5R per inch; Type IX expanded polystyrene—3.2R per inch; Type X extruded polystyrene—4.5R per inch. NR indicates that insulation is not required.

d. Vertical insulation shall be expanded polystyrene insulation or extruded polystyrene insulation.

e. Horizontal insulation shall be extruded polystyrene insulation.

FIGURE 5.20b Minimum insulation requirements for a concrete slab based on Table R403.3(1) of the IRC.

fixtures, communication elements and fixtures, special rooms and spaces, and built-in furnishings and equipment. Chapter 10 of the ICC A117.1 standard applies specifically to access within units, with Section 1003 devoted to type A units and Section 1004 devoted to type B units. Major guidelines apply to bathroom and kitchen design. The main consideration in bathroom design is wheelchair access. Figure 5.21 shows possible layout alternatives for access in a bathroom. A major consideration in kitchen design is access to work areas. Figure 5.22 shows counter requirements.

Accessible Route

An *accessible route* is the walking surface from the exterior access through the residence. The exterior access (the front door) may not be located in a bedroom. At least one route must connect all spaces that are part of the dwelling unit. If there is only one route, it must not pass through a bathroom, closet, or similar space.

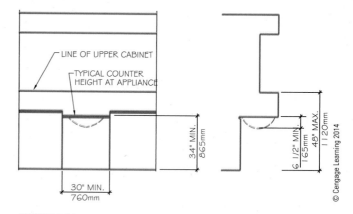

FIGURE 5.22 A major consideration of kitchen guidelines for type A dwelling units is access to work areas.

The access route must have a minimum width of 36" (914 mm) except at doors. Vertical changes in floor height must not exceed 1/4" (6.4 mm). Changes in floor level up to 1/2" (13 mm) are allowed if there is a bevel with a slope not exceeding 1:2. Ramps may not have slopes greater than 1:20. Floor surfaces of a turning space may have slopes no steeper than 1:48.

Operating Controls

This portion of the accessibility standards regulates placement of and access to controls for electrical, environmental, security, and intercom controls. Figure 5.23 shows

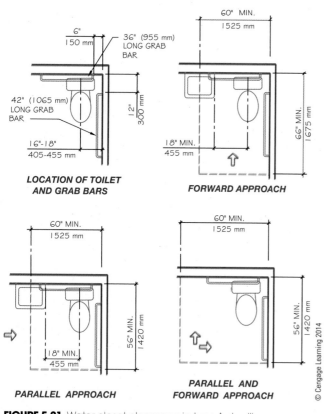

FIGURE 5.21 Water closet clearance in type A dwelling units based on ICC A117.1 requirements for multifamily units. Although not required for single-family homes, many homeowners opt to incorporate accessibility requirements to ensure that their family can remain in the home should a debilitating injury or illness occur.

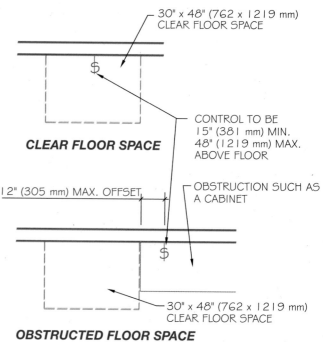

FIGURE 5.23 A clear floor area of 30 × 48" (762 × 1219 mm) must be provided to access controls.

guidelines for placement of controls. The control should be centrally located in a clear floor space measuring a minimum of 30 × 48" (762 × 1219 mm), and should be no more than 48" (1219 mm) and no less than 15" (381 mm) from the finished floor. Exceptions to these locations include:

- Electrical receptacles serving dedicated uses such as a 110 convenience outlet (C.O.) for a refrigerator.
- Appliance-mounted controls or switches.
- A single receptacle located above a portion of a countertop uninterrupted by a sink or appliance. This receptacle does not need to be accessible as long as one receptacle is provided.
- Floor electrical receptacles.
- Plumbing fixture controls.

Doorways

All doors in type A units must provide a minimum clear opening of 32" (815 mm), as shown in Figure 5.24. Although maneuvering space is not required on the dwelling unit side of the door, good design dictates that space for turning a wheelchair be provided. Figure 5.25 shows required clear access for type A units.

Kitchens

Figure 5.26 shows the required minimum clearances for kitchen base cabinet placement. A clear floor area of 30 × 48" (762 × 1219 mm) is required for the cooktop,

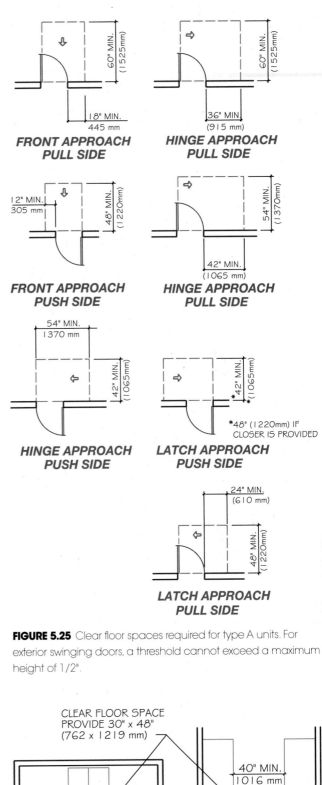

FIGURE 5.25 Clear floor spaces required for type A units. For exterior swinging doors, a threshold cannot exceed a maximum height of 1/2".

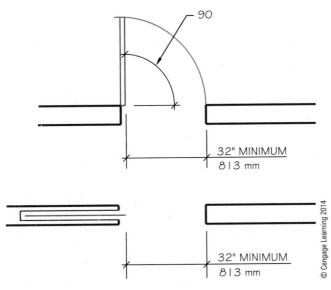

FIGURE 5.24 Doorways must have a minimum clear opening of 32" (813 mm) measured between the face of the door when open 90° and the stop. A maximum tolerance of 1/4" (6.4 mm) is allowed.

FIGURE 5.26 Clear floor spaces required between cabinets in a kitchen.

dishwasher, freezer, oven, range, refrigerator, sink, and trash compactor when provided.

Toilet and Bathing Facilities

Figure 5.27 shows a typical bathroom layout. Doors are not allowed to swing into the clear floor spaces required for any fixture unless there is a clear floor space at least 30" × 48" (762 × 1219 mm) beyond the swing of the door. This space allows a person to enter, close the door, and then move to a fixture. If this space is provided, the door may swing into the required space for each bath fixture. Figure 5.28 shows the required space for a lavatory. As shown in Figure 5.29, a water closet must have a minimum of 18" (457 mm) from the centerline of the fixture and a minimum of 15" (381 mm) on the other side when located between a bathtub or lavatory. When a toilet is located by a wall, a distance of 18" (457 mm) must be provided from the centerline of the fixture to the wall. Figure 5.30 shows access methods and clear floor

space required for a toilet. For each access method, vanities or lavatories located on a wall behind the water closet are permitted to overlap the clear floor space. Where a tub and/or shower is provided, it must comply with Figure 5.31. If a separate shower and tub are provided, the guidelines apply to only one of the fixtures. Figure 5.32 shows the clear floor requirements when only a shower is provided.

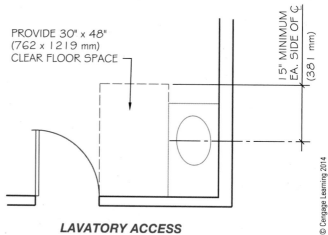

LAVATORY ACCESS

FIGURE 5.28 Required space for a lavatory. A water closet must be at least 18" (457 mm) from the centerline of the fixture and 15" (381 mm) on the other side when located between a bathtub or lavatory. When a lavatory is located by a wall, 18" (457 mm) must be provided from the centerline of the fixture to the wall.

MINIMUM BATHROOM SIZE

MINIMUM ACCESSIBLE BATHROOM

FIGURE 5.27 A typical bathroom layout (top) is often too small to provide accessibility. Doors are not allowed to swing into the clear floor space required for any fixture unless a 30 × 48" (762 × 1219 mm) minimum clear floor space is provided beyond the swing of the door.

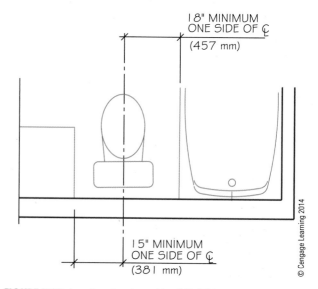

FIGURE 5.29 A water closet must be 18" (457 mm) from the centerline of the fixture and 15" (381 mm) minimum on the other side when located between a bathtub or lavatory. When the toilet is located by a wall, 18" (457 mm) must be provided from the centerline of the fixture to the wall.

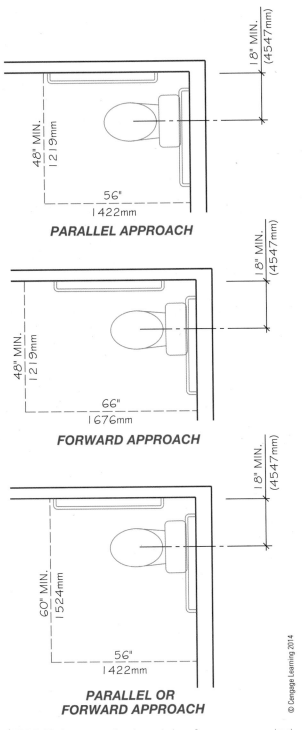

PARALLEL APPROACH

FORWARD APPROACH

PARALLEL OR
FORWARD APPROACH

FIGURE 5.30 Access methods and clear floor space required for a toilet. For each access method, vanities or lavatories located on a wall behind the water closet are permitted to overlap the clear floor space.

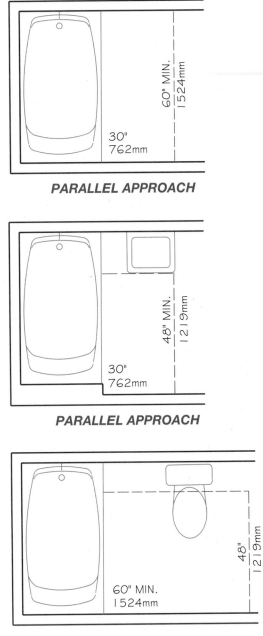

PARALLEL APPROACH

PARALLEL APPROACH

FORWARD APPROACH

FIGURE 5.31 Where a tub and/or shower is provided, it must have a clear floor area of 30 × 60" (762 × 1524 mm). A lavatory placed at the control end of the tub may extend into the clearance if a 30 × 48" (762 × 1219 mm) clear area is maintained. When the forward approach is used, the floor space must be 48 × 60" (1219 × 1524 mm). A toilet placed at the control end of the tub may be placed in the clear floor area as long as the minimum requirements for the toilet are still met. Access to the toilet can be achieved using the parallel or the parallel/forward approach.

© Cengage Learning 2014

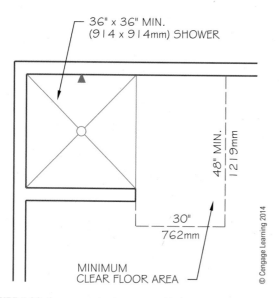

FIGURE 5.32 If a separate shower and tub are provided, the guidelines apply to only one of the fixtures. If only a shower is provided, minimum clear floor requirements must be met.

INTERNATIONAL GREEN CONSTRUCTION CODE

New to the 2012 ICC I-codes is the ***International Green Construction Code*** (IgCC). The IgCC moves from guidelines to required codes and has the potential to produce large-scale environmental benefits in the construction industry that would be impossible to attain with voluntary green building programs and rating systems. Although the 2012 edition applies only to commercial structures, the trend within the industry is to incorporate green standards to all levels of construction.

This code incorporates project electives that are designed to encourage the construction of buildings that exceed the minimum requirements of the International Residential Code, similar to the LEED rating systems do. In addition the IgCC contains features that allow jurisdictions to customize and tailor the code to address environmental concerns of a local nature and to respond to environmentally related political agendas.

The IgCC provides jurisdictions with a document that allows them to specify enhanced building performance in many specific critical areas of concern, including energy, water, natural resources, and material conservation. Rather than relying on an overall score attained by allowing owners and design professionals a wide array of choices in all environmental categories with few mandatory requirements, as is typical of most green building rating systems, the IgCC takes the opposite approach consisting mainly of mandatory requirements.

Going Green

Green Codes

Building codes address how the environment affects a structure. Stresses resulting from gravity, wind, snow, water, and seismic activity have always been a major concern of the model codes. The National Green Building Standard ICC 700-2012 now addresses how the building affects the environment. The ICC and the NAHB have jointly developed the National Green Building Standard that provides a common national benchmark for designers. Although primarily aimed at residential construction, the standard does apply to multifamily construction. The standard requires designers and builders to address:

- Land conservation
- Water conservation
- Material resource conservation
- Energy conservation
- Indoor and outdoor air quality

In addition to the Green Building Standard, the ICC has developed the 2012 IgCC. At the time of publication of this text, the 2012 IgCC applied only to commercial construction. Because green code development is such a fluid area, it is imperative that you constantly monitor the websites of the ICC, USGBC, ANSI, and NAHB for the most current information on green building and developing codes that might affect your projects. The address for each site is listed at the end of this chapter.

Additional Resources

Use the following websites as resources to help you keep current with changes in guidelines, codes, and major regulating agencies that are related to residential construction.

Major Building Code Organizations

Address

www.thegreendestination.com
www.iccsafe.org

Company, Product, or Service

Delmar Cengage/ICC (essential information for green building)
The International Code Council (ICC)—The 2012 IRC is
    their current code; the 2015 codes will be available in the
    spring of 2015

United States and Federal Agencies Related to Construction

Address	Company, Product, or Service
www.ada.gov	Americans with Disabilities Act (ADA)
www.eere.energy.gov	Department of Energy (DOE), Energy Efficiency & Renewable Energy
www.energystar.gov	ENERGY STAR
www.epa.gov	Environmental Protection Agency (EPA)
www.federalregister.gov/agencies/ government-printing-office	Federal Register, Government Printing Office
www.nist.gov	National Institute of Standards and Technology (NIST)
www.osha.gov	Occupational Safety & Health Administration (OSHA)
www.access-board.gov	U.S. Access Board (also known as the U.S. Architectural and Transportation Barriers Compliance Board)

The following sites are listed in the IBC and IRC for their reference standards.

Address	Company, Product, or Service
www.aamanet.org	American Architectural Manufacturers Association®
www.aci-int.org	American Concrete Institute®
www.afandpa.org	American Forest & Paper Association©
www.aisc.org	American Institute of Steel Construction©
www.aitc-glulam.org	American Institute of Timber Construction©
www.ansi.org	American National Standards Institute (ANSI)
www.apawood.org	APA—The Engineered Wood Association
www.asce.org	American Society of Civil Engineers (ASCE)
www.asme.org	American Society of Mechanical Engineers© (ASME©)
www.astm.com	ASTM International©
www.awpa.org	American Wood Protection Association™
www.aws.org	American Welding Society®
www.cedarbureau.org	Cedar Shake and Shingle Bureau©
www.gypsum.org	Gypsum Association
www.passivehouse-international.org	International Passive House Association
www.iso.org	International Organization for Standardization©
www.masonrysociety.org	The Masonry Society©
www.naamm.org	National Association of Architectural Metal Manufacturers©
www.nahb.org	National Association of Home Builders
www.ncma.org	National Concrete Masonry Association
www.nfpa.org	National Fire Protection Association
www.passivehouse.com	Passive House Institute
www.pci.org	Precast Prestressed Concrete Institute©
www.post-tensioning.org	Post-Tensioning Institute©
www.tpsgc-pwgsc.gc.ca/ongc-cgsb/ index-eng.html	Canadian General Standards Board
www.seinstitute.org	Structural Engineering Institute
www.spri.org	Single Ply Roofing Institute
www.steel.org	American Iron and Steel Institute©
www.steeljoist.org	Steel Joist Institute©
www.tpinst.org	Truss Plate Institute
www.ul.com	Underwriters Laboratories
www.usgbc.org	United States Green Building Council
www.wdma.com	Window & Door Manufacturers Association
www.wirereinforcementinstitute.org	Wire Reinforcement Institute®

Construction-related organizations that ensure the quality of materials include:

Address	**Company, Product, or Service**
www.approvals.org	International Approval Services, Inc.
www.iafc.org	International Association of Fire Chiefs (IAFC)
www.csa.ca	Canadian Standards Association©
www.mbinet.org	Modular Building Institute©
www.nfrc.org	National Fenestration Rating Council
www.nibs.org	National Institute of Building Sciences (NIBS)
www.nmhc.org	National Multi-Housing Council® (NMHC®)
www.wwpa.org	Western Wood Products Association®

Guidelines and Codes That Affect Design Test

Follow these instructions to access and complete an electronic copy of the Chapter 5 Guidelines and Codes That Affect Design Test:

1. Go to cengagebrain.com
2. Enter the email address and password you used to register for the site (see Preface for full instructions).
3. Select the website from the **My Course & Materials** area of your home page. Select the chapter you want from the pull-down menu at the top of the page. Choose the resources for that chapter from the menu on the left.
4. Type your name, the chapter number, and the date at the top of the sheet.
5. Answer the following questions with short, complete statements using a word processor.
6. Base your answers on the code that governs your area unless otherwise noted.

NOTE:

The answers to some questions may not be contained in this chapter and will require you to do additional research using the Internet. Use your favorite search engine to search for specific governmental agencies or professional organizations.

Questions

5.1. What is the minimum required size for an entry door?

5.2. List the five major building codes used throughout the United States, starting with the code that governs your area.

5.3. All habitable rooms must have a certain percentage of the floor area provided in window glass for natural light. What is the required percentage?

5.4. What is the required width for hallways?

5.5. List the minimum width for residential stairs.

5.6. What is the minimum ceiling height for a kitchen?

5.7. What is the maximum height that a bedroom window sill can be above the finish floor?

5.8. Toilets must have a space how many inches wide?

5.9. Are bathrooms in a single-family residence required to be handicapped-accessible?

5.10. List three sanitation requirements for a residence.

5.11. What are the area limitations that a spiral stair can serve?

5.12. What is the minimum window area required to meet the ventilation requirements for a bedroom that is 10' × 12'?

5.13. List the minimum square footage required for habitable rooms.

5.14. For a sloping ceiling, what is the lowest height allowed for usable floor area?

5.15. What is the minimum size opening for an emergency egress?

5.16. When are guardrails required?

5.17. The 36" wide entry door is to be secured with a dead bolt lock that requires a key on each side to open the lock. Is it legal? Explain your answer.

5.18. What are the requirements for controlling drainage in a window well?

5.19. If a home is to comply with A117.1, what is the minimum clear opening required for a door located in an access route?

5.20. What are the requirements for locating the operating controls based on A117.1?

5.21. What is the required floor space for a forward approach toilet?

5.22. What is an accessible route?

5.23. At what height should an accessible kitchen counter with the sink be located?

5.24. A home has a LEED credit of 37. What category does the home qualify for, and how many points are needed to advance to the next stage?

5.25. You're part of the design team that will try to qualify for LEED certification. If the Integrative Process credit is desired, how long will the meeting to earn this credit last, and who could you expect to be at the meeting?

5.26. A home is to be built on a 100' × 35' site. One of the 35' sides of the property faces a street, the other 35' side opens to a golf course, and the two 100' property lines face developed property. Will this site qualify for LEED credits under the Location and Transportation credit?

5.27. Describe two methods of reducing heat islands on a LEED site.

5.28. What is the maximum allowable water pressure to qualify for a LEED Water Efficiency credit?

5.29. Visit the website of the building department that governs residential construction in your area. List the site address and determine the following current design criteria:
   a. Roof live loads
   b. Wind pressure
   c. Risk of weathering
   d. Frost-line depth
   e. Snow loads
   f. Seismic zone
   g. Risk of termites

5.30. Visit the website of the agency that regulates your state's building code. List the site address and describe any code changes currently under consideration.

5.31. Visit the website of one of the testing labs and obtain information related to a class drawing project. List the site address and information specific to your project.

5.32. Visit the website of one of the regulatory agencies that influence construction in your area. List the site address and information specific to your project.

5.33. Visit the USGBC webpage and research and write a 500-word report about the importance of the LEED program and how it relates to home building in your area. Be sure to include information about what resourses are available to you in your current educational setting.

5.34. Visit the ENERGY STAR website and determine what homes are required to meet the standards contained in the ENERGY STAR Version 3 Prescriptive Pathway.

5.35. Write a 500-page report to describe how a home can qualify for the ENERGY STAR Version 3 Prescriptive Pathway. REPORTS should indicate that students have visited the ENERGY STAR Perscriptive Pathway site and researched key points of the standards including what the standard is, and how it impacts heating, cooling, the building envelope, water heating, lighting, thermostats, and ductwork.

Chapter 8
Environmental Design Considerations

Previous chapters consider the home style, the number of floors, and key factors that control the layout of the interior and exterior living spaces. This chapter explores site-related design features that make the home energy-efficient and environmentally friendly. This chapter also covers design features such as zoning restrictions on design, methods of integrating the structure to the site, and environmentally friendly design.

Key Terms

Berm

Coniferous

Contours

Deciduous

Earth-bermed

Fire suppression
   system

Infill sites

Magnetic declination

Prevailing wind

Review boards

Solar orientation

Terrain

Variance

Zoning regulations

ZONING CONSIDERATIONS

Several site factors affect the design of a house. Among the most important are the zoning of the property, the neighborhood, and access to the lot.

Zoning Regulations

Each municipality has the right to regulate how property will be used. One of the first jobs of the design team is to identify the governing agency that regulates the building site and then to determine how the construction site is zoned. Keep in mind that zoning regulations are separate from building regulations. *Zoning regulations* control the density of an area by regulating the number of structures that can be built per acre. These regulations for density are often based on a comprehensive plan developed at the county or state level for 5-, 10-, 20-, and 50-year growth patterns. Although regulations vary greatly for each area, common examples of zoning divisions include:

- Urban Low-Density Residential (R-2.5, R-5, R-7, R-10, R-15, R-20, R-30)
- Medium-Density Residential (MR-1)
- High-Density Residential (HDR)
- Special High-Density (Residential) (SHD)
- Recreational Residential (RR)
- Mountain Recreational Resort (MRR)
- Rural (Agricultural) Residential (RA-1)
- Rural Residential Farm Forest 5-Acre (RRFF-5)
- Farm Forest 10-Acre (FF-10)

Notice after each zone is a listing of sub-zones. Although they may be called by a different name in your area, the zones in the Urban Low-Density Residential group are similar in most areas. These zones regulate the minimum average lot or parcel area per dwelling of the building site, similar to Table 8.1.

After determining the specific zone for the construction site, the usable area of the site can be determined. Setbacks regulate the building area. If a 100 × 100' site is to be developed, it is considered an R-10 zone. Zoning departments establish common minimum setbacks to protect structures on adjoining properties from the risk of fire or other structural damage. The setback size will vary greatly, but examples for the minimum design requirements for primary structures in these Urban Low-Density Residential Districts are as follows:

Minimum front yard setback: 20'

Minimum rear yard setback: 20'

TABLE 8.1 Minimum Average Lot or Parcel Area per Dwelling

DISTRICT	LOT AREA
R-2.5	2500 sq ft.
R-5	5000 sq ft.
R-7	7000 sq ft.
R-8.5	8500 sq ft.
R-10	10,000 sq ft.
R-15	15,000 sq ft.
R-20	20,000 sq ft.
R-30	30,000 sq ft.

© Cengage Learning 2014

Minimum side yard setback: 5'

Maximum building height: 35'

Maximum lot coverage of the primary use structures: 40%

Using these guidelines, the 100 × 100' site is reduced to a usable area 90' wide × 60' deep. The zoning guidelines for a 10,000 square-foot site allow:

- 5400 sq ft of buildable area within the setbacks (60 × 90').
- A maximum height of 35'.
- A maximum of 4000 sq ft of residence (40% of 10,000).
- An area of 6000 sq ft of open space (60% of 10,000 sq ft).

In addition to these guidelines, zoning regulations may vary based on the number of levels or on solar access guidelines. A designer should always verify the site limitations with the zoning department website prior to starting the planning process.

The home in the previous example is unrealistic for many urban settings. A large open space may be available in rural areas, but most urban areas are fairly well developed. Because of the previous development of most buildable sites, many urban areas allow established areas to be subdivided to create small building sites. Notice that the R2.5 site (25 × 100') allows the owner of an R5 or larger property to subdivide and create a new buildable site. Because of the narrow width of the site, many municipalities allow home construction with one zero side-yard setback. Figure 8.1 shows an example of three narrow *infill sites* in a high-density residential zone. Even though the zoning department allows high-density construction,

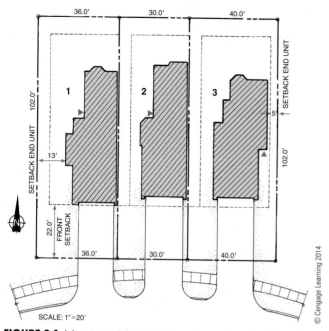

FIGURE 8.1 Many municipalities allow homes in a high-density residential zone to be constructed with one zero side-yard setback.

the construction of a wall that abuts the property line requires different construction methods. The design team must coordinate zoning regulations with building department regulations.

After determining the zoning and building regulations that govern the site, the design team can proceed. If the zoning regulations hinder the intended project, the design team can search the complete zoning regulations for exceptions or substitutions to allow the project to proceed. The code offers exceptions based on the specific zone and the size of the proposed structure. Common exceptions to the stated building setbacks include:

- Architectural features may project into the required yard not more than one-third the distance of the setback requirement and not exceeding 40" (1000 mm) into any required yard adjoining a street right-of-way.

- Open, unenclosed fire escapes may project a distance not exceeding 48" (1200 mm).

- An uncovered porch, terrace, patio, or underground structure extending no more than 30" (750 mm) above the finished elevation may extend within 3' (900 mm) of a side lot line or within 10' (3000 mm) of a front or rear lot line.

If the code restricts the design of the project once the listed exceptions have been applied, the owner can apply for a design review or a *variance,* or apply to have the land rezoned to a less restrictive use. A design review allows the

owner and the design team to meet with the regulating agency to obtain a solution that will ensure the safety of the occupants of the home. A variance is a legal request to allow a specific project to vary from the general guidelines.

Neighborhood Restrictions

After considering the legal restrictions of the zoning department, the practical aspects of design must be considered. In the initial planning of a residence, the neighborhood must be considered. Given a choice, it is extremely poor judgment to design a $500,000 residence in a neighborhood of $200,000 houses. This is not to say that the new occupants and existing neighbors would not be able to coexist, but the house will have poor resale value because of the lower value of the other houses in the neighborhood. The style of the houses in the neighborhood should also be a consideration. It's not necessary for all houses to look alike, but some unity of design can help maintain the value of all the properties in the neighborhood.

Review Boards

To help keep the values of the neighborhood uniform, many areas have architectural review committees. These are *review boards* made up of residents who determine what may or may not be built. Although once found only in the most exclusive neighborhoods, review boards are now common in undeveloped subdivisions, recreational areas, and retirement areas. These boards often set standards for minimum square footage, height limitations, and the type and color of siding and roofing materials. A potential homeowner or designer usually must submit preliminary designs showing floor plans and exterior elevations to the review board.

Site Access

Site access can have a major effect on the design of the house. Access will be influenced by the size of the building site, the location of streets or alleys, and the site terrain. The narrower the lot, the more access will affect the location of the entry and the garage. Figure 8.2 shows typical access and garage locations for a narrow lot with access from one side. Usually, because of space restrictions, interior lots have straight driveways.

There is much more flexibility in garage and house placement when developing a corner lot. To enhance livability, some municipalities are moving away from the layouts shown in Figure 8.2. The traditional layout has produced what is referred to as a snout house, meaning a home that is dominated by a view of the garage. In a design in which the garage dominates the home, the main entrance is often secondary to the entrance for cars,

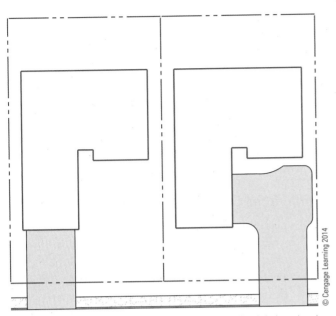

FIGURE 8.2 Access to an inner lot is limited by the lot size, street, and garage location.

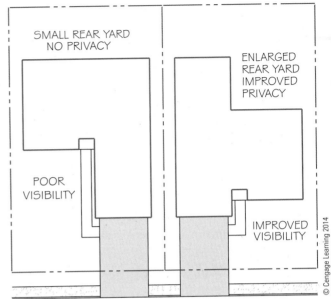

FIGURE 8.3 Limiting the distance that the garage can project from the balance of the home improves visibility and provides for a friendlier neighborhood atmosphere.

and the driveway often dominates the front yard. In an attempt to eliminate barriers between homes and enhance visibility, building covenants may call for

- At least one main entrance to the house that meets one of the following requirements:
- The main entrance can be no further than 6'-0" (1800 mm) behind the longest wall of the house that faces the street.
- The main entry must face the street or be at an angle of up to 45°.
- At least 15% of the area of the street-facing facade of the home must be windows.
- The length of the garage wall facing the street may not be greater than 50% of the length of the home's entire facade.
- A garage wall that faces a street may be no closer to the street property line than the longest street-facing wall of the home (see Figure 8.3).

Figure 8.4 shows an example of a pleasing relationship between the garage and the balance of the home.

Another popular way to make a neighborhood more livable is to remove the garage from the front of the site altogether. Many planned areas in Florida, Maryland, Oregon, and Tennessee have moved the garages to the rear of the site so that no driveway or parking is available on the entry or front side of the home. Automobile access is available to the rear of the lot by an alley. Figure 8.5 shows a garage carefully blended into a home on a large site.

FIGURE 8.4 A pleasing relationship between the residence and the garage.

FIGURE 8.5 On larger sites, the entrance to the garage can often be moved away from the main entry so that it is not a part of the front elevation.

Driveway Planning

After determining the location of the driveway, the driveway, turnaround, and exterior parking can be planned. Design options include:

- Position the driveway at a 90° angle to the access road when possible. A range of 60° to 90° to the access road is acceptable.

- Position the driveway to provide good visibility of the access road.

- Provide a minimum space of 10 × 20' (3000 × 6000 mm) for off-street parking.

- If possible, maintain a 5 percent grade for the driveway.

- Provide a minimum driveway slope of 1/4" per foot.

  - Single-car driveway minimum width is 10'-0" (3000 mm).

  - Double-car driveway minimum width is 18'-0" (5400 mm).

- The minimum turning radius for a driveway is 15'-0" (4500 mm), with a turning radius of 20' (6000 mm preferred if space permits).

In addition to providing access to the home for the owners, plan for additional parking space for guests and future drivers. Figure 8.6 shows a variety of driveway parking and turnaround options. The dimensions are given as commonly recommended minimums for small to standard-size cars.

Rural Access

When planning a residence for a rural site, weather and terrain can affect access. Studying weather patterns at the site helps reveal areas of the lot that may be inaccessible during parts of the year due to poor water drainage or drifted snow. The terrain of the site often determines where access to the house can be placed. In addition to incorporating the design features for urban drives and turnarounds, access for emergency vehicles must be considered. Standards will vary with each municipality and must be verified with the

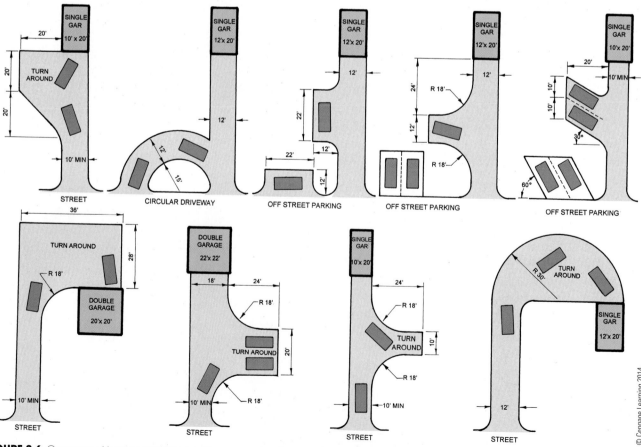

FIGURE 8.6 Common driveway, parking, and turnaround options and sizes.

local building department and fire marshal. Additional requirements for fire safety include:

- An all-weather surface of gravel, concrete, or asphalt paving.
- A minimum driveway width of 15' (4500 mm) with an additional 3' (900 mm) of space of vegetation-free space on each side of the roadway.
- A driveway slope that does not exceed 15 percent.
- Support for all bridges and culverts in the driveway up to 75,000 lbs (34 019 kg).
- A radius of 30' (9000 mm) or greater for emergency vehicles, delivery trucks, or vehicles pulling trailers.
- A pull-off equal to twice the road width 40' (12 000 mm) long near the midpoint of the driveway, but at no more than 1/4-mile intervals.
- Maintenance of tree limbs above the driveway for 15' (4500 mm) of clear access.
- A water access location that is obvious in appearance, cleared, and has safe footing and a footpath that will facilitate the use of portable pumps for lakefront properties.
- Requirements for a turnaround area at or near the end of the drive include:
  - For ambulance and smaller fire trucks, access to the turnaround must have a turning radius of 25' (7500 mm) and/or a pull-out of 30 × 12' (9000 × 3600 mm).
  - For large fire trucks, there must be a turnaround with a radius of 60' (18 000 mm) and/or a pull-out of 60 × 20' (18 000 × 6000 mm).
  - A turnaround with a minimum outside turning radius of 36' (10 800 mm) for all dead-end driveways with a length in excess of 150' (45 000 mm).

Fire Protection

In addition to access for emergency vehicles, provisions may be necessary for the home and site to meet the requirements of the Life, Fire, and Safety Code. Even if the 2012 IRC has not been adopted, many municipalities require single-family homes larger than 3,500 sq ft in rural settings to have protection from the *fire suppression system.* These requirements are often based on the proximity of the home to fire hydrants, water pressure at the hydrant, and the travel time to the home from a fire station. Insurance underwriters may also require a fire suppression system even when not required by the building department. Chapter 14 introduces the use of interior fire suppression systems. Some municipalities waive this requirement for sprinklers when certain guidelines are met, including:

- The fire-retardant roofing and siding materials.
- A 30' (9000 mm) minimum firebreak around the entire perimeter of the home that contains no vegetation exceeding 24" (600 mm) in height.
- A sprinkler system at the top of all exterior banks controls the possible spread of fire.
- A water storage system, swimming pool, pond, or storage tank containing 20,000 gal (75 708 L) of water for use in fire suppression

INTEGRATION OF THE HOME TO THE SITE

The location of the residence on the site has a major effect on the livability, energy efficiency, and cost of building and maintaining the home. Each of these features influences view orientation, the integration of the home to the terrain, solar orientation, and the orientation of the home to prevailing winds. For home construction in a subdivision, the design team may have little control over how the structure relates to the site. The street location will dictate the front of the home as well as the main entry and the garage locations. As the area of the site increases, the options for integrating the home with the environment also increase. Blending the home with the site becomes a preliminary factor that the design team must consider when starting the design process. Chapter 2 and Appendix A introduce guidelines for the evaluation of site features during the initial stages of the design process. Further integration of the home to the site, requires the design team to consider how the view, terrain, solar access, and prevailing summer and winter winds will affect the design.

View Orientation

Most homeowners purchase a building site before they begin designing the home. Many factors will influence the choice of an area for construction, such as the price of the site, the availability of necessary utilities, and access to schools and other features important to the owner's lifestyle. After determining the area, a key basis for selecting the actual site is often the view from the site. What makes a beautiful view depends on the taste of each individual and the available features such as a specific mountain peak or even a mountain range, forest, city skyline, or body of water such as a lake, stream, or ocean. Sites offering a view similar to that

© Jerry Harpur/Harpur Garden Library/Corbis

FIGURE 8.7 An orientation that captures a specific view can greatly increase the value of a home and be a priceless asset to the owner.

from the home in Figure 8.7 are usually more expensive than comparable sites without a view. The designer's obligation to the client is to design a home that will optimize the view. The ideal design provides an environment that allows the occupants to feel as though they are part of the view.

Rarely will a site be perfect for each aspect of a home's design. A home with a gorgeous view may have a poor solar or wind orientation. The design team must work closely with the owners to evaluate orientation conflicts and evaluate tradeoffs. A home designed to take advantage of a view will generally have large amounts of glass on the view side. The openings for the glass may require the help of a structural engineer to ensure the home meets the lateral design loads caused by wind or earthquakes. If the home is situated to take advantage of a view but has poor solar or wind orientation, design alternatives or energy-saving building materials can be required to offset possible problems. Section 6 includes construction options to overcome poor solar orientation.

View orientation should be a consideration even if a home is being built in a subdivision with no spectacular view. Although the size of the lot and building setbacks may limit the placement of the home, consideration should be given to the view from each window. If homes are on the adjacent sites, plan room to minimize views directly into the windows of an adjoining home. In areas where no other homes currently exist, plan for where potential new homes may be constructed and add or delete windows accordingly.

Integration of the Home to the Terrain

The land at the building site greatly influences the type of available structures and the drawings necessary for completing the construction documents. Land considerations

such as natural features, contour, and soil-bearing capacity play important roles in determining the number of floor levels in a home, the placement of structure, and how loads will be transferred into the ground.

Natural Features

Few if any reputable designers would consider bulldozing a site of its major natural features to have a clean site at which to begin work. Quite the opposite: one of the first considerations in planning how the home will blend with the site is to map key natural features for incorporation into the design. This includes locating streambeds, marshlands, major clusters of natural vegetation, and natural rock clusters. Most areas have strict environmental regulations protecting natural features, even to the point of requiring that no soil leave the construction site, either by erosion or on the wheels of construction equipment. Because great care must be taken in locating each feature, hiring a civil engineering firm to locate key natural features will help to ensure accuracy. In working with bodies of water such as creeks or streams, the design firm must research state or federal regulations that may regulate development within specified distances. Minimum distances from a stream, for example, may be based on a minimum distance such as 100' (30 000 mm) from the average yearly stream edge. Minimum distances may also be based on a minimum height above a 50- or 100-year flood plane. The local building department will usually determine the method of measurement.

Determining the location of existing trees is often required for preliminary design review in some municipalities. Planning departments often require information regarding the type of tree, the diameter of the tree trunk, the average diameter of the ground coverage, and the estimated size of the root ball.

After locating key natural features, the home can be designed so that each feature can safely remain. Figure 8.8 shows Frank Lloyd Wright's Fallingwater. It is what many architects consider to be the best example of a home that blends with its environment. A second major consideration in planning how the home will fit the site is to carefully plan how it will match the terrain.

Terrain

Terrain refers to the shape or contour of a specific parcel of land. Although stock plans are usually drawn as if the construction site is flat, in reality, most of the flat, easy-to-build sites in urban areas have already been developed. Custom home plans are drawn to blend with a specific area at a specific construction site. In working on a site with a gentle slope, for example, someone from the design team may visit the site to determine spot elevations and

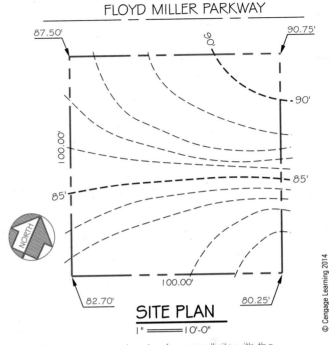

FLOYD MILLER PARKWAY

87.50'   90   90.75'

100.00'   90'

85'   85'

NORTH

82.70'   100.00'   80.25'

SITE PLAN
1" = 10'-0"

© Cengage Learning 2014

FIGURE 8.9 A topography plan for a small site with the elevations for each property corner and the contours for each foot of elevation change.

© Richard A. Cooke/CORBIS

FIGURE 8.8 Fallingwater, designed by Frank Lloyd Wright, is considered by many architects to be the best example of a home that blends in with its environment.

general trends in drainage. When a large area of land or a slope is involved, a civil engineering firm is typically hired by the owner to develop a map of the topography.

Figure 8.9 shows a topographic drawing for a small site. Notice that the elevation for each property corner is given in engineering units. Chapter 10 presents the process for creating a topographic drawing. The dash lines represent the *contours* for each foot of elevation change. As the effect of terrain is considered on the design of a home, it's important to remember a few basic concepts about reading a topographic plan. Notice that the contour lines on the east side of the site are closer together than those on the west side. The spacing of the lines indicates the slope of the terrain. The closer the lines are to each other, the steeper the slope. For this site, the east side is steeper than the west side of the property.

A second method of describing the slope of land is to use slope percentages. Slopes can be specified by percentages, such as 2%, 8%, or 25% slope. The number

represents the rise in inches for 100 inches, or the number of feet per 100 feet. A 2% slope rises 2' over a distance of 100'. The east side of the property falls 10', or has an approximate 10% slope. The west side slopes approximately 5' per 100' for a 5% slope. The term *approximate* is used to describe each slope because the slopes are not uniform throughout the property length. Figure 8.10 shows various slopes expressed in percentages.

Modifying Terrain. Adding or removing soil alters the contours of the land at a construction site. Removing soil from a site is referred to as a cut. Soil can be cut to form a vertical bank, but this will lead to landslides. An incline of 1.5 horizontal units to 1 vertical unit (1.5/1) is typical for cut banks. To represent a cut bank on a site plan, lines must be placed 1.5' apart. Fill is the process of adding soil over the existing grade. An incline of 2 horizontal units to 1 vertical unit (2/1) is typically used to create fill banks. To represent a fill bank on a site plan, lines must be placed 2' apart. Chapter 10 provides methods for creating and representing cut and fill banks. During the design process, it's important to remember that any portion of the home being built over fill material needs a special foundation design. (Section 7 covers foundation design.) Remember that it is possible to modify the land to fit the design and style of the home as it is being designed. In planning the portion of the site where the

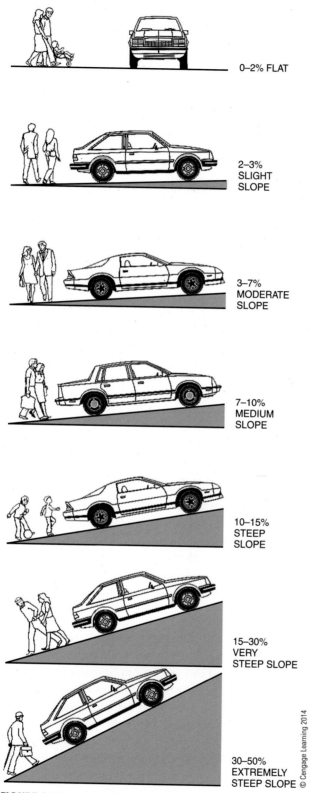

FIGURE 8.10 Many zoning departments specify the grade for a driveway by a percentage of slope. A slope of 10% is the maximum that many municipalities will allow.

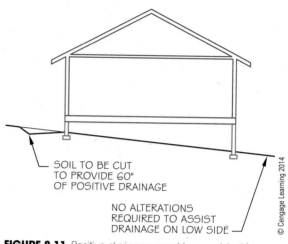

FIGURE 8.11 Positive drainage must be provided for a distance of 5' (1500 mm) on all sides of the residence. On the high side of the home, the existing soil will need to be cut to provide positive drainage.

house will be located, two key points must be considered before altering the site:

- The soil must slope away from the residence on all sides for a distance of 5' (1500 mm). The IRC refers to this as positive drainage. On the low side of the house, this is quite easy. On the high side, this requires cutting some of the existing soil to provide drainage, as shown in Figure 8.11. The low point formed between the two slopes must also be inclined to allow water to drain away from the house.

- The practical maximum grade for a driveway is 10%, although some municipalities allow a 14% slope. When a car is parked on such a steep grade, it will be awkward to open its doors. Many municipalities have regulations covering the length, grade, width, and turning radius of residential driveways to ensure that service vehicles can navigate the driveway. A slope of 3% to 7% is convenient for access.

The slope of the driveway also plays an important role in determining the finish floor level of the home. Chapter 10 introduces methods of moving soil to provide positive drainage and introduces the process of planning the driveway access to the home.

Soil Considerations

In addition to the slope of the site, the type of soil must be considered during the design stage. The type of soil will affect the design of the foundation. Although you do not want the foundation to dictate the design of the home, the type of foundation should be considered as the home is designed. The type of soil, its drainage capacity, and its tendency to freeze should all be known prior to starting the design. A soils engineer can provide the design team with this information.

Floor Layout and Terrain Design

The terrain of the site will affect the design of the home. A single-level or two-story home is well suited to a level or a gently sloping site. Land at the upper end of the site can be cut and pushed to the lower portion to form a level pad for a floor (see Figure 8.12a). On sites with a gentle slope, a multilevel floor similar to that in Figure 8.12b, which steps with the site may be used. A single-level home on a sloped site will require extra construction cost for excavation or building up the foundation. If a single floor is used on a sloping site similar to that in Figure 8.12c, a wood-framed floor will need to be used. A crawl space will be created on the low side of the site. This space can generally be developed into a lower floor formed with a concrete slab, similar to that in Figure 8.12d. The cost of excavation will increase, but the additional living space is more economical than using the crawl space for storage. A multilevel home or a home with a daylight basement, similar to that in Figure 8.12e, is well suited to a sloped site. Another alternative for a steep site is to design a home built on stilts. This requires that the design team coordinate with a structural engineer to design the supports and a soils engineer to study the soil and determine its bearing capacity. The steel frame for a multilevel home constructed on a steep site is shown in Figure 8.13. An alternative to building up is to build down. Subterranean construction is used for some high-end homes in frigid regions of the country. Underground homes have increased excavation and material cost but have economical advantages in energy consumption over above-ground homes.

Solar Orientation

The orientation of a home to the sun is referred to as **solar orientation.** Depending on the area of the country where the home will be built, the solar orientation of a home may be based on heating or cooling requirements. If you're building in a southern state, blocking the summer heat is a goal of the solar design. In northern states, maximizing the winter sun is the goal of solar design. In either case, the position of the sun throughout the day and the year is an important factor in home orientation. Even if the home is not designed to take advantage of solar heat, its orientation to the sun should be an important consideration. Chapter 6 explores the relationship of rooms and their usage to

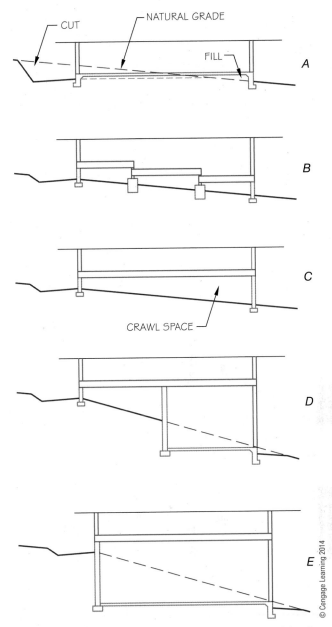

FIGURE 8.12 The shape of the building will affect the style of the home to be built. A. On mild slopes, land at the upper end of the site can be cut and pushed to the lower portion of the site to form a level pad for a level floor. B. A multilevel floor is well suited to a gentle slope. C. A single-level home on a sloped site will require a floor framed with wood or extra excavation for building a concrete slab. D. A wood-framed floor over a partial basement. E. A multilevel home or a home with a daylight basement is well suited to a steep site.

the sun during the day. Factors such as placing bedrooms on the east side of the home and living areas on the west side will allow the family to take advantage of natural lighting throughout their daily activities. Figure 8.14 shows considerations of the sun's position throughout the day.

FIGURE 8.13 Construction sites with steep slopes will require additional input from structural and soils engineers. The site for this multilevel home required the use of steel pilings driven 27' into the soil to reach solid rock. At the far corner of the home, stilts 20' high were required

Locating the Home to Maximize Sunlight

The location of the sun throughout its yearly cycle is as important as its daily effect on room layout. As seen in Figure 8.15, the sun is higher in the sky during the summer, when it rises in the northeast and sets in the northwest.

During the winter, the sun is much lower in the sky, rising in the southeast and setting in the southwest. Depending on your location, on December 21 the sun may be as low as 20° above the horizon. This difference in sunrise, sunset, and height above the horizon must be a consideration for planning window placement and the size of the roof overhang. Careful planning of the location and the angle of the windows where sunlight can enter the home will affect the heat gained within the residence. Knowing the location of the sun at specific times of the year allows the designer to size and place glazing to maximize heating and cooling effects. Glazing can be as much as 25° away from perpendicular to the sun's rays and still receive 90% of the radiation. Chapter 11 explores window placement and Chapter 16 explores how to determine the size of the roof overhang based on heating and cooling needs.

In developing a site with a solar orientation, allow for full sun exposure from about 8:00 a.m. through 3:00 p.m. to make the most efficient use of the sun's radiation for heating. Place the home in a northern portion of the sunny area of the site to maximize the exposure of the southern face of the home to the sun. This limits the chance that future development will cast shade on the residence and maximizes southern outdoor living areas.

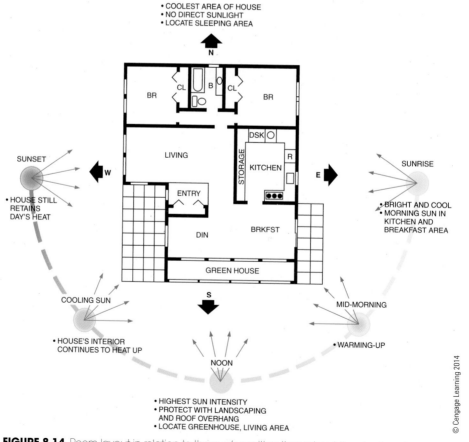

FIGURE 8.14 Room layout in relation to the sun's position throughout the day is an important design consideration.

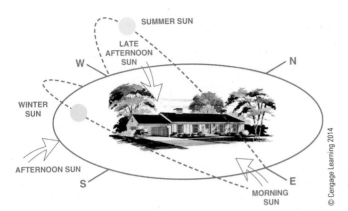

FIGURE 8.15 The sun is higher in the sky during the summer, rising in the northeast and setting in the northwest. During the winter, the sun is much lower in the sky, rising in the southeast and setting in the southwest. This difference in sunrise, sunset, and height above the horizon will need to be considered as the home is designed.

Consider obstacles such as tall homes, evergreen trees, or other obstructions that may block the sun. Many areas restrict the height and the placement of the home on the site based on solar access laws to ensure that each site will have such access. Tall obstructions to solar access, their locations and effects on the site should be mapped to determine the extent of the solar blockage. The types of trees on the site also affect solar heat gain. *Coniferous* trees on the south side of the home will hinder solar gain. *Deciduous* trees on the south side of the home provide shade from the summer sun. In the winter, when these trees have lost their leaves, winter sun exposure is not substantially reduced.

Building Shape and Solar Planning

In addition to the home's location on the site, its shape will affect the solar gain. A rectangular home that is elongated along the east-west axis will maximize solar gain. This orientation is the most efficient shape for both heating and cooling in all climates. A home with a long south face maximize solar gain during the winter and minimizes the solar gain in summer by having short east and west faces. Most of the summer sun, including the hottest sun of the day, will be on the southern roof, with glazing protected by overhangs. Glazing on the east and west walls is not exposed to the hottest sun of the day. By placing rooms that require heat on the south face of the home and rooms that produce heat on the cool north face, the solar gain can be maximized.

The depth of the home along the east-west axis is also an important consideration in maximizing solar gain. Studies by the Illuminating Engineering Society of North America conclude that the depth of rooms along the south

face of a home should not exceed 2.5 times the window height from the floor. Using this guideline allows sunlight to penetrate the entire room. Installing skylights in a south-sloping roof will provide sunlight to areas exceeding the window height ratio.

A third consideration for the shape of the home is minimizing the height and length of the structure's north face. This can be done by berming earth against the wall or by sloping the roof so that its low side is on the north face of the structure. Building taller south walls with glazing and shorter north walls with minimal glazing will minimize heat loss. The low north walls will also reduce the shadow cast by the home and increase outdoor living areas on its north side. A roof pitch that approximates the sun's winter angle will maximize exterior living areas on the home's north face. On a multilevel home, position the upper floor on the south side when possible and protect the north side with attic space over the lower portion of the home.

Establishing South

To maximize solar gain, determine true south when evaluating the site's solar potential. If view orientation requires a slight turn of the structure away from south, the solar potential may not be significantly reduced. The exact amount will vary based on your location, but the south face of the home can vary up to 45° to the east or west and still maintain efficiency. True south is determined by a line that stretches from the North Pole to the South Pole. When using a compass to establish north, the compass points to magnetic north, which is different from true north. The difference between true north and magnetic north is referred to as *magnetic declination.* The amount of magnetic declination differs throughout the country. Figure 8.16 shows the magnetic declination at various locations in the United States. A magnetic declination of 15° east, which occurs in central California, means that the compass needle points 15° to the east of true north and 15° to the west of true south. If you face magnetic south, true south is 15° to the left.

Wind Orientation

The term *prevailing wind* refers to the direction in which the wind typically blows. The prevailing winds in the United States are from west to east. If you live on the West Coast, the winds generally flow from the southwest off the Pacific Ocean. The prevailing winds are said to be southwesterly. During the late summer and early fall, winds come from the northeast and produce hot, dry weather. These differences in prevailing winds are caused by differences in atmospheric pressure. These types of patterns are large, regional patterns. The Rocky Mountains,

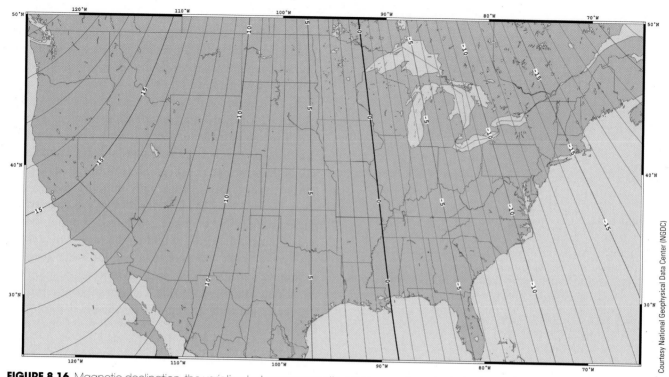

FIGURE 8.16 Magnetic declination, the variation between magnetic and true north, varies based on your location.

Courtesy National Geophysical Data Center (NGDC)

the Great Lakes, the Gulf of Mexico, the Atlantic Ocean, and the Great Plains are all examples of natural features that greatly influence the winds in specific regions. Within each region, wind patterns can vary because of the mountains, valleys, canyons, or river basins. A third type of pattern exists within local areas. On hillside sites, heat causes a breeze to blow uphill during the daylight hours and cooler air settling in the evening causes a breeze to flow downhill. The design of the home should be based on the winds expected for the construction site. You can find conditions that influence site location on the Internet, in almanacs, or at the local library by researching subjects such as climate, microclimate, prevailing wind, and wind conditions. The local weather bureau can also provide information regarding prevailing winds in an area.

In planning the home site, select an area with protection from the prevailing winter winds. Landmass, other buildings, and vegetation can all provide protection from the prevailing winds. When the view will not be blocked, place the structure so that existing structures can block winds. Placing a home on the crest of a hill usually provides the best view, but it also maximizes the force of the wind. Locating a home just below the ridge of a sloping site allows the land to block the wind. As shown in Figure 8.17, the orientation of the home to the site affects wind currents. By altering the home's shape,

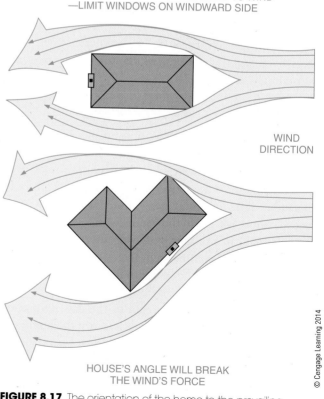

NARROW SIDE OF HOUSE EXPOSED TO WIND
—LIMIT WINDOWS ON WINDWARD SIDE

WIND DIRECTION

HOUSE'S ANGLE WILL BREAK THE WIND'S FORCE

© Cengage Learning 2014

FIGURE 8.17 The orientation of the home to the prevailing winds and the shape of the home will affect wind flow around it.

you can protect pockets for outdoor living. The shape of the roof can also aid in deflecting wind. A sloping roof can be used to deflect wind currents. Placing the low edge of the roof toward the direction of the prevailing wind causes the wind to rise up and over the structure. Another method of blocking strong prevailing winds is to sink the home into the grade. This includes such options as daylight basements, earth-bermed, and earth-sheltered homes. ***Earth-bermed*** homes have soil on three sides and earth-sheltered homes have soil on the roof as well as on three sides. Figure 8.18 shows options for earth-sheltered homes. Be sure to verify emergency egress requirements with the local building department if bermed or sheltered options are to be used.

Room location and construction methods can also influence wind protection. Place rooms such as utility rooms, pantries, and bathrooms that do not require large areas of glass for view or solar use on the north side or the side toward severe winter winds. The kitchen produces heat, so it can be placed on the windward side of the house. A garage can also be used to provide a break between cold winter winds. Bedrooms with fairly small windows may also provide a barrier between the wind and the balance of the home.

In addition to natural features or other structures, landscaping is an effective means of blocking wind. Plantings and windbreaks such as fences or decorative barriers can also be used to moderate the effects of winter winds. Be sure to balance the decision to plant deciduous or conifer trees for wind protection with view considerations. Coniferous trees or other evergreen landscaping planted in staggered rows can provide an effective windbreak. Consult a landscape architect or other landscaping professional to verify tree choices. If the wrong types of trees or too few of them are planted, they can become a danger to the home during high winds. Figure 8.19 shows a home built in a wooded area that provides an effective wind buffer.

Cooling Summer Winds

In coastal regions and areas affected by large bodies of water, summer winds are usually mild and contribute to a more comfortable living environment. In inland areas, summer breezes may be nonexistent or hot and dry. In areas where cooling is the goal, it is especially important for the home design to take advantage of any cooling available. Comfort can be achieved through design for natural ventilation and by landscape design. The use of high ceilings, ceiling fans, and large south- and west-side eave overhangs can all also contribute to keeping a home cool. Dormer windows and openable skylights on the north side of the roof allow hot air to escape. Windows on the windward and leeward sides of the home allow for cross ventilation. In multiple-level homes, stairwells provide for continuous ventilation. Window placement on the low and high ends of the stair creates a draft as hot air rises up the stairwell and cooler air is drawn in through the low window.

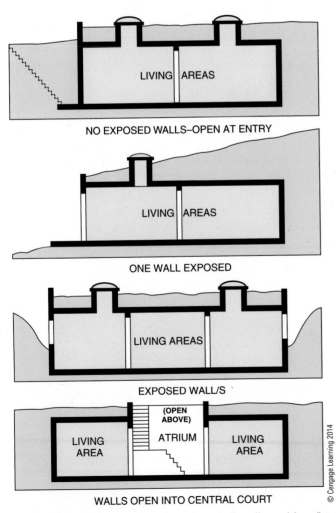

NO EXPOSED WALLS–OPEN AT ENTRY

ONE WALL EXPOSED

EXPOSED WALL/S

WALLS OPEN INTO CENTRAL COURT

© Cengage Learning 2014

FIGURE 8.18 Earth-sheltered homes have soil on three sidewalls and the roof. Four options often used for earth-sheltered homes are seen here.

Courtesy William E. Poole Designs, Inc.

FIGURE 8.19 Trees and bushes provide an effective barrier to wind.

Landscaping can also provide relief from summer heat. Coniferous and deciduous trees help block the sun and funnel summer winds into the site. Deciduous trees serve a triple purpose. In the summer they provide needed shade and act as filters to cool heated wind. In the winter they lose their leaves, allowing the sun's rays to help warm the house.

Sound Orientation

If the construction site is in a rural setting, sound orientation may not be a concern. In an urban setting the sound of neighbors and traffic 24/7 can make life unbearable. Positioning the home in relation to neighboring structures will help filter out unwanted noise. A building site that is level with or slightly below a road may have less noise than a site that is above and overlooking the sound source.

Good landscaping design can contribute to a quiet living environment. *Berms,* trees, hedges, and fences can all be helpful. Some landscape materials deflect sounds; others absorb them. The density and thickness of the sound barrier will also influence sound reduction. The greater the width of the plantings for sound insulation, the better the control. Trees planted in staggered rows provide the best design.

Construction methods and materials can also reduce the transmission of sound into the building. Masonry is effective at blocking noise, for example, as are wood and sheetrock®. Providing breaks in floors or double-wall construction are common methods to stop sound carrying from room to room. Sound-deadening board and some types of insulated foams have excellent ability to stop sound. Triple-glazed windows can also help reduce outside sound.

Going Green

Environmental Design Considerations

Much of the information presented throughout this chapter is intended to help a home blend with its site. The concept of green building involves considering not only the building site but also how the home integrates with its total environment. A well-designed structure, such as the home in Figure 8.20, may be called environmentally friendly, earth-friendly, or green construction, but increasingly the goal of design is to blend a home that is efficient at all stages of design, construction, habitation, and as it is recycled at the end of its life. Ideally a green building is:

- Designed, constructed, and maintained for the health and well-being of the occupants.
- Operated to maximize present and future beneficial impacts on the environment.
- Designed with an integrated approach to be resource efficient.
- Designed to promote resource conservation with features that encourage energy-efficiency, use of renewable energy, and water conservation.

Green buildings are resource and efficient buildings. They are designed to be energy-efficient and to use construction materials wisely—including recycled, renewable, and reused resources to the maximum extent practical. They are designed and constructed to make sure that they will be healthy to live in, are typically more comfortable and easier to live in due to lower operating and owning costs, and they are good for the planet. The overall environmental impact of new home and community development and the choices made when we either

(Continued)

FIGURE 8.20 A well-planned home will be constructed with the health and well-being of the occupants as a prime consideration. It must also be designed to maximize present and future beneficial impacts on the environment and offer an opportunity to create environmentally sound and resource-efficient buildings by using an integrated approach to design.

reuse or demolish existing structures are important. Examples of materials that are often featured in green homes include:

- Tankless water heaters
- Low-flow plumbing fixtures
- Gray-water reuse
- Air-admittance vents
- Solar water heaters
- Radiant barriers
- Mini-duct air distribution systems
- High-efficiency air conditioners without HCFCs (hydro-chlorofluorocarbons)
- Low-impact development techniques
- ENERGY STAR windows, doors, appliances, and insulation levels
- Bamboo flooring
- Low- or no-VOC (volatile organic vapor) paints

Each of these features is explored in the chapters that follow. Members of the building industry have banned together to form the U.S. Green Building Council (USGBC) to help promote the use of these materials and to develop new materials. The council has created a standard called the Leadership in Energy and Environmental Design (LEED) to measure the effectiveness of green buildings. LEED has become the national standard to measure high-performance sustainable homes. Major areas defined by LEED include:

- Sustainable sites: This portion of the standard evaluates the selected site, the amount of site disturbance, erosion and sedimentation control, urban redevelopment, public transportation, storm water management, landscaping, and light pollution.
- Efficient use of water for living purposes and landscaping, as well as wastewater management and dispersal.

(Continued)

- Efficient use of energy and low impact on the atmosphere: This portion of the standard affects the heating and cooling systems, reduction of CFCs (chlorofluorocarbons) in HVAC equipment, ozone depletion, and renewable energy.
- Efficient use of materials: This portion of the standard affects the storage and collection of recyclables, material reuse, management of construction waste, resource reuse, recycled content, use of local and regional materials, use of rapidly renewable materials, and certified wood.
- Indoor environmental quality: This portion of the standard affects indoor air quality, carbon dioxide monitoring, and ventilation effectiveness.

The complete guidelines for green certification are available at the USGBC website.

Additional Resources

Use the following websites as resources to help you keep current with environmental issues.

Address	Company or Organization
www.buildinggreen.com	Building Green
www.envirolink.org	Environmental resources
www.greenbuilder.com	Sustainable Building Sourcebook
www.iesna.org	Illuminating Engineering Society of North America
www.nesea.org	Northeast Sustainable Energy Association
www.nfpa.org	National Fire Protection Association
www.oikos.com	Green Building Source
www.ourcoolhouse.com	Energy-efficient home construction
www.physicalgeography.net	Fundamentals of physical geography
www.renewableenergyaccess.com	Renewable Energy Access
www.usgbc.org	U.S. Green Building Council
www.wbdg.org	Whole Building Design Guide

Environmental Design Considerations Test

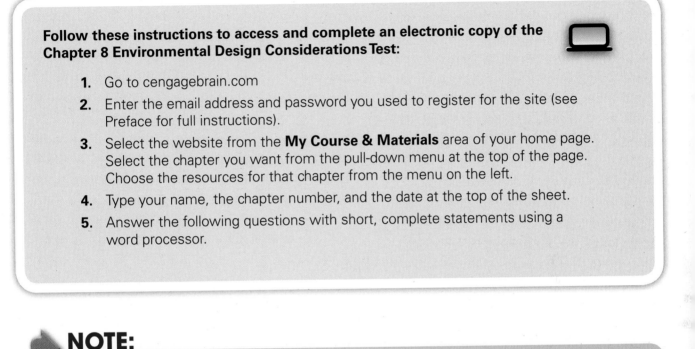

Follow these instructions to access and complete an electronic copy of the Chapter 8 Environmental Design Considerations Test:

1. Go to cengagebrain.com
2. Enter the email address and password you used to register for the site (see Preface for full instructions).
3. Select the website from the **My Course & Materials** area of your home page. Select the chapter you want from the pull-down menu at the top of the page. Choose the resources for that chapter from the menu on the left.
4. Type your name, the chapter number, and the date at the top of the sheet.
5. Answer the following questions with short, complete statements using a word processor.

NOTE:

The answers to some questions may not be contained in this chapter and will require you to do additional research using the Internet. Use your favorite search engine to search for specific professional companies or general categories of information.

Questions

8.1. Explain how the neighborhood can influence the type of house that will be built.

8.2. List four functions of a review board.

8.3. Define site orientation.

8.4. List and briefly describe five factors that influence site orientation.

8.5. Define magnetic declination.

8.6. Use the Internet to determine the magnetic declination of the area where you live.

8.7. Describe how trees can be an asset in solar orientation.

8.8. Describe what influences the prevailing summer and winter winds in your area.

8.9. Describe features that can protect a structure from wind.

8.10. Describe how to use landscaping as effective sound control.

8.11. List three methods of construction common to subterranean construction.

8.12. What is a common goal of the zoning department?

8.13. Why does construction on any site require that a slope be graded away from the structure?

8.14. Define terrain.

8.15. Why might view orientation be more important than other orientation considerations?

Section 2

Site Plans

Palladian Design Group, Inc. Laurence Taylor Photography

Chapter 9
Land Descriptions and Drawings

The drawings required to specify the information for the site plan are usually the first drawings started in a residential project. As described in Chapter 2, a preliminary site plan is drawn to help study and access the design criteria. To complete the working drawings for the permit process, the preliminary site plan is converted to a working site plan. Every construction project requires one or more site-related drawings to describe the work to be done. To complete this process, a CAD technician must understand the use of legal descriptions to describe land, site-related drawings, and the general process of completing drawings.

Key Terms

Angle of repose	Grading plan	Lot and block	Site plan
Bearing	Irrigation plan	Meridian	Subdivision
Catch basin	Landscape plan	Metes	Swale
Chain	Legal description	Metes and bounds	Topography plan
Contour lines	Lateral	Profile	Township
Drainage grate	Latitude	Rod	True point of beginning
Elevation	Longitude	Section	Vicinity map

CAD Commands and Tools

The following AutoCAD commands and tools are concepts that you should be familiar with to successfully understand and complete the CAD skills referenced in this chapter.

LINETYPE   TEXT   Dimension   PEDIT

LEGAL DESCRIPTIONS

For legal purposes, each piece of land is referenced in official documents by a description of the property known as a **legal description.** The term is used by municipalities to specify land parcels as they are bought, sold, and taxed. The legal description of a parcel of land can be obtained from the local zoning department that governs the property or from a title company. The legal description for any parcel of land is a matter of public record and can be obtained if the mailing address is known. The legal description may be given in several forms such as a metes-and-bounds system, a rectangular system, or a lot-and-block system. The type of description to be used depends on the contour of the area to be described or the requirements of the municipality reviewing the plans.

Metes and Bounds

A **metes and bounds** description is also referred to as a long description. A copy of the description can be obtained from a title company, the zoning department, or the tax assessor's office. A complete description can be added to the site plan or attached to the drawings on a separate sheet of paper. This system provides a written description of the property in terms of measurements of distance and angles of direction from a known starting point. The known starting point is referred to as the **true point of beginning** in a legal description. The true point of beginning is usually marked by a steel rod or a benchmark established by the U.S. Geological Society (USGS). These are referred to as monuments.

Metes

The **metes** are measured in feet, yards, rods, or surveyor's chains. A **rod** is equal to 16.5' (4950 mm) or 5.5 yd. A **chain** is equal to 66' (19 800 mm) or 22 yd. Directions are given from a monument such as a benchmark established by the USGS or an iron rod set from a previous survey.

The point of beginning may be several hundred feet away from the property to be described. Directions are given from the point of beginning to a specified point on the perimeter of the property to be described. Directions are then given to outline the property, with all distances set in units of feet expressed in one hundredth of a foot rather than the traditional feet and inches normally associated with construction. Metric units should be expressed in either millimeters or meters. Centimeters are not used on construction drawings.

Bounds

The boundaries of property are described by **bearings,** which are angles referenced to a quadrant on a compass. Figure 9.1 shows the four compass quadrants and descriptions of lines within each quadrant. Bearings are always described by starting at north or south and turning to the east or west. Bearings are expressed in degrees, minutes, and seconds. Each quadrant of the compass contains 90°, each degree contains 60 minutes, and each minute can be divided into 60 seconds. A degree is represented

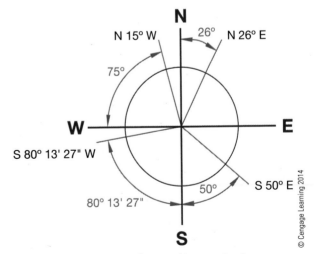

FIGURE 9.1 Bearings are referenced by quadrants on a compass beginning at either north or south.

© Cengage Learning 2014

by the ° symbol, a minute is represented by the ' symbol, and seconds are represented by the " symbol. Bearings are used to describe the angular location of a property line. Some properties are also defined by their location to the centerline of major streets. When property abuts a body of water such as a creek or river, a boundary in angles may not be given and the property boundary is defined by the centerpoint of the body of water. A metes-and-bounds legal description would resemble the following description:

A TRACT OF LAND SITUATED IN THE SOUTHEAST QUARTER OF THE NORTHEAST QUARTER OF SECTION 17, T3S, R1W OF THE WILLAMETTE MERIDIAN, CLACKAMAS COUNTY, OREGON, BEING MORE PARTICULARLY DESCRIBED AS FOLLOWS, TO WIT: BEGINNING AT THE 5/8 INCH IRON ROD AT THE SOUTHWEST CORNER OF THE SOUTHEAST QUARTER OF THE NORTHEAST QUARTER OF SAID SECTION 17; THENCE NORTH 0°06'10" EAST ALONG THE WEST LINE OF THE SOUTHEAST QUARTER OF THE NORTHEAST QUARTER, 322.50'; THENCE LEAVING SAID WEST LINE NORTH 89°38'15" EAST 242.00 FEET; THENCE SOUTH 0° 06'10" WEST PARALLEL WITH SAID WEST LINE OF THE SOUTHEAST QUARTER OF THE NORTHEAST QUARTER, 50.00 FEET, THENCE NORTH 89° 38' 15" EAST 310.74 FEET TO THE WESTERLY RIGHT OF WAY LINE OF BELL ROAD NO. 113; THENCE SOUTH 3° 31' EAST ALONG SAID WESTERLY RIGHT OF WAY LINE, 272.91 FEET TO A 5/8 INCH IRON ROD; THENCE LEAVING SAID WESTERLY RIGHT OF WAY LINE, SOUTH 89° 38' 15" WEST 569.97 FEET TO THE POINT OF BEGINNING.

This description would be listed on legal documents describing the property as well as the site plan. Figure 9.2 shows the land described by the metes-and-bounds legal

description. A short description of the property should be copied exactly onto the site plan. The short description would read:

A TRACT OF LAND SITUATED IN THE S.E. 1/4, OF THE N.E. 1/4 OF SECTION 17, T3S, R1W OF WILLAMETTE MERIDIAN, CLACKAMAS COUNTY, OREGON.

Rectangular Systems

Many areas of the country refer to land based on its *latitude* and *longitude.* Parallels of latitude and meridians of longitude were used by the U.S. Bureau of Land Management in states that were originally defined as public land states. As the land was divided, large parcels of land were defined by what are known as basic reference lines. There are thirty-one pairs of standard lines in the continental United States and three in Alaska. Principal *meridians* and base lines can be seen in Figure 9.3. These divisions of land are described as the great land surveys. As the initial division of land was started, the first six principal meridians were numbered. The last-numbered meridian passes through Nebraska, Kansas, and Oklahoma. All subsequent meridians are defined by local names. The great land surveys were further divided by surveys that define land by townships and sections.

Townships

Baselines and meridians are divided into 6-mile-square parcels of land called townships. Each *township* is numbered based on its location to the principal meridian and baseline. Horizontal tiers are numbered based on their position above or below the baseline. Vertical tiers are defined by their position east or west of the principal meridian. Township positions are shown in Figure 9.4. The township highlighted in Figure 9.4 would be described as Township No. 2 North, Range 3 West because it is in the second tier north of the baseline and in the third row west of the principal meridian. The name of the principal meridian would then be listed. This information is abbreviated as T2N R3W on the site plan.

Sections

Land within the townships can be further broken down into 1-mile-square parcels known as *sections.* Sections are assigned numbers from 1 to 36 as shown in Figure 9.5, beginning in the northeast corner of the township. Each section is further broken down into quarter sections. Each section contains 640 acres or 43,560 square feet. Quarter sections can be further broken down as seen in Figure 9.6. The areas are defined by quarters of quarters or halves of quarters. These small segments are further broken down by quarters or halves again.

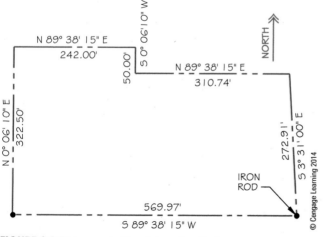

FIGURE 9.2 The parcel of land described in the metes-and-bounds legal description.

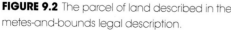

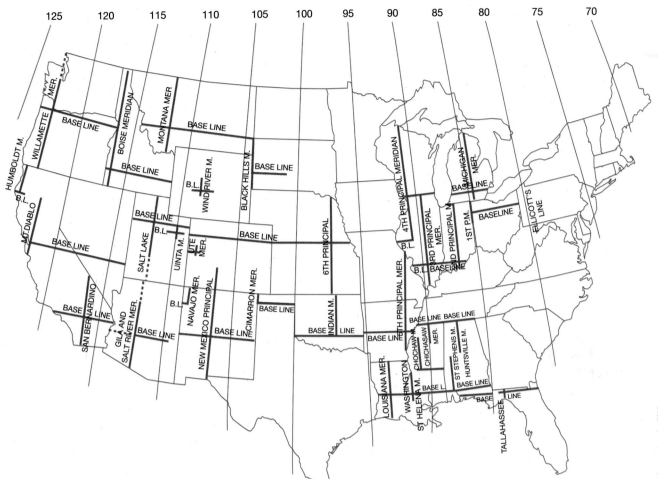

FIGURE 9.3 Principal meridians and basic reference lines are used to divide land in the continental United States.

© Cengage Learning 2014

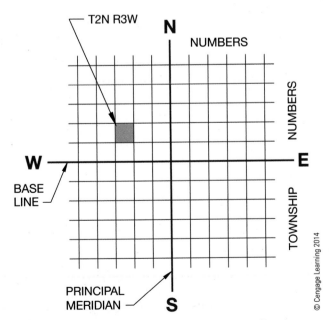

FIGURE 9.4 A township is a 6-square-mile portion of land defined by its position in reference to a principal meridian and a baseline. The indicated township is referred to as T2NR3W because it is in the second tier north of the baseline and three rows west of the principal meridian.

© Cengage Learning 2014

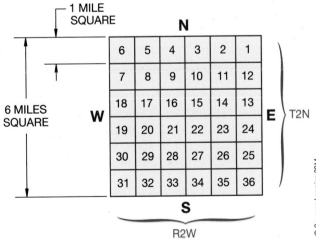

FIGURE 9.5 Land within a township is divided into thirty-six 1-mile-square portions called sections.

© Cengage Learning 2014

Specifying the Legal Description

The legal description, based on the rectangular system, lists the portion of the land to be developed described by its position within the section, the section number,

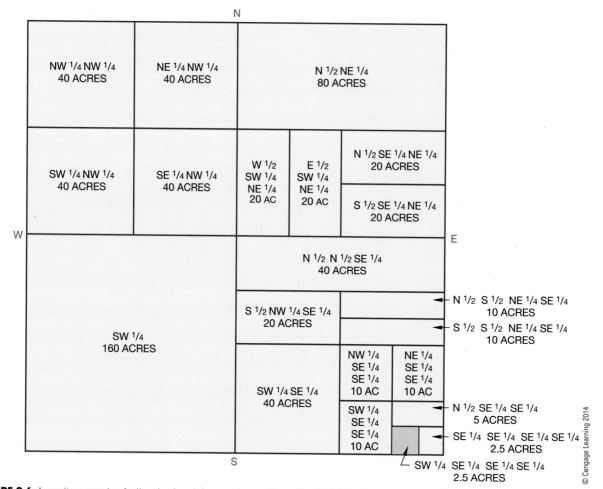

N

W

E

S

NW 1/4 NW 1/4 40 ACRES	NE 1/4 NW 1/4 40 ACRES	N 1/2 NE 1/4 80 ACRES

SW 1/4 NW 1/4 40 ACRES

SE 1/4 NW 1/4 40 ACRES

W 1/2 SW 1/4 NE 1/4 20 AC

E 1/2 SW 1/4 NE 1/4 20 AC

N 1/2 SE 1/4 NE 1/4 20 ACRES

S 1/2 SE 1/4 NE 1/4 20 ACRES

SW 1/4 160 ACRES

N 1/2 N 1/2 SE 1/4 40 ACRES

S 1/2 NW 1/4 SE 1/4 20 ACRES

← N 1/2 S 1/2 NE 1/4 SE 1/4 10 ACRES

← S 1/2 S 1/2 NE 1/4 SE 1/4 10 ACRES

NW 1/4 SE 1/4 SE 1/4 10 AC

NE 1/4 SE 1/4 SE 1/4 10 AC

SW 1/4 SE 1/4 40 ACRES

SW 1/4 SE 1/4 SE 1/4 10 AC

← N 1/2 SE 1/4 SE 1/4 5 ACRES

← SE 1/4 SE 1/4 SE 1/4 SE 1/4 2.5 ACRES

⌐ SW 1/4 SE 1/4 SE 1/4 SE 1/4 2.5 ACRES

© Cengage Learning 2014

FIGURE 9.6 A section can be further broken into quarter sections (the NW 1/4 of the NW 1/4) and then divided again into a quarter of a quarter section (the NW 1/4 of the SE 1/4 of the SE 1/4) and then divided one more time into quarters (the SE 1/4 of the SE 1/4 of the SE 1/4 of the SE 1/4).

the township, and the principal meridian. A typical legal description resembles the following description:

THE SOUTHEAST ONE QUARTER, OF THE SOUTHWEST ONE QUARTER OF THE SOUTHWEST ONE QUARTER OF SECTION 31, TOWNSHIP NO. 2 NORTH, RANGE 3 WEST OF THE SAN BERNARDINO MERIDIAN, CITY OF EL CAJON, IN THE STATE OF CALIFORNIA.

On the site plan, this is often abbreviated into a legal description as follows:

THE SE 1/4, OF THE SW 1/4 OF THE SW1/4, S31, T2N, R3W, SAN BERNARDINO MERIDIAN, EL CAJON, CALIFORNIA.

Because the method of describing quarters of quarters of quarters can become confusing, many municipalities have gone to a labeling system using letters. Quarter sections are labeled as A, B, C, or D. Quarter sections are further divided into quarters by the letters A, B, C, or D. The

northeast quarter of the northeast quarter would then be listed as Parcel AA. This method of land description works especially well in areas where the land contour is fairly flat. In areas with irregular land shapes, the rectangular land description can be linked with a partial metes-and-bounds description to accurately locate the property.

Lot-and-Block System

The *lot-and-block* system of describing land is usually found within incorporated cities. Most states require the filing of a subdivision map, similar to the one in Figure 9.7, that defines individual lot size and shape as land is being divided. Each lot is defined on a *subdivision map* by a length and angle of each property line as well as a legal description. On older subdivision maps, land is first divided into areas based on neighborhood, called subdivisions. The subdivision is, in turn, broken into blocks based on street layout. The block is further divided into lots. On newer maps, most municipalities assign a number to a parcel of

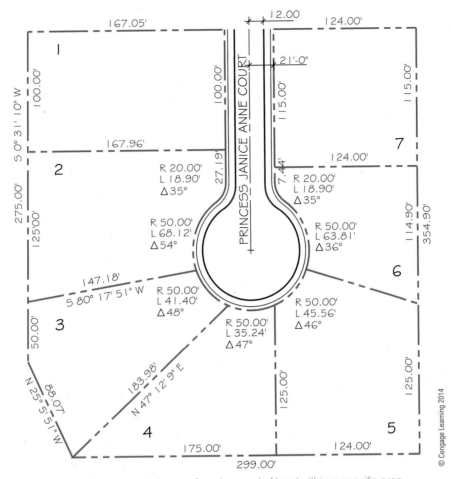

FIGURE 9.7 A subdivision map shows the size and shape of each parcel of land within a specific area.

land that corresponds to either a tax account or a map number. Lots can be irregularly shaped or rectangular. The shape of the lot is often based on the contour of the surrounding land and the layout of streets. A typical legal description for a lot-and-block description would resemble the following:

LOTS NO. 1, 2, AND 3 OF MAP #17643 OF THE CITY OF BONITA, COUNTY OF SAN DIEGO, CALIFORNIA.

LAND DRAWINGS

The most common plan used to describe property is the *site plan.* The site plan is started before or in conjunction with the floor plan, although it probably will not be finished until other architectural drawings are completed. With the property boundaries drawn, the preliminary design for the floor plan can be inserted into the site plan. Preliminary designs for access, walkways, landscaping, and parking can then be determined and adjustments to both the site and floor plans can then be made.

The size of the project and the complexity of the site will dictate the drawings required to describe site-related construction, who will do them, and when they will be done. In addition to the site plan, a *vicinity map* as well as topography, grading, landscape, sprinkler, freshwater, and sewer plans may be required to describe the alterations to be made to the site. On simple construction projects, all of these plans can be combined into one site plan. This plan is typically the first sheet of the architectural drawings and labeled A-1. On most plans, the site-related drawings are placed at the start of the architectural drawings and listed as civil drawings. On a complicated custom home, the topography, grading, demolition, landscape, sprinkler, freshwater, and sewer plans may comprise the civil drawings (C-1 or L-1) and precede the site plan.

Another consideration in the placement of the site plan is municipal regulations controlling the size of the site plan. Many municipalities require a copy of the site plan to be submitted on 8 1/2 × 11" or 8 1/2 × 14" paper with specific scale required for submittal. The mandatory uses of small scale for a complex site will often require a simple site plan to locate the residence. Large-scale drawings on a paper size that matches the balance of the drawings may be used to represent landscaping, irrigation, and topography information.

Drawing Origin

The size and complexity of the project will determine who will draw the project. On most projects, the architectural team will draw the site plan. These drawings are usually completed by a CAD technician working for a civil engineer, surveyor, or landscape architect and then given to the architectural team to be incorporated into the working drawings. On simple projects, the architectural team, under the supervision of a landscape architect and a civil engineer, may complete the drawings.

Vicinity Map

A vicinity map is used to show the area surrounding the construction site. It is placed near the site plan and is used to show major access routes to the site. This could include major streets, freeway on and off ramps, suggested routes for large delivery trucks, and rail routes. A CAD technician working for the architectural team will prepare a vicinity map. It is not drawn to scale, but it should show an area that reflects the size of the project in proportion to the area represented. If building components primarily come from the surrounding area, the map only needs to reflect the immediate construction area. If materials come from several different cities or states, the area of the vicinity map should be expanded to aid drivers who may not be familiar with the area. Figure 9.8 shows an example of a vicinity map.

Site Plan

The site plan for a residential project is the basis for all other site-related drawings. It shows the layout and size of the property, the outline of the structure to be built, north arrow, ground and finish floor elevations, setbacks, parking and access information, and information about utilities. The results of engineering studies and soils reports related to the site may be summarized on the site plan.

Common Linetypes

The shape of the construction site can be drawn based on information provided by the legal description or subdivision map. Common linetypes used to represent major materials based on the National CAD Standards include:

- Property lines, represented by a line with a long-short-short-long pattern. PHANTOM2 or PHANTOMX2 from the AutoCAD line file can be used for representing property lines.
- Centerlines of access roads or easements represented by a long-short-long line pattern using CENTER, CENTER2, or CENTERX2.

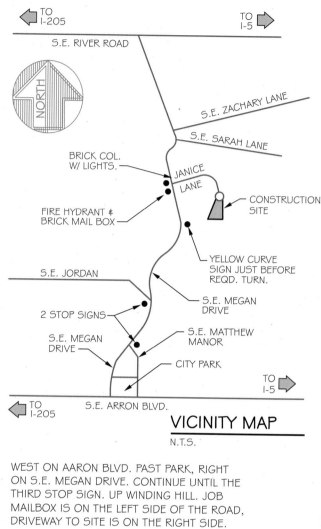

WEST ON AARON BLVD. PAST PARK, RIGHT ON S.E. MEGAN DRIVE. CONTINUE UNTIL THE THIRD STOP SIGN. UP WINDING HILL. JOB MAILBOX IS ON THE LEFT SIDE OF THE ROAD, DRIVEWAY TO SITE IS ON THE RIGHT SIDE.

FIGURE 9.8 A vicinity map is used to show the surrounding area and major access routes to the construction site.

- Sidewalks, patios, stairs, driveway, and exterior parking outlines, typically represented by a continuous linetype.
- Edges of easements and building setbacks, often represented by dashed or hidden lines using DASHED or HIDDEN lines.
- Utility lines are usually represented by thick lines using either a dashed or hidden pattern. Each line is labeled with a G (gas), S (sewer), W (water), P (power), or T (communications) to denote its usage. See Chapter 14 for requirements and drawing standards when the home is not on public sewers.

Specifications must also be provided to distinguish between existing utilities and those that must be extended within the site. The location of each utility referenced to the property should also be provided. Figure 9.9 shows a site plan for a residence and the appropriate linetypes.

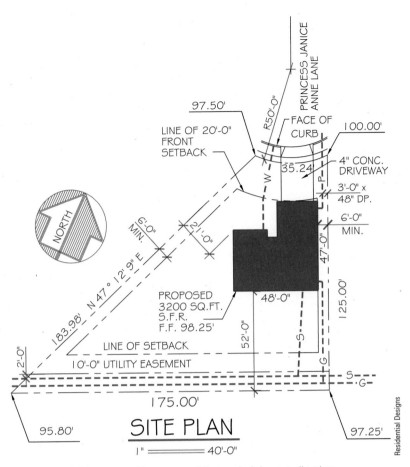

SITE PLAN

1" ══════ 40'-0"

FIGURE 9.9 Varied linetypes and lineweights are used to represent the materials on a site plan.

Representing the Structure

The outline of the residence, also known as the building footprint, must be accurately represented and easily distinguishable from the property and utilities. Common methods to represent a structure include the use of a thick line to define the perimeter and a hatch pattern such as ANSI31 or ANSI37 to further highlight the structure. This method is shown in Figure 9.10. A common alternative is to draw the outline of the residence with a dashed line and bold lines for the outline of the roof. The complexity of the project and building department requirements will determine which method is used. Many firms X-REF the floor plan into the site plan. This offers the advantage of an up-to-date site plan each time the drawing is opened. This can be especially important when the footprint of the structure is altered or door locations are moved.

The use of the structure should also be specified within its outline, with titles such as PROPOSED 2 LEVEL SFR (single-family residence). Consideration must also be given by the drafter to accurately distinguish between portions of the structure that are in contact with the ground and those that are supported on columns or

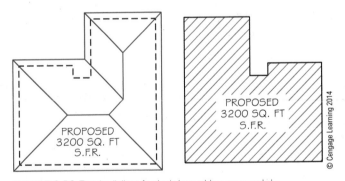

FIGURE 9.10 The building footprint must be accurately represented and easily distinguishable from the property and utilities. On a simple plan, the structure can be shown with dashed lines and the outline of the roof can be represented. When the plan is more complex, a hatch pattern can be used to distinguish the home from surrounding features.

cantilevers. Projects often include structures that are to be demolished to make way for the new project. These structures must be accurately located and distinguished from new construction. A separate demolition plan may be used to supplement the site plan. See Chapter 35 for site plan requirements when demolition or alterations are required.

Access, Walks, and Parking Information

Information about access must be shown on the site plan including driveways, walks, areas to be paved, parking spaces, and ramps. With the exception of the centerline for access roads, continuous lines are used to represent each. As shown in Figure 9.11, many offices hatch concrete walkways with a random pattern of dots so they can be easily distinguished from asphalt paving areas.

Off-Street Parking Information. Common driveway and access arrangements for residential projects were presented in Figure 8.6. Multifamily projects will require off-street parking, but requirements will vary from city to city. The drafter must verify requirements for each project. Off-street parking may be in a garage or open-air parking area. When a parking structure is provided, it can be represented with the same methods used to represent the residence. The size and location of each open air space must be represented and specified. Parking spaces are specified as full, compact, handicapped, or van-handicapped. Common sizes include:

- 9 × 20' (2700 × 6000 mm) for a full space
- 8 ×16' (2400 × 4800 mm) for a compact space
- 14 ×19' (4200 × 5700 mm) for an ADA-approved handicapped space
- 16 × 19' (4800 × 5700 mm) minimum for an ADA-approved handicapped van space

Many municipalities require a parking schedule to be part of the site plan. A parking schedule can be used to specify the number, type, and size of each type of parking space.

It is important to remember that there is a wide variance in sizes depending on the municipality and the direction of entry into the space. Figure 9.12 shows an example of common alternatives for parking based on the angle of entry. Perpendicular spaces can be shorter than spaces that require parallel parking. Spaces placed on an angle require different lengths, widths, and a different driveway size as the entry angle is varied. Parking spaces next to obstructions such as raised planters or building supports should have added width to ease access and allow the minimum required width to be maintained.

Wheel stops must be drawn and specified for individual spaces. Wheel stops 6 ft (1800 mm) long are typically used for spaces that are 90° to the access drive. Stops are normally placed 24" (600 mm) from the front end of the stall and straddle the dividing line between spaces so that one stop is shared by two spaces. Building supports often require a permanent protective device to be installed for protection from vehicle damage. A steel column filled with concrete added near each structural column is a common method of protecting the structure from damage caused by careless drivers. These columns must be represented and specified on the site plan and the floor plan. Building supports and wheel stops can be represented as shown in Figure 9.13.

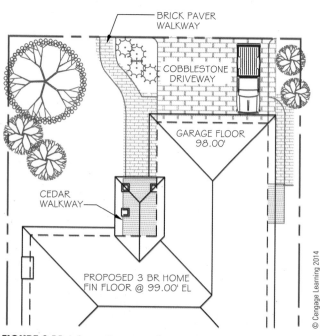

FIGURE 9.11 Information regarding access—including driveways and walks, areas to be paved, parking spaces, and ramps—is typically represented with continuous lines.

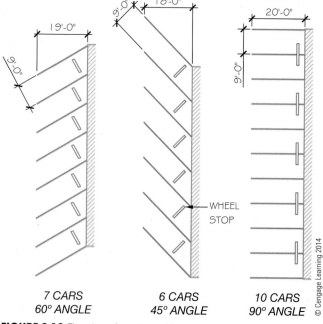

FIGURE 9.12 The size of each parking space will vary depending on the angle of approach. Each city has it own parking requirements, which the CAD technician should verify prior to starting the site plan.

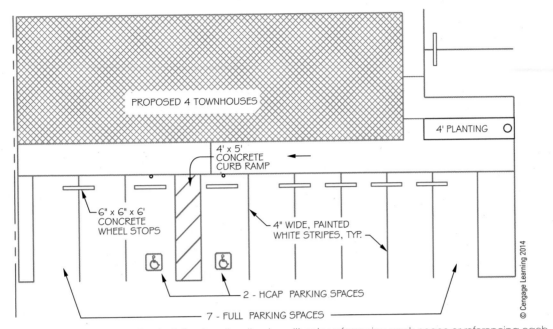

FIGURE 9.13 Parking spaces must be clearly defined on the site plan either by referencing each space or referencing each group of spaces.

Elevations and Swale

Projects with major changes of contour that require large quantities of soil to be excavated usually require a grading plan. A CAD technician working for the architectural team or for a civil engineer will help prepare the grading plan. Sites that do not require extensive excavation often reflect finished grade elevations on the site plan. Four common methods of denoting elevation are shown in Figure 9.14. The elevation of ground level is indicated on the site plan with a note similar to:

FINISHED FLOOR ELEVATION 101.25'

A symbol similar to a leader line is used to indicate the *elevation* of each property corner as well as other important features. The elevation of the specified location is indicated above the leader line. An elevation marker should be placed on each corner of the property. Comparisons of elevations can also be specified by indicators such as TW (top of wall), which are placed above the symbol, or BF (bottom of footing), which is placed below the symbol. When abbreviations are used to define the elevation, a schedule should be provided to explain each term that is represented.

A third method to show minor change of elevation is with a swale indicator. A *swale* is a small valley used to divert water away from a structure. The slope of the swale is dependent on the surface material being drained. A minimum slope of 2% should be provided for dirt, and a slope of 1% to 2% is used for asphalt or concrete paving areas.

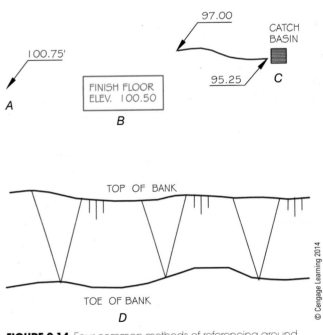

FIGURE 9.14 Four common methods of referencing ground elevation include (A) an elevation symbol, (B) a note to describe the elevation, (C) a swale line with elevation symbols, and (D) a bank indicator to represent the top and toe of a bank.

The fourth method to show change of contour is with a bank indicator. A bank indicator is represented by a V placed between lines that indicate the top and toe of the bank. The bottom of the V is placed at the bottom of the bank. Three short lines are normally placed between the V's to indicate the top of the bank. Figure 9.15 shows how each could be used on a site plan.

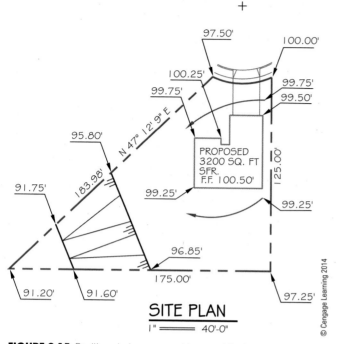

FIGURE 9.15 Positive drainage must be provided on each side of the residence. This can be assured by the use of elevation symbols, notes, swales, and bank indicators.

© Cengage Learning 2014

Drainage

On complex projects, the drainage system may be shown on a separate drainage plan. An underground concrete box called a **catch basin** is often placed at the low point of swales to divert water from the site. A catch basin acts as a funnel to collect water and channel it into the storm system. It is covered by a metal cover with slotted openings level with the ground surface called a **drainage grate.** The grate allows water to flow into the catch basin without letting anyone fall in. Water flows through the grate, into the catch basin, and then into pipes leading to public storm sewers. The pipe that connects the construction site to the public sewer pipe is referred to as a **lateral.** The location of the lateral should be indicated on the site plan and be noted as existing or new.

An engineer designs the system and determines the required change of elevation to ensure proper runoff. Elevation markers referred to as spot grades should be established on the plan to specify the finished grading to ensure runoff. The elevation, size, type, and location of all grates and drainage lines should also be specified on either the site or drainage plan. The grate elevation is shown using a symbol, as in Figure 9.14c. If a drainage plan is drawn, the elevation of the inside surface of the bottom of the drainage pipe is also specified. This elevation is known as an invert elevation. Either the minimum slope required or specific elevations along the drainage pipe are specified on a drainage plan.

Common Site Plan Details

The details required for a site plan vary widely from office to office and will vary based on the complexity of the construction. Common areas requiring details on a site plan include sidewalks, curbs, planting details for planters, large plants, irrigation controls, decorative walls, and retaining walls. Figure 9.16 shows examples of two common site details for a multifamily project. Each is considered a standard detail and could be stored in a detail library as a WBLOCK that is edited for specific job requirements. The engineer or project coordinator will generally note for the drafter the details that should be inserted into the site plan, and the CAD technician is expected to compile and edit the details to match project requirements.

Annotation

In addition to drawing and locating information, notes must be placed on the site plan to completely specify required construction. General text on a site drawing is

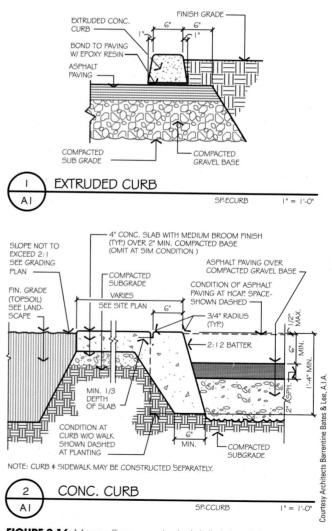

Courtesy Architects Barrentine Bates & Lee, A.I.A.

FIGURE 9.16 Many offices use stock details to explain site-related construction.

placed per the guidelines presented in Chapter 4. Text giving the names of streets and describing the proposed structure should be treated as titles. A notation such as PROPOSED 3000 SQ FT SFR is used to define the proposed construction. Local and general notes are used to define the construction to be completed. On complex drawings, general notes should be broken into categories to make specific information easier to find. Categories such as paving, flatwork, landscaping, and irrigation are common. In addition to the general notes, which gives a full specification, a local note is usually placed on the plan, with a partial note to clarify what each symbol represents. Abbreviations exclusive to site-related drawings are also used. Common abbreviations include:

BF	Bottom of footing	EP	Edge of pavement
BW	Bottom of wall	FF	Finish floor
CB	Catch basin	FH	Fire hydrant
CO	Clean out	FP	Flagpole stanchion
D/W	Driveway	M	Meter
G	Gas	MH	Man hole
EG	Edge of gravel	O/H	Overhead utility line
PL	Property line	TP	Top of paving
ROW	Right-of-way	TW	Top of wall
SD	Storm drain	UP	Utility pole
SOV	Shutoff valve	W	Water
SS	Sanitary sewer line	WCR	Wheel chair ramp
TC	Top of curb	WM	Water meter
TG	Top of grate	WV	Water valve

On large projects, plans include common abbreviations used throughout the drawings on a title page. Common abbreviations used on construction drawings are given at the end of this text.

Text to describe the property lines for each site must be provided using distances and bearings. This text is placed parallel to the property lines. Figures 9.7 and 9.9 each show examples of required annotation to describe the property lines. In Figure 9.9, the south property line is described with a distance of 175.00', with no bearing given. If no bearing is listed for the property line, it can be assumed that the property line runs either north-south, or, as in this case east-west. The northwest property line is described with a length of 183.98' and a bearing of N47°12'9"E.

Many sites similar to parcel 4 in Figure 9.7 have property lines that curve. Three notations can be used to describe curved property lines, including R 50.00', L 35.24', and Δ 47°. R is the radius of the curve and L is its length. The symbol Δ represents the delta angle, which is the included angle of the curve. The included angle is the angle formed between the center and the endpoints of the arc.

In addition to information used to describe the construction site, general information is also placed on the site plan. General information might include a table of contents, list of consultants, and information about the overall construction project. An alternative to placing this general information on the site plan is to provide a title sheet that includes the vicinity map.

Site Dimensions

Each item represented on the site plan needs to be located by dimensions. Three types of dimensions are often found on a site plan, including:

- Land sizes, which are represented in feet and hundredths of a foot, using notations such as 100.50', or in meters (30.6 m)

- Property line dimensions, which are placed parallel to the property line with no use of dimension or extension lines

- Overall sizes of structures, which are often placed parallel to the side of the structure and specified in feet and inches using notations such as 75'-4" or 22.8 m for meters

These overall dimensions also are usually placed without the use of dimension lines. Parking boundaries and the structure are located using dimension and extension lines. Objects such as sidewalks or planters can often be described in a note rather than by dimensions. Figure 9.9 shows examples of each type of dimension. Notice the symbol used to designate each property corner. It is often omitted from rectangular lots but is very helpful in locating small changes of angle on irregularly shaped lots.

SITE-RELATED DRAWINGS

In addition to the site demolition plan, several related drawings can accompany a set of working drawings. Related drawings include a topography plan, grading plans, profile drawings, landscaping plan, and sprinkler plan. A *topography plan* shows the existing contour of the construction site. This plan is normally prepared by a licensed surveyor developed from notes provided by a field survey. It is based on existing municipal drawings describing the site, on measurements taken by the surveyor, or by aerial photography methods. Once the shape of the site is prepared, the results of the field survey are translated onto the drawing by a drafter working for a civil engineer. A *grading plan* is used to show the finished configuration of the building site. A grading plan may be designed and completed by a drafter under the supervision of the architectural team project manager or a civil engineer. A *landscape plan* may be provided to show the location, type, size, and quantity of all vegetation required for the project. It will typically show patios, walkways, fountains, pools, sports courts, and other landscaping features.

Drafters working for the architectural team or a landscape architect usually complete a landscaping plan. On small projects, drafters working for the architectural team may complete the project under the supervision of the project architect. In arid climates, an *irrigation plan* may be required to show how landscaping will be maintained. The same team that provides the landscape plan usually completes the irrigation drawings. Because the landscape and sprinkler drawings usually fall under the supervision of the landscape architect, procedures to create these drawings are not presented in this chapter.

Topography Plans

A topography plan provides a description of land surface using lines to show variation in elevation. Lines used to represent a specific elevation are referred to as *contour lines.* A contour line connects points of equal elevation. The elevations may be based on a USGS benchmark or the highest corner on the site. If the elevations are not related to a known benchmark, the highest property corner is usually assigned a height of 100.00'. All other elevations for the site are then expressed relative to this base point. If the nearest property corner were 5.5' lower it would receive an elevation of 94.50'. Figure 9.17 shows the contour lines for the site plan shown in Figure 9.15.

The location of contour lines is determined by a land survey. A survey team will record the elevations of the job site at specified distances in what are referred to as field notes. When the slope is uniform, the survey team will typically record elevations at intervals of 25' (7500 mm). When the grade changes, spot elevations are recorded at the top and bottom of banks that fall between the base intervals. For small sites, the land will be divided into grids by the survey team, which will take spot elevations at each grid point. For larger sites, the survey may be made only for the area where construction will occur. Once the survey is complete, a CAD drafter working for the civil engineer will convert the field notes to a topography plan. A grid will need to be drawn on the site plan that matches the grid used by the surveyors at the job site.

Figure 9.18 shows an example of a sketch provided to reflect the existing surface elevations. A grid is drawn to represent each known elevation location. Notice the six elevations in the northwest corner of the survey. Between

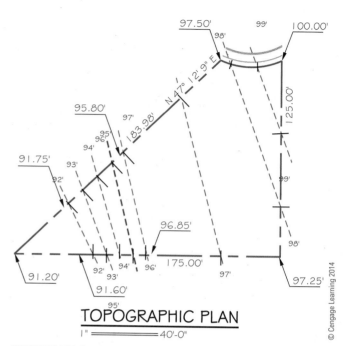

TOPOGRAPHIC PLAN
1" ══════════ 40'-0"

FIGURE 9.17 Contour lines have been added to the site plan shown in Figure 9.15. Each line represents soil that is at the same elevation. Contour lines help a skilled print reader understand the terrain at the construction site. Contour lines that are close together indicate a steep slope. Lines that are farther apart indicate a gentle slope.

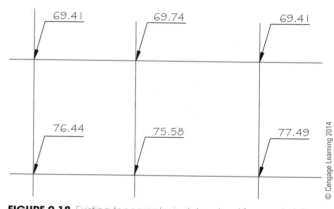

FIGURE 9.18 Existing topography is determined from a sketch or drawing, provided by the civil engineer, that lists the known elevation at specific points at the site.

grid 69.41 and 76.44, seven contour lines are required to represent the change of elevation. It can be assumed the contours fall at an even spacing because the surveyor did not change the distance between grids to reflect a rise or depression. The seven lines should be evenly spaced between the two spot grades and will represent the contours for 70 through 76. Because a rise of .6' is required to reach the contour for the next whole foot, the distance between 69.41 and the first line should be slightly more than half the distance between any two of the 1' markers. The distance between the 76' contour and the spot grade for 76.44 should be slightly less than half the distance between any two of the 1' markers.

Six contour lines are required between grids 69.74 and 75.58, and eight contour lines are required to reflect the change in elevation between grids 69.41 and 77.49. Once the distance between grids has been divided into the required divisions, points of equal elevation can be connected, as seen in Figure 9.19. The use of a polyline aids in finishing the drawing. As the distance between contour lines is decreased, the land becomes steeper. As the distances between contour lines increase, the land becomes flatter. The topography plan must be completed before accurate estimates of soil excavation or movement can be planned.

Representing Contours

Once the known elevations have been converted to contour lines, the lines can be curved and altered to provide clarity. Dashed lines are generally used to represent existing contours. Unlike the real contour of the site, in the initial layout stage the lines run from point to point and have distinct directional change at each known point. PEDIT leaves each vertex in its exact location but changes the straight line to a curved line. The WIDTH option of the PEDIT command can also be used to alter the width of the contour lines. The line width used to represent contours will vary based on the drawing scale and

the accuracy of the contours to be shown. On many residential sites, contours are shown to represent each 1' of elevation change. Lineweights on such drawings should be selected that provide clear contrast between 1' and 5' (300 and 1500 mm) intervals. Depending on the spacing of the contours, lines representing every 5' or 10' (1500 or 3000 mm) are usually highlighted and labeled as shown in Figure 9.20. Site plans with a large difference in elevation may show the elevation change in 2' or 5' intervals.

Grading Plans

The grading plan shows the proposed structure and its relationship to the contours of the building site. On simple projects, a drafter working for the architectural team may complete the grading plan. A drafter working for the civil engineer translates preliminary designs by the architectural team and the topography drawings into the finished drawings. The grading plan shows the finished contour lines, areas of cut and fill, building footprint, driveways, walkways, patios, steps, catch basins, and drainage provisions. Figure 9.21 shows the grading plan based on the topography shown in Figure 9.17.

A grading plan uses contour lines to represent existing and finished grades. This would include:

- Natural grade: Land in its unaltered state.
- Finish grade: The shape of the ground once all excavation and movement of earth has been completed.
- Cut material: Soil that is removed to lower the original elevation.
- Fill material: Soil that is added to the existing elevation to raise the height.
- Daylight: The point that represents the division between cut-and-fill.

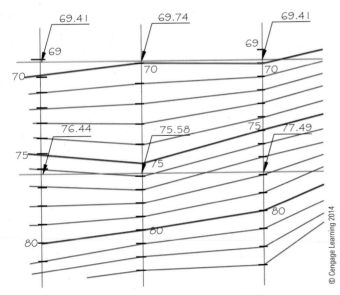

FIGURE 9.19 Once known elevations are located, lines can be placed to represent specific elevations. Grades can be determined by estimating the rise or fall between two known points. Because lines for grades 70 through 76 occur in the upper left grid, the distance between the two points is divided to represent each elevation.

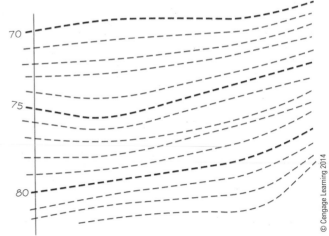

FIGURE 9.20 A dashed line is generally used to represent existing contours. The angular contour lines from Figure 9.19 were curved using the FIT CURVE option of the PEDIT command.

© Cengage Learning 2014

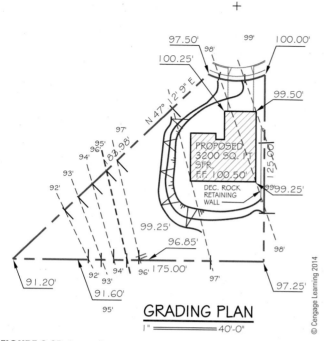

GRADING PLAN
1" ════════ 40'-0"

© Cengage Learning 2014

FIGURE 9.21 A grading plan is used to show changes in topography required by a construction project.

The project manager determines the finish elevation of floor levels and major areas of concern. It is then typically the drafter's job to indicate the extent of cut-and-fill material based on the desired angle of repose.

Angle of Repose

The angle of the cut or fill bank created is referred to as the *angle of repose.* The maximum angle of repose is based on the soil type. The municipality that governs the construction project determines the maximum angle. Common limits include:

- For fill banks, a common angle of repose is often set at a 2:1 angle. For every two units of horizontal measurement, one vertical unit of elevation change can occur.

- A common angle for cut banks is 1.5:1. The engineer specifies variations in the angle of repose that will be allowed near footings or retaining walls to minimize loads that must be supported.

Representing Contours

Contours for new and existing elevations are usually combined on one plan. Thin dashed lines are typically used to represent existing 1' (300 mm) contours and thick dashed lines are used to represent 5' (1500 mm)

contours. Thin continuous lines are typically used to represent new contours for 1' (300 mm) intervals. New 5' (1500 mm) contours are usually represented by thick continuous lines. Figure 9.22 shows the representation of new cut-and-fill banks placed on the topography drawing.

The drawing in Figure 9.22 shows the cut-and-fill banks created to place a one-level home with a concrete slab on a level pad. To determine what the floor level will be requires that the access to home be considered. Figure 9.23 shows the grading that resulted for a two-level home on the same site used in Figure 9.22. For this example, the following assumptions were made:

- A 5% slope for the driveway
- A 20' front setback
- Cut banks of 1 1/2 / 1
- Fill banks of 2 / 1
- 9' between floor levels

Placing the home in the desired position and then locating the driveway will allow the floor level to be determined. The home was placed 32' from the front property line to allow for a gentle slope in the driveway. The soil in the front yard was cut to allow the 100' elevation to be pulled close to the property line to help flatten the slope. With a distance of 32' or 420" (10 500 mm), it would seem that a 21" (525 mm) fall is allowed. Remember that positive drainage must be provided for 60" (1500 mm). This will reduce the effective length to 27' or 324" (8100 mm) with a maximum slope of 16" (400 mm). The 16" must be converted to decimal fractions of a foot to determine the driveway slope (16" is equal to 1.33'). If the east edge of the driveway is assumed to be 100.5', the west edge of the garage will be set at 99.17' (100.5' − 1.33'). The remaining 60" of the driveway must have a slope of 1.25" (5 × 0.25") or 0.10'. This will set the east edge of the garage slab at 99.27'. This can be rounded to an elevation of 99.25'. A 6" slope for the garage floor will place the west edge of the garage slab at 99.75'. Adding 8" (0.66') for the step up to the house places the upper floor level at a height of approximately 100.41'. For planning purposes, round up to assume a height of 100.50' for the upper floor and a lower floor elevation of 91.50'. If the lower slab must be a minimum of 6" above the soil, it will require that the ground be no higher than 91.00'. To provide positive drainage, the edge of the bank was set at 90'. This will provide a gentle slope for a small yard on top of the bank. Figure 9.23 shows the resulting grading plan with the building footprint and the required cut-and-fill banks.

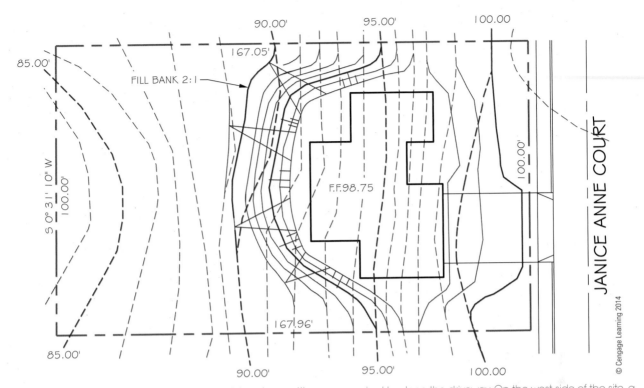

FIGURE 9.22 To keep the home as high as possible, minor cutting was required to place the driveway. On the west side of the site, a fill bank was created.

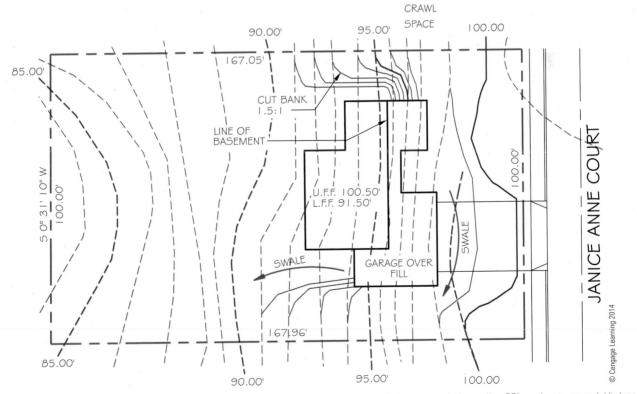

FIGURE 9.23 The grading required for a two-level home. To allow for the basement, the ground above the 90′ contour was cut. Higher grades were run into retaining walls on the north and south ends of the basement. The garage area will require gravel fill to bring it up to the required level. The northeast portion of the home will be over a crawl space, allowing the natural grade to remain.

Site Profile Drawings

A ***profile*** is a drawing showing the surface of the ground and underlying earth taken along any desired fixed line. Figure 9.24 shows a profile cut near the center of the site, as in Figure 9.22. The drawing is created by placing a line to represent the cutting plane on the grading plan and then projecting each grade that touches the line into the profile. The horizontal scale of the profile should be plotted at the same scale used for the grading plan. The vertical scale can be the same as the horizontal scale, or it can be exaggerated to give a clearer representation of the contour. The vertical scale in Figure 9.24 is 2 times the horizontal scale.

Several profile drawings are often made during the preliminary process to help the owners visualize how the home will relate to the site. Profile drawings are generally not required by most municipalities to obtain a building permit but are used by the architectural team to help define how the home will blend with the site. Figure 9.25 shows the altered profile drawing through the center of the home shown in Figure 9.23.

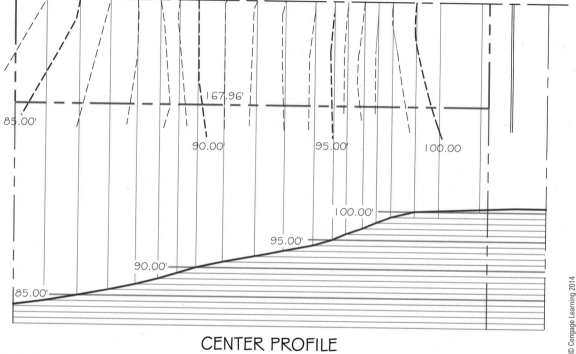

CENTER PROFILE

FIGURE 9.24 A profile for the site shown in Figure 9.22, showing the existing contours.

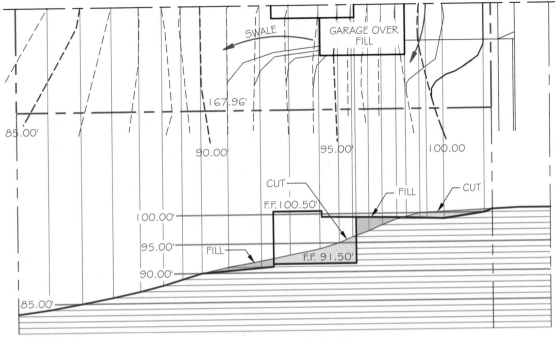

FIGURE 9.25 A profile for the site shown in Figure 9.23, showing the structure and the finished grading.

Additional Resources

The following websites can be used as a resource to help you keep current on issues of land use.

Address	Company or Organization
www.blm.gov	Bureau of Land Management
www.blm.gov/ca	California Bureau of Land Management
www.usgs.gov	United States Geological Survey (USGS)
http://earthquake.usgs.gov	USGS Earthquake Hazards Program

Land Descriptions and Drawings Test

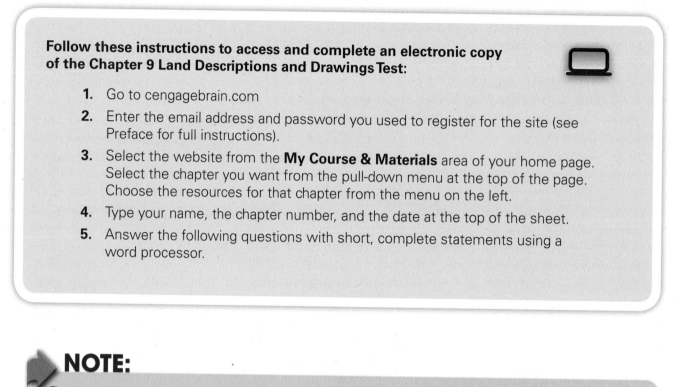

Follow these instructions to access and complete an electronic copy of the Chapter 9 Land Descriptions and Drawings Test:

1. Go to cengagebrain.com
2. Enter the email address and password you used to register for the site (see Preface for full instructions).
3. Select the website from the **My Course & Materials** area of your home page. Select the chapter you want from the pull-down menu at the top of the page. Choose the resources for that chapter from the menu on the left.
4. Type your name, the chapter number, and the date at the top of the sheet.
5. Answer the following questions with short, complete statements using a word processor.

NOTE:

The answers to some questions may not be contained in this chapter and will require you to do additional research using the Internet. Use your favorite search engine to search for specific professional companies or general categories of information.

Questions

9.1. What is a monument as it relates to a site drawing?

9.2. List four units of measurement that might be referred to in a rectangular system legal description.

9.3. What two directions are used to commence a bearing?

9.4. What would a designation of 100.67' S37° 30'45"W represent on a site plan?

9.5. What would a designation of S28AA, T 3S, R1E represent on a site plan?

9.6. List three components of a legal description commonly used for incorporated areas.

9.7. List two common sources of site drawings.

9.8. Explain the difference between a topography plan and a grading plan.

9.9. What is the purpose of a vicinity map?

9.10. Sketch examples of linetypes to represent the following materials: property line, centerline, easement, sewer, and water line.

9.11. List and describe two common hatch patterns that can be used to highlight a building.

9.12. Sketch a bank indicator representing a slope.

9.13. How are existing and new grades typically represented on a plan?

9.14. Describe the process of changing field sketches to a topography map.

9.15. What is an angle of repose?

9.16. Give the common proportions of cut-and-fill banks.

9.17.   Obtain a land map and legal description from a local title company of the property your place of residence is built on or for a site provided by your instructor.

9.18.   Interview a local landscape architect, civil engineer, and landscape contractor to assess the drafting opportunities in your area and to obtain examples of the types of drawings local professionals expect drafters to draw.

9.19.   Take a minimum of 15 photographs representing the installation or completion of work specified on a site, grading, landscape, or sprinkler plan.

9.20.   Use the Internet to research the local building department in your area and determine common residential zones and the required front, side, and rear setbacks for each.

Chapter 10
Site-Related Drawing Layout

Chapter 9 includes examples of a subdivision, site plan, topography plan, and grading plan. This chapter introduces drawing methods to create site-related drawings. Consideration is given to how to develop files for site drawings; methods to establish common drawing parameters such as scales, paper sizes, and layers; and layout methods for each type of drawing.

Key Terms

No new terms are introduced in this chapter.

CAD Commands and Tools

In addition to basic drawing, editing, text, and dimensioning commands, the following AutoCAD commands and tools are concepts that you should be familiar with to successfully understand and complete the CAD skills referenced in this chapter.

BLOCK	LAYER	LINEWEIGHT	SAVE	XREF
FILE	LIMITS	PEDIT	SNAP	
FOLDER	LINETYPE	PLINE	UNITS	

PROJECT STORAGE METHODS

The method for developing the site plan depends on the complexity of the project and the types of drawings to be created. Because the site plan serves as a basis for so many other drawings, it is important for the CAD technician to have a clear understanding of what additional site drawings will be required and who will complete them. Storing all of the site-related drawings in one file, using a separate drawing file for each drawing, and using external referencing are the most common methods for developing a site plan. See Chapter 4 for a review of drawing and layer prefixes and titles.

One Drawing File

On small-scale projects, one firm often prepares each of the site drawings and then stores them within one drawing file. Site-related drawings should be stored in one file only if each drawing is stored on a separate layer. You should give layers names describing both the base drawing and the contents of the layer, as outlined in Chapter 4. Titles such as *C BLDG, C PROP,* or *C ANNO* will clearly describe the contents. To plot the topography plan, basic items from the site plan, such as the building and property and all *TOPO* layers, should be set to THAW, with all other layers such as SITE ANNO set to FREEZE. Using separate layouts in one drawing file can also serve to store multiple drawings in one file. Separate layouts can be created for the site plan, topography plan, and landscape plan in one drawing, allowing easy selection of the desired drawing for plotting.

Separate Drawing Files

Using separate drawing files is the least effective use of disk space. To effectively create separate model and sheet files, place necessary information for each of the related drawing files in a base drawing and store it as a wblock. This information can then be reused, saving valuable drafting time on each new drawing and without wasting disk space.

External Reference

Site-related drawings are an excellent example of drawings that can be referenced to other drawings. A drafter working for the architectural team can draw the basic site plan information in a base drawing that will be reflected on all other site drawings. Copies of this drawing file can be given to the other consulting firms that will develop the landscape, sprinkler, and grading drawings. Using external referencing allows each firm to have a current drawing file as a base while progressing with its work independently.

SETTING SITE PLAN PARAMETERS

Site drawings require a template drawing that reflects either engineering or metric values instead of architectural values. Parameters such as UNITS, LIMITS, SNAP aspect, GRID sizes, layer parameters, dimension and text variables, and plotting requirements can then be set to meet the specific needs of the site plan. Common layers can also be set up to separate site information from other information that will be stored with the site file. Offices usually have stock template drawings containing common site-related linetypes, dimension and text variables, notes, and symbols. As a student, you may need to develop your own template drawing for site plans.

Drawing Scales

Site plans are plotted at a scale factor such as 1" = 10' (1:120) or 1" = 20' (1:240). Table 4.1 on the website lists common architectural and engineering scales for site plans. Tables 3.3 and 3.4 list preferred metric scales for civil drawings. Factors that influence the scale include building department requirements and the amount of detail required. For single-family projects, many municipalities regulate either the scale of the site plan or the size of the sheet on which the plan is plotted. For multi-family drawings, varied scales may be required for the site plan depending on the stage of the design review or permit process. Verify scale requirements with the governing municipality. If the building department does not mandate a scale, use the largest scale possible for the paper size to be used as well as large enough to show all required information clearly.

Paper Sizes

Site plans are drawn on media ranging in size from A through D. The choice of material is often based on requirements from building departments and lending institutions and the purpose of the plan. Many municipalities require site plans on specific paper sizes for easy filing. Common sizes include 8 1/2 × 11", 14", or 17" (215 × 275, 350, or 425 mm). When specific paper sizes are not required, use a size that matches the size used for the balance of the project. When the site plan is placed on paper larger than A, the sheet is often used as a title sheet. On projects for multi-family developments, the site plan often includes a table of contents, a list of consulting firms involved in the project, and a list of abbreviations used throughout the project.

Layer Guidelines for Civil Drawings

The list below includes common layers for site-related drawings. Many of the layers are not necessary for a single-family residence but will be useful on site-related plans for multifamily developments.

C BLDG	Proposed building footprints
C COMM	Site communications
C COMM OVHD	Overhead communications lines
C COMM UNDR	Underground communications
C FIRE	Fire protection
C NGAS	Natural gas
C NGAS UNDR	Underground natural gas lines
C PKNG	Exterior parking areas
C PKNG CARS	Graphic illustrations of cars
C PKNG DRAN	Parking lot drainage slope indicators
C PKNG ISLD	Parking islands
C PKNG STRP	Parking lot striping, handicapped symbols
C PROP	Property lines
C PROP BRNG	Bearings and distance labels
C PROP CONS	Construction controls
C PROP ESMT	Easements, rights-of-way, and setback lines
C ROAD	Roadways
C ROAD CNTR	Centerlines
C ROAD CURB	Curbs
C SSWR	Sanitary sewer
C SSWR UNDR	Underground sanitary sewer lines
C STRM	Storm drainage catch basins and manholes
C STRM UNDR	Underground storm drainage pipes
C TOPO	Proposed contour lines and elevations
C TOPO RTWL	Retaining walls
C TOPO SPOT	Spot elevations
C WATR	Domestic water, manholes pumping stations, storage tanks
C WATR UNDR	Domestic water underground lines

Gathering Information

Before beginning the layout of the site plan, gather information to explain the site. The site size and a legal description are available in legal documents for the property that are provided by the client, a title company, a surveyor's map, the local assessor's office, or the local zoning department. Other information necessary before starting the site plan includes:

- Legal description.
- Zoning information including front, rear, and side yard setbacks; height limitations; and methods of determining building height.
- North.
- Existing roads and alleys.
- All utilities including telephone, gas, water, sewer, or septic disposal.
- Drainage and slope requirements.
- Size of proposed structures and outbuildings.
- Minimum drawing standards based on municipal standards.

Figure 10.7 shows a subdivision map that will be used for preparing the site plan. For this example, parcel 1 will be used and the plan will have a scale of 1" = 10' (1:50). Other information not found on the subdivision map but required by the building department includes:

- Legal description: Lot 1 of the Schmitke addition in S20, T2S, R5E of the Willamette Meridian, Clark County, Washington.
- Front setback = 20' (6000 mm), rear setback 20' (6000 mm), side yard setback = 5' (1500 mm) one level, 6' (1800 mm) for two levels.
- Gas and water are located in the street. Sewer is available in the street, but the sewer line for this site will connect to a line in the easement.

- 10' sewer easement on west property line.
- 5' utility easement on east property line for phone, with utility box 3' south of the north property line.
- Cut bank = 1.5/1; fill bank = 2/1.

See the home used throughout Chapter 12 for footprint size.

Minimum Drawing Standards

The following standards are assumed to be the minimum requirements for the site based on the "local building department." Although they are common, each time you draw a site plan, you must verify the requirements of the governing body. The site plan must show:

- Site and building sizes.
- Setback dimensions.
- Property corner elevations.
- Contours: if site includes more than a 4' elevation differential, the plan must show 1' contour intervals.
- Location of easements, driveway, footprint of structure and decks.
- Location of all utilities.
- Site area, building coverage area, and building height. The height is to be measured by subtracting the average height of the corners of the structure from the average height of the site corners.
- Surface drainage.

COMPLETING A SITE PLAN

A site plan can be completed using the following steps:

Step 1. Before starting your drawing at a computer, gather all the information required to complete the drawings.

Step 2. Select or create the proper template to create the site plan. If a new template drawing is required, establish all required parameters for site-related drawings including: UNITS, LIMITS, SNAP aspect, GRID sizes, layer parameters, dimension and text variables, and plotting requirements.

Step 3. Working from a plat map, draw the property lines of the site on the *SITE PROP* layer. For this example the site in Figure 10.7 will be drawn.

Step 4. Establish the center of all access roads, alleys, and easements on the *SITE PROP ESMT* layer.

Step 5. Locate all public sidewalks on the *SITE CURB* layer.

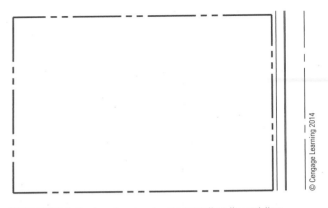

FIGURE 10.1 Start a site plan by representing the existing features of the building site, including the property lines, easements, access roads, and any public utilities.

© Cengage Learning 2014

Your drawing now shows the existing features of the building site and should resemble Figure 10.1. The next steps will help you proceed in an orderly fashion to show all new features to be included in the project. Steps 6 through 13 can be seen in Figure 10.2.

Step 6. Draw lines to indicate the required setback distances on the *SITE PROP ESMT* layer.

Step 7. Locate the proposed structure on the site plan on the *SITE BLDG* layer by following the dimensions on the preliminary floor plan or by inserting a block of the home. Create the block by tracing the footprint of the floor plan.

Step 8. Represent all paved areas such as the driveway, curb cuts, ramps, exterior parking spaces, and walkways on the *SITE CURB* layer.

Step 9. Draw all utilities, including electrical, gas, water, sewer, telephone lines, and utility easements, on the *SITE UTIL* layer.

Step 10. Draw any decks, balconies, or patios on the *SITE BLDG* layer.

Step 11. Draw any landscaping features such as planting areas, fountains, pools, spas, benches, or fences on the *SITE BLDG* layer.

Step 12. Draw drainage swales and catch basins on the *SITE PROP ESMT* layer.

Step 13. Draw special symbols such as property corner markers, a north arrow, fire hydrants, and cleanouts on the *SITE PROP BRNG* layer.

Step 14. Multifamily projects may require showing additional man-made features that are specific to the site, such as trash enclosures, patio furniture, flagpoles, retaining walls, and signs. Draw these features on the *SITE BLDG MISC* layer.

Once all man-made items are drawn, each should be located with dimensions. Place dimensions on the *SITE*

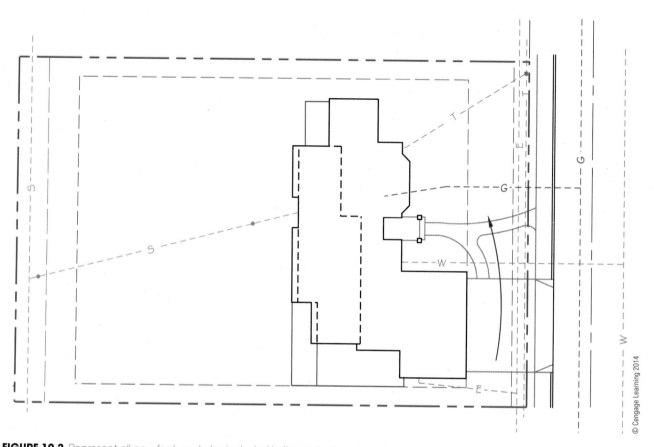

© Cengage Learning 2014

FIGURE 10.2 Represent all new features to be included in the project, such as the structure, decks, driveway and walkways, public utilities, required planting areas, landscaping features, and drainage patterns.

ANNO DIMS layer by locating major items first. Express dimensions as feet and inches unless noted below. Use the following order to place dimensions:

Step 15. Dimension property boundaries using decimal feet and list the required bearings parallel to the property lines.

Step 16. Dimension the location of the structure to the property lines.

Step 17. Dimension the minimum required yard setbacks or list the minimum required setback size in a table placed near the site plan.

Step 18. Dimension the overall size of the building footprint by placing the dimensions parallel to the edge of the building.

Step 19. Dimension the locations of streets, public sidewalks, and easements from the property line.

Step 20. Dimension all paved areas as well as individual parking spaces and catch basins relative to the property boundaries.

Step 21. Dimension all utility locations relative to the property boundaries.

Step 22. Dimension all other miscellaneous man-made features relative to the property boundaries.

Figure 10.3 includes steps 15 through 22. With all features drawn and located, add any special symbols necessary to describe the material being used on the *SITE BLDG MISC* layer. Typically this includes hatching concrete walkways with a dot pattern or hatching the footprint of the structure.

The next stage in completing the site plan is to provide annotation to define all man-made features for the site. Care should be taken to distinguish between existing material and new material that is to be provided. Occasionally it is necessary to specify the removal of existing material from the site. Place the required notes on the *SITE ANNO NOTE* layer unless noted. Include the following notes a site plan:

Step 23. Proposed building use (SFR can be used to represent a single-family residence), square footage, and building height placed inside the structure.

Step 24. Site area and site coverage in a table near the site plan.

Step 25. Use the *SITE PROP BRNG* layer to specify elevation markers for each property corner and each building corner.

Step 26. Finished floor elevation placed inside the structure or referenced to the structure with a leader line.

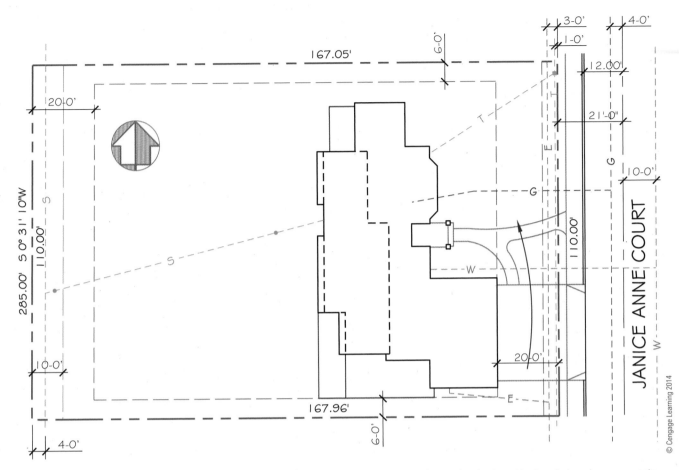

FIGURE 10.3 All man-made items must be located with dimensions. Express dimensions using feet and inches to locate man-made objects and engineering units to dimension the site boundaries.

Step 27. Legal description placed near the site plan.

Step 28. Specify all streets, public walkways, curbs, and driveways.

Step 29. Describe all utilities with local notes referenced to the utility with a leader line.

Step 30. Describe all paved areas and specific parking areas with local notes referenced to the area with a leader line.

Step 31. Describe specific features that are added to the site, including furniture, flagpoles, retaining walls, fencing, and planting areas with local notes referenced to the item with a leader line.

Once all items on the site plan have been drawn, dimensioned, and noted, complete the drawing using the following steps:

Step 32. Add details to show construction of man-made items.

Step 33. Add general notes to describe site-related construction requirements.

Step 34. Specify a drawing title and scale.

The site plan is now complete and should resemble Figure 10.4. Use the drawing checklist from Appendix D located on the website to evaluate your drawing before submitting it to your instructor or placing the drawing into production.

COMPLETING A TOPOGRAPHY PLAN

A topography plan is created using field notes from the surveying team. Spot elevations are located on the site plan using the *TOPO OUTL* layer; then points that represent uniform elevations are connected using the *TOPO CONT* layer. Figure 10.5a shows the spot elevations for the site plan that was just created. The topography plan can be completed using the following steps.

Follow steps 1 through 5 that were used to create the site plan, or use an electronic copy of the plan as a base for the topography plan. If using an electronic copy, freeze all unnecessary information.

Step 6. Draw grid lines on the site plan that match the grid used on the field drawings. Place the grid on a layer such as *TOPO OUTL* so that it can be frozen and not be part of the finished drawings.

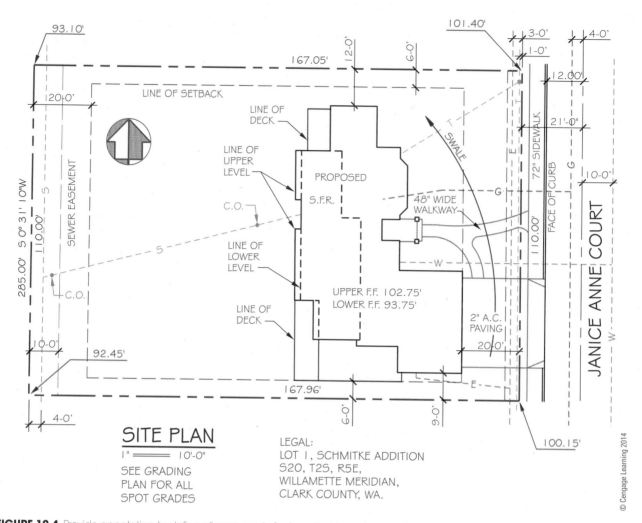

FIGURE 10.4 Provide annotation to define all man-made features that have been added to the site. Care should be taken to distinguish between new and existing features and material that is to be demolished.

Step 7. Determine the desired contour interval to be used on the drawing. Common intervals include 1, 2, 5, or 10' (300, 600, 1500, or 3000 mm). For this example, contours are shown for each 1' of elevation change. Accent will be provided to each 5' (1500 mm) contour.

Step 8. Locate points to represent each of the spot grades on the *TOPO OUTL* layer.

Step 9. Using the *TOPO OUTL* layer, divide the space between each spot grade to represent the height between each spot grade.

NOTE:

To locate each contour, use the PLINE command to place the lines between the grid points. Place these marks on a separate layer so they can be frozen after establishing all contour lines.

The drawing should now resemble Figure 10.5b with each spot grade located and the distance between each spot grade equally divided.

Step 10. Select either the highest or lowest whole-foot elevation and establish a contour line on the *TOPO CONT* layer. Place the lines by picking points on the grid that represent the desired elevation. Use the PLINE command to place the lines between each grid to locate each contour.

Figure 10.6 shows the layout of the 101', 100', and the 99' contours.

Step 11. Draw the balance of the contour lines by connecting points of equal elevation. Work from highest to lowest or lowest to highest.

Step 12. Use the Fit option of the PEDIT command to provide a curve to each contour line.

Step 13. Freeze all layout information such as grids and spot elevations that is not required for the final drawing.

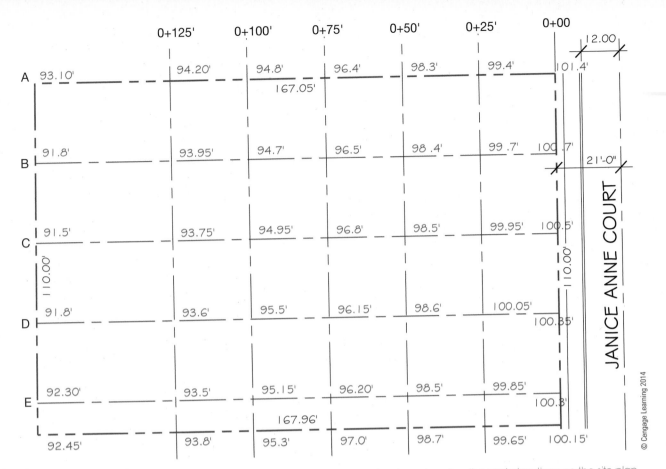

FIGURE 10.5a A topography plan is created using field notes for the surveying team, locating the spot elevations on the site plan, and then connecting the dots that represent uniform elevations.

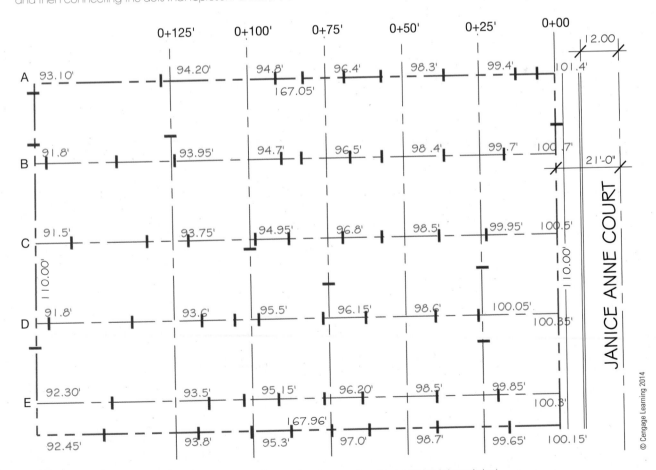

FIGURE 10.5b Once the field notes are located on the site plan, spot grades can be interpolated.

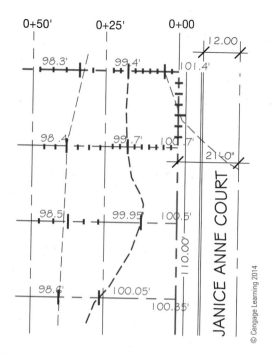

FIGURE 10.6 A contour line can be represented by picking points on the grid that represent the desired elevation. Knowing that 0 + 50 represents 98.3' and 0 + 25 represents a height of 99.4', it can be assumed that the ground slopes evenly between these two known elevations. If a major change occurred between those two points, the surveyor would have added a spot grade. The first mark to the right of 0 + 50 represents 98.4', with each of the following marks representing 98.6', 98.8', 99.0', and 99.2', respectively. Lines to connect each point of the 101', 100', and the 99' contours are shown.

Step 14. Change the line weight of every fifth contour line to highlight the 5' intervals.

Step 15. Provide spot grades for each property corner elevation on the *TOPO ANNO ELEV* layer.

Step 16. Provide labels at the ends of each 5' elevation on the *TOPO ANNO* layer.

Step 17. Display text from the site plan, including property lengths and bearings, labels for the street name, curb, sidewalk, a title and scale, and a north arrow.

The completed topography plan should now resemble Figure 10.7.

COMPLETING A GRADING PLAN

A grading plan should be provided when the proposed construction requires extensive excavation. The grading plan shows the existing topography and the elevations of the site that require excavation. Complete the plan using the following steps:

Steps 1 through 5. Follow steps 1 through 5 that were used to create the site plan or use an electronic copy of the site and topography plans as a base for the grading plan. If an electronic copy is used, freeze all unnecessary information.

Step 6. Determine the angle of repose for cut-and-fill banks based on municipal requirements or standards recommended by the soils engineer who supervised the topography drawings and geology report recommendations. The slope of cut surfaces for this site must not exceed 1.5/1 and fill banks must not exceed 2/1.

Step 7. Insert a block to represent the outline of the upper and lower floor plans or XREF the floor plan to the site plan. For this project, the floor plan from Chapter 12 will be used.

Step 8. Show the outline of the driveway and proposed walks.

Your grading plan should now resemble Figure 10.8, showing the existing topography and all existing features such as curbs and sidewalks. Take information for steps 1 to 8 from the site and topography plans if an electronic copy of the site plan is not available. If you have access to the electronic drawings, use the site and topography plans as a base drawing and freeze unnecessary information.

Step 9. Use a print of the grading plan to plan the finished soil elevations.

Step 10. Use the print to evaluate the finish elevations for the garage, the upper floor plan, and the lower floor. Sketch the proposed changes on your print.

10a. Because the existing grade at the driveway flows down into the garage, a swale is required.

10b. If the 100' contour is pulled closer to the property line, the garage can be set at an elevation of 101'. This allows for:
- The driveway and garage to be placed on a small amount of fill creating positive drainage.
- Raising the lower floor to minimize cutting.
- Front of garage floor at 101.00'.
- Rear of garage floor at 101.50'.
- Upper finish floor elevation at 102.75'.
- Lower finish floor elevation at 93.75'.
- A concrete pad at 97.5' in the crawl space for the utilities.

10c. The north, east, and south walls of the basement require retaining walls.

Step 11. Use your freehand sketch as a guide to locate all proposed contour changes on the *TOPO CONT NEW* layer. Assume that no grading will be allowed in the setback area. Use continuous thin lines to represent new contours. Use continuous thick lines to represent 5' contours.

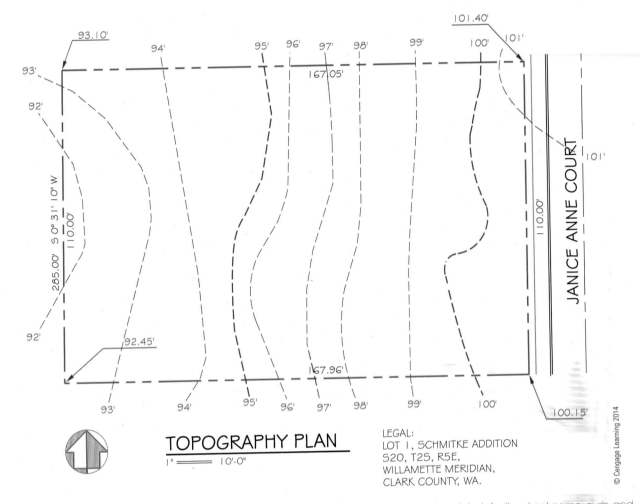

TOPOGRAPHY PLAN

1" === 10'-0"

LEGAL:
LOT 1, SCHMITKE ADDITION
S20, T2S, R5E,
WILLAMETTE MERIDIAN,
CLARK COUNTY, WA.

© Cengage Learning 2014

FIGURE 10.7 The completed topography plan should include property lengths and bearings; labels for the street name, curb, and sidewalk; a title and scale; and a north arrow.

The grading plan should now resemble Figure 10.9. Complete the grading plan using the following steps:

Step 12. Place the needed text to represent the elevation of each contour line on the *TOPO CONT ANNO* layer.

Step 13. Represent swales required to divert water from the residence on the *TOPO DRAN* layer.

Step 14. Provide spot grades for each corner of the site on the *TOPO DRAN ANNP* layer.

Step 15. Provide spot grades for each corner of the residence on the *TOPO BLDG ANNO* layer.

Step 16. Label the elevation of each floor level on the *TOPO BLDG ANNO* layer.

Step 17. Thaw, insert, or copy information from the site plan to show information that describes the site such as the property size, legal description, north arrow, street name, sidewalks, driveways, and walks.

Step 18. Place a title and scale below the drawing on the *TOPO ANNO* layer.

Step 19. Establish the proper scale values for the viewport and prepare a check print to evaluate your work.

The completed grading plan can be seen in Figure 10.10.

COMPLETING A PROFILE DRAWING

A profile is a section that shows the contour of the ground along any line extending through the site. Once a line is drawn on the grading plan, the profile is drawn from the contour lines at the section location. The contour map and its related profile are commonly referred to as the plan and profile. The following example places the viewing line at the north edge of the driveway in Figure 10.10. Information needed to lay out the project can be placed on the *SITE OUTL* layer and frozen for plotting. Use the *SITE GRID* layer to display the profile base. Create a profile using the following steps:

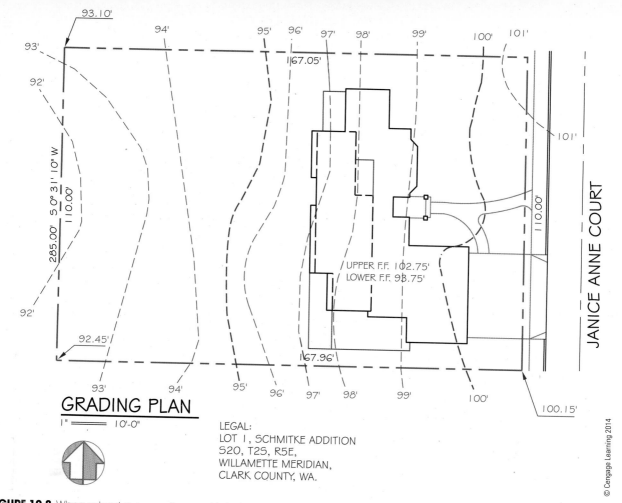

GRADING PLAN

1" = 10'-0"

LEGAL:
LOT 1, SCHMITKE ADDITION
S20, T2S, R5E,
WILLAMETTE MERIDIAN,
CLARK COUNTY, WA.

UPPER F.F. 102.75'
LOWER F.F. 98.75'

JANICE ANNE COURT

© Cengage Learning 2014

FIGURE 10.8 When extensive excavation must take place, a grading plan is provided to show the existing topography and the elevations of the site requiring excavation. Start the plan by using a topography plan as a base, and locate all proposed work, such as the structure, walks, and the driveway.

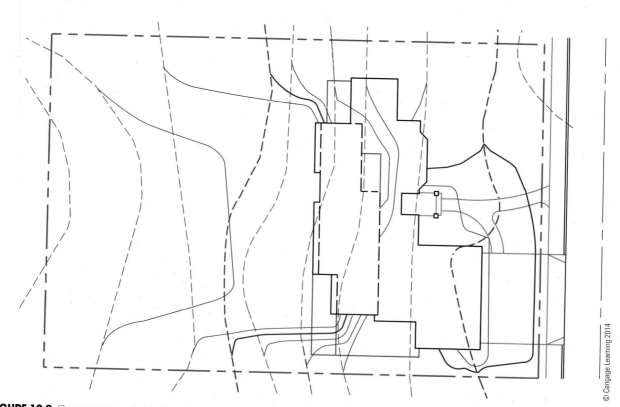

© Cengage Learning 2014

FIGURE 10.9 Once proposed elevations have been placed on a sketch, new contour locations can be represented using continuous thin lines. Continuous thick lines are used to represent 5' contours.

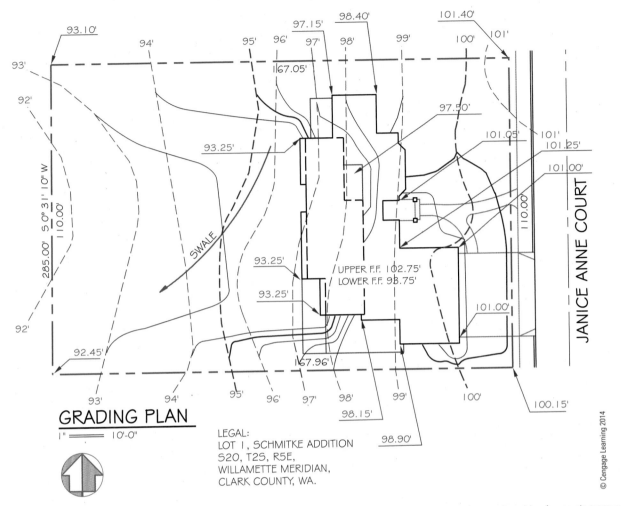

GRADING PLAN
1" = 10'-0"

LEGAL:
LOT 1, SCHMITKE ADDITION
S20, T2S, R5E,
WILLAMETTE MERIDIAN,
CLARK COUNTY, WA.

© Cengage Learning 2014

FIGURE 10.10 The completed grading plan will represent existing and new contours, drainage swales, spot grades for each corner of the site and the residence, and the finish floor elevations. Information should also be provided to describe the site, such as the property size, legal description, north arrow, street name, sidewalks, driveways, and walks.

Step 1. Draw a straight line on the topography or grading plan at the location of the desired profile.

Step 2. Draw a horizontal line to represent the base of the drawing.

Step 3. Project a line at 90° from the cutting plane to indicate where each existing contour line touches the cutting plane.

Step 4. Determine the vertical scale to be used. For this drawing the vertical scale is 3 times the horizontal scale. Figure 10.11 shows the grid created to establish the profile.

Step 5. Draw a line to connect the corresponding existing contour elevations on the *SITE GRID NEW* layer.

Step 6. Freeze the grid used to establish the contours or set the plotting parameters to display it with grayscale.

Step 7. Provide spot grades at the high and low points of the profile and at any significant elevation changes on the *SITE GRID ANNO* layer.

Step 8. Place a title and list the horizontal scale on the *SITE GRID ANNO* layer.

The completed existing profile drawing should resemble Figure 10.12. Use the completed profile to show the proposed grading and the new structure.

Complete the profile using the following steps:

Step 9. Thaw the grid to help represent the new grades.

Step 10. Project lines at 90° to the cutting plane to represent the outline of the structure and the new grade contour locations on the *SITE OUTL* layer.

Step 11. Draw a line on the *SITE OUTL* layer to connect the corresponding new contour elevations on the *SITE CONT NEW* layer.

Step 12. Provide spot grades at any significant elevation changes, floor levels, and walkways on the *SITE GRID ANNO* layer.

Step 13. Place a title and list the horizontal scale on the *SITE GRID ANNO* layer.

The completed profile drawing should resemble Figure 10.13.

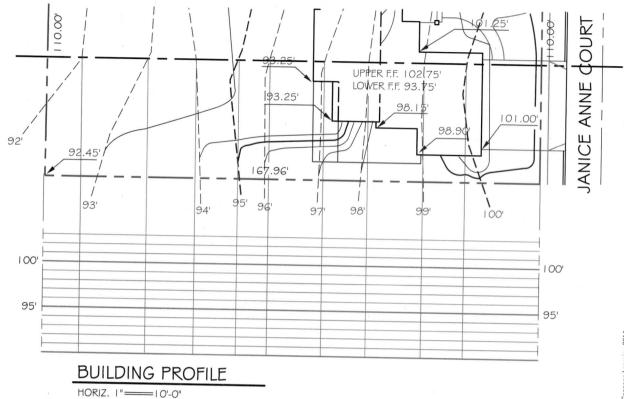

FIGURE 10.11 A profile shows the contour of the ground along any line extending through the site. Once a line is drawn on the grading plan, the profile is drawn from the contour lines at the section location.

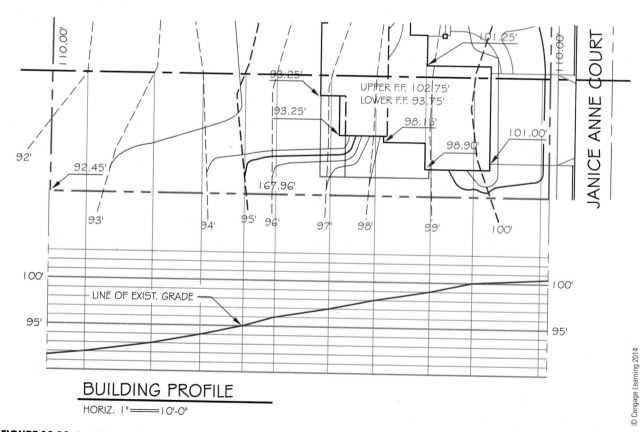

FIGURE 10.12 A profile drawing is created by drawing a straight line on the topography or grading plan to represent the cutting plane. Once the desired profile location is selected, a line is projected at 90° from the cutting plane where each existing contour line touches the cutting plane.

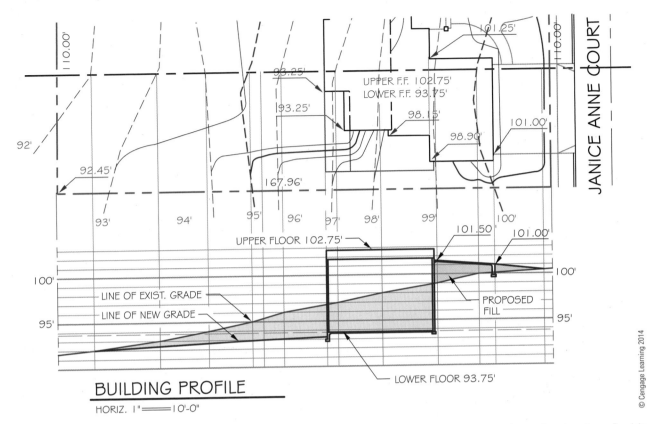

FIGURE 10.13 The completed profile drawing should show the outline of the structure and the new grade contour locations. Provide spot grades at significant elevation changes, floor levels, and the walkways. Provide a title and list the horizontal scale.

Site-Related Drawing Layout Test

Follow these instructions to access and complete an electronic copy of the Chapter 10 Site-Related Drawing Layout Test:

1. Go to cengagebrain.com
2. Enter the email address and password you used to register for the site (see Preface for full instructions).
3. Select the website from the **My Course & Materials** area of your home page. Select the chapter you want from the pull-down menu at the top of the page. Choose the resources for that chapter from the menu on the left.
4. Type your name, the chapter number, and the date at the top of the sheet.
5. Answer the following questions with short, complete statements using a word processor.

Questions

10.1. How is the sheet size for a site plan determined?

10.2. What factors influence the drawing scale selection for a site plan, a topography plan, and a grading plan?

10.3. List five pieces of information you should gather before starting a site plan.

10.4. List five sources of information for site-related drawings.

10.5. Define setbacks and explain how they affect a site and grading plan.

10.6. Explain factors that influence the spacing of contour lines on a grading plan.

10.7. What is a spot grade and how does it relate to a topography plan?

10.8. What is the distance to station point 0 + 50 from the base point?

10.9. In addition to the elevation of the site excavation, what does the grading plan show?

10.10. Explain how information on a site plan is transferred to a topography or grading plan.

Drawing Problems

Unless your instructor assigns a specific site, select one of the following site plans using the following guidelines.

- Visit the website for the municipality that governs your area and use the setbacks for the given size of the lot you have chosen, or use the following setbacks:
  —Minimum front setback, 25'-0"
  —Minimum rear yard setback, 20'-0"
  —Minimum side yard setback: one level, 5'-0"; two level, 6'-0"

- Use the paper size specified by the municipality that governs your area. If your zoning department does not specify a size, make your drawing fit on an 8.5" × 14" sheet of paper.

- Select the appropriate scale to draw the required site drawing. Use the Internet to access the zoning department website to verify the requirements that apply to the site you've selected for your project. Be sure to verify allowable site coverage limits, height requirements, and setbacks appropriate for the size of the site.

Before starting this drawing, demonstrate your understanding of the drawing problem with your client (your instructor). After reviewing the drawing criteria for this project on the student website, either verbally or in a written memo, confirm with your client your understanding of the project, and list the amount of time you expect the drawing to take and any resources you require to complete it. Provide verbal instructions to your client addressing any questions they might have, and let them know when the project will be complete. Ask for clarification of any questions you have regarding the drawing criteria. If you complete your project preview verbally, have your questions written down so that you can ask relevant questions in a professional manner and be prepared to take notes regarding your client's comments.

Once you've confirmed the work to be done on this drawing project, using the guidelines presented in this chapter, make a list of the work to be completed that includes the minimum contents as well as an estimate of the time you require to complete each aspect of the drawing:

Research.

Major steps to complete the drawing.

Applicable codes that will apply to this drawing.

Applicable local requirements that apply to the drawing.

Adjusting drawing templates to set plotting standards, text heights, dimensions, and linetypes.

Completing all required annotation and dimensioning.

Evaluation.

Track the amount of time.

Compare the estimated completion time for each aspect of the project with the actual required time.

Use the appropriate checklist from the student website prior to submitting your drawing to your instructor.

Problems

The following paragraph describes problem 10.1 through 10.7. Use the subdivision map in Figure 9.7 and draw the site plan for one of the parcels of land. Begin the selected site plan problem by representing the given information in preparation to complete a preliminary design study for one of the homes in Chapter 12. Once your preliminary floor plan is approved, complete the required site drawings.

10.8   Draw a vicinity map of your school showing major access routes and important landmarks within a five-mile radius.

10.9   Use the following legal description to draw the site plan for a tract of land situated in the SW 1/4 of the NE 1/4 of section 17, T2S, R1W of Mount Diablo Meridian, Rancho Santa Barbara:

Beginning at a 5/8" iron rod marking the true point of beginning of the southwest property corner that lies 32' directly north of the center of Rancho Santa Barbara Place, proceed N 3° 15' W 115.0', thence N8° 30' E 140.0', thence proceed N 90° 00'E a distance of 92.10; thence proceed S38° 30' E 91.5'; thence proceed due south a distance of 181.5'; and thence proceed due West 163.25' back to the true point of beginning.

10.10   Use the following legal description to draw the site plan for the following tract of land:

Parcel 12, tax lot 215682 of the Miller Addition, situated in section 12, T3N, R1E, 6th Principal Meridian, Cloud County, Kansas. Beginning at a 5/8" iron rod marking the southerly corner and the true point of beginning of the southeast property corner, go a distance of 185.0' N49° 50' W to the far westerly corner. Said property line lies 32.00' north of the center of Miller Drive. Thence N 65° 15' E a distance of 104.50'; thence N49° 00' W a distance of

147.0'; thence N43° 30' E a distance of 93.0' back to the true point of beginning.

10.11   Use the following description to draw and label a site plan that can be plotted at a scale of 1/8" = 1'-0":

Beginning at a point that is the NE corner of the G.M. Smith D.L.C., which lies 250 feet north of the centerline of N.E.122 Street which is in Section 1AB, Township 6 north, Range 1 west of Los Angeles County, California, thence south 225.00 feet to a point which is the southwest corner of said property, thence North 85.00 feet 1° 25' 30" west along the easterly edge which lies along N.E. Sweeney Drive (25' to street centerline) to the northwest property corner, thence 140.25 feet South 89° 15' 00" East, thence south 85.25 feet 1° 25' 30" east, thence westerly along the north boundary of N.E. 122 street to the true point of beginning.

10.12   Use the attached drawing and the drawing on the website to complete a site plan. After you complete the site plan, determine the square footage of the site and the zone for this property based on local zoning standards. Assign a legal description to the site that would be appropriate for a suburban site in your area.

10.13   Use the corresponding drawing on the website to lay out the represented grades. Draw the site plan using a scale of 1" = 10'-0". Show grades at 1' intervals and highlight contours every 5'.

10.14   Use the site plan created in problem 10.9 and the corresponding field notes on the website to create a topography plan for this site. Show grades at 1' intervals and highlight contours every 5'.

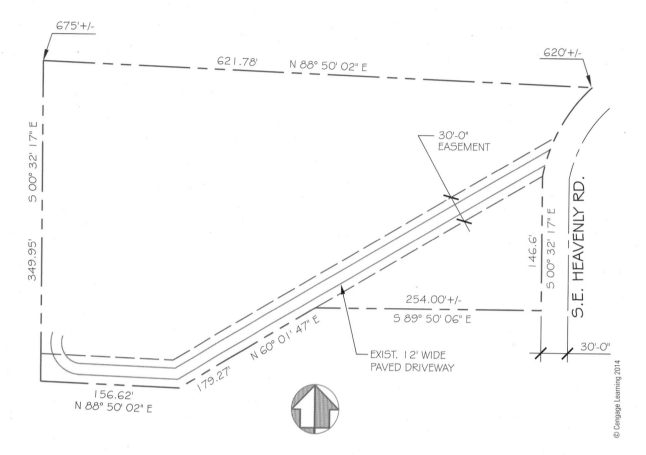

675'+/-

621.78'   N 88° 50' 02" E

620'+/-

S 00° 32' 17" E

30'-0"
EASEMENT

349.95'

146.6'

S 00° 32' 17" E

S.E. HEAVENLY RD.

254.00'+/-
S 89° 50' 06" E

N 60° 01' 47" E

30'-0"

EXIST. 12' WIDE
PAVED DRIVEWAY

179.27'

156.62'
N 88° 50' 02" E

© Cengage Learning 2014

10.15 Use the site plan created in problem 10.10 and the field notes on the website to create a topography plan for this site. Assume point H/0 + 00 to be the south corner of the property and line A-H is the southerly property line.

10.16 through 10.22 Use the field notes on the website to complete a topography plan for one of the sites created in problems 10.1 through 10.7.

10.23 through 10.29 Complete one of the following projects once you have selected and done a preliminary layout of one of the homes from Chapter 12. Use the completed topography plan for one of the sites created in problems 10.16 through 10.22 and the footprint of a home from Chapter 12 to create a grading plan. Assume that all fill banks are at a maximum angle of 2/1 and all cut banks are at a maximum angle of 1.5/1.

10.30 Use the drawing on the website to complete a site plan for four townhouse units. Prepare the drawing so that it can be plotted at a scale of 1" = 10'-0". The site is 120 ×110' and is Lots 4 and 5 of Arrowhead Estates, Rapid City, South Dakota. The project fronts onto Sioux Parkway with 36' from the property line to centerline of the roadway. Tee water to the property 75' east of the westerly property line from a main line 30' south of the property line. Provide a water shutoff valve in the garage of each unit. Access the city sewer line, which is 25' south of the property, with a new line 25' east of the westerly property line. Provide a clean out in the lower planting strip of each unit. Provide a continuous drainage grate across each driveway. Set each drain 3" below the finish floor level at each door. Provide a 7.5' wide easement along the northerly property line for a telephone easement. Provide each unit with a fenced yard. Dimension each unit as needed and specify all grades. Interpolate as needed to determine the grades for each corner of the structure.

Section 3

Floor Plans and Supplemental Drawings

Chapter 11
Floor Plans—Symbols, Annotation, and Dimensio

The floor plan provides a representation of where to locate the major items of a home. The plan shows the location of walls, doors, windows, cabinets, appliances, and plumbing fixtures.

Chapter 2 includes the development of a set of house plans and instructions for developing the floor plan. The drawing allows the homeowner to evaluate the project in terms of how it will meet the family's current and future needs after construction. The floor plan also serves as a key tool in the communication process between the design team and the building team. This chapter introduces the symbols, annotation, and dimensions typically associated with residential floor plans.

For the design team, the floor plan becomes the skeleton for developing other plan views required for the project, including the electrical plan, fire-protection plan, framing plan, plumbing plan, and HVAC drawings. The team will also use it as a base to create the site plan, roof plan, and roof-framing plan. The floor plan shows the material required for these related drawings. There are two common methods for placing related information on the floor plan. If the entire set of drawings will be drawn by one office, the team uses layers to control the display of information related to the various plan views. Common layers for controlling multiple drawings in one file are listed in Chapter 4 and throughout this chapter. If multiple firms consult on a project, the architectural team often completes the floor plan and provides an electronic copy of it to each consultant. This allows each firm to bind information to the base drawing using external referencing (XREF).

Key Terms

Accordion door	Casement window	Firebox	Handrail
Awning window	Chase	Fireplace insert	Hearth
Bay window	Combustion air	Firewall	Hopper window
Bidet	Double door	Flue	Hose bibb
Bifold door	Double-hung window	French door	Jalousie window
Bow window	Dutch door	Garden window	Jamb
Café door	Fanlight	Guardrail	Landing

Legend	Palladian window	Pocket door	Skylight
Low-E glass	Parametric	Radius window	Sky window
Mullions	Party wall	Riser	Sun tunnel
Muntins	Picture window	Run	Transom window
Nosing	Plenum	Single-hung window	Tread

CAD Commands and Tools

In addition to basic drawing, editing, text, and dimensioning commands, the following AutoCAD commands and tools are concepts that you should be familiar with to successfully understand and complete the CAD skills referenced in this chapter.

| AREA | BREAK | HATCH | OFFSET | TRIM |
| BLOCK | DIST | LAYER | TABLE | |

COMMON FLOOR PLAN SYMBOLS

Whatever method you use, you must clearly represent the information on the plan so it is consistent with common drawing practices. In theory, the floor plan is created by passing an imaginary horizontal cutting plane through the structure approximately 4' (1200 mm) above the floor. The portion of the structure above the cutting plane is then removed, allowing the viewer to look down into the structure. The relationship of the structure to the floor plan is shown in Figure 11.1. To create the plan view, you will work in model space using full scale. If the home is 70' long, adjust the drawing area so the structure will fit in the viewing area. As the floor plan is developed, the scale to be used to plot the plan must be considered. Most professionals plot floor plans using a scale of 1/4" = 1'-0" (1:50). Other scales such as 1/8" = 1'-0" or 3/16" = 1'-0" are common for large projects such as multifamily residential projects. To be consistent with professional practice, you will also need to use standard symbols to represent common features such as walls, doors, windows, cabinets, appliances, and plumbing features.

NOTE:

Most of the symbols in this chapter are in the Floor Blocks subfolder of the DRAWING BLOCKS folder on the website. Any text that is displayed with the block is set for display when plotting at a scale of 1/4" = 1'-0". Verify all layers and dimension sizes prior to inserting these blocks or any others into your drawing. Once an object is in your drawing, you assume responsibility that the object is correct.

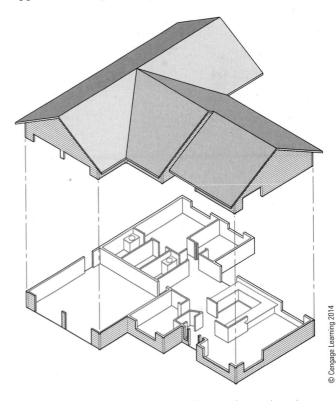

FIGURE 11.1 The floor plan is created by passing an imaginary horizontal cutting plane through the structure approximately 4' (1200 mm) above the floor. The portion of the structure above the cutting plane is then removed, allowing the viewer to look down into the structure.

© Cengage Learning 2014

Wall Symbols

Use pairs of thick (0.024"/60 mm) parallel lines to represent walls on the floor plan. The distance between the lines will vary based on office practice. Represent wood walls based on the following common methods:

- Nominal thickness of the building material which will produce 6 or 4" (150 or 100 mm) wide walls for wood construction.

- Thickness of the construction materials to be used.

Wall Thickness for Wood Walls

When the thickness of wood walls is drawn to the exact construction dimensions, the values are based on the material in use. Use 2 × 6 (50 × 150) or 2 × 4 (50 × 100) studs based on the region where the construction will take place to build exterior walls. Studs are the vertical members for constructing walls (see Chapter 21). Their finished size is 1 1/2 × 3 1/2" (40 × 90 mm) for a 2 × 4 (50 × 100) and 1 1/2 × 5 1/2" (40 × 140 mm) for a 2 × 6 (50 × 150). The thickness of the exterior and interior construction materials must added to the stud width. For a 6" exterior wall, the common thickness is:

Studs	5.5"	140 mm
Interior sheet rock	0.5"	13 mm
Exterior sheathing	0.5"	13 mm
Exterior stucco	1.0"	25 mm
Total wall thickness	7.5"	191 mm

© Cengage Learning 2014

Because the wall covering may not be known when starting the preliminary drawings, it is common to represent the wall thickness based on the stud width. Remember that while the computer is very accurate, you are creating only a representation of the structure. The contractor determines the necessary sizes based on your dimensions, not on the exact thickness of the walls on the floor plan.

When the studs are the basis for the wall thickness, four common sizes are usually represented on a floor plan. These sizes include:

- 6" (150 mm) wide for exterior heated walls.

- 4" (100 mm) wide for exterior unheated walls.

- 4" (100 mm) wide for interior walls.

- 6" (150 mm) wide for walls to hide plumbing for toilets on the lower level of multilevel structures.

(Pipes for toilets in a single-level home and other plumbing fixtures can be placed in a 2 × 4 (50 × 100) stud wall, but 2 × 6 (50 × 150) studs are often used to aid the plumbers.)

- 2" (50 mm) wide for furring (furring is material placed over the interior side of concrete walls to provide a smooth finish).

- 6–8" (150–200 mm) party walls and firewalls for multifamily units.

Although not found in a single-family residence, multifamily projects contain party walls and often contain firewalls. The *party wall* is the wall between two adjoining units. Two separate walls usually form a party wall to minimize sound transmission. A *firewall* separates units so that the floor area of multifamily projects does not exceed a specified size. Verify the need for firewalls with local codes, but a firewall is typically required when the floor area exceeds 3000 sq ft. Firewalls are typically constructed from wood studs covered with 5/8" type "X" gypsum board on each side. Chapter 22 explains party and firewall construction.

Wall Thickness for Non-wood Walls

In addition to wood, other materials can be used to frame walls. Walls framed with steel studs are drawn using the same methods used to draw wood walls. Masonry walls are represented in plan view with thick (0.024"/60 mm), parallel lines to represent the edges of the masonry. Thin lines for hatching are placed at a 45° angle to the edge of the wall using approximately 0.125" (3 mm) spacing. The AutoCAD ANSI31 hatch pattern is the common method of hatching masonry. The type, size, and reinforcement used to build the wall are not represented on the floor plan but are specified in note form. Common masonry wall thicknesses include:

- 4" (100 mm) wide for masonry veneer

- 8 to 10" (200 to 250 mm) wide for structural brick

- 8" (200 mm) wide for poured concrete walls

- 8" (200 mm) wide for concrete masonry units (CMUs)

Representing Walls

Represent walls on a layer that describes their function. A layer name such as *FLOR WALL* clearly describes the contents. A modifier can be added to further describe the contents using names such as *FLOR WALL NEW, FLOR WALL EXST, FLOR WALL REMOV, FLOR WALL CMU, FLOR WALL PRHT,* or *FLOR WALL MASN.*

⧉ Going Green

Alternative Materials

Energy-efficient homes often use various methods for constructing walls ranging from using common materials such as wood with advanced framing methods to bermed poured concrete or concrete blocks. Other materials and methods for energy-efficient construction may include strawbales, cob, mud and straw, rammed earth, poured earth, stone, bamboo, cordwood, papercrete, earth bags, used tires, or a hybrid method combining one of these methods with traditional framing method. Common wall thickness for these materials include:

- Strawbales   16–24" (400–600 mm)
- Cob   10–36" (250–900 mm)
- Rammed earth   12–24" (300–600 mm)
- Poured earth   12–18" (300–450 mm)
- Papercrete   8–12" (200–300 mm)
- Earth bags   8–18" (200–450 mm)

Sizes vary based on project and the design specifications. Chapter 21 introduces each of these methods. No matter the material, it can be represented in plan view using the methods described in the next section.

Figure 11.2 shows common methods of representing each type of wall in plan view. Although most offices do not use shading in walls, some projects require differences in wall construction to be highlighted. Shading partial-height walls differentiates them from full-height walls. New construction will need to be contrasted from existing walls and walls that will be removed. Figure 11.3 shows methods of highlighting varied wall construction. In planning wall layouts, common sizes include:

- Hallways: 36" (900 mm) minimum clearance
- Entry hallways: 42" to 60" (1060 to 1500 mm) minimum
- Bedroom closets: 24" (600 mm) minimum depth; 48" (1200 mm) minimum length

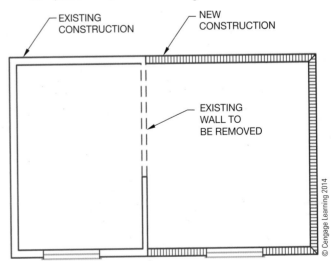

FIGURE 11.3 Methods of highlighting varied wall construction such as new walls, existing walls, and walls to be demolished are often found on residential remodeling projects.

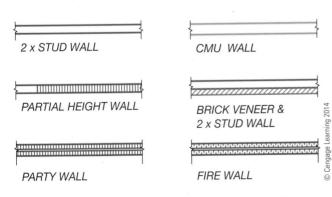

FIGURE 11.2 Common methods of representing each type of wall in plan view. Party walls and firewalls are found on multifamily projects.

USING CAD

The ability to draw walls and other symbols that will be introduced in this chapter with a CAD program is critical to your success. Methods vary from programs that require individual lines to be drawn to represent walls to programs that draw pairs of parallel lines to represent walls. These programs typically use X and Y coordinates to track lines. Although you may not be aware of it, a Z value representing a vertical height above a base plane is typically used with a default value of zero. Advanced programs such as those introduced in Chapter 4 allow a model to be created by entering Z coordinates. Models range from simple wire frame drawings to realistic images that can be rotated to see how various areas of a proposed project will look once it's finished. See the figure below.

4-UNIT BUILDING – KENDALL SQUARE APARTMENTS

Courtesy Terrel Broiles

- Linen closets: 14" to 24" (350 to 600 mm) deep (not over 30", or 760 mm)
- Washer/dryer space: 36" (900 mm) deep, 5'6" (1675 mm) long minimum
- Stairways: 36" (900 mm) minimum wide

Door Symbols

The AEC industry has developed standard symbols that represent common door types. AutoCAD and third-party vendors supply blocks to represent common door symbols, or they can easily be made and saved as part of your architectural template. Figure 11.4 shows common types of doors found on floor plans including swinging, sliding, folding, and overhead.

The door symbol on the floor plan reflects the type of door to be used. The size and material are specified in a schedule. The creation of schedules is discussed later in this chapter. Although traffic patterns dictate door placement, doors are usually placed in one of three locations:

- Within 3" (75 mm) of a corner to allow space for the doorframe and trim.
- Approximately 24" (600 mm) from a corner to allow for furniture placement behind the open door.
- Centered on the wall.

Swinging-Door Symbols

A swinging door is represented on the floor plan with thin lines showing the door and its swing. Symbols should be placed on a layer with a title such as *FLOR DOOR*. Common types of swinging doors include exterior, interior, double, French, double-acting, and Dutch. Each can be seen in Figure 11.5. Each swinging-door type can be used as both an exterior or interior door. A ***double door*** consists of two or more single swinging doors mounted in one frame, similar to Figure 11.6. Double swinging doors are often used as the main entry door in a large formal entry

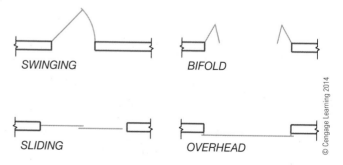

SWINGING   BIFOLD

SLIDING   OVERHEAD

© Cengage Learning 2014

FIGURE 11.4 Common doors found on a floor plan include swinging, sliding, folding, and overhead types.

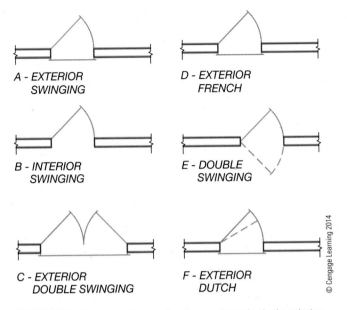

A - EXTERIOR SWINGING

D - EXTERIOR FRENCH

B - INTERIOR SWINGING

E - DOUBLE SWINGING

C - EXTERIOR DOUBLE SWINGING

F - EXTERIOR DUTCH

© Cengage Learning 2014

FIGURE 11.5 Common types of swinging doors include exterior, interior, double, French, double-acting, and Dutch doors.

© Cengage Learning 2014

FIGURE 11.6 Double doors consist of two or more single swinging doors mounted in one frame.

or to access decks and other outside living areas. If more than two doors are installed in one frame, they are usually installed as fixed panels.

A **French door** contains one or more glass panes referred to as lites. A single-lite French door contains one large piece of glass surrounded by a wood frame. A ten-lite door contains ten glass panes with a muntin between each pane. The most common French doors contain 1, 5, 10, or 15 lites. French doors can have multiple panes of glass or have one panel of glass with surface-mounted **muntins.** The surface-mounted muntins are removable to allow for easy cleaning.

Double-acting doors swing in either direction for easy passage. See Figure 11.5e. The access between kitchen and dining area is a common place for a double-acting door. **Dutch doors** (see Figure 11.5f) are divided in half, allowing one portion to be closed while the other is open. Typically the top portion can be opened and used as a pass-through while the lower portion is closed. Common widths for single swinging doors range from 2'-0" through 3'-6" (600 to 1050 mm) in 2" (50 mm) increments. Pairs of doors range from 2'-6" through 12'-0" (750 to 3600 mm) wide in 6" (150 mm) increments. Doors are typically 6'-8" (2000 mm) high, although 8'-0" (2400 mm) doors are available.

A final type of swinging door is a **café door**. It can be full height but is generally 36" to 42" (900 to 1050 mm) high and ranges from 28" to 42" (700 to 1050 mm) wide. Café doors are often used to block the view into the kitchen. They normally have louvered and raised-panel patterns.

Exterior Swinging Doors. Notice, in Figure 11.5, that an exterior door is represented with a thin line across the opening on its outside edge. This line represents the sill, which provides weatherproofing at the bottom of the door, and the step from the finish floor to the landing. (See Chapter 5 for a review of door/step relationships). The sill is commonly drawn projected about 1" (25 mm) from the exterior side of the wall. Some companies draw the sill line flush with the wall, but this tends to make the symbol harder to find on a complicated plan. Common sizes for swinging doors include:

- Main entry door   3'-0" (900 mm) wide
- Garage to utility   2'-8" (800 mm) wide
  room or outside
- Pairs of swinging doors   4' to 12' (1200 to
                          3600 mm) wide

Place exterior doors so the door swings in and opens toward the common direction of travel. By doing so, the hinges are on the interior side of the door, preventing the door from swinging over a step. Figure 11.7 shows

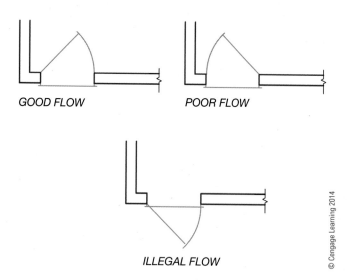

GOOD FLOW

POOR FLOW

ILLEGAL FLOW

FIGURE 11.7 Exterior doors should be placed so that they swing in and open toward the common direction of travel. The inward swing places the hinges on the interior side of the door and avoids swinging the door over a step.

common considerations in door placement. Exterior doors are made of solid wood components, fiberglass, or hollow metal with insulation. Doors may be either smooth (referred to as slab) or have decorative panels.

Interior Swinging Doors. Interior doors use the same symbol as exterior doors without sill lines, as shown in Figure 11.5b. Interior doors should swing into the room being entered and against a wall. Common interior door sizes are:

- Utility rooms   2'-8" (800 mm)
  and garages
- Bedrooms, dens,   2'-8" to 2'-6" (800 to 750 mm)
  family, and
  dining rooms
- Bathrooms   2'-6" to 2'-4" (750 to 700 mm)
- Closets   2'-4" to 2'-0" (700 to 600 mm)
- ADA access route 2'-8" (800 mm)

When two sizes are listed, the first, larger size is normally used for custom homes and the smaller is the standard size. Although the added cost for a larger door is minimal, providing wider halls for access can be costly. The smaller door sizes are for homes where space is critical. Keep in mind that the door size plus 6" (150 mm) for trim [3" (75 mm) each side] should be provided. Interior doors are usually 6'-8" (2000 mm) high. Taller doors are available for custom situations. Interior doors are usually made of wood, fiberglass, or vinyl panels that have a hollow core and a smooth surface on each side. This type of door is referred to as a hollow-core flush door. Interior doors can also be purchased with raised panels or glass panels.

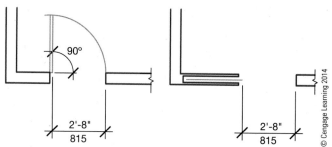

FIGURE 11.8 All doors for egress must have a minimum clear opening of 32" (815 mm) for wheelchair access.

ADA Access. The Americans with Disabilities Act (ADA) specifies that all doors must have a minimum opening of 32" (815 mm) for wheelchair access. This size is the clear, unobstructed dimension, measured to the edge of the door when opened at 90° (see Figure 11.8).

Non-swinging Doors

Common alternatives to swinging doors include pocket, slider, bypass, bifold, accordion, and overhead doors.

Pocket Doors

A **pocket door** is a door that slides into a wall cavity. This type of door is used when space for the door swing is limited. It is also used where a door may occasionally be desired for privacy, but the open position is the normal preference. Do not place a pocket door in heavy-traffic areas, where the pocket is in an exterior wall, or where it will interfere with plumbing or electrical wiring. Pocket doors may be hollow-core flush, raised-panel, or louvered. They range in width from 2'-0" through 3'-6" (600 to 1050 mm) in 2" (50 mm) increments. Figure 11.9 shows the representation for a pocket door.

Sliding Doors

Exterior sliding doors are made with wood, vinyl, or aluminum frames that contain tempered glass panels. Figure 11.10 shows a sliding door and the floor plan symbols for representing exterior sliding doors. These doors provide glass areas that meet code-mandated light and

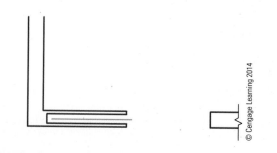

FIGURE 11.9 A pocket door that slides into a wall cavity can be used when space for the door swing is limited.

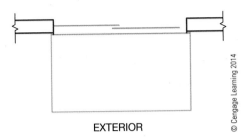

EXTERIOR

© Cengage Learning 2014

FIGURE 11.10 An exterior sliding glass door.

Courtesy Marvin Windows & Doors®

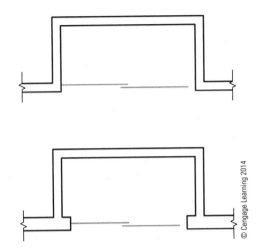

© Cengage Learning 2014

FIGURE 11.11 A bypass door is often used for a closet.

As doors increase in width, the number of panels also increases. Common panel arrangements include:

- Up to 8' (2400 mm) two-panel door
- 8' to 10' (2400 to 3000 mm) three-panel door
- 10' and larger (3000 mm+) four-panel door

Folding Doors

Common interior folding doors include bifold and accordion doors.

Bifold doors are always used in pairs—either two doors folding to one side or four doors split in the center of the opening with two doors folding back to each side. Bifold doors often provide full access to storage areas, but they can also hide appliances such a washer or dryer and, in some cases, folding doors are used between rooms. Bifold doors may be hollow-core slab, raised-panel, louvered, or French doors. Figure 11.12 shows the floor plan symbols for representing folding doors. Because hinges support the doors, framing support is required at the edges. They are usually centered between walls, but the door opening can be flush with a closet edge if hinge support is available. Common widths range from 4'-0" through 9'-0" (1200 to 2700 mm) in 6" (150 mm) increments.

Accordion doors are often used for closets or wardrobes, as room dividers, or as acoustical barriers between living areas such as basement or family room recreation areas or galley-style kitchen facilities. As room dividers, accordion doors can also provide separation between sleeping and living areas within an efficiency-style housing unit. Figure 11.13 shows the floor plan symbol for accordion doors. Accordion doors range in width from 4'-0" through 15'-0" (1200 to 4500 mm) in 1' (300 mm) increments, but most suppliers provide custom widths. Door panels are made of vinyl or wood veneer panels and are supported from a ceiling-mounted track.

ventilation requirements and are excellent for access to outdoor living areas. Common sizes for exterior sliding doors are 6'-0" and 8'-0" (1800 and 2400 mm), but they range in width from 5'-0" through 12'-0" (1500 to 3600 mm) in 12" (300 mm) increments.

Interior sliding doors are referred to as bypass doors and are often used for closets that require complete access. Figure 11.11 shows the floor plan symbol for a bypass door. Because the doors are supported on rollers on either the top or bottom, they do not require special framing at their edges. They are usually centered between walls, but the door opening can be flush with the closet edge. Bypass doors normally range in width from 4'-0" (1200 mm) through 12'-0" (3600 mm) in 1' (300 mm) increments.

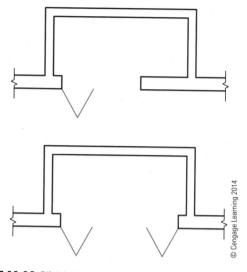

FIGURE 11.12 Bifold doors are often used to provide full access to storage areas, but they can also be used to hide appliances such as a washer or dryer.

Garage Doors

Overhead or sectional roll-up doors typically provide access to a garage. The floor plan symbol for a garage door is shown in Figure 11.14. The dashed lines represent the size and extent of the garage door when open. The extent of the garage door should be shown when the door interferes with something on the ceiling. Overhead doors range in width from 8'-0" through 18'-0" (2400 to 5400 mm). An 8'-0" (2400 mm) door is a common width for a single car. A 9'-0" (2700 mm) width is common for a single door that will accommodate a pickup truck or large van. A door 16'-0" (4800 mm) wide is common for double-car access. Doors are 7'-0" (2100 mm) high, although doors 8'-0" (2400 mm), 10'-0" (3000 mm), or 12'-0" (3600 mm) high are common for campers or recreational vehicles.

Creating Door Blocks

Blocks that represent each type of door can be created and stored in a block library or template drawing if third-party blocks are not available. Use thin, continuous lines to represent each type of door except pocket doors. Pocket doors are usually represented by a thick line. Figure 11.15

FIGURE 11.13 Accordion doors are often used at closets or wardrobes, as room dividers, or as acoustical barriers between living areas.

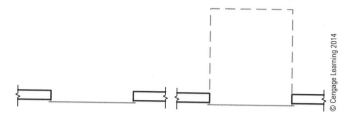

FIGURE 11.14 An overhead garage door can be simplified as shown with the left symbol, or dashed lines can be used to represent the size and extent of the garage door when the door interferes with something on the ceiling.

shows the process for creating a block for a swinging door. Use the following steps to create an exterior door:

- Create the block on the 0 layer.
- Draw two lines to represent the wall thickness [6" (150 mm)] for exterior walls. Use the OFFSET command to place the lines at the desired spacing.
- Draw two thick lines perpendicular to the wall lines to represent the door width. Use the TRIM command to place the lines exactly between the walls (Figure 11.15b).
- Use the intersection of the interior wall line and one edge of the door as the center point for a circle (Figure 11.15c). Use the opposite edge of the door to determine the radius of the circle.
- Draw a line at 45° to represent the door swing (Figure 11.15d).
- Use the BREAK command to remove a portion of the circle so that only an arc remains from the wall to just past the door swing (Figure 11.15e).
- Remove the wall lines that cross the door opening.
- Add the line to represent the sill (Figure 11.15f).
- Save the symbol as a block with a name that describes the size and style (*DOOR-SWING-EXT-36*).
- In creating the block, pick an insertion point that will be useful for inserting the block into the floor plan. Common insertion points include:
  - The intersection of the door edge and the door swing
  - A point 3" (75 mm) from the hinge point
  - The midpoint of the door
- Insert the block on a layer with an appropriate title, such as *FLOR-DOOR*.

Window Symbols

Design professionals have developed standard symbols to represent common window types. AutoCAD and

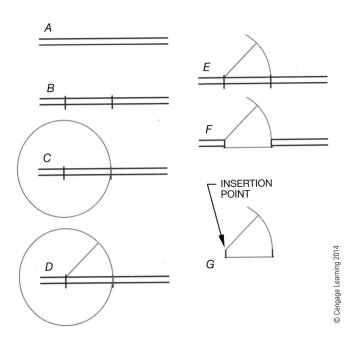

FIGURE 11.15 Blocks for doors can easily be created and stored for multiple use.

© Cengage Learning 2014

code requirements for windows. Only the window size is represented on the floor plan by the window symbol. A window schedule specifies the style, frame, and glass type. The creation of schedules is discussed later in this chapter.

Types of Windows

Sliding windows (Figure 11.16a) are popular because of their moderate price and the amount of ventilation they provide. A single sliding window is 50% openable. Windows wider than 6'-0" (1800 mm) typically include a fixed glass panel with a sliding window on each end.

Craftsman, Tudor, Mission, and various twentieth-century styles often have **casement windows** (Figure 11.16b) that are 100% openable. **Jamb** mounted hinges allow the window to open outward for maximum ventilation and egress. Single casement windows usually range in width from 18" to 42" (450 to 1050 mm), but most manufacturers bind multiple units into one frame to create a larger window.

A rectangular, fixed panel of glass is referred to as a **picture window** or fixed window, as seen in Figure 11.16c. Although they do not provide ventilation, picture windows do provide maximize view exposure. They can be combined with sliding, casement, or awning windows to meet ventilation requirements. Picture windows usually come in widths ranging from 1'-6" through 12'-0" (450 to 3600 mm). Larger windows are available but are difficult to handle.

Awning windows are hinged at the top and swing outward (Figure 11.16d). They are often placed below picture windows to provide ventilation when no egress

third-party vendors supply blocks to represent common styles, or they can easily be made and saved as part of your architectural template. Common types of windows on a floor plan include sliding, picture, casement, single-hung, awning, bay, bow, garden, radius, and specialty windows. Each window type is shown in Figure 11.16. In planning windows for a project, the designer must consider code requirements for light, ventilation and egress, the type of window to be used, the type of glass, and the size of the window. Chapter 3 covers

USING CAD

In addition to drawing walls as 3D objects, most CAD programs, including the standard AutoCAD program, includes common door blocks and other common symbols for use on a floor plan to represent doors, windows, plumbing symbols, cabinets, furniture, and identification symbols. Third-party vendors also have free libraries of blocks and details for adding to CAD drawings to cut drafting time and eliminate the need to draw your own symbols. Use the Internet and your favorite search engine to search these libraries for common manufacturers of specific products. For instance if you need plumbing blocks, a search of PLUMBING FIXTURES will produce a list of large companies such as American Standard©, Crane©, Delta©, Kohler©, and Moen©. You can reduce the search results by searching the websites of one or more of these companies with suitable blocks for your project. Along with their drawings blocks, many companies include key attributes that can be used to assemble schedules. Most companies also supply specifications that can be added directly into project manuals explaining the product and how it is to be stored on the site and installed.

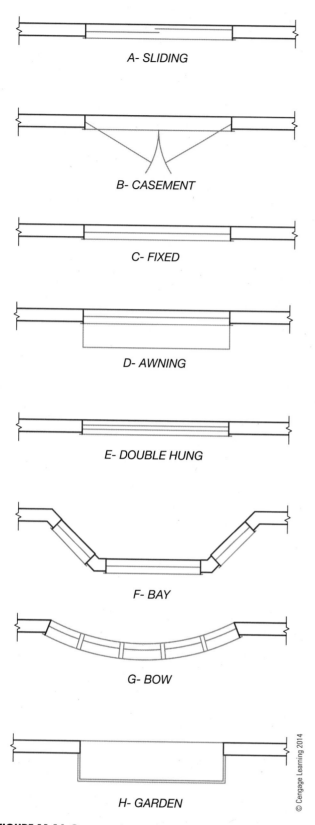

A- SLIDING

B- CASEMENT

C- FIXED

D- AWNING

E- DOUBLE HUNG

F- BAY

G- BOW

H- GARDEN

© Cengage Learning 2014

FIGURE 11.16 Common types of windows found on a floor plan.

Single- *or **double-hung windows*** (Figure 11.16e) replicate the look of traditional double-hung windows with bottom panels that slide up and upper panels that slide down. A single-hung window has a lower panel that slides vertically, with a fixed upper panel. A double-hung tilt window allows the lower portion of the window to slide vertically and both panels of the window to tilt inward for easy cleaning. Single- and double-hung tilt windows typically range in width from 1'-6" to 4'-0" (450 to 1200 mm), but it's possible to bind multiple units together into one frame to create larger windows.

Bay windows (Figure 11.16f) project beyond the exterior walls of the structure to increase the illusion of a large interior. Used when a traditional style is desired, they can be purchased as a unit or built by the framer to increase the floor space. When purchased as a unit, a picture window is centered between two fixed single-hung, or casement windows. Usually the side panels are placed at a 45° or 30° angle to the picture window. The projection of the bay from the outer wall is usually between 18" and 24" (450 to 600 mm). The size of the center window determines the total width of a bay. Bays constructed at the job site can have more than one center panel.

Bow windows (Figure 11.16g) project beyond the exterior wall of the structure to increase the illusion of a larger interior. Bow windows usually consist of four to six panels that may be fixed, casement, or single-hung. The windows are arranged to form an arc and typically range in width from 6 to 12' (1800 to 3600 mm).

A ***garden window*** (Figure 11.16h) projects out from the exterior wall to provide an interior shelf at the base of the window. A garden window is often used above the kitchen sink to provide extra space behind the sink. They usually project between 12" and 18" (300 to 450 mm) from the exterior wall and range in width from 24" to 60" (600 to 1500 mm). The large glass panel parallel to the wall is fixed with vertical sliding side panels. Depending on the manufacturer, either the side or the top panels open.

A ***radius window*** provides a half-round arc to the top of the window. As seen in Figure 11.16b, a radius can be added to a fixed window without creating a mullion that would disturb the view. A radius can also be added to a single-hung, double-hung, or casement window, but doing so creates a mullion (horizontal divider between glass panels).

Most window manufacturers provide lines of *specialty windows* including fixed panels that are round, half-round, quarter-round, arched, multiple arched, gable 3-sided, gable 4-sided, gable-doghouse, hexagon, and octagon units in standard and custom sizes. Each of these

is required. A ***transom window*** is hinged at the top and swings in. These windows are often used on custom homes above a door or another window. A fixed transom window may also be placed over an interior door.

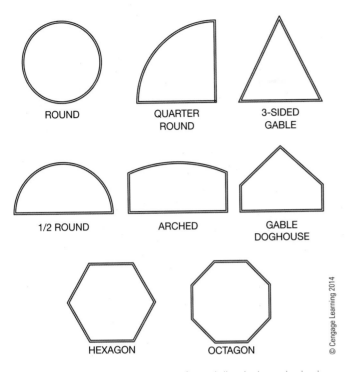

FIGURE 11.17 Common shapes of specialty windows stocked by most window manufacturers.

© Cengage Learning 2014

windows are shown in Figure 11.17. Additional window shapes that copy a specific historical era include:

- **Pointed arch:** Rooted in the tradition of medieval cathedrals and common on Victorian homes, these are narrow windows with pointed arches. Wider, squat Gothic arches are characteristic of Tudor homes.

- **Rounded arch:** Rounded or Roman arches date from Renaissance Italy and are modeled after ancient Greek and Roman forms. These windows feature a gently curved archway and are often found on Italian Renaissance and Victorian Italianate homes.

- **Palladian:** A *palladian window* is divided into three parts by *mullions* with rectangular panes on each side of a wide arch. Placed at the center on an upper story, a palladian window is an elegant focal point in Federal, Queen Anne, and Classical Revival homes.

- **Semicircular and oval:** Like rounded arches, half-circles and ovals are classically inspired. These accent windows are a hallmark of Victorian homes.

- **Triangular and trapezoid:** Angular shapes add drama to contemporary homes. A cathedral window forms a narrow triangle as it stretches across the room, following the line of a slanted roof.

Although they are not available from all manufacturers, two additional types of windows—hopper and

jalousie—are popular in some regions of the country. *Hopper windows* are hinged at the bottom and swing inward. This design allows the window to remain open with a minimum of water penetration. Hopper windows are often used in basements if egress is not required. *Jalousie windows* are made with horizontal vinyl, aluminum, wood, or glass blades that can be opened to allow ventilation. The blades overlap each other to form the panes of a jalousie window. Operated with a crank or turn-screw, the louvers tilt to open, permitting airflow. This is also their greatest disadvantage: they allow ventilation so well that they are almost impossible to seal. When closed, each louver rests against the one below it, rarely if ever making an airtight seal, and the hinges along the sides are almost impossible to seal without covering the entire window. These windows are not energy-efficient and because each pane is easily removed, they are a security risk. Some building codes no longer allow jalousie windows.

Window Locations. The placement of windows can be as important as their shapes. Common window locations based on historical home styles include:

- **Ribbon:** Common in Prairie, Craftsman, and twentieth-century homes, several ribbon windows are placed in a row with their frames abutting.

- **Five-ranked:** Georgian-style homes have five rectangular windows equally spaced across the second story.

- **Sidelights:** Neoclassical and Greek Revival homes often have tall, narrow sidelight windows flanking the entry door.

- **Fanlights:** Many classically styled homes have a semicircular *fanlight* above the entry door.

- **Projecting windows:** Bay, bow, and oriel windows are the most common types of projecting windows. Bay and oriel windows became popular during the Victorian era. Bay windows jut out from the side of the house while oriel windows project from an upper story and are supported by decorative brackets.

Common Window Sizes Based on Use

Windows typically come in widths that range from 2' through 12' (600 to 3600 mm) at intervals of about 6" (150 mm). The exact size varies based on the manufacturer and the type of frame to be used. Vinyl, aluminum, and fiberglass window frames generally fall within the range of these nominal sizes, but custom sizes are readily available. Wood-frame window sizes are different for each manufacturer and should be confirmed with the manufacturer's specifications. The location of a window in the house and the way the window opens has an effect on the size. Common sizes include:

ROOM	WIDTH	DEPTH
Living, dining, and family rooms	6' to 12' (1800 to 3600 mm)	4'-5' (1200 to 1500 mm)
Bedrooms	3' to 6' (900 to 1800 mm)	3'-6" to 4' (1050 to 1200 mm)
Kitchen	3' to 6'-0" (900 to 1800 mm)	3' to 3'-6" (900 to 1050 mm)
Bathrooms	2' to 3' (600 to 900 mm)	18" to 36" (450 to 900 mm)

© Cengage Learning 2014

Windows in the main living areas range from 6' to 12' (1800 to 3600 mm) wide and between 4' and 6' (1200 and 1800 mm) tall, allowing occupants to take advantage of a view while sitting. Windows in bedrooms are often smaller to allow for the placement of furniture. The type of bedroom window is important because of the IRC emergency egress requirements. (See Chapter 5 for a review of egress codes.) The width of the kitchen windows affects the placement of the upper cabinets. In a small kitchen, the tradeoff between natural light and sufficient cabinet space is critical. Generally placed behind the sink, kitchen windows range between 3' and 5' (900 and 1800 mm) in width and between 3'-0" and 3'-6" (900 and 1050 mm) in height. Wide windows are nice to have in a kitchen for the added light they provide, but having them will require the elimination of some of the upper cabinets. Because the tops of windows are normally set at 6'-8" (2000 mm), windows deeper than 42" (1050 mm) will interfere with the countertop.

The size of bathroom windows varies depending on their location in the room. When placed over a toilet or in a shower, the window often ranges between 2' and 3' (600 and 900 mm) in width. When the window is over a tub or spa, its width is usually a close match to the width of the plumbing fixture. Windows installed in showers are usually set higher than the standard header height to minimize water buildup on the windowsill. According to the IRC, windows by a spa or tub must be tempered. Tempered glass is also required for all windows located within 18" (450 mm) of a door or where the window could be used as a backrest at a window seat.

Privacy Considerations. Using obscure or tinted glass are common ways to provide privacy. Obscure glass includes a pattern, color, or texture in the glass that disrupts the view

while still allowing light to pass through. Tinted glass uses shading to provide protection from direct sunlight and warm conditions.

Glazing Patterns. Although windows usually are made from a single sheet of glass, a variety of glazing patterns or windowpane arrangements are available.

- Windows set in wood frames may be set in six, nine, or twelve panes. Windows with many small square panes suggest a Colonial, Georgian, or Federal influence.
- Diamond-shaped panes are characteristic of Tudor, English Cottage, and some Mission-style homes.
- Leaded glass windows have panes secured with thin strips of lead; pieces of clear, frosted, beveled, or stained glass can be arranged in dazzling patterns. Leaded glass should be installed over a standard fixed glass panel to increase energy efficiency.

Representing Windows on the Floor Plan

A wide range of methods is used to represent windows on a floor plan. Many professionals use a thin line for the glass and thick lines for the surrounding walls, similar to Figure 11.18. Some professionals draw windows with two thin lines representing the panes of glass. These symbols can represent any style of window: They appear on the floor plan to identify the window location, but the style may not be known until after the designer begins the preliminary and presentation drawings.

A second consideration in drawing the window symbol is the representation of the sill. Most professionals draw windows, like exterior doors, with a projecting sill—usually projected about 1" (25 mm) from the exterior side of the wall—although some companies draw it flush. On the interior side of the window, a thick line represents the wall below the window. If the window extends to the floor, the line is omitted.

Figure 11.16 shows alternative methods of representing various types of windows. Although these symbols provide a graphic representation of the window type, a window schedule can clearly describe the window type. Whatever the method, it should be consistent throughout the plan and should be determined by the preference. Window symbols should be placed on the *FLOR GLAZ* layer.

Creating Window Blocks

Blocks to represent windows can be created and stored in a template drawing if third-party blocks are not available. Use thin, continuous lines to represent the glass and thick lines to represent the walls surrounding the window. It's only necessary to create one block if using the single-line symbol. The process for creating a window block is shown

Going Green

Window Considerations Affecting Design

Although the window sizes listed earlier are common, consideration must be given to the relationship of the window to the sun. Increasing the size of south-facing windows helps to achieve direct gain from sun in winter but may cause the home to overheat during the summer. The size of non-south-facing windows and their affects on heat loss should be another consideration. Balance the size of windows based on the view, orientation, roof overhangs, glass type, and landscaping. With proper planning, windows can provide energy by harnessing the sun in winter, breezes in summer, and natural daylight all year.

Glass Options

Windows are made with many options for glass. Although double-glazing is common, single-pane windows are available for special conditions. Other common glazing options include "Low-E" and insulated glass to help control heat loss and obscure and tinted glass to control privacy.

Heating Considerations

Windows are rated for energy efficiency by R-values and U-values. R-values indicate the energy efficiency of the window unit. The U-value is the rate of heat flow through the window.

Low-E glass is designed to increase the U-factor of a window. A thin, invisible, metallic layer several atoms thick, coats the glass making it transparent to short-wave solar energy. This coating also allows most of the solar spectrum, including visible light, to pass through. The glass is opaque to long-wave infrared energy, reflecting most heat energy. This helps retain interior heat in the winter and prevents radiated heat from outside objects from entering. One negative aspect of the Low-E coating is a slight loss of solar contribution; however, this loss is offset by its insulated value at night.

In addition to coating the panes of glass, reducing the conduction of heat in the air space between the glass layers can improve thermal performance. Manufacturers include argon and krypton gas in the sealed space between windowpanes. Argon is inexpensive, nontoxic, non-reactive, clear, and odorless.

in Figure 11.19. Use the following steps to create a window block:

- Create the block on the 0 layer.
- Draw two lines to represent the wall thickness [6" (150 mm)] for exterior walls. Use the OFFSET command to place the lines at the desired spacing.
- Draw two thick lines 12" (300 mm) apart to represent the window width. Use the TRIM command to

place the lines exactly between the walls. (The true window size will be determined when the block is inserted into the drawing.) See Figure 11.19a.

- Draw a line centered on the wall lines to represent the glass.
- Add the line to represent the sill and trim the exterior wall line between the window edges. See Figure 11.19b.

- Save the symbol as a block with a name that describes the size and style, such as *WINDOW FLOOR*. See Figure 11.19c.

- In creating the block, pick an insertion point that will be useful for inserting the block into the floor plan. The center of the wall line of the symbol is a convenient location. This will allow the midpoint of a wall to be used for inserting the block.

- Insert the block on a layer with an appropriate title, such as *FLOR GLAZ*.

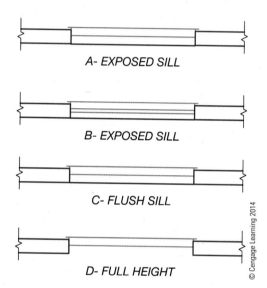

FIGURE 11.18 Common methods of representing windows on a floor plan. The symbols are used to represent any style of window, with the type specified in a note or schedule.

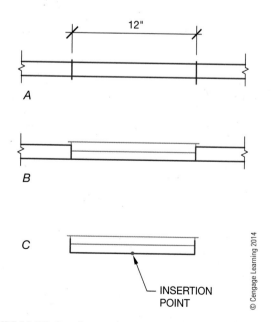

FIGURE 11.19 Creating a window block.

Placing CAD Blocks on the Floor Plan

Windows are usually centered in the wall of a room. When inserting one window symbol into a room, the center point of the block can be aligned with the center point of the interior wall, as seen in Figure 11.20a. If providing two or an even number of windows, base the locations of the window blocks on the center of the wall between the windows, as seen in Figure 11.20b. A minimum of 3" (75 mm) is required to represent the (2) 2× studs (vertical wall framing members) to frame a window opening. (See Chapter 21 for a discussion of framing methods.) Place the center post or wall relative to the midpoint of the wall. If providing three or an odd number of windows, locate the window blocks on the middle of the center window relative to the center of the room, as seen in Figure 11.20c. An alternative to having the framer place a post between windows is having the manufacturer bind multiple windows together. The vertical support between the combined windows is referred to as a mullion (Figure 11.20d). The individual panes of a window can be further divided by muntins (Figure 11.20e).

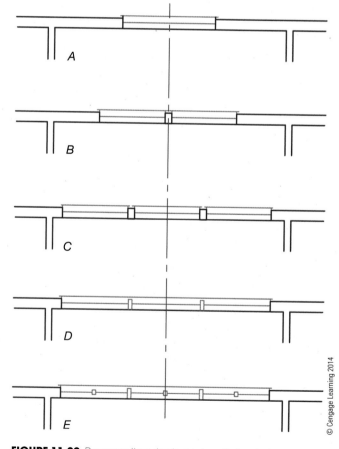

FIGURE 11.20 Representing single and multiple windows on a floor plan. Examples A, B, and C represent individual openings created by the framer. Windows D and E represent multiple windows joined together by the manufacturer. Only single openings would be required for windows D and E.

Roof Openings

Sky windows, skylights, and sun tunnels are common methods of delivering light through the roof and ceiling. Each can be seen in Figure 11.21a. **Skylights** are openings in the roof that bring additional daylight into a room and let natural light enter an interior room. Skylights are available in fixed and openable units. They are made of double-domed plastic or flat tempered glass. Skylights are approximately 24" (600 mm) wide. The length is usually a minimum of 24" (600 mm) long. Common sizes include 2' × 2', 2' × 3', and 2' × 4' (600 × 600, 600 × 900, and 600 × 1200 mm). Exact sizes vary based on the manufacturer. A **sky window** combines features of a skylight and a window, using glazing on a wall that extends to meet glazing on a portion of the roof. An alternative to a skylight is a **sun tunnel**, which passes light into a room through a reflective tunnel that connects the roof opening to the opening in the ceiling. Unlike the chase connecting the skylight to the ceiling, the tunnel is flexible, allowing sharp bends that do not disrupt the amount of light being delivered. A diffuser is mounted at the ceiling end of the tunnel to disperse the light.

Figure 11.21b shows the representation of a skylight on the floor plan. Represent skylights using thin lines. The linetype used will vary in width based on office practice. Place the skylights on a layer with a title such as *FLOR OVHD* (overhead). Skylights must also be represented on the roof plan. If possible, place the skylight so that it fits between the roof trusses. If the roof is framed with rafters, skylights can be placed based on design requirements

Courtesy Velux®-America Inc.

FIGURE 11.21a Skylights, sky windows, and sun tunnels all can be used to provide light and ventilation to habitable rooms.

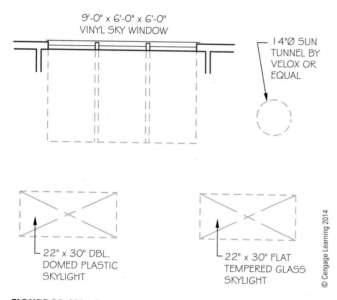

FIGURE 11.21b *Common representations of skylights, sky windows, and sun tunnels on the floor plan. Some professionals use dashed lines to represent the skylights.*

and the roof framing can easily be altered to meet the design. Up to four separate skylights can usually be bound together to create one consecutive unit.

REPRESENTING CABINETS, APPLIANCES, AND PLUMBING SYMBOLS WITH CAD

Cabinets are found in the living, sleeping, and services areas of a home. Specialized cabinets such as a desk, hutch, bookcase, entertainment unit, window seat, or built-in dresser are found in bedrooms, family rooms, dens, dining rooms, home offices, and garages. In general, the cabinets drawn on the floor plans are built-in units. To complete a floor plan, the cabinets the contractor will provide must be represented. When drawing the cabinets on the floor plan, include the appliances and plumbing fixtures associated with the cabinets.

Represent cabinets, appliances, and plumbing features using thin lines. The linetype used will vary in width based on office practice. Common linetypes include:

- Continuous lines for lower cabinets, the outline of the upper cabinets, changes in cabinet height, plumbing fixtures, the front of the dishwasher, and closet shelves.

- Hidden lines for appliances that are under the counter, the refrigerator, the furnace, water heater, limits of knee space under counters, washers, dryers, and fold-down ironing boards.

- Centerlines for rods in closets.

The use of linetypes also varies greatly with each office. Figure 11.22 shows common options. The objects drawn with continuous lines are fairly consistent throughout the industry. The upper cabinets may be drawn using continuous lines, but they are sometimes drawn with hidden lines because they are above the cutting plane. Other items, such as a dishwasher or trash compactor, are drawn with hidden lines because they are below the counter. Items such as the refrigerator, washer, and dryer are drawn with hidden lines because the contractor does not provide them. A final group of items, such as the water heater and furnace, may be drawn with hidden lines based on office practice. Your boss or instructor is the final word on which method to use.

Base cabinets are usually drawn 24" (600 mm) deep and upper cabinets are 12" (300 mm) deep. Custom base cabinets may be 27" and 30" (675 and 750 mm) deep. Custom homes often use base cabinets with varied depths to create the illusion of built-in furniture. Add a width of 12", 15", or 18" (300, 375, or 450 mm) to the counter depth to accommodate a food bar. Place the cabinets on a layer with a title such as *FLOR CASE* (casework-manufactured cabinets) or *FLOR WDWK* (field-built architectural woodwork).

Kitchens

In addition to representing the cabinets, fixtures such as sinks, butcher-block cutting boards, countertops, appliances, and plumbing fixtures as well as common appliances including the range, refrigerator, dishwasher,

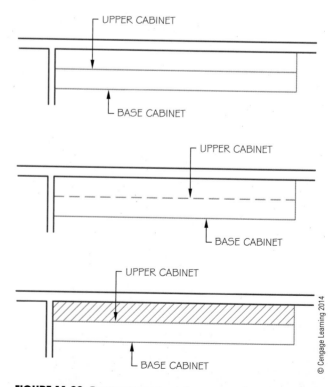

FIGURE 11.22 *Common methods for representing upper and base cabinets.*

trash compactor, and garbage disposal must be represented. Also include plumbing fixtures such as the main and vegetable sinks, water to the refrigerator, and possibly a faucet in the wall above the range or cooktop. Figure 11.23 shows common kitchen features. Appliances and plumbing fixtures can be placed on the same layer as the cabinets or on a layer with a title such as *FLOR APPL* (appliances) and *FLOR PLMB* (plumbing fixtures).

Cabinets

If prefabricated cabinets are to be used, represent the length of each cabinet in 3" (75 mm) increments. Custom units can be built to any desired length. Pantries, broom closets, and other cabinets that extend from floor to ceiling are drawn with two parallel lines spaced approximately 1" (25 mm) apart. Common widths of prefabricated pantries range from 12" to 48" (300 to 1200 mm) in 3" (75 mm) increments. Broom closets generally range from 12" to 24" (300 to 600 mm) wide × 24" (600 mm) deep. A pantry may be designed to be part broom closet and part shelves for

storage. If a desk unit is to be represented, lower the counter to a height of approximately 32" (800 mm). Provide a space between 30" to 48" (750 to 1200 mm) wide. Chapter 20 includes additional information related to cabinet drawings.

Plumbing

Common kitchen plumbing fixtures include the main sink, a vegetable sink, and a bar sink. Each can be placed on the *FLOR PLMB* layer. The use and location of each type of sink was introduced in Chapter 6 as work areas in the kitchen were explored. Figure 11.24 shows common kitchen sink symbols. Common kitchen sink options, which vary by manufacturer, include:

- Single: 19" × 25", 19" × 30", and 21" × 24" (475 × 625 mm, 475 × 750 mm, and 525 × 600 mm)
- Single apron front: 22" × 22", 22" × 25", and 22" × 30" (550 × 550 mm, 550 × 625 mm, and 550 × 750 mm)
- Double: 32" × 21" (800 × 525 mm)
- Triple: 42" × 21" (1050 × 525 mm)
- Vegetable sink and/or bar sink: 16" × 16" or 16" × 21" (400 × 400 mm or 400 × 525 mm)

The water supply line for a refrigerator icemaker or a door-mounted chilled water dispenser requires a 1/4" water line. Some custom kitchens include a wall-mounted faucet in the wall behind the range or cooktop to aid in food preparation. Both features can be represented by a note and usually require no special symbol, as shown in Figure 11.25.

Appliances

Common appliances found in a kitchen include the refrigerator, cooking units, dishwasher, and trash compactor. Each can be represented on the *FLOR APPL* layer. The refrigerator can be either freestanding or built in and may or may not contain the freezer. Figure 11.25 shows

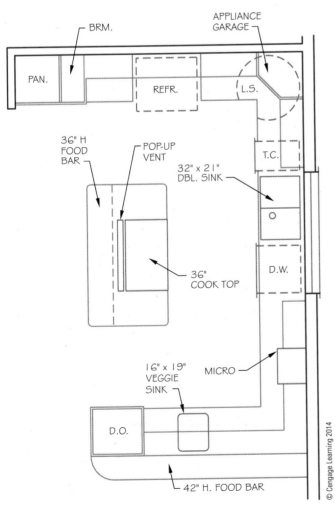

FIGURE 11.23 Standard symbols used to represent kitchen cabinets, fixtures, and plumbing features.

© Cengage Learning 2014

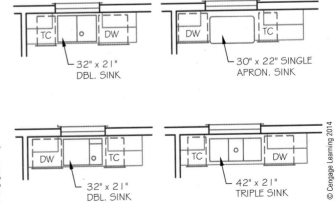

FIGURE 11.24 Standard kitchen sink symbols. Symbols for a dishwasher and trash compactor have also been added.

© Cengage Learning 2014

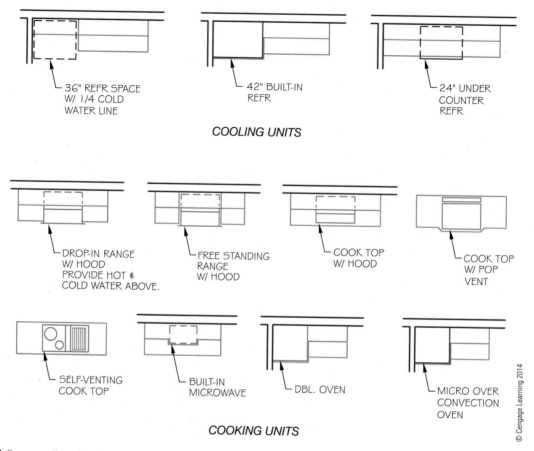

FIGURE 11.25 Representing standard kitchen cooling and cooking appliances.

common kitchen appliances. Common widths of refrigerators include:

- Freestanding refrigerator: side by side, 36" (900 mm) typical; 28" to 42" (700 to 1150 mm) available; 27" (675 mm) deep.

- Built-in refrigerator: 42" (1050 mm) common; 36" to 54" (900 to 1250 mm) available; 27" (675 mm) deep.

In addition to the refrigerator, a custom kitchen may include an icemaker and a small under-counter cooling unit called a wine cellar or cooler.

- Freestanding and built-in icemakers are typically 15" or 18" (375 or 450 mm) wide.

- Built-in wine cellars are 24" (600 mm) wide.

Several options are available for cooking units, including a range or cooktop and oven. A range (Figure 11.25) contains the cooking elements over the oven. It can be either gas, electric, or dual-fuel, and can be either freestanding or drop-in. The most common size is 30" × 26" (750 × 650 mm). Other common range sizes include:

- 36" × 26" (900 × 650 mm)
- 48" × 27" (1200 × 675 mm)
- 60" × 28" (1800 × 700 mm)

A standard cooktop (Figure 11.25) contains gas or electric cooking elements. Larger units can include simmer plates, grills, griddles, and a rotisserie. A standard cooktop is 30" × 21" (750 × 525 mm), but sizes range from 15" to 48" (375 to 1200 mm) wide. A built-in oven (Figure 11.25) may contain one or more baking units. A cooking unit can include a standard baking unit, convection oven, microwave, and warming oven. A standard built-in oven is 27" (675 mm) wide and 24" deep. Common width options include 24", 30", and 36" (600, 750, and 900 mm).

Some method of ventilation must be provided for a range and a cooktop. Venting typically consists of a hood, a popup vent, or a self-contained vent. A self-contained vent does not require a symbol, but the vent should be specified on the floor plan. Figure 11.25 shows symbols for a cooktop hood and a popup vent. The width of each type of vent usually matches the width of the cooking unit.

Other common appliances found in a kitchen include the dishwasher, microwave, trash compactor, and range hood. A dishwasher (Figure 11.23) is usually placed beside the sink. A standard dishwasher is 24" (600 mm) wide and is placed about 3" (75 mm) from the edge of the sink. It should not be more than 24" (600 mm) from the sink to avoid dripping water on the floor causing a slipping hazard.

The microwave (Figure 11.25) can be freestanding or built-in. Common sizes for countertop units vary widely but are usually about 22" × 20" (550 × 500 mm). Built-in units are generally 27" or 30" (675 or 750 mm) wide with a cabinet depth of 15". Built-in units can be mounted at eye level as part of the upper cabinets or below the counter of the base cabinets. Trash compactors can be built-in or freestanding. The symbol for a trash compactor resembles that of a dishwasher. The common width of a trash compactor is 15" (375 mm).

Utility Rooms

The utility room may have upper, lower, and full-height cabinets and can contain several plumbing fixtures and appliances. Draw the upper and lower cabinets using the same layer and linetypes used to represent the kitchen. The symbols for the clothes washer, dryer, laundry sink, and fold-down ironing board are shown in Figure 11.26. The symbols for the clothes washer and dryer are drawn with dashed lines, since they are not part of the construction contract. Sizes vary widely, but generally a 28" (700 mm) square can be used to represent the washer and dryer symbols. Stacked units with a typical width of 27" (675 mm) and vertical dryers that are 36" (900 mm) wide × 29" (725 mm) deep × 74" (1850 mm) high are also available. Laundry sinks are usually drawn using a symbol that is 21" × 21" (525 × 525 mm). Larger sizes are available that are similar to the sizes of kitchen sinks. Ironing boards are often built into the laundry room wall or attached to the wall surface, as shown in Figure 11.26. Drawer mounted

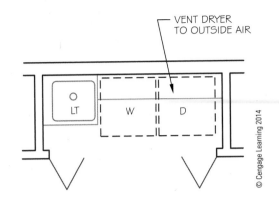

FIGURE 11.27 Representing laundry facilities in a closet.

units are also available. Each type of unit typically ranges in width from 12" to 15" (300 to 375 mm). Laundry utilities may be placed in a closet when only minimum space is available, as shown in Figure 11.27.

When a laundry room is below the bedroom area, a laundry chute is often provided from a convenient area near the bedrooms through a ceiling and into a cabinet in the utility room. The cabinet should be above or next to the washing machine. Figure 11.28 shows how to represent a laundry chute on the floor plan. Place a note on the floor plan to indicate the laundry chute is to be lined

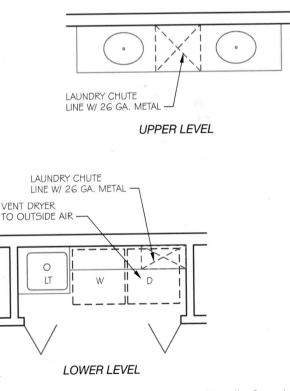

FIGURE 11.28 Representing a laundry chute on the floor plans. The laundry chute is located in the base cabinet of a bathroom located above the utility closet. Although the upper and lower levels of the chute do not need to match, a smooth inclined surface should be specified for the chute so that laundry does not get stuck in the chute.

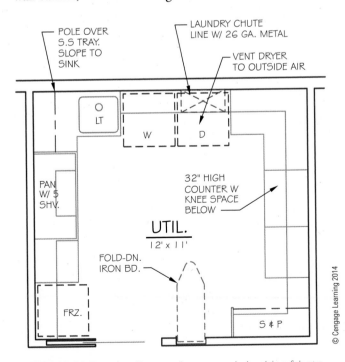

FIGURE 11.26 Representing appliances and plumbing fixtures of a laundry room.

with 26-gauge metal or gypsum board to help prevent the spread of fire between floors.

Bathrooms

Common bathroom cabinets and fixtures are shown in several typical floor plan layouts in Figure 11.29. If a bathroom counter or vanity is to be provided, represent it on the floor plan like any other base cabinet. The counter depth generally ranges from 22" to 24" (550 to 600 mm). Specify the width on the cabinet elevations or in a general note if no interior elevations will be provided. The counter can be eliminated if the lavatory (sink) is wall-mounted or freestanding. If a counter is provided, 30" (900 mm) is the smallest length that should be used. Provide a counter length of 36" to 42" (900 to 1050 mm) for each user if more space is available. Provide a minimum counter space of 9" (225 mm) on the wall side of the lavatory and 12" (300 mm) between lavatories. If a makeup counter is to be represented, a minimum space 30" (750 mm) wide and 30" (750 mm) high is usually specified. See Chapter 5 for additional ADA requirements for vanity sizes. Represent the cabinets and changes in counter height with thin lines on the *FLOR CASE* layer.

Other standard features in a bathroom include multiple lavatories, toilet, bidet, tub, shower, a combination tub and shower unit, and spa. Each of these items can be represented with thin lines on the *FLOR PLMB* layer. The bathroom sink or lavatory is usually oval, but rectangular, round, and square fixtures are also available. Common sink sizes include:

- ADA wall-hung: 20" × 27" (500 × 675 mm)
- Oval: 19" × 16" and 20" × 17" (475 × 400 mm and 500 × 425 mm)
- Pedestal: 22" × 18" and 26" × 20" (550 × 450 mm and 625 × 500 mm)
- Round: 19" (475 mm) diameter

Toilets

Most people refer to what the IRC calls a *water closet* as a *toilet, commode, potty*, or the *royal throne*. The IRC requires a minimum space of 21" (525 mm) from the front of the toilet to any obstruction and a space of 15"(375 mm) from a side wall or cabinet to the centerline of the toilet. Keep in mind that the minimum distances in Figure 4.21 are for multifamily units, which require ADA minimums. Except in the smallest of bathrooms, the IRC minimum requirements are rarely a concern. A 36" (900 mm) wide space between obstructions is much preferred over the 30" (750 mm) space that results from using the minimum code requirements. Also a 30" (750 mm) space in front of the toilet will also make the fixture more pleasant to use. In larger bathroom suites, the toilet is often placed in a

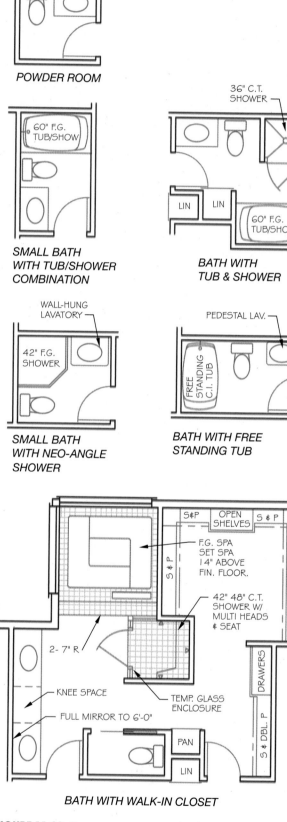

POWDER ROOM

SMALL BATH WITH TUB/SHOWER COMBINATION

BATH WITH TUB & SHOWER

SMALL BATH WITH NEO-ANGLE SHOWER

BATH WITH FREE STANDING TUB

BATH WITH WALK-IN CLOSET

FIGURE 11.29 Common arrangements of cabinets and plumbing fixtures for small bathrooms. Options for the master suite are endless but typically provide private space for each area of the bathroom. The wall behind a toilets is often framed with 6" material to ease the installing of the drain and vent pipe.

© Cengage Learning 2014

NOTE:

The wall behind a toilet is often framed with 6" (150 mm) studs to allow for easy installation of the waste line and vent pipe. If the toilet is on an upper floor, a wall on the lower level near the upper toilet location should be framed from 6" (150 mm) material to allow space for the waste pipe to reach the basement, crawl space, or to run beneath the floor slab.

separate room within the bathroom to provide privacy. When this is the case, exceeding the minimum code standards will decrease the feeling of confinement.

Bidet. A *bidet* is a basin-like plumbing fixture for personal hygiene of the private area. Its looks are similar to the lower portion of a toilet, but water is sprayed up onto the user who straddles the fixture. Both hot and cold water must be supplied to the fixture, and knobs similar to a sink are part of the fixture to be used to adjust the water temperature. Depending on the manufacturer, electricity may also be required for the fixture. While the IRC does not regulate the space requirements for a bidet, providing similar clearance to a toilet will be adequate.

Tubs

Tubs can be freestanding or built in and made of fiberglass, cast iron, or ceramic tile. A wide variety of options are available within each category of material and style. Sizes vary with manufacturers based on the style and the material used to make the tub. Lengths range from 4' to 7' (1200 to 2100 mm) and widths from 32" to 48" (800 to 1200 mm). Common tub sizes include:

- Standard fiberglass: 60" × 32" (1500 × 800 mm)
- Built-in corner: 60" × 60" (1500 × 1500 mm)
- Freestanding: 72" × 38" (1800 × 950 mm)
- Oval: 66" × 36" (1650 × 900 mm)

Tub sizes also vary if the unit uses jets. Common jetted tub sizes include 60" × 42" and 72" × 48" (1500 × 1050 mm and 1800 × 1200 mm).

Showers

A shower is often added over a tub unit for a bathroom that children will use. This type of unit is specified as a tub/shower on the floor plan. The shower in a master bathroom suite is often separate from the tub or bathing fixture. Shower sizes vary based on the manufacturer, style, shape, and material to be used.

- The standard fiberglass tub shower unit is 60" × 32" (1500 × 800 mm), which can be purchased as a square, rectangular, or neo-angle type if it is separate from the tub fixture.
- Common sizes for square showers are 34", 36", 42", and 48" (850, 900, 1050, and 1200 mm).

An example of a neo-angle shower is shown in Figure 11.29. Two surfaces are mounted to the walls in a corner, and the other three sides are freestanding. Neo-angle showers are specified by their overall size and by the size of the opening.

- Common widths for neo-angle units are 34", 36", and 42" (850, 900, and 1050 mm). Common door widths are 16", 18", and 23" (400, 450, and 575 mm).

Custom shower units can also be made of ceramic tile. These showers are made by craftsmen at the job site and may be any shape or size.

Spas

A homeowner often uses the term *spa* when he or she really means a jetted tub. Common sizes for jetted tubs have been introduced earlier. A true spa is typically placed outside the residence but may be inside a master bedroom or master bath suite. See Figure 11.29 for common floor plan symbols. The size of a spa is based on its number of seats. Common seating arrangements and sizes for built-in fiberglass spas include:

- Three-person size: 76" × 66" (1900 × 1650 mm).
- Four-person size: 84" × 76" (2100 × 1900 mm).
- Five-person size: 84" × 84" (2100 × 2100 mm).
- Six-person size: 91" × 84" (2275 × 2100 mm).
- Seven-person size: 94" × 94" (2350 × 2350 mm).

Spas can also be freestanding and portable. Verify the seating capacity and the location of the pump access prior to drawing a spa on the floor plan. If the spa is inside the home or on a deck, the size and capacity will also need to be considered when completing the structural drawings. See Chapters 23 and 24 for structural considerations.

Miscellaneous Plumbing Symbols

Floor drains should be used in any room where water could accumulate and damage the finished floor material. Laundry rooms, bathrooms, and garages are common locations to place pans under specific appliances that might cause water damage. Figure 11.30 shows a floor drain in a utility room. A floor drain should be placed on the *FLOR PFIX* layer and specified with a note such as

30" SQ. METAL PAN BELOW WASHER W/ 3" DIA. DRAIN.

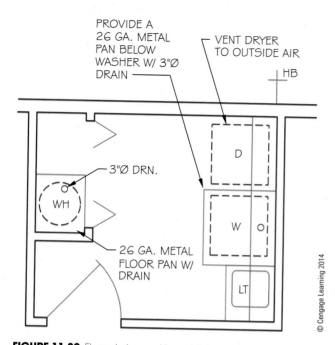

FIGURE 11.30 Floor drains and hose bibbs may also be specified on a floor plan.

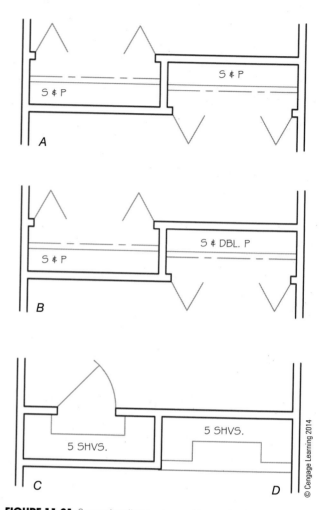

FIGURE 11.31 Several options are used by professional designers to represent shelves and poles.

A **hose bibb** is an outdoor water faucet for connecting a garden hose to the plumbing system. Place hose bibbs at locations convenient for watering lawns or gardens and washing cars, as well as near other plumbing runs. The floor plan symbol for a hose bibb is shown in Figure 11.30. Depending on the complexity of the home, each of these fixtures may be shown on a separate plumbing plan. See Chapter 14 for a discussion of plumbing plans.

Closets, Wardrobes, and Other Storage

Closets are used in each of the three main areas of the residence to provide various types of storage. Building codes do not regulate closet sizes, but FHA and HUD regulations affect their depth and length. The common depth of a closet is 24" (600 mm), but a depth of 30" (750 mm) is preferred in damp areas. The added space allows air to circulate around damp clothes. In the living area, a closet with a shelf and pole should be provided near the entry to store coats for the family and guests. Figure 11.31 shows two common methods for drawing the shelf and pole. Some professionals use two dashed lines to symbolize the shelf and pole. The shelf is typically placed at 72" (2100 mm), with the rod directly below it. Represent the shelves and other storage material with thin lines on a layer with a title such as *FLOR FIXT* or *FLOR WKWD* (woodwork).

Service Area Storage

In the service area, provide storage in the kitchen, utility room, and garage. Storage for the kitchen and utility rooms was discussed as cabinets were explored. In addition to the pantry provided with the cabinetry, many custom homes have walk-in pantries for long-term storage (see Chapter 6). This storage may consist of base and upper cabinets that match the kitchen cabinets, exposed shelves, or a combination of shelves over enclosed cabinets. Shelves ranging in depth from 9" to 24" (225 to 600 mm) are common. A space of 36" to 42" (900 to 1050 mm) between banks of shelves is desirable, but a distance of 30" (750 mm) is tolerable if no space for pull-out units is required. Figures 11.31c and 11.31d show how to represent shelves on the floor plan.

Sleeping Area Storage

Three types of storage are common in the sleeping area of a home, including a linen closet, a bedroom wardrobe closet, and walk-in closets. A storage closet with either five or six shelves with an approximate depth of

storage space or provide a premanufactured closet organizer (see Figure 11.31b).

Master bedrooms often have walk-in closets similar to that in Figure 11.32a. A minimum of 6' × 6' (1800 × 1800 mm) is adequate space for clothes storage; however, 6' × 8' (1800 × 2400 mm) provides better access to all clothes. Multiple rods allow short clothes to be hung above each other. Provide an area with a single pole to hang dresses and seasonal coats. An area containing shelves, baskets, and drawers is also desirable if space permits. Closet packages are available from companies that customize the wardrobe closet to meet the specific needs of family members. Figure 11.32b shows a well-planned wardrobe area for a master suite.

REPRESENTING STEPS, STAIRWAYS, AND RAILINGS WITH CAD

Steps are required even on a single-level home. Steps or a *landing* are required at each exterior door to provide a surface for the home's entry. Allow a minimum width of 36" (900 mm) for a landing at each exterior door. The step from the landing to walkways or the ground must not exceed 7 3/4" (196 mm). Represent and specify these steps as shown in Figure 11.33. A second area requiring steps is where floor levels change elevation. Figure 11.34 shows how to represent and specify changes in floor elevation on a floor plan. Place stairs on a layer with a name such as *FLOR STRS* (stair). If the home must meet ADA requirements or universal living standards, provide a ramp instead of a step. The ADA requires the ramp to have a slope of 1:48 or less.

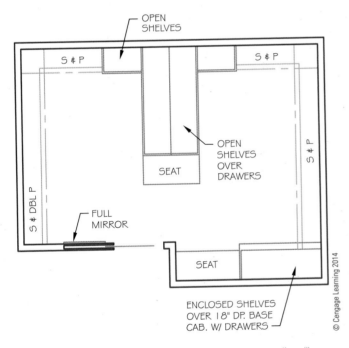

FIGURE 11.32a, b The closet of a master bedroom suite will typically comprise multiple types of storage, including the traditional shelf and pole, double poles, shelves, baskets, and drawers. A full-length mirror and seating should also be provided. Each should be clearly labeled on the floor plan.

24" (600 mm) should be provided for bath and bed linens. A linen closet can be represented as shown in Figures 11.31c and 11.31d. Each bedroom should also include a wardrobe closet unless it will have an armoire. The FHA recommends a length of 48" (1200 mm) of space for males and 72" (1800 mm) for females. The practical minimum for resale should be 6' (1800 mm) if there is a traditional shelf-and-pole storage system. Space can be reduced if using closet organizers. The minimum closet depth is 24" (600 mm). A 30" (750 mm) depth is desirable to keep clothing from becoming wrinkled. If a closet must be small, a double-pole system will double the

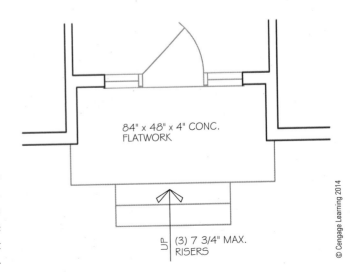

FIGURE 11.33 Steps from the landing to walkways or the ground cannot exceed 7 3/4" (195 mm).

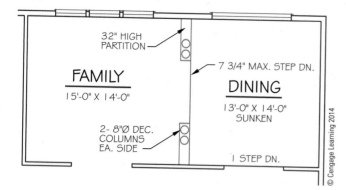

FIGURE 11.34 *Changes in floor elevation can be represented using thin, continuous lines and explained with local notes.*

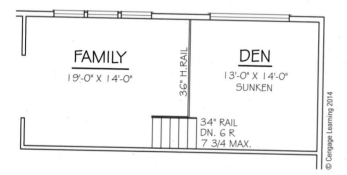

FIGURE 11.35 *In representing the steps for sunken rooms or split-level homes, each end of the stair run must be shown.*

If the difference in floor elevation exceeds 30" (750 mm), a *guardrail* must be provided. The IRC requires rails to be 36" (900 mm) above the floor. Represent rails on the floor plan as shown in Figure 11.35, using a layer name such as *FLOR HRAL* (handrail). Many professionals use two thin, continuous lines with a 1" offset. A partial wall is sometimes used as a guard at the floor edge.

To represent the steps for sunken rooms or split-level homes, show each end of the stair run. You can depict the steps between these two types of floor changes as shown in Figure 11.35. In addition to representing the steps, specify the number of required risers and a *handrail*. Use an arrow to show the direction of travel. Chapter 31 provides a complete description for planning stairs, but completing a floor plan requires a few key sizes. Minimum stair sizes include:

- Stairs must be a minimum of 36" (900 mm) wide, but a width such as 48" to 60" (1200 to 1500 mm) is preferred if space is available.
- The *tread* depth should be 10" to 12" (250 to 300 mm) with a 10" (250 mm) minimum.
- Individual *risers* may range from 4" to 7 3/4" (100 to 195 mm) in height but must be a consistent size within the stair run. A flight of stairs must not exceed 12' (3658 mm) between floor levels or landings.

- Landings at the top, bottom, or in the stair run must be equal in size to the width of the stairs.
- A minimum clear height of 6'-8" (2000 mm) is required for the length of the stairs.
- The stairs must have a handrail that measures between 34" and 38" (850 and 950 mm) above the tread *nosing*.
- Guardrails at landings above stairs, at balconies, lofts, or any area above another floor must be at least 36" (900 mm) above the floor.

The design of a multistory home requires more coordination to provide adequate length and height while still meeting the aesthetic requirements of the owners. There are several common methods of arranging the stairs to meet the design needs. Figure 11.36 shows three common arrangements for steps. A key point in drawing a multilevel stair run is that neither end of the stairs are seen on the same floor plan. A second consideration for stair layout is to show the stairs if more than two levels will be accessed. The middle-level floor plan shows the top end of the lower stair and the bottom portion of the upper stair (see Figure 11.37).

Determining the Number of Steps Required

Keep in mind that the goal is to represent stairs on the floor plan. See Chapter 31 for a complete discussion of stair design. The height between floor levels must be known to determine how many steps to represent on the floor plan. This height is a decision made by the designer. For this introduction, the common height of 8' (2400 mm) between floors is used; 12" (300 mm) for the thickness of the floor framing will be assumed and 7 3/4" (195 mm) for the rise. Although these heights are not exact, they allow the stairs to be represented on the floor plan. Determine the exact size for the riser (the vertical height of the step) and the tread (the horizontal depth of the step) while drawing the stair section. (See Chapter 31 for additional information on stairs.)

With a total rise of approximately 9' (2700 mm) and a maximum riser of 7 3/4" (195 mm), the number of risers can be determined by dividing the total height by the maximum riser size. Dividing 108" by 7 3/4" (2700 by 195 mm) gives 13.9 risers. Since all risers must be of equal height, provide 14 risers (the vertical portion of the step) in the stair run. There will always be one less tread, the horizontal portion of the step, than there are risers. Determine the total stair run once the number of risers and treads are known. If each tread is 10 1/2" (263 mm) deep, the total run is found by multiplying 10 1/2" (263 mm), the depth, by 13, the number of treads required. A run of 136 1/2"

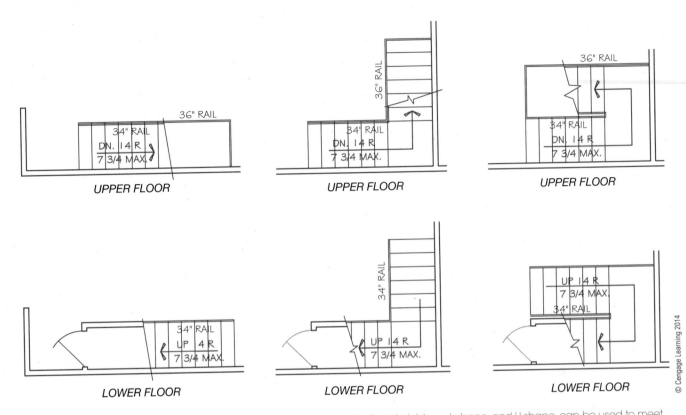

FIGURE 11.36 Several common methods of arranging the stairs, including straight run, L shape, and U shape, can be used to meet the design needs.

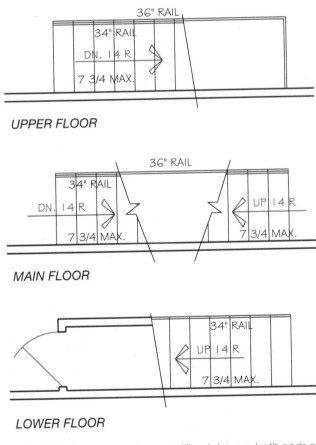

FIGURE 11.37 When drawing a multilevel stair run, both ends of the stair are never seen on the same floor level. The middle-level floor plan will show the top end of the lower stair and the bottom

(3413 mm) is the minimum length for the stairs. Complete the layout of the stairs with this basic information.

Use thin lines to represent the members of the stairway and place the stair information on a layer with a title such as *FLOR STRS*. Usually the starting or ending point will be determined by the location of the surrounding walls. In the example in Figure 11.38, the lower end of the stair is based on the location of the first step from the exterior wall. The design requires a hallway 42" (1050 mm) wide. With the location of the first riser known, the total length of the stairway can be located. Show enough of the treads on the floor plan to reveal a repetitive pattern. Use a break line to end the stair pattern and show what will be under the upper end of the stair.

On the upper floor plan, determine the end of the stair run based on the beginning of the run on the lower floor. Show the end of the stair run and enough of the treads to produce a pattern. Provide a break line on the upper run to terminate the stair pattern, but show the guardrail that surrounds the entire opening for the stair. On the upper floor, walls may be placed over the first few steps of the stair run. For planning purposes, the upper floor can extend over the first two steps of the lower floor and still remain level. As seen in Figure 11.39, once the upper floor extends over the third step, the 6'-8" (2000 mm) minimum headroom no longer exists. Depending on how the floor above the lower steps will be used, an inclined floor may be suitable. If a closet is placed over the steps, the inclined floor will provide

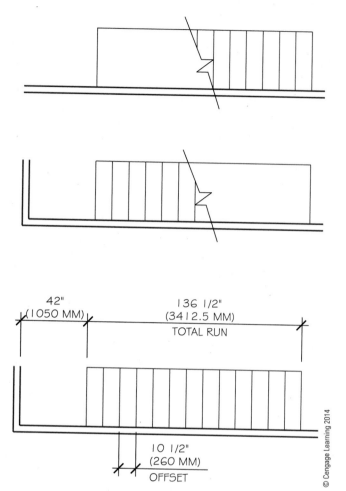

© Cengage Learning 2014

FIGURE 11.38 The number of risers can be determined by dividing the total height by the maximum rise. Once the number of risers and treads is known, the total stair run can be determined by multiplying the tread width by the number of treads required. With this basic information, the layout of the stairs can be completed.

an excellent place to display shoes. An inclined floor will not be suitable if there is a bathroom above the stairs unless it can be hidden beneath a cabinet.

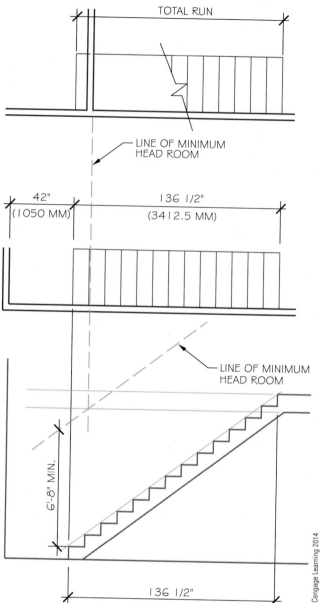

© Cengage Learning 2014

FIGURE 11.39 Walls on the upper floor can be placed over the first few steps of the stair run. For planning purposes, the upper floor can extend over the first two steps of the lower floor and still remain level. Once the upper floor extends over the third step, the minimum required headroom no longer exists.

> ## ▶ NOTE:
>
> *Many of the CAD programs introduced in Chapter 4 include tools for the design and layout of stairs on the floor plan. Stair runs that are straight, L-shaped, U-shaped, spiral, and circular can be designed and drawn using CAD programs that are specifically designed for the AEC industry. Not only do **Parametric** programs allow the stairs to be represented on the floor plan, by providing the basic design data such as the rise, run, and the total rise from floor to floor, but they also will automatically create stair sections. Some programs allow design parameters to be set based on common building code requirements.*

REPRESENTING A FIREPLACE AND CHIMNEY WITH CAD

Several types of fireplaces may be represented on a floor plan, including single- and multilevel masonry, prefabricated zero clearance, direct vent, and freestanding wood burning. Chapter 32 provides a detailed description of each type. This chapter provides the information needed to represent each type of fireplace on a floor plan.

Single-Level Masonry Fireplace

Figure 11.40 shows the symbol and the minimum sizes to represent a single masonry fireplace. Represent the edge of the fireplace with thick lines that match the wall lineweight. Draw a masonry fireplace on a layer with a name such as *FLOR MASN*. Place the hatch pattern on the *FLOR PATT* layer. Notice that the face of the interior masonry laps over the interior face of the exterior wall to provide a tight seal. The hatch pattern and all other lines are thin lines. The hatch pattern to represent the masonry can be placed using ANSI31 set at a 0° angle. Adjust the pattern so the hatch lines are approximately 1/16" (2 mm) apart when plotted. Do not place the dimensions that describe the fireplace on the floor plan. Common fireplace opening sizes include:

OPENING HEIGHT	OPENING WIDTH	OPENING DEPTH
36" (900 mm)	24" (600 mm)	22" (550 mm)
40" (1000 mm)	27" (675 mm)	22" (550 mm)
48" (1200 mm)	30" (750 mm)	25" (625 mm)
60" (1500 mm)	33" (825 mm)	25" (625 mm)

Natural gas may be provided to the fireplace, either for starting a wood fire or for fuel to provide flames on artificial logs. Specify the gas supply on the floor plan, as shown in Figure 11.41, with the notation of FG placed by the symbol to represent fuel gas.

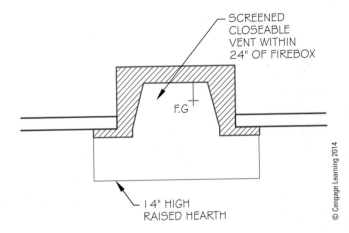

FIGURE 11.41 Representing gas, venting for combustion air, and the hearth on the floor plan.

Common Shapes

Several common arrangements are available for masonry fireplaces, but shapes are limited by the designer's imagination and the skills of the mason. Figure 11.42 shows several fireplace symbols often found on a floor plan. In addition

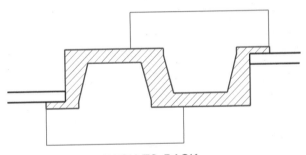

BACK-TO-BACK

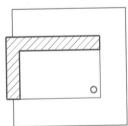

FRONT/END

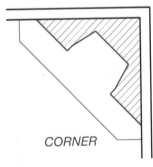

CORNER

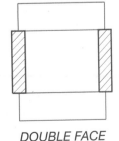

DOUBLE FACE

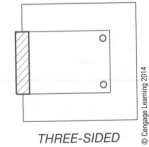

THREE-SIDED

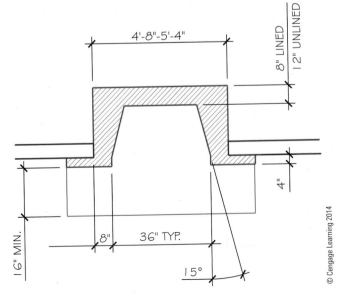

FIGURE 11.40 Minimum dimensions for a single masonry fireplace. See Figure 32.8 for a complete listing of IRC minimum sizes and construction requirements.

FIGURE 11.42 Common arrangements of masonry fireplaces.

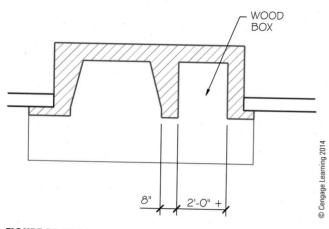

FIGURE 11.43 Masonry fireplace with an area for wood storage.

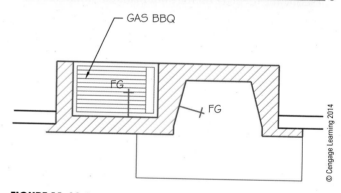

FIGURE 11.44 A masonry fireplace with an outdoor sink and barbecue. Each item would need to be specified on the floor plan, as well as any utilities that may be required.

to considering the shape and location of the *firebox*, provide a wood compartment next to the fireplace opening to store small amounts of wood. The floor plan representation of a wood storage box is shown in Figure 11.43. Support below the fireplace must be shown on the foundation plan if a fireplace is represented on the floor plan. See Sections 7 and 8 for a discussion of fireplace support.

Barbecues. When a home has a fireplace in a room next to the dining room, nook, or kitchen, the masonry structure may also incorporate a built-in barbecue. If incorporating a barbecue into the exterior side of the fireplace, represent it as shown in Figure 11.44. A prefabricated built-in unit can be set into the masonry structure surrounding the fireplace. Specify gas and electricity to supply the barbecue. As an alternative, the barbecue unit may be built into the exterior structure of a fireplace for outdoor cooking. The barbecue may also be installed separately from a fireplace.

Multilevel Masonry Fireplaces

Represent a multilevel masonry fireplace using a symbol similar to that for a single-level fireplace. On the lowest level, the firebox must be offset from the firebox on the upper level to allow the lower-chimney to vent. Provide adequate space for the lower level to support the additional upper-level fireplaces. On the upper level, represent an area for the lower flue so it is separate from the upper firebox. A *flue* is a heat-resistant, noncombustible passageway in a chimney used to carry combustion gases from the fireplace. There must be a separate flue for each fireplace. Figure 11.45 shows how to represent a multilevel masonry fireplace on the floor plan. Base overall sizes on the opening size of the firebox. The chimney above the upper fireplace can taper to a smaller size, but it must be large enough to house the flues and still provide the minimum surrounding masonry material.

Prefabricated Metal Fireplaces

Fireplace fireboxes made of steel are available from various manufacturers. These prefabricated fireplaces are popular because they are efficient and easy to install. Metal wood-burning fireplaces can be installed using a masonry or metal chimney. The metal chimney is usually hidden in a wood-framed chimney called a chase. Figure 11.46 a,b shows how to represent a metal fireplace and chimney. Metal fireplaces, referred to as zero-clearance units, can be enclosed by wood walls. Units are available that burn wood, natural gas, or propane, or they may use electricity to produce heat. Sizes vary greatly among the several major suppliers, and there are many models from which to choose. An area of 48" × 24" (1200 × 600 mm) provides ample space on the floor plan during the preliminary design stage. Draw the fireplace on the *FLOR CHIM* layer. Once a specific model has been selected, the exact size is specified based on the manufacturer's specifications. To specify a zero-clearance fireplace, provide the model number and other specific information next to the fireplace symbol on the floor plan or in a general note. The gas supply should also be shown with a symbol and a note, similar to the examples in Figure 11.41.

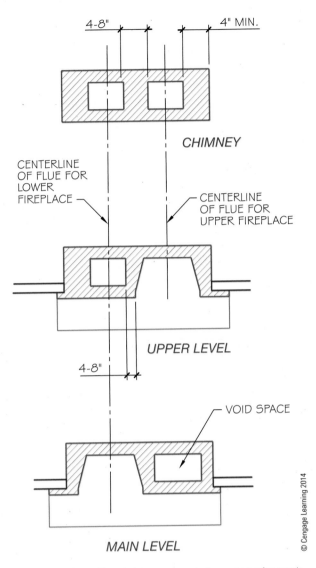

FIGURE 11.45 A multilevel chimney must allow space for each flue beside the fireplace opening.

FIGURE 11.46a A metal fireplace and chimney supported by wood framing.

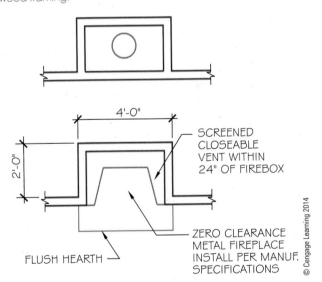

FIGURE 11.46b Representing a zero-clearance fireplace and metal chimney in plan view.

Fireplace Alternatives

Common alternatives to a fireplace include inserts, logs, and stoves. A *fireplace insert* is a metal fireplace that is inserted into an existing masonry fireplace and vented using the existing chimney. Inserts are often used for renovations to get better energy efficiency from an old firebox. Inserts can be installed that burn gas, propane, wood, and wood pellets or that use electricity. A chimney liner may be provided for the existing chimney and should be specified on the floor plan based on the manufacturer's recommendations. Figure 11.47 shows a metal insert and how to represent it on a floor plan.

Freestanding stoves are excellent radiant heating units. Models are available that burn wood, pellets, gas, and coal. Sizes vary widely based on the manufacturer and the fuel that is burned. Use a rectangle 30" × 27" (750 × 675 mm) to represent a stove on a floor plan.

Figure 11.48 shows a freestanding fireplace represented on a floor plan. Gas and propane log units are available that can be installed in existing masonry fireplaces or placed in a freestanding pit to imitate the effect of an open wood fire. Design values determine the size of the pit. Common widths for log units range from 18" to 24" (450 to 600 mm). Draw each type of heating unit on the *FLOR APPL* layer.

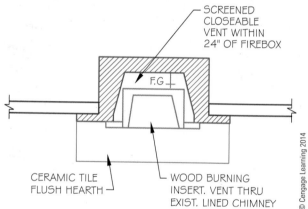

FIGURE 11.47 Representing an insert on the floor plan.

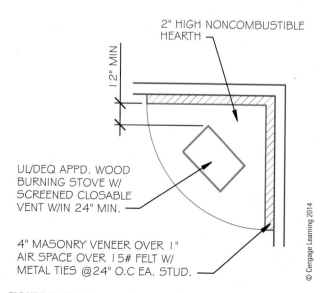

FIGURE 11.48 Representing a freestanding wood stove.

Floor and Wall Protection

Floor and wall protection for a fireplace, insert, and stove must also be represented on the floor plan. Combustible floors must be protected from hot embers from an open firebox. A **hearth** is the noncombustible protection for the floor that is usually constructed from brick, stone, tile, or concrete. The exact size required for the hearth varies depending on the size and type of the heating unit. A hearth must extend a minimum of 16" (406 mm) in front and 8" (203 mm) to the side of the firebox. A projection of 20" (500 mm) is required if the firebox opening is larger than 6 sq ft. The hearth may be flush with the floor or raised approximately 14" (350 mm) to provide a place to sit. Self-contained zero-clearance units are available that do not require special floor protection. Chapter 32 explores hearth options.

Unless a solid masonry fireplace meets the minimum sizes shown in Figure 11.40 or there is a zero-clearance unit, the walls near a heating unit must be protected. Exact distances from the heating unit to an unprotected wall will vary based on the specifications of the manufacturer. A minimum distance of 18" (450 mm) is required between unprotected walls and the backs of most units. This distance can be reduced to between 8" and 12" (200 and 300 mm) if a noncombustible surface such as masonry, stone, or tile is laid over a cement asbestos board. Draw protective surfaces on a layer with other masonry products and place the hatch pattern with other hatch patterns.

Metal Chimneys

The type of chimney must also be considered, based on the manufacturer's recommendations, if a prefabricated metal fireplace or stove is specified. Flues must be designed to provide proper ventilation and draft for the fireplace. Draft is a current of air and gases that pass from the fireplace through the chimney. The fireplace opening and the chimney height determine the size of the flue. Common options for venting include a direct vent, rear vent, and self-vent. The direct-vent models have a chimney that is vented through the roof or out the wall and extended above the roof, either exposed or in a framed enclosure. A triple-wall metal chimney with an approximate diameter of 14" (350 mm) is common when the chimney is to be vertical. Draw the metal chimney on the *FLOR CHIM* layer. Metal fireplaces are also available that vent out the back, with vents similar to dryer vents. Self-venting units vent directly out the wall behind the fireplace. A vent-free fireplace does not have a flue.

Combustion Air

Combustion air is supplied to the firebox to allow fuel combustion. The IRC requires a closable vent to outside air within 24" (600 mm) of the firebox to provide combustion air. Providing outside air ensures that the fireplace does not draw heated air from the interior. The vent allows indoor oxygen levels to be maintained and keeps heated air from going up the chimney. The vent does not have to be shown on the floor plan, but place a note near the fireplace to indicate how the combustion air will be provided.

MISCELLANEOUS FLOOR PLAN SYMBOLS

Common symbols that may be shown on a floor plan include a north arrow, miscellaneous appliances, decks and porches, attic and crawl access openings, miscellaneous plumbing symbols, cross-section symbols, and structural symbols. Provide a legend to explain the symbols represented on the floor plan.

North Arrow

An arrow must be placed on the floor plan to indicate north. It should be simple and easy to reproduce. It is usually placed near the drawing title using the *FLOR SYMB* layer. Figure 11.49 shows common symbols used for the north arrow.

Miscellaneous Equipment

Common equipment that may be necessary to represent on a floor plan includes a heating unit, air conditioner, water heater, and a built-in vacuum system.

Heating Units

The type of heating unit will determine what is placed on the floor plan. Chapter 15 introduces major types of residential heating systems. Generally, only a forced-air furnace must be represented on the floor plan. Other types of heaters are represented on the electrical plan. When drawing a simple residence, place the electrical symbols on the floor plan. For most custom plans, provide a separate plan to represent all electrical fixtures. Chapter 13 explores how to represent electrical fixtures and symbols on the floor plan. The furnace is often placed in a location central to the house, or in the garage, basement storage area, attic, or closet. Do not locate units that burn a fuel such as gas under a stairway. Figure 11.50 shows a common method of representing a forced-air unit. Sizes vary depending on the fuel source, but common sizes for representing the heating unit include:

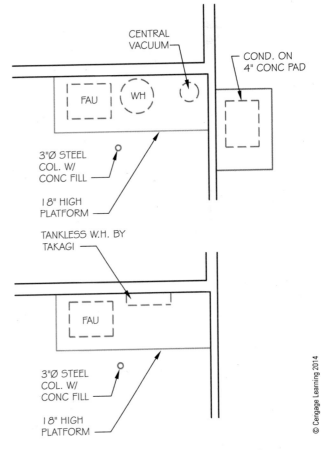

FIGURE 11.50 Heating, cooling, and cleaning appliances are often located in the garage to conserve living space. The burning element for a gas unit is required by code to be 18" (450 mm) above the floor level. Most modern appliances meet this requirement, but an 18" high platform is often specified to ensure code compliance. Many homeowners are moving away from the traditional round water heater for the more efficient tankless heater with instant hot water.

© Cengage Learning 2014

FIGURE 11.49 A north arrow must clearly define the direction without being a distraction.

© Cengage Learning 2014

- Gas forced-air unit: 18" (450 mm) square (minimum)
- Electric forced-air unit: 24" × 30" (600 × 750 mm)

Provide a 6" (150 mm) space on each side of the unit for airflow. Space is also necessary to service the unit. Draw the furnace on the *FLOR HVAC* layer.

Air Conditioning

A compressor for the cooling unit should be drawn on the floor plan. The size of the unit varies greatly depending on the size of the house. For planning purposes, use a 27" × 27" (675 × 675 mm) square to represent the compressor (see Figure 11.50). Place the compressor on a concrete pad that is typically about 6" (150 mm) larger than the unit. Place the unit outside of the house in a location near the heating unit. Draw the air conditioning unit on the *FLOR HVAC* layer. Chapter 15 explores options to cool a residence.

Planning for HVAC Ducts

Ducts for a forced-air system for a single-level structure are usually placed in a crawl space or attic. In a multilevel home, consideration must be given to where the ductwork can be placed. When supply ducts cannot be confined to a crawl space or attic, they must be run inside the occupied areas of the home. When possible, conceal ducts between floor and ceiling members. Figure 11.51 shows a multilevel home, the required HVAC registers, and possible locations for ductwork. As a drafter, it is usually not your job to plan the ductwork; you only indicate its placement to supply treated air to each room. In this example, as the main supply ducts leave the furnace, they travel through unfinished rooms and can be run below the ceiling. When the supply ducts run parallel to structural members and the duct size is equal to or smaller than the size of the construction members, they can be placed within the space between the structural members. Framing covered with gypsum or other finish material can be used to enclose ducts that must be placed in habitable areas. When possible, place duct runs in the ceiling of a hallway, kitchen, or bathroom. These rooms can be framed and finished with a 7'-0" (2100 mm) ceiling. Figure 11.52 shows how to represent a chase on a floor plan. Show the chase on the *FLOR HVAC* layer. If the chase is to be hatched, place the pattern on the *FLOR PATT* layer.

When ducts must be run between floor levels, they must be run in an easily concealed location, as in a closet or in the stud space. Use the stud space for ducts that are 3 1/2" deep for 2 × 4 studs, 5 1/2" deep for 2 × 6 studs, or 7 1/2" deep for 2 × 8 studs. If the duct can be run up through a closet, place it in a chase. A ***chase*** is a continuous recessed area built to conceal ducts, pipes, or other construction products. If the duct cannot be easily concealed, it might need to be framed into the corner of a room. The framing for a chase is shown on the floor plan

as a wall surrounding the duct to be concealed; place a note indicating its size and use. A typical note reads:

CHASE FOR 22 × 24 RETURN DUCT.

Return air ducts are usually placed between enclosed construction members called a ***plenum***. When this is possible, no extra framing is required to conceal the ducts. When ducts are run in an area such as an unfinished basement, it is possible to leave them exposed.

Water Heaters

The water heater is generally located in a central area of the home. It is often placed near the furnace, not because they have common elements but because they often share leftover space. Figure 11.50 shows a water heater by the furnace in a garage. Represent the water heater with a circle drawn with dashed lines and a diameter of 18" to 24" (450 to 600 mm). The actual size varies based on the fuel type, the number of bathrooms and bedrooms, and the manufacturer. Chapter 14 provides further guidelines that determine the size of the water heater.

Draw the water heater on the *FLOR PFIX* layer. If the water heater is in a garage, use a steel column filled with concrete, called a ballard, to protect the unit from impact by a car. Install gas units so the burning element is 18" (450 mm) above the floor level. Most gas water heaters are manufactured to meet this minimum height, but many professionals specify that the unit be on an 18" (450 mm) platform to ensure compliance. If the water heater is in a room with a finished floor, provide a metal pan with a drain connected to the sewer system.

A tankless system is a popular alternative to the traditional water heater. Tankless water heaters do not store water but heat it as needed. As the hot water tap is opened at a fixture, water flows over a heating element to the fixture. When the fixture is turned off, the heater is turned off. Draw tankless water heaters as shown in Figure 11.50. Sizes vary based on fuel type and manufacturer, but they are approximately 16" (400 mm) wide and 8" (200 mm) deep. Draw a tankless water heater on the *FLOR APPL* layer. Use thin continuous lines for wall-mounted units and dashed lines for under-cabinet models. Provide a note to specify the manufacturer, model number, and fuel type.

Built-in Vacuum

Represent a central vacuum system on the floor plan and the electrical plan. The outlets are shown on the electrical plan and are discussed in Chapter 13. The central unit should be shown on the floor and the electrical plans (see Figure 11.50). A central vacuum is about 12" (300 mm) in diameter and is usually mounted on a wall in a location that provides noise dampening and easy access. This may

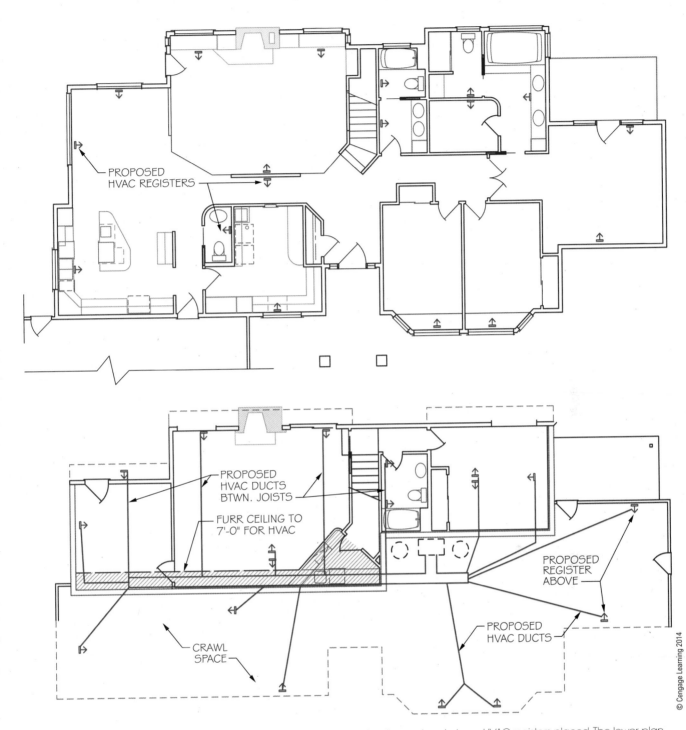

FIGURE 11.51 The upper floor plan of this home shows where the design team plans to have HVAC registers placed. The lower plan shows how possible ductwork can be placed. Neither the ducts nor the vents are shown on the floor plan, but possible locations must be determined so that the HVAC contractor has room to place needed equipment.

be in the same area as the furnace and water heater. Place the central vacuum on the *FLOR APPL* layer.

Decks and Porches

Show decks and porches on a floor plan using thin, continuous lines on a layer such as *FLOR DECK*. When the deck is higher than 30" (750 mm) above the ground,

place a guardrail around the deck using the same methods and layer title used to represent interior rails. On multi-level homes, use a dashed, hidden, or centerline on the lower plan to represent the outline of the deck above. Place the outline of the deck on the *FLOR DECK OTLN* layer. Use continuous bold lines to represent support posts. The posts should be placed on the same layer as the lower wood walls. If exterior stairs are required, represent them

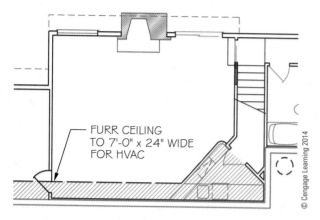

FIGURE 11.52 Although the main supply duct could be run through the crawl space, the designer has planned to provide a lowered ceiling parallel to the interior wall. Ductwork can then be run to registers through the joist space. The ceiling was also lowered over the bar to help hide the chase.

using the same techniques used to represent interior stairs. Figure 11.53 shows common methods of representing deck information.

Specify concrete slabs for patios, walks, or driveways on the floor plan. Common notes that might be used to describe hardscape include:

4" THICK CONCRETE WALK

4" THICK CONCRETE STOOP

4" THICK CONCRETE FLATWORK

Stoop and flatwork are terms for describing concrete slabs. Concrete flatwork is usually sloped 1/4" per foot to drain water. Place decks, porches, and concrete flatwork on the *FLOR DECK* layer.

Attic and Crawl Access

Access is necessary to crawl space and attics. Locate the crawl access for homes with a wood-framed floor in an exterior foundation wall or on the floor plan in any convenient location. An exterior access provides an excellent method for inserting pipes or other long materials for making repairs under the structure. An access opening in the interior helps stop wild critters from getting free rent. The master bedroom closet or a utility room is a common place to hide the crawl access. Avoid placing it in a child's closet. If locating crawl access in the floor, the access must be a minimum of 18" × 24" (457 × 610 mm). Figure 11.54 is an example of representing the crawl access. Section 7 explores providing access in the foundation wall.

Attic access must be provided if an attic exceeds an area of 30 sq ft (2.8 m²) and has a height of 30" (762 mm). The attic

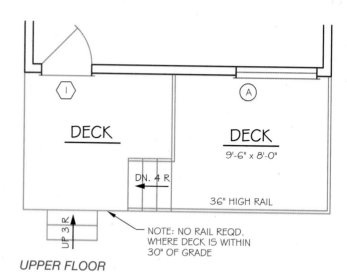

UPPER FLOOR

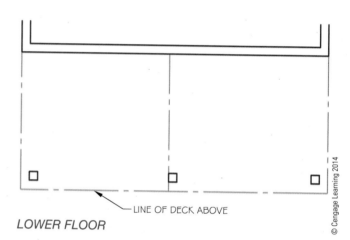

LOWER FLOOR

FIGURE 11.53 Thin lines should be used to represent the outline of the deck and any required guardrails. On multilevel homes, a dashed or centerline can be used on the lower plan to represent the outline of the deck above. Continuous bold lines should be used to represent support posts. If exterior stairs are required, they can be represented using the same techniques that were used to represent interior stairs.

access must be a minimum of 22" × 30" (559 × 762 mm), and it must be located in an area of the house that has 30" (762 mm) of unobstructed headroom above the access opening. The attic access is often placed at the end of a hallway, in the master bedroom walk-in closet, or in a utility room. The attic access cannot be located in a closet that requires shelving to be moved to gain access to the attic. The attic access may include a fold-down ladder if the attic is to be used for storage. A fold-down access door is usually between 48" and 60" (1200 and 1500 mm) long. Figure 11.54 shows attic access and crawl access symbols and related notes describing them. Draw the symbols with thin lines and, depending on the office preference, continuous or dashed lines. Place the access opening on the *FLOR OVHD* (overhead) layer.

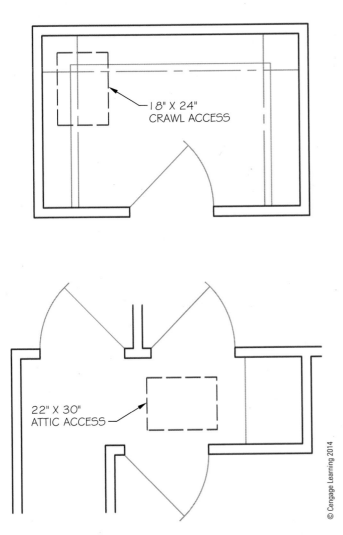

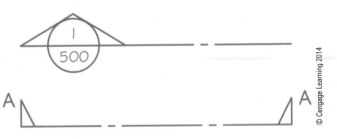

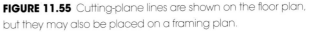

FIGURE 11.55 Cutting-plane lines are shown on the floor plan, but they may also be placed on a framing plan.

FIGURE 11.54 The attic access cannot be located in a closet that would require shelving to be moved to gain access to the attic. The attic access may include a fold-down ladder if the attic is to be used for storage. The crawl access for a home with a wood-framed floor may be located in an exterior foundation wall or placed on the floor plan in any convenient location.

DRAWING ANNOTATION

The first portion of this chapter introduced the symbols to represent the features shown on a floor plan. Once drawn, most of the symbols need some form of annotation to explain the size, material, or function of the symbol. The challenge to the CAD technician is to include all the necessary notes for the various phases of construction and yet make the plan easy to read. Drawing annotation includes general notes, local notes, schedules, legends, annotation symbols, and title block text. Annotation can also include title and text categories. Room names and the actual title of the drawings are examples of titles. General notes, local notes, and other notes in schedules and legends are all considered text. Titles placed on the drawing are usually 1/4" high. When plotting at a scale of 1/4" = 1'0" (1:50) and creating the titles in model space, the titles should be 12" (300 mm) high. Drawing titles may be as large as 24" (600 mm) high. Secondary headings such as the subtitles in schedules are often placed using letters 8" (200 mm) high. Text is usually 1/8" (3 mm) high. When creating in model space and plotting at a scale of 1/4" = 1'-0", text must be 6" (150 mm) high. No matter the size choice, use an architectural font such as StylusBT or a similar third-party font.

Cross-Section Symbols

The location on the floor plan where a cross section is taken is identified with symbols known as cutting-plane lines. These symbols are discussed in detail in Chapter 30. Figure 11.55 shows options for the symbol representing the cutting-plane line. The method used depends on your school or office practice and the drawing complexity. Place the symbol on the *FLOR SYMB* (symbol) layer. Cutting planes may be omitted from the floor plan and shown only on the framing plan of complicated plans.

Structural Materials

Structural materials may be identified on simple floor plans with notes and symbols or on the framing plan. Framing information and symbols are discussed in Chapter 25.

General Notes

General notes apply to the overall drawing or to a specific group of items in the drawing. The lower right corner of the sheet is an ideal location for general notes, but they can be placed in any open area of a sheet that surrounds the drawing. Notes may also be placed in large open areas inside the drawings, as in the garage. Notes should not be placed closer than 1/2" (13 mm) from the drawing border or the actual drawing. Common general notes that might be found on a floor plan are shown in Figure 11.56. General notes are typically saved as a block and inserted into the floor plan drawing so it's not necessary to type them for each project. Always be sure to edit stock notes so they comply with the current project. Place general notes on the *FLOR ANNO NOTE* layer.

GENERAL NOTES:

1. ALL CONSTRUCTION TO BE IN COMPLIANCE W/ THE 2012 IRC.

2. CONTRACTOR & ALL SUBCONTRACTORS TO VERIFY ALL DIMENSIONS BEFORE ORDERING OR INSTALLING MATERIALS.

3. INSTALL ALL MATERIALS PER THE MANUF. SPECIFICATIONS.

4. ALL PENETRATIONS IN THE TOP OR BOTTOM PLATES FOR PLUMBING OR ELECTRICAL RUNS TO BE SEALED. SEE CAULKING NOTES.

5. PROVIDE 1/2" WATER RESISTANT GYPSUM BD. AROUND ALL TUBS, MODULAR SHOWERS, & SPAS.

6. PROVIDE 1/4"Ø COLD WATER LINE TO REFR.

7. VENT DRYER AND ALL FANS TO OUTSIDE AIR THROUGH VENTS W/ DAMPERS.

8. INSULATE THE WATER HEATER TO R-11. GAS W.H. TO BE ON 18" HIGH PLATFORM.

9. PROVIDE 1-HOUR FIREWALL BETWEEN GARAGE AND RESIDENCE BY PROVIDING 5/8" TYPE 'X' GYP. BD. FROM FLOOR TO ROOF SHEATHING. PROVIDE ALTERNATIVE BID FOR 1/2" GYP. BD. ON ALL GARAGE WALLS AND CEILINGS.

Residential Designs

FIGURE 11.56 General notes can be saved as a block and inserted into the floor plan drawing so that they do not have to be typed for each project. Be sure to edit the notes to meet specific needs of each project.

Local Notes

Local or specific notes relate to specific features within the drawing, such as an appliance or plumbing fixture. A specific note should be connected to a feature with a leader line. Figure 11.57 shows a portion of a floor plan and the local notes required to explain it. Place local notes on the *FLOR ANNO TEXT* layer. When possible, place all notes so lines of text run parallel to the long edge of the drawing paper. Some local notes that are too complex or take up too much space may be placed with the general notes. These notes are then keyed to the floor plan with a short identification symbol or with a phrase such as

SEE NOTE #5.

Common information that may be specified in the form of local notes includes:

- Windows
- Doors
- Room titles, size, and building area
- Appliances

- Plumbing
- Fireplace and chimney
- Stairs
- Storage
- Miscellaneous notes

Windows

Place window size and type directly on the floor plan as long as the plan is not complicated. For a complex plan, place window information in a schedule. Figure 11.57 shows window symbols that reference the windows to a schedule. The creation of schedules is explored later in this chapter. When placed on the floor plan, specifications should resemble Figure 11.58. Some professionals use this method to save time. There are three common methods of specifying windows on a floor plan:

- 6036, represents 6'-0" $\times$ 3'-6"
- $6^0 \times 3^6$, represents 6'-0" $\times$ 3'-6"
- 6'-0" $\times$ 3'-6"

Although these methods are easy to use, they should not be used when specific data must be identified. If window text is placed on the floor plan, use the *FLOR ANNO TEXT GLAZ* layer.

Doors

Place door size and type directly on the floor plan or in a schedule. When placed on the floor plan, notation should resemble that in Figure 11.58. Place door text on the *FLOR ANNO TEXT DOOR* layer. Some drafters use the same system they use for windows to place door information. Common methods to represent a door include:

2868 represents 2'-8" wide $\times$ 6'-8" high

$2^8 \times 6^8$ represents 2'-8" wide $\times$ 6'-8" high

2'-8" $\times$ 6'-8"

Room Titles, Size, and Building Area

Place the room name in the center of all habitable rooms with the interior size below the name. Use text 1/4" (6 mm)

NOTE:

The height of doors may be omitted from the specification if a note is provided to indicate that all doors are 6'-8" high unless noted. This simplified method of identification is best suited for housing in which the manufacturer of doors is not specified in the plans. Completing door schedules is covered later in this chapter.

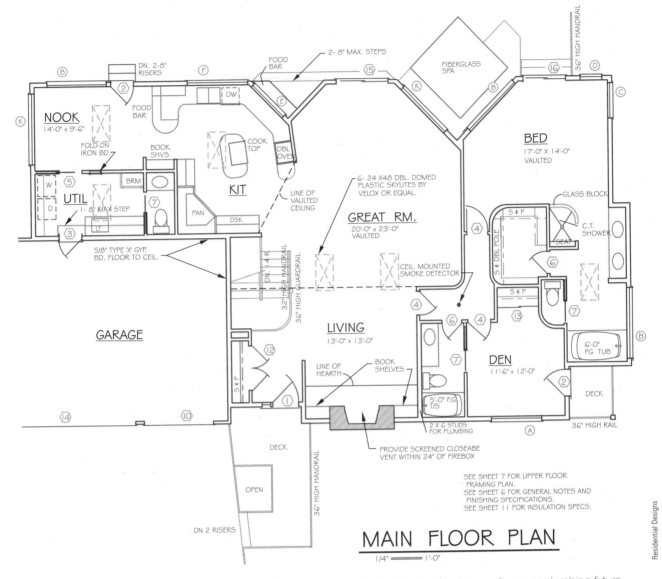

MAIN FLOOR PLAN
1/4" = 1'-0"

Residential Designs

FIGURE 11.57 Local or specific notes relate to a specific feature within the drawing, such as an appliance or plumbing fixture. A specific note should be connected to a feature with a leader line.

high for the title and 1/8" (3 mm) high for the room sizes. Most professionals list the width (left/right) followed by the depth (top/bottom). For an irregularly shaped room similar to the room in Figure 11.59, show the size of the room based on the size that represents most of the room. Place the room title and size on the *FLOR ANNO TEXT IDEN* layer.

Determining Room Size. Use the DIST (distance) or the LINE command of AutoCAD to determine the room size. The best accuracy is determined by setting OSNAP to ON. If using the LINE command, select point A in Figure 11.59 as the first point of the line. To determine the distance between A and B, move the cursor to B, but do not select the "to point." As the cursor rests at B, check the coordinate display for the distance between A and B. Once you note the distance, move to point C to check the coordinate display for that distance. Use this method to move through

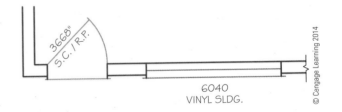

FIGURE 11.58 On a simple plan, the types and sizes of windows and doors can be placed directly on the floor plan.

© Cengage Learning 2014

each room and write each room size on a sheet of paper. Once all sizes are recorded, place the data in the drawing.

Determining the Building Area. In addition to listing the approximate size of all rooms, determine the area of each floor and list them on the drawing. Use the AREA command of AutoCAD to determine the size of the structure. Toggle OSNAP to ON to increase accuracy as you select

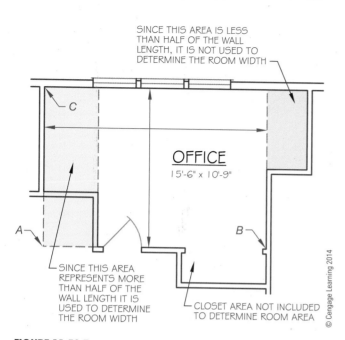

SINCE THIS AREA IS LESS THAN HALF OF THE WALL LENGTH, IT IS NOT USED TO DETERMINE THE ROOM WIDTH

OFFICE
15'-6" x 10'-9"

C

A

B

SINCE THIS AREA REPRESENTS MORE THAN HALF OF THE WALL LENGTH IT IS USED TO DETERMINE THE ROOM WIDTH

CLOSET AREA NOT INCLUDED TO DETERMINE ROOM AREA

© Cengage Learning 2014

FIGURE 11.59 The names and sizes of all habitable rooms should be placed in the center of the room. The size can be determined using the LINE command with OSNAP set to ON. Select point A as the first point of the line. To determine the distance between A and B, move the cursor to B, but do not select the "to point." As the cursor rests at B, check the coordinate display for the distance between A and B. Once the distance has been noted, move to point C and check the coordinate display for that distance.

UPPER FLOOR	1250	SQ. FT.
LOWER FLOOR	2175	SQ. FT.
TOTAL LIVING AREA	3425	SQ. FT.
GARAGE	822	SQ. FT.
TOTAL BLDG. AREA	4247	SQ. FT.

© Cengage Learning 2014

FIGURE 11.60 The size of each floor, including all walls, should be listed and a total building area provided. These sizes are often used by the lender and building department to determine minimum safety requirements.

each "next point." Use the exterior corners of the structure to include the walls in the area. Determine the area of each floor and the garage area. Arrange the answers as you would an addition problem similar to the display in Figure 11.60.

Appliances and Equipment

Label equipment such as furnace, water heater, dishwasher, compactor, refrigerator, and range. Place this text on the *FLOR ANNO TEXT* layer. Examples of notes to be placed can be seen throughout this chapter. Common notes include:

- FAU (forced air unit). List the power/fuel type (gas, electric, propane), manufacturer, and size in BTUs if known.

- W.H. (water heater). List the size in gallons if known and the fuel type.
- D.W. (dishwasher).
- T.C. (trash compactor).
- REFR. (refrigerator). List the size, style if known, and specify a water line if an icemaker will be provided. A typical note would read:

PROVIDE 38" WIDE SPACE FOR SIDE/SIDE REFR & SUPPLY 1/4" COLD WATER LINE TO REFR.

For cooking units, list the size, type, venting method, and fuel source. Common options include:

- 30" GAS COOKTOP W/ POP-UP VENT.
- 30" FREESTANDING RANGE. PROVIDE HOOD W/ LITE AND FAN. VENT TO OUTSIDE AIR.
- 30" DROP-IN RANGE. PROVIDE HOOD W/ LITE AND FAN. VENT TO OUTSIDE AIR.
- 27" WIDE DOUBLE OVEN
- 30" WIDE MICRO OVER CONVECTION OVEN.

Plumbing

Label all tubs, showers, or spas by describing the size, type, and material of each unit. It is not necessary to identify items that can be distinguished by shape, such as toilets and sinks. Place this text on the *FLOR ANNO TEXT* layer. Common notes include:

- 60" F.G. T/S (fiberglass tub/shower)
- 60" C.I. FREE-STANDING TUB (cast iron)
- 42" F.G. SHOWER (fiberglass)
- 48" C.T. SHOWER W/ MULTIPLE HEADS (ceramic tile)
- 84" × 96" F.G. SPA W/ TILE SURROUND.

Fireplace

Label each fireplace or solid fuel-burning appliance with a note such as:

- MASONRY FIREPLACE W/ SCREENED CLOSABLE VENT W/IN 24" OF FIREBOX. PROVIDE 18" WIDE × 14" HIGH C.T. HEARTH.
- MAJESTIC 0-CLEARANCE FIREPLACE W/ DIRECT VENT METAL CHIMNEY.
- 32" × 21" WOOD STOVE BY MAJESTIC W/ TRIPLE LINED METAL CHIMNEY. SET ON FLUSH MASONRY HEARTH. PROVIDE 4" MASONRY WALL PROTECTION OVER 1" AIR SPACE. PROVIDE SCREENED CLOSABLE VENT WITHIN 24" OF FIREBOX.

Stairs

Label stairs with direction of travel, number of risers, and rail height. Common notes include:

- UP 14 R (risers)
- 34" HANDRAIL
- 36" HIGH GUARDRAIL
- 4" CONC. FLATWORK W/ 7 3/4" MAX. STEP
- 48" × 42" × 4" CONCRETE STOOP

Storage

Label all closets by their uses or their storage methods. Common notations include:

- 5 SHELVES, S&P (shelf and pole)
- DBL POLE & SHELF
- CLOSET ORGANIZER
- LINEN
- BROOM or BRM
- PANTRY or PAN

Miscellaneous Notes

Specify access openings, masonry veneer, firewalls, changes in ceiling or floor levels, and upper-level projections.

- Specify attic crawl access openings with notes such as:
  - 22" × 30" ATTIC ACCESS
  - 22" × 48" PULL-DN. ATTIC ACCESS W/ STEPS
  - 22" × 30" CRAWL ACCESS
- Specify masonry veneer with a note similar to:
  - MASONRY VENEER OVER TYVEK AND 1" AIR SPACE W/ METAL TIES @ 24" O.C. EA. STUD
- Designate a 1-hour firewall between the garage and residence with a note similar to one of the following notes:
  - 1/2" GYP. BD. ON WALLS & CEILING OF GARAGE
  - 5/8" TYPE X GYP. BD. FROM FLOOR TO CEILING.
- Specify changes in ceiling and floor levels. Notes can be placed below the room title or placed with a local note similar to the following:
  - LINE OF VAULTED CEILING
  - LINE OF SUNKEN FLOOR
- On multilevel structures, call out projections with notes such as:
  - LINE OF UPPER FLOOR
  - LINE OF BALCONY ABOVE
  - LINE OF LOWER FLOOR.

Schedules

Schedules allow drawings to be simplified by removing information from the drawing and placing it in a table. Although window, door, and finish information can be referenced as local notes, it is usually represented in a schedule. Information regarding appliances, fixtures, hardware, and finishes can also be placed in a schedule. To accurately convey information, place symbols on the floor plan to represent a material, such as a window; then a create a schedule to explain each specific window. Include the schedule on the floor plan or place it on a separate sheet that contains all of the schedules and general notes for the entire project. The exact contents of the schedule will vary depending on the materials being referenced, but common components include:

- Manufacturer's name
- Product name
- Model number
- Type
- Quantity
- Size
- Rough opening size
- Color

During the early stages of plan development, the designer works with the clients to determine their preferences. A CAD technician may then be assigned the task of research, working with manufacturers' catalogs to find the preferred products. In addition to material supplied directly by vendors, use the Internet and Sweets website for information to complete the schedules. Place schedules on the *FLOR ANNO SCHD* layer and symbols related to the schedule on the *FLOR ANNO SYMB* layer. The website contains skeletons to develop a window schedule.

Creating a Window Schedule

Office practice dictates how to create schedules. One method is to create a schedule in model space as previously discussed. An alternative method is to create the schedule in paper space. This method provides the benefit that the schedule can be inserted directly into a sheet without changing the text and title scale for a drawing of a different scale. Use the following guidelines to create a window schedule:

- Use text 1/8" high (6").
- Place window symbols on a layer separate from the schedule and other text.
- Place all schedules and notes on a separate layer.

- Place all general notes related to windows by the schedule on the *FLOR ANNO SCHD* layer.
- List skylights in the window schedule if they are supplied by the window manufacturer.

Before working at a computer, plan the schedule on a print of the floor plan. Use the following steps to create a window schedule:

1. Start at the front door and work counterclockwise or clockwise to identify window sizes.
2. Represent each different window with a letter starting with A. Do not use the letters I or O.
   - Each window that is similar in every way should have the same letter.
   - If a window is different in any way from other similar windows, it should have a separate symbol from other similar windows.
   - Windows from all floors should be included in one schedule.
3. Keep track of symbols to be used: the size, type, model number, and quantity of the windows. If wood windows are used, you will also need to create a column for rough opening size. Use roman numerals to track the quantity.

Once a rough schedule has been determined, create the schedule using the TABLE command. Figure 11.61 shows an example of a window schedule using vinyl windows. Figure 11.62 shows an example of similar windows using wood frames. Use the following steps to create the schedule:

WINDOW SCHEDULE

SYM	SIZE	TYPE	QUAN
A	5'-0" X 3'-6"	SLDG. W/ GRIDS	1
B	2'-6" X 4'-0"	CASEMENT W/ GRIDS	2
C	6'-0" X 4'-0"	SLIDING W/ GRIDS	2
D	3'-0" X 5'-0"	CASEMENT - TEMP.	1
E	7'-0" X 5'-0"	FIXED - TEMPERED	1
F	3'-0" X 2'-0"	SLDG.	2
G	1'-0" X 5'-0"	FIXED	2
H	1'-0" X 2'-0"	TRANSOM	2
J	5'-0" X 5'-0"	SLDG.	3
K	5'-0" X 2'-0"	TRANSOM	2
L	6'-0" X 5'-0"	FIXED	1
M	9'-0" X 2'-0"	TRANSOM	1
N	5'-0" X 2'-6"	1/2" ROUND	1
P	6'-0" X 5'-0"	SLDG.	1

WINDOW NOTES:
1. ALL WINDOWS TO BE U-.40 MIN.   PROVIDE ALT. BIDD FOR U=.54. IF FLAT CEILINGS ARE INSULATED TO R=49
2. ALL WINDOWS TO BE MILGARD OR EQUAL W/ VINYL FRAMES.
3. ALL BEDROOM WINDOWS TO BE WITH IN 44" OF FIN. FLOOR.
4. ALL WINDOW HEADERS TO BE SET AT 6'-10" UNLESS NOTED.
5. UNLESS NOTED ALL HDRS. OVER EXT. DOORS AND WINDOWS TO BE 4" WIDE WITH 2" RIGID INSUL. BACKER. SEE TYP. SECTION.

SKYLITES NOTES:
1. ALL SKYLITES TO BE VELOX OR EQUAL DOUBLE DOMED PLASTIC OPENABLE SKYLITES.   U=.50 MIN.

FIGURE 11.61 A window schedule is a convenient method of listing required window information and at the same time keeping the floor plan from becoming cluttered. A letter is used to represent each type of window, with all windows from each floor located in one schedule. An additional column may be added to the schedule for comments.

WINDOW SCHEDULE — ALL WINDOWS TO BE POZZI OR EQUAL

SYM	SIZE	TYPE	MODEL *	ROUGH OPENING	QUAN
A	6'-10 1/4" X 4'-0"	CSM/PIC.	CR14/CP24/CR14	6'-10 3/4" X 4'-0 1/2"	2
B	7'-1 3/8" X 4'-0"	CASEMENT	CW14-3	7'-1 7/8" X 4'-0 1/2"	1
C	4'-8 1/2" X 4'-0"	CASEMENT	CW24	4'-9" X 4'-0 1/2"	1
D	4'-8 1/2" X 3'-4 13/16"	CASEMENT	CW235	4'-9" X 3'-5 3/8"	5
E	2'-4 3/8" X 4'-0"	CASEMENT	CW14	2'-4 7/8" X 4'-0 1/2"	1
F	2'-4 3/8" X 1'-4 1/2"	1/2 ROUND	CTCW1	2'-4 7/8" X 1'-5"	2
G	2'-4 3/8" X 2'-11 15/16"	CASEMENT	CW13	2'-4 7/8" X 3'-0 1/2"	
H	5'-11 7/8" X 4'-0"	PICTURE	CP34		
J	4'-0" X 3'-4 3/4"				

FIGURE 11.62 In addition to the information normally found in a window schedule, a schedule for wood-frame windows must include columns for the model number and the rough opening size. The rough opening size is determined by consulting the manufacturer's specifications.

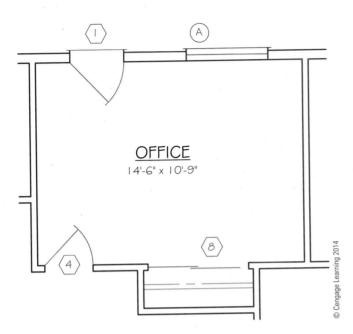

OFFICE
14'-6" x 10'-9"

© Cengage Learning 2014

FIGURE 11.63 Symbols for windows and doors should be placed near the appropriate fixtures. Place symbols on the exterior side of the fixture when it is located in an exterior wall and centered in or near objects in the interior of the house.

1. Use text 12" (300 mm) high for the titles, 8" (200 mm) high for subtitles, and 6" (150 mm) high for the text.

2. Use thick lines to represent the schedule box and provide a space equal to half of the height of the lettering between the text and the lines.

3. List the width and height of windows in a schedule. Always use foot, inch, and dash symbols, so a listing resembles 6'-0" × 4'-0".

4. Place text in a circle 1/4" (12") in diameter to represent the window on the floor plan. Place the symbol on the outside of the window and offset from the center. Figure 11.63 shows how window symbols should be represented on the floor plan.

The window schedule should resemble Figure 11.61 when completed. Add notes as necessary to describe windows. Common notes include:

- ALL WINDOWS TO BE U-0.40 MIN.
- ALL WINDOWS TO BE VINYL FRAMED BY MILGARD OR EQUAL.
- ALL BEDROOM WINDOWS TO BE WITHIN 44" OF THE FIN. FLOOR.
- ALL WINDOW HEADERS TO BE SET AT 6'-8" UNLESS NOTED.
- ALL WINDOWS WITHIN 18" OF THE FLOOR OR A DOOR ARE TO BE TEMPERED.

- UNLESS NOTED, ALL HEADERS OVER EXTERIOR WINDOWS TO BE 4" WIDE W/ 2" RIGID INSULATION BACKER. SEE TYPICAL SECTION.
- PROVIDE AN ALTERNATE BID FOR ALL WINDOWS TO BE WOOD-FRAMED BY HILLSDALE POZZI OR EQUAL.

Creating a Door Schedule

Create a door schedule using similar steps to those used to create the window schedule:

- Use text 1/8" high (6").
- Place door symbols on a layer separate from the schedule and other text.
- Place the door schedule and notes on a layer separate from door symbols and text.
- Place the schedule and all general notes related to the doors by the schedule on the *FLOR ANNO SCHD* layer.

Before working at a computer, plan the door schedule on a print of the floor plan. Use the following steps to create the schedule:

1. Start at the front door and list all exterior swinging doors sequentially from the largest to smallest.
   - Each door that is similar in every way should have the same number.
   - If a door is different in any way from other similar doors it should have a separate symbol.
   - Doors from all floors should be included in one schedule.

2. List all interior swinging doors from largest to smallest.

3. List all doors by group, such as swinging, pocket, folding, bifold, and so on, from largest to smallest. The last door listed should be the overhead garage door.

4. Represent doors on the floor plan with a number 6" high placed in a hexagon (circumscribed around a 12" diameter circle). Place the hexagon near the door swing.

5. Common door abbreviations:
   - MI (metal insulated)
   - RP (raised-panel)
   - SC (solid-core)
   - SC/SC (solid-core/self-closing)

The door schedule should resemble Figure 11.64 when completed. Add notes as necessary to describe doors. Common notes might include:

DOOR SCHEDULE

SYM.	SIZE	TYPE	QUAN.
1	3'-6" X 8'-0"	S.C. RAISED PANEL	1
2	2'-8" X 6'-8"	METAL INSUL.	3
3	2'-8" X 6'-8"	1-LITE FRENCH	1
4	9'-0" X 6'-8"	SLIDING - TEMPERED	1
5	9'-0" X 6'-8"	1-LITE FRENCH	1
6	6'-0" X 6'-8"	SLIDING - TEMPERED	1
7	2'-8" X 6'-8"	M. I./ SELF CLOSING	1
8	2'-8" X 6'-8"	INTERIOR	7
9	2'-6" X 6'-8"	INTERIOR	4
10	2'-8" X 6'-8"	POCKET	1
11	2'-6" X 6'-8"	POCKET	4
12	PR. 2'-6" X 6'-8"	PR. 1-LITE FRENCH	1
13	6'-0" X 6'-8"	BI-PASS	2
14	4'-0" X 6'-8"	BI-PASS	1
15	9'-0" X 8'-0"	OVERHEAD GARAGE	3

DOOR NOTES:

1. FRONT DOOR TO BE RATED AT U 0.54 OR LESS.

2. EXTERIOR DOORS IN HEATED WALLS TO BE U 0.20 OR LESS.

3. DOORS THAT EXCEED 50% GLASS ARE TO BE U 0.40 OR LESS.

4. ALL INTERIOR DOORS TO BE RAISED 6 PANEL DOORS.

FIGURE 11.64 A simplified door schedule is often used on homes that are drawn as spec homes. When a home is drawn for a specific owner, the schedule may include the door thickness, the manufacturer's model number, the side of the door to be hinged, finish, threshold type, hardware type, and rough opening size.

- FRONT DOOR TO BE RATED AT .54 OR LESS.
- EXTERIOR DOORS IN HEATED WALLS TO BE U.20 OR LESS.
- DOORS THAT EXCEED 50% GLASS ARE TO BE U.40 OR LESS.
- ALL GLASS IN DOORS TO BE TEMPERED.

Finish Materials Schedules

Representation of finish materials is usually restricted to the presentation floor plan, and not shown on the floor plan associated with the working drawings. The finish materials are usually specified on the floor plan with notes or key symbols that relate to a finish schedule. Figure 11.65 shows a typical interior finish schedule. Listing each room and then providing a menu of options is a common method of creating a finish schedule. Another option is to provide a column for each wall of each room and a listing of finishing materials. Place the finish schedule on the *FLOR ANNO SCHD* layer and the finish symbols related to the schedule

Residential Designs

on the *FLOR ANNO LEGN* layer. When floor finishes are identified, the easiest method is to label the material directly under the room designation.

Legends

Legends explain symbols that are referenced to a specific plan. Common legends found on a set of residential plans include those for explaining electrical, HVAC, and plumbing symbols. A legend explaining types of wall construction should be provided for renovations or additions to explain existing, new, and partial walls as well as walls to be removed. If legends are used on the floor plan, place them on the *FLOR ANNO SCHD* layer. You may also place legends on a separate sheet with the schedules and general notes.

Title Block Text

The title block consists of two types of text. Some text is based on the office logo and includes the office name, legal disclaimers, and other types of information that appears on every sheet. Chapter 4 covers this text that is part of the office template used for all drawings. It is usually created on layers such as *TITL BLCK ANNO* and should not be altered. Other text includes information that must be altered for each project such as:

- Sheet number
- Date of completion
- Revision date
- Client name
- Sheet contents

Place text for the title block on the *FLOR ANNO TTLB* layer. By providing a separate layer, text can be frozen, allowing the base floor drawings to be used for the electrical drawings without displaying floor-related text. Because information such as the date of completion and the revision date is the same for all drawings within the project, this can be placed on the *TITL BLOCK TEXT* layer.

PLACING DIMENSIONS ON A FLOOR PLAN WITH CAD

Introduced in Chapter 4, the use of dimensions on the floor plan varies with office practice and the complexity of the project. On a simple project similar to the residence in Figure 11.66, dimensions and other information related to the framing of the structure are included with the floor plan. If used, dimensions on the floor plan describe the location of walls, windows, doors, and

INTERIOR FINISH SCHEDULE

ROOM	FLOOR					WALLS															CEILING	
	CARPET	CERAMIC TILE	SHEET VINYL	HARDWOOD-OAK	CONCRETE	PAINT				PAPER				WAINSCOT LOWER 36"				SPRAY			SMOOTH	SPRAY
						N E		S W		N E		S W		N E		S W		N E		S W		
LIVING				●		ALL								ALL									●
DINING				●		ALL								ALL									●
BED. 1	●					● ●		● ●		● ●				●		● ●		●					●
BED.2	●					ALL												ALL					●
BED. 3	●					ALL												ALL					●
FAMILY	●					ALL								●				ALL					●
DEN					●	ALL												ALL					●
KITCHEN		●					ALL															●	
UTILITY		●																				●	
STAIRS																							

© Cengage Learning 2014

FIGURE 11.65 A finish schedule is often provided for custom homes to specify floor, wall, and ceiling treatments. General categories are typically listed in the schedule, but specific manufacturers, styles, and types of materials may also be listed in notes that accompany the schedule.

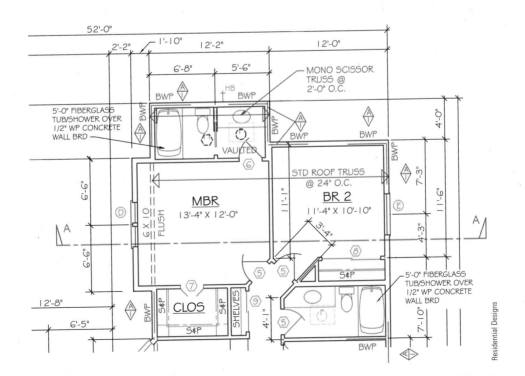

FIGURE 11.66 Dimensions and other information related to the framing of the structure can be included with the floor plan.

interior features. Not all windows, doors, and interior features have dimension lines to locate them if they can be located by their position to a known wall. For instance, if a window is located in the apparent center of a room, or a door is located in a corner, the exact location is usually not specified with a dimension. The material being represented also affects the method of placing dimensions.

For most residential projects, there must be a separate plan so dimensions and framing-related information can remain separate from the architectural information on the floor plan. Chapter 25 explains the use of dimensions related to the framing plan. Figure 11.67 compares similar portions of a floor plan and a framing plan.

Dimension Placement

Dimensions placed on a plan view are divided into the areas of interior and exterior dimensions. The exterior dimensions are used to describe the location of exterior walls or interior walls that intersect exterior walls. Whenever possible, place the dimensions that describe the exterior shape of the structure outside of the exterior walls. Interior dimensions are dimensions used to describe the location of features that are note referenced to a location on an exterior wall.

Exterior Dimensions

Most offices start the dimensioning process by placing an overall dimension on each side of the structure that is

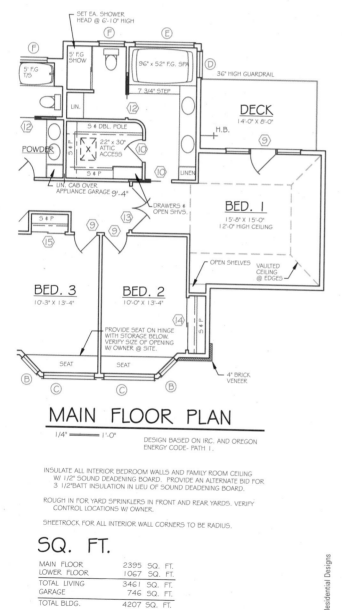

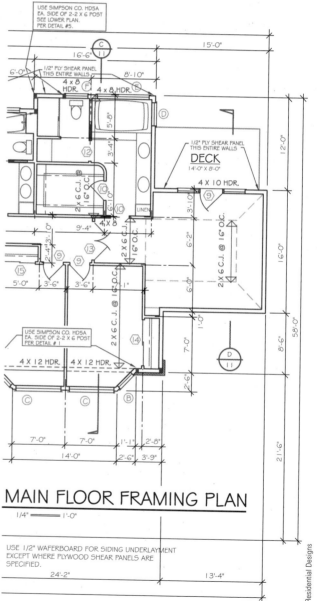

FIGURE 11.67 (left) A floor plan with architectural information only. (right) A framing plan can be used to display all dimensions and structural information needed by the framing crew.

approximately 2" (50 mm) from the exterior wall when plotted. Moving inward, place approximately 1/2" (13 mm) between lines that describe major jogs in exterior walls, the distance from wall to wall, and the distance from wall to opening. Most exterior dimensions lines are placed so that the dimension provides the distance from the face of stud of one wall to the face of stud of the next wall. If the location of the dimension is unclear, place the letters FOS parallel to the extension line. Occasionally the design will call for the dimension to reference the face of finish. When required, place the letters FOF parallel to the extension line to clearly define the dimension being given. The exact method to place these dimensions varies slightly depending on the material being used. Figure 11.68 shows an example of exterior dimensions for a structure.

In placing dimensions, it is important to adjust the use of four dimension lines to the shape of the structure. If one side of the structure has no offsets, the wall-to-wall and wall-to-opening lines of dimensions can be moved out from the structure. If one portion of a structure has no interior walls and several windows, the dimensions for wall-to-windows would be moved out as far as possible from the structure. It is not important to maintain four lines of dimensioning. It is critical, however, that each line of dimension adds up to the corresponding dimension on each succeeding dimension line, as seen in Figure 11.68.

Interior Dimensions

The three main considerations in placing interior dimensions are clarity, groupings, and addition. Place dimension lines and text so they can be read easily and so neither interferes with other information on the drawing. Group information together as seen in Figure 11.69, so construction workers can find dimensions easily. Place interior dimensions so they extend between the location of a surface described by the exterior dimensions. It is important that interior strings of dimensions add up to match their corresponding exterior string of dimensions. Interior walls are generally dimensioned to the center of stud. Some architectural firms dimension interior walls to each face of interior studs. Doors located in the corner or centers of rooms are generally not dimensioned.

Dimensioning Small Spaces

Often small areas that do not allow enough space for placing text between extension lines must be dimensioned. Although options vary with each office, several alternatives to place dimensions in small spaces can be seen in Figure 11.70.

Metric Dimensioning

Structures dimensioned using metric measurement are defined in millimeters. Large distances may be defined in meters. When all units are given in millimeters, the unit of measurement requires no identification. For instance, a distance of 2440 mm is written as 2440. Dimensions other than millimeters should be labeled with their unit descriptions, such as 24 m. See Chapter 4 for metric conversions and equivalents.

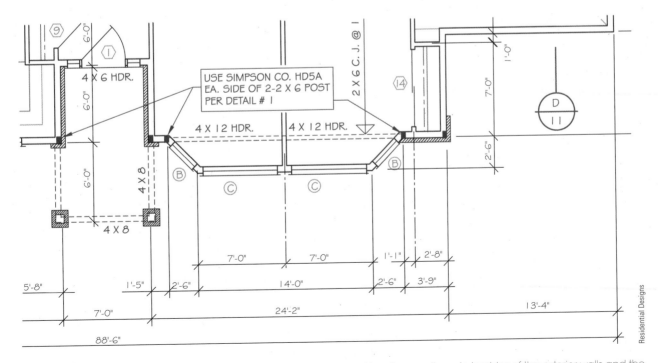

FIGURE 11.68 Exterior dimensions for light frame construction are placed to reference the exterior sides of the exterior walls and the centers of interior walls.

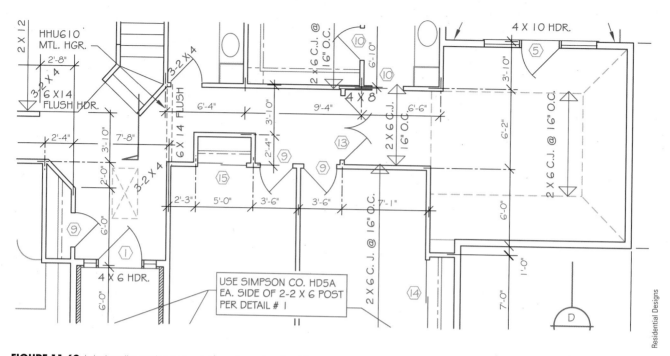

FIGURE 11.69 Interior dimensions should be placed so that they can be read easily and do not interfere with other information that must be placed on the drawing.

Light Frame Dimensions

Light frame structures are usually dimensioned by using the four dimension groupings just presented. Dimensions are placed on each side of the structure to define:

- The overall limits of the structure (the outer line).

- Changes in shape or major jogs. The changes are dimensioned from exterior face of the material used to build one wall to the exterior face of the next wall. The extension line is sometimes labeled with text parallel to the extension line that reads F.O.S. or F.S., representing the face of stud (the second line).

- The distance from the edge of exterior walls to the center (edge for some architectural offices) of interior walls (the third line).

- The location of openings from a wall to the center of the openings.

Figures 11.68 and 11.69 show dimensioning methods for a light frame structure.

Masonry Dimensions

Dimension structures made of concrete block, poured concrete, or tilt-up concrete using similar line placement methods as with light frame construction. Differences include the following:

- Masonry walls are always dimensioned to edge and never to center.

- Openings for doors and windows are also dimensioned from edge rather than from center.

- When the structure is made of concrete block, all dimensions should be based on 8" (200 mm) modules. Distances in odd numbers of feet should always end in 4" (100 mm) increments, such as 15'-4". To be modular, even-numbered distances must end in 0" or 8" increments such as 8'-0" or 10'-8" to be modular. Interior light frame walls are dimensioned to their centers as previously described. Figure 11.71 shows examples of common dimensioning practices for masonry structures.

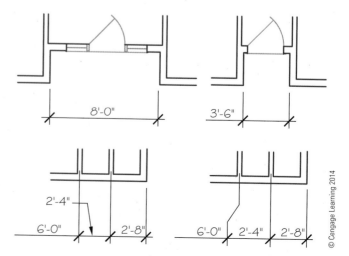

FIGURE 11.70 Several alternatives are available for placing dimension in small spaces.

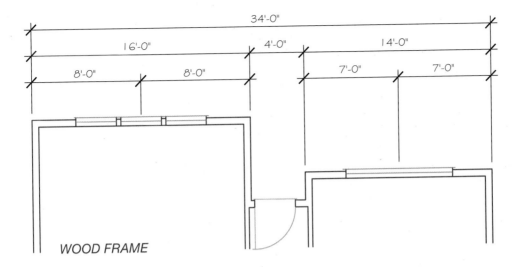

WOOD FRAME

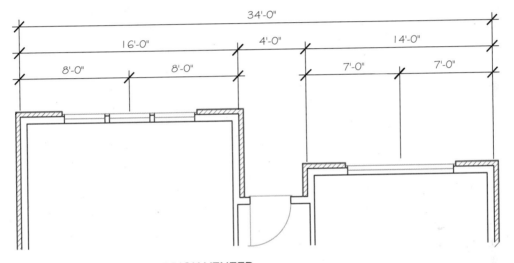

WOOD FRAME W/ BRICK VENEER

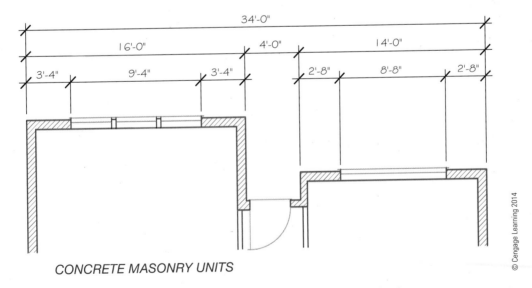

CONCRETE MASONRY UNITS

FIGURE 11.71 Placing dimensions for wood, wood with masonry veneer, and masonry structures.

Additional Resources

Use the following websites as resources to help you keep current with changes in floor plan-related materials.

Address   **Company or Organization**

Appliances

www.geappliances.com   Home appliances
www.homedepot.com   The Home Depot© (home improvement)
www.jacuzzi.com   Jacuzzi® (jetted spas and tubs)
www.kitchenaid.com   KitchenAid® (appliances)
www.lowes.com   Lowe's®
www.nutone.com   NuTone®
www.subzero-wolf.com   Sub-Zero, Inc. (refrigerators)
www.whirlpool.com   Whirlpool® (home appliances)

Cabinets and furniture

www.aristokraft.com   Aristokraft® Cabinetry
www.homecrestcabinetry.com   Homecrest® Cabinetry
www.kraftmaid.com   KraftMaid® (kitchen and bath cabinets)
www.schultestorage.com   Schulte (storage systems)
www.ssina.com   The Stainless Steel Information Center
www.temafurniture.com   TEMA Furniture (bedroom furniture)
www.lowes.com   Cabinets

Doors and windows

www.andersonwindows.com   Anderson® Corporation
www.crestlineonline.com   Crestline
www.jeld-wen.com   Jeld-Wen® Windows & Doors®
www.milgard.com   Milgard Windows & Doors® (vinyl, aluminum, fiberglass, and
                                 wood windows, doors, and skylights)
www.marvin.com   Marvin Windows and Doors ®
www.pella.com   Pella®

Fireplaces

www.heatilator.com   Heatilator®
www.heatnglo.com   Heat & Glo®
www.majesticfireplaces.com   Majestic Fireplaces (prefabricated)
www.optiflame.com   Dimplex®

HVAC

www.waterfurnace.com   WaterFurnace®

Miscellaneous

www.beamvac.com   Beam Central Vacuum Systems
www.builtinvacuum.com   M.D. Manufacturing (central vacuum)
www.easyclosets.com   EasyClosets (storage units)
www.generalshale.com   General Shale (masonry supplier)
www.homedepot.com   The Home Depot (kitchen, bath, and lighting supplies)
www.homecenter.com   HomeCenter.com (kitchen, bath, and lighting supplies)
www.lowes.com   Lowe's (kitchen, bath, and lighting supplies)

Plumbing

www.americanstandard-us.com American Standard (bath and kitchen plumbing fixtures)
www.jacuzzihottubs.com Jacuzzi
www.us.kohler.com Kohler (kitchen and bath fixtures)
www.peerlesspottery.com Peerless Pottery (bath and kitchen fixtures, bath and kitchen hardware)

Software

www.abracadata.com The Liquid Ate Her (architecture software)
www.autodesk.com Autodesk (engineering software great and small)
www.builderswebsource.com Builders Websource
www.chiefarchitect.com Chief Architect (3D home design software)
www.caddepot.com CAD depot (symbol libraries)
www.cadprosoftware.com CADPro (drawing program)
www.catalog.com Catalog.com (symbol libraries)
sketchup.google.com Google SketchUp
www.graphisoft.com GRAPHISOFT (ArchiCAD software)
www.bentley.com Bentley Systems (software solutions for sustaining infrastructure)
www.softplan.com SoftPlan (architectural design software)

Floor Plans—Symbols, Annotation, and Dimensions Test

Follow these instructions to access and complete an electronic copy of the Chapter 11 Floor Plans—Symbols, Annotation, and Dimensions Test:

1. Go to cengagebrain.com
2. Enter the email address and password you used to register for the site (see Preface for full instructions).
3. Select the website from the **My Course & Materials** area of your home page. Select the chapter you want from the pull-down menu at the top of the page. Choose the resources for that chapter from the menu on the left.
4. Type your name, the chapter number, and the date at the top of the sheet.
5. Answer the following questions with short, complete statements using a word processor.

NOTE:

The answers to some questions may not be contained in this chapter and will require you to do additional research using the Internet. Use your favorite search engine to search for specific professional companies or general categories of information.

Questions

11.1. How thick are exterior walls for a wood-frame residence usually drawn in your area?

11.2. How thick are interior walls are commonly drawn?

11.3. How does the floor plan symbol for an exterior door differ from the symbol for an interior door?

11.4. What are the recommended spaces for the following?
   a. Wardrobe closet depth
   b. Fireplace hearth for a 36" wide opening
   c. Stair width
   d. Fireplace hearth depth

11.5. Describe an advantage of using schedules for windows instead of placing the information on the floor plan.

11.6. Describe an advantage of placing window and door information on the floor plan.

11.7. Sketch the following floor plan symbols:
   a. Pocket door
   b. Bifold closet door
   c. Casement window
   d. Sliding window
   e. Skylight
   f. Hose bibb

11.8. What is the minimum required height of a guardrail?

11.9. Does a deck that is 32" above the ground require a guardrail?

11.10. When is a guardrail required for interior floor changes?

11.11. What style of window is 100% openable?

11.12. What does the note 6040 CSM next to a window on a floor plan mean?

11.13. What is the required minimum headroom height above an attic access?

11.14. List possible reasons that an appliance might be shown with dashed lines on the floor plan.

11.15. Explain options for representing the upper cabinets on the floor plan.

11.16. List factors that may influence window sizes.

11.17. What is the purpose of a flue?

11.18. Determine the minimum size for a fireplace based on current code requirements.

11.19. Give the flue size for a standard fireplace opening 36" W × 28" H × 20" D.

11.20. Describe a local note and give an example of a local note that might be found in a bathroom.

11.21. After scheduling an appointment, interview a contractor who specializes or homeowner who lives in a home built of one of the materials listed in the Alternate Materials section of this chapter. Write a report to describe the merits and pitfalls of the method you chose.

11.22. After scheduling an appointment, interview at least three different principals of architectural firms and research the software programs they use. Find out, beyond cost, why they chose these programs and the strengths of the programs. Write a 500-word report on what you discover. Include how your discoveries will affect your educational plan regarding what software you may need more experience with.

11.23. Contact the local branch of the NAHB and research and report on major trends in the housing market in your area. If there is no branch of the NAHB in your area, visit the website of a regional branch for your research.

11.24. Contact the local building department to see if any local codes have been created to cover the construction of a home built with one of the alternate materials listed in this chapter. Report on how a designer might obtain a building permit, any special drawings that are required, and any special inspections necessary if an alternative material is used for construction. Write a report on your findings.

11.25. Contact the local branch of the NAHB and then write a report on current building trends of single-family construction.

Chapter 13
Electrical Plans

The electrical needs of a residence may be the fastest-changing area of residential design. The use of computers and smart phones to control almost every function of a home, smart appliances, and demands for increasing energy efficiency have been fueling the development of electrical and electronic items that must be represented on the construction drawings. Kitchens in many custom homes have moved beyond a microwave oven and electric ovens to include warming drawers, pizza ovens, rotisseries, built-in espresso and cappuccino machines, heated towel drawers, dishwasher drawers, and refrigerators that tell you when the milk is spoiled. The electrical plans for a residence must display all of these electrical systems as well as the specialty systems for the entire project. This chapter introduces the principles of electrical distribution, key considerations in the design of electrical fixtures, basic code restrictions and design considerations that influence the development of electrical drawings, and skills needed to complete an electrical plan. This chapter will also help you plan a well-designed home similar to that shown Figure 13.1, which will satisfy a wide variety of needs.

Key Terms

Amps	Ground fault circuit interrupter	Meter	Single-pole switch
Circuit		Motion-detection switch	Soffit
Circuit breaker	Habitable room		Three-way switch
Conduit	Half-hot receptacle	Non-habitable room	Turbine
Convenience outlet	Inverter	Outlet	Volt
Demand factor	Junction box	photoelectric switch	Watt
Dimmer switch	Lux	Photovoltaic	
Footcandle	Master switch	Receptacle	

CAD Commands and Tools

In addition to basic drawing, editing, text, and dimensioning commands, the following AutoCAD commands and tools are concepts that you should be familiar with to successfully understand and complete the CAD skills referenced in this chapter.

BLOCK   INSERT   Object Tracking   XREF

ELECTRICAL DISTRIBUTION

The electricity to power a home can come from the local power company that uses water, fossil fuel, wind, or nuclear power to generate electricity, or it may be generated by private wind, solar, or geothermal methods. With the exception of solar photovoltaic cells, each method can produce a rotary mechanical motion that converts the rotary movement of a generator into electricity. Transformers are used at the generation point to increase the electrical power to hundreds of thousands of volts for transmission over long distances. Transformers are then used at local substations to step down the voltage to a few thousand volts for distribution to neighborhoods. Local transformers are also used within the neighborhood to step down the power to 120/240 volts for delivery to a home. Older designations list the service drop as 110/220 volts. Appliances are rated to be 110 or 220 volts. The service is supplied at higher voltages to compensate for increased starting loads. Once in the home, power flows from the service entrance, to the distribution box, through individual circuits, and finally, into individual fixtures.

FIGURE 13.1 A well-designed home must meet a variety of needs and provide a pleasant environment throughout the year in a variety of conditions.

Courtesy Brent Roland, Roland Builder, Inc.

Electrical Measurement

Knowing that electrical power is delivered to a home in 240- and 120-volt supplies is important to understanding residential power usage. Any technician with knowledge of computing can place symbols on a drawing and call it an electrical plan. Understanding the use of electricity in a circuit will help you advance from a technician placing symbols to a designer working with a client to plan complex electrical needs. Key terms for measuring the electrical requirements of fixtures include volt, ampere, and watt.

A **volt** is a unit of measurement of electrical force or potential. It's voltage that makes electricity flow through an electrical wire. For a specific load, the higher the voltage, the more electricity will flow. The flow of electricity is the current. The rate of the current flow is measured in amperes or amps. An **amp** measures the number of electrons passing a specific location each second. The electrician must know the number of amps that will pass through a circuit to determine proper wire sizes and breaker sizes. Watts measure the actual power required to operate a specific fixture or appliance. A **watt** is a unit of power measurement based on the potential and the current. To determine the amount of power to be used per fixture (watts), multiply the current (amps) by volts (potential). In residential construction, except for the largest of custom homes, the electrician determines the electrical loads that need to be considered in the design. Remembering these three terms will allow you to have an informed discussion with the electrician.

Electrical Service Entrance

The 240 and 120 volts that are supplied to a residence enter the home at the service entrance. Three wires are either dropped from a utility pole or run underground to the electric meter of the home to provide power. Overhead wires enter a service head mounted to the residence and pass through a conduit, which leads to the electric meter. A **conduit** is a metal or plastic tube used to enclose one or more electrical wires. The contractor is responsible for providing minimum clearance heights between the ground and the service head, but the design team may provide details to mount the meter and service head to ensure compliance with local laws. If service to the home is underground, a conduit is used to bring the electrical service up to the meter. Each condition is shown in Figure 13.2. The electric *meter* is mounted on the wall where the power enters the structure and is used by the electrical supplier to measure the amount of electricity used by a structure.

All systems must be grounded at the service entrance, and some municipalities require lightning protection and brownout equipment. The contractor and electrician are generally responsible to plan for these needs as well as to determine the exact location for the service drop. On homes designed to appeal to the local market conditions, the contractor determines the location of the meter. For a custom home, the design team is responsible for coordinating the meter location with the owner and the contractor and representing the location on the electrical drawings. The service location and required trenches are often represented on the site plan, and the meter is represented on the electrical drawings. The design team may also need to locate a transformer on the site plan for homes in rural settings.

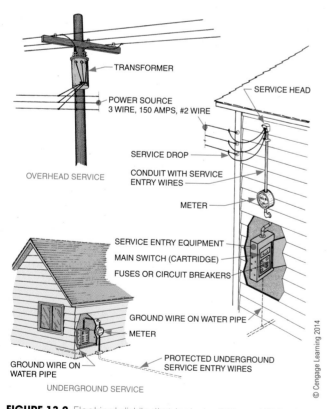

OVERHEAD SERVICE

TRANSFORMER

POWER SOURCE
3 WIRE, 150 AMPS, #2 WIRE

SERVICE HEAD

SERVICE DROP

CONDUIT WITH SERVICE ENTRY WIRES

METER

SERVICE ENTRY EQUIPMENT
MAIN SWITCH (CARTRIDGE)
FUSES OR CIRCUIT BREAKERS

GROUND WIRE ON WATER PIPE
METER

GROUND WIRE ON WATER PIPE

PROTECTED UNDERGROUND SERVICE ENTRY WIRES

UNDERGROUND SERVICE

© Cengage Learning 2014

FIGURE 13.2 Electrical distribution includes 240- and 120-volt service, which is delivered to a service entrance using either an overhead drop or an underground conduit that leads to the electric meter.

Distribution Panel

From the meter, power flows to the distribution panel, which is also referred to as the service panel or circuit box. The distribution panel contains circuit breakers, which control each of the individual circuits in the home. The total load requirement in watts for the entire project determines the minimum size of the panel in amperes. To convert watts to amperes, divide the total watts needed by the amount of voltage delivered to the distribution box. In determining the total watts needed, consider any possible future additions. The National Electrical Code® (NEC) requires a minimum of 60 amps, but most residential projects require a distribution panel with a capacity of between 100 to 200 amps. If heating, cooking, water heating, and similar heavy loads are supplied by gas, a 100-amp distribution panel will be suitable. A 200-amp panel is common for most residential projects and is required by some local codes for each single dwelling.

The distribution box must be located on the electrical plan (see Figure 13.25). The box is generally placed on the interior side of the wall where the meter is mounted. On custom homes, the circuit box may be placed in a more convenient location such as the master bedroom closet, in a closet in the utility room, or by the door leading from the house to the garage. Place the circuit box in a location that provides easy access in the dark and away from areas where there is a risk of injury from falling in the dark.

Branch Circuits

The distribution panel contains circuit breakers that control the individual circuits of the home. A *circuit breaker* is a safety switch that automatically opens a circuit when excessive amperage occurs. A *circuit* is a closed loop that electricity follows from the circuit box to one or more fixtures and then back to the power source. The circuit is controlled by a circuit breaker that is rated in the amount of amps the breaker allows to flow through the circuit. A distribution panel typically contains breakers that control 50-, 40-, 30-, 20-, and 15-amp circuits. Appendix E contains the amps required for common residential appliances. Figure 13.3 lists the amp requirements for common residential circuits.

When the breaker is closed, it allows electricity to flow through the circuit. If too many fixtures are used on a circuit at one time, the circuit may overheat and cause a fire. If the circuit requires more amps than the breaker is rated to allow, the breaker will trip, or open. When the breaker is open, the flow of electricity to the circuit is disrupted.

If you've lived in an older home, you know the joy of not using the microwave while the dishwasher is on. For most residential projects, the electrician is responsible for determining the number of fixtures to place on each

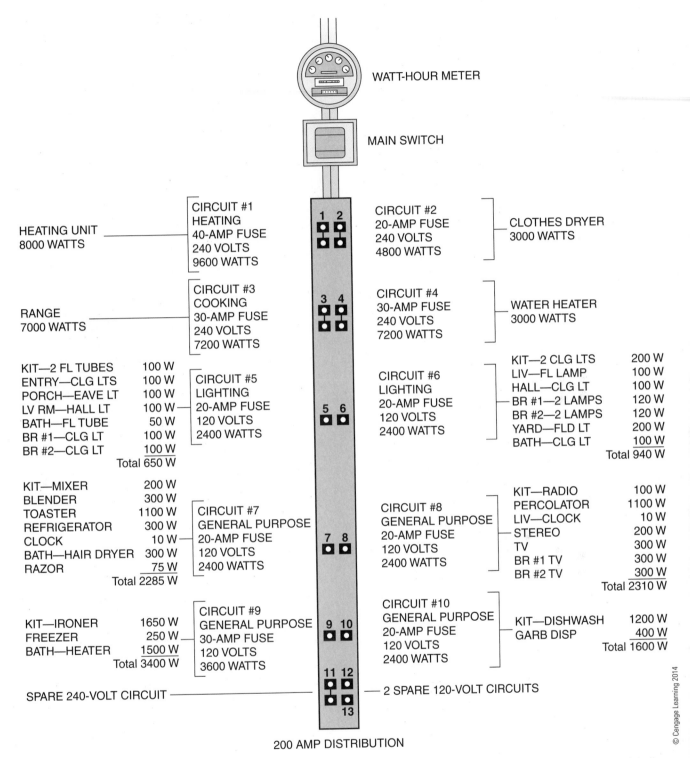

WATT-HOUR METER

MAIN SWITCH

HEATING UNIT
8000 WATTS

CIRCUIT #1
HEATING
40-AMP FUSE
240 VOLTS
9600 WATTS

1 2

CIRCUIT #2
20-AMP FUSE
240 VOLTS
4800 WATTS

CLOTHES DRYER
3000 WATTS

RANGE
7000 WATTS

CIRCUIT #3
COOKING
30-AMP FUSE
240 VOLTS
7200 WATTS

3 4

CIRCUIT #4
30-AMP FUSE
240 VOLTS
7200 WATTS

WATER HEATER
3000 WATTS

KIT—2 FL TUBES	100 W
ENTRY—CLG LTS	100 W
PORCH—EAVE LT	100 W
LV RM—HALL LT	100 W
BATH—FL TUBE	50 W
BR #1—CLG LT	100 W
BR #2—CLG LT	100 W
	Total 650 W

CIRCUIT #5
LIGHTING
20-AMP FUSE
120 VOLTS
2400 WATTS

5 6

CIRCUIT #6
LIGHTING
20-AMP FUSE
120 VOLTS
2400 WATTS

KIT—2 CLG LTS	200 W
LIV—FL LAMP	100 W
HALL—CLG LT	100 W
BR #1—2 LAMPS	120 W
BR #2—2 LAMPS	120 W
YARD—FLD LT	200 W
BATH—CLG LT	100 W
	Total 940 W

KIT—MIXER	200 W
BLENDER	300 W
TOASTER	1100 W
REFRIGERATOR	300 W
CLOCK	10 W
BATH—HAIR DRYER	300 W
RAZOR	75 W
	Total 2285 W

CIRCUIT #7
GENERAL PURPOSE
20-AMP FUSE
120 VOLTS
2400 WATTS

7 8

CIRCUIT #8
GENERAL PURPOSE
20-AMP FUSE
120 VOLTS
2400 WATTS

KIT—RADIO	100 W
PERCOLATOR	1100 W
LIV—CLOCK	10 W
STEREO	200 W
TV	300 W
BR #1 TV	300 W
BR #2 TV	300 W
	Total 2310 W

KIT—IRONER	1650 W
FREEZER	250 W
BATH—HEATER	1500 W
	Total 3400 W

CIRCUIT #9
GENERAL PURPOSE
30-AMP FUSE
120 VOLTS
3600 WATTS

9 10

CIRCUIT #10
GENERAL PURPOSE
20-AMP FUSE
120 VOLTS
2400 WATTS

KIT—DISHWASH	1200 W
GARB DISP	400 W
	Total 1600 W

11 12

13

SPARE 240-VOLT CIRCUIT — 2 SPARE 120-VOLT CIRCUITS

200 AMP DISTRIBUTION

FIGURE 13.3 The distribution panel, also known as a circuit panel, is used to control the flow of power from the power source into the structure. Although the exact appearance will vary with each structure, each panel will contain 50-, 40-, 30-, and 20-amp circuit breakers to regulate each electrical fixture in the home. See Appendix E for specific requirements for common home appliances.

circuit. For very large custom projects, an electrical consulting company will design the circuits and provide the electrician a plan of how to establish circuits. In considering circuits, it is important to know how the NEC defines branch circuits as lighting circuits, small appliance circuits, and individual circuits.

Lighting Circuits

The lighting circuits control the light fixtures for the home. Outlets that provide power for small appliances such as clocks, radios, and fans can also be placed on lighting circuits. The NEC requires the minimum number of lighting circuits to be based on a lighting load of three watts per square foot of floor space. For a 2000-sq ft home, it would seem that a lighting load of 6000 watts must be provided. The NEC allows this number to be reduced based on what it refers to as the demand factor. The **demand factor** assumes that not all lights will be on at the same time, so the lighting load can be reduced. The demand factor allows:

100% based on the first 3000 watts

35% for the next 17,000 watts

Based on the reduced demand factor, the 2000-sq ft home requires

$$\text{First 3000 watts} = 3000 \text{ W}$$
$$\text{Next 3000 watts} \times 35\% = 1050 \text{ W}$$
$$4050 \text{ watts required}$$

If each lighting circuit supplies 2400 watts (120 V × 20 A = 2400 W), a 2000-sq ft house will require a minimum of two lighting circuits.

Small Appliance Circuits

The small appliance circuits provide power to outlets where small appliances are likely to be located. The NEC considers small appliances to be irons, toasters, skillets, crockpots, and computers. These appliances do not produce a power surge when started. Small appliance circuits cannot supply power to lighting fixtures. The NEC requires a minimum of two small appliance circuits per residence. When the locations of home computers are known, it is ideal to provide a separate circuit for each computer station. The actual number of circuits is usually determined using a 3600-watt load (30 A × 120 V = 3600 W).

Dedicated Circuits

A dedicated circuit serves a single large electrical appliance such as a dryer, range, or heating unit. Any large motor-driven appliance such as a dishwasher or washing machine that produces a surge of power when started (the starting load) should also have its own circuit.

Fixture Boxes

The final destination of each wire in a circuit is a **junction box**. Such a box, also known as an outlet box or j-box, protects and seals the connection of the wires associated with the fixture and the wiring that runs through the walls. The wires for a ceiling fixture are connected to the circuit wires and hidden in the junction box. Wall-mounted boxes usually contain either a switch or an outlet with a direct connection to the circuit wires. Some appliances, such as a dishwasher and some garbage disposals, have wires

FIGURE 13.4 Wires from the circuit box to a fixture terminate in a box that is hidden in the wall, ceiling, or floor. The box is used to provide a sealed termination point between the circuit and the fixture. (Top) The wall-mounted box will be used to provide for two switches on the left and a 130-volt convenience outlet on the right. (Bottom) A ceiling-mounted light fixture contains its own termination box.

without end plugs. These appliances connect directly to the circuit wires and are hidden in the box. When no plug is provided, the appliance is said to be "hard-wired." Figure 13.4 shows examples of wall and ceiling boxes.

PLANNING FOR ELECTRICAL FIXTURES

Your job captain may provide you, as a new employee, with a copy of a floor plan including all the required symbols marked on the plan. As you advance as a CAD technician, you'll be expected to make a print of the floor plan and make your own plan. Many municipalities do not require an electrical plan to obtain a permit for a residence. The contractor or homeowner can apply for an electrical permit and pay fees based on the number of

Going Green

Reducing Energy Grid Dependence

There are three major energy supply grids that provide electricity to homes and businesses across America. Although most of the country gets its power from one of these energy grids, reducing their energy demand or getting off the grid entirely has become a goal of many homeowners. Although the phrase "living off the grid" originally meant not being connected to the public-utility electricity grid, the term has taken on varied meaning with the growing sustainability movement. Two popular, alternative-energy substitutes have become common for reducing a home's dependence on a public-utility: photovoltaic systems and wind-powered systems. Chapter 15 covers additional methods for reducing energy demands related to alternative heating systems.

Photovoltaic Systems

Photovoltaics (PV) is a field of technology and research related to the application of solar cells for energy by converting sunlight directly into electricity using solar cells or semiconductors. Semi-conducting cells are usually made of silicon and do not contain any corrosive materials or moving parts. As long as the solar cells are exposed to light, they will produce environmentally clean, quiet, and safe energy.

Individual photovoltaic cells are electrically connected together to form photovoltaic modules or solar panels. Light striking the solar modules contains energy in the form of photons. When the photons hit the module's silicon solar cells, energy is transferred, freeing up electrons. These electrons move through the silicon to the nearest wires and create positive and negative charges. When the millions of electrons flow through the wires of the solar electric system, they create electric power. These modules as seen in Figure 13.5 can then connect to create photovoltaic arrays for powering homes. The resulting output of photovoltaic energy is dependent on the size of the array. The size may vary, depending on the amount of available sunlight and the amount of power needed.

The electricity produced by a photovoltaic solar array is much like a high-voltage battery producing direct current (DC). Because appliances and fixtures operate on alternating current (AC), DC power can't be used in a home. To make the electricity produced by a photovoltaic system useful, the wires joining all the solar modules carry this DC

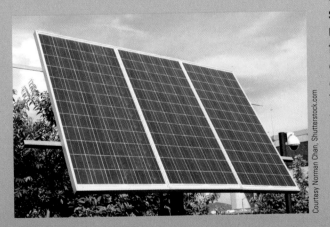

FIGURE 13.5 Photovoltaic systems create electricity by using the photons in the light that strikes the solar modules. When the photons hit the module's silicon solar cells, energy is transferred, freeing up electrons. When the millions of electrons flow through the wires of the solar electric system, electric power is created.

Courtesy Norman Chan, Shutterstock.com

(Continued)

electricity from the solar array to an inverter. The ***inverter*** monitors the output of the solar modules and then transforms the DC into AC electricity and feeds that electricity into the home's wiring, through a circuit breaker in the electrical panel. The inverter also monitors the voltage and frequency of the electricity coming from the public-utility system, so that it's electric output matches the utility supplied electricity.

Photovoltaic systems can produce electricity during cloudy weather but the power output of the system depends on the overall amount of light exposure. Between sunset and sunrise and during very cloudy weather, the system does not produce electricity. To store energy for later transmission, a variety of reliable storage systems using a combination of rechargeable batteries and energy-storing capacitors are available. When the photovoltaic array does not produce enough electricity to meet the demands of the home, then additional electricity from the public-utility system flows in to supply the balance needed.

In a typical residential photovoltaic system, the solar array often produces more electricity than is presently being consumed. The extra electricity produced flows out of the house and onto the utility wires. The outward flow registers on the utility meter by spinning it in reverse, giving the homeowner full credit for the excess electricity that is produced.

Wind-Powered Electricity Generating Systems

Turbines are a type of machine for producing continuous power in which a wheel or rotor turns by a fast-moving flow of water, steam, gas, or air. A wind turbine provides motion for a generator to produce electricity. Wind turbines generate electricity by harnessing the kinetic power of the wind. In the past, wind turbines like windmills were used to turn machinery or pump water. Modern wind turbines use the force of wind over their blades to turn a shaft. As the blades attached to the turbine are turned, a shaft in the turbine spins, powering a small generator. Commercial wind turbines known as wind farms are usually clustered together, either on the land or in the sea. The power from each turbine is combined before being distributed. Individual turbines have become popular for rural residential uses.

Residential wind systems usually consist of a pole-mounted wind turbine similar to Figure 13.6 installed

Courtesy Andrei Nekrassov, Shutterstock.com

Figure 13.6 Wind turbines generate electricity by harnessing the kinetic power of the wind to turn a shaft in the turbine. As the turbine is turned, a shaft in the turbine spins, powering a generator that creates electricity.

(Continued)

in an unobstructed area. Most manufacturers recommend mounting turbines at a height of 35' (10 500 mm), but a greater height may be necessary to capture steady prevailing winds. The three blades that turn the turbine shaft usually have a diameter range between 4 to 15' (1200 to 4500 mm) long. The size needed is largely dependent on the average wind speed in the area. Similar to a photovoltaic system, the electricity produced by the wind turbine goes through the electric meter to supplement the existing electric supply from a public-utility. When the wind blows, the electricity it produces is used.

During still periods when electrical production is low, power is drawn from the grid. If the turbine produces more electricity than the home consumes at any given time, the excess electricity is fed back into the public-utility grid, turning the consumer's electricity meter backwards.

A residential wind power system is usually not suitable for urban locations with small lots. Most manufacturers recommend a property size of one acre or more to accommodate a wind turbine's large scale. The exact location of the wind turbine varies based on the size of the turbine and local codes. The turbine must be higher than nearby buildings and mature trees. Support towers are usually installed at least 20' (6000 mm) above any obstructions that could block or redirect wind and 250' (75 000 mm) away from obstructions in all horizontal directions.

fixtures and outlets to be installed. The general contractor may rely on a skilled electrician when the home is being built for an unknown buyer. An electrical plan is given careful consideration when a home is designed for a specific owner. Planning for the electrical needs of a home requires considering the type and placement of lighting fixtures, placing outlets based on code and practical use, and the placement of switches to control each fixture.

Lighting Design

The type of lights, how light is dispersed, and the method to provide lighting should be considered in planning the lighting requirements of a home. Too much light casts a glare on objects, ruins a mood, and causes the electric bill to skyrocket. Insufficient lighting can require the use of unwanted table or freestanding lights. Within a room, if lighting is ample in one area and inadequate in another, shadows result, making the area difficult to use. Good planning, including carefully balancing the light provided by the sun, outside lights in the neighborhood, and lighting that is part of the home, allows all areas of a home to be used throughout the day and in each season.

The intensity of a light is measured in units of footcandles. A *footcandle* is the amount of light a candle casts on an object 12" (300 mm) away. Table 13.1 provides a listing of the minimum amount of footcandles electrical designers agree are necessary for basic activities. Values are listed in footcandles with the metric equivalent measured in lux (lx). One *lux* is equal to .093 fc (footcandles). To convert footcandles to lux, multiply by 10.764. Knowing the light required to perform the expected tasks of a room will help to determine the lighting needs of a room.

Types of Lighting

The type of lighting to be provided affects the number and placement of lighting fixtures. Lighting needs are considered to be general, specific, or decorative.

General Lighting. General lighting provides a comfortable level of illumination for an entire room. One or more ceiling-mounted lights, a chandelier, a series of recessed ceiling fixtures, or several wall-mounted lights are common methods of providing general light to a room. Each of these fixtures allows a shade or globe to be used to diffuse the light and avoid direct viewing of the light source. Track lighting and other adjustable lighting fixtures can also be used to light the room. The placement of windows and skylights and their relationships to the movement of the sun must be considered in planning general lighting needs. Figure 13.7 shows a chandelier and recessed lights for providing general lighting to a dining room.

TABLE 13.1 Comparison of Natural Sunlight and Artificial Sunlight Levels

By providing adequate lighting levels, each area of the home can be efficiently used at any time throughout the day

SUNLIGHT

Beaches, open fields	10,000 fc (107 640 lx)
Tree shade	1000 fc (10 764 lx)
Open park	500 fc (5382 lx)
Inside 38" from window	200 fc (2153 lx)
Inside center of room	10 fc (108 lx)

ACCEPTED ARTIFICIAL LIGHT LEVELS

Casual visual tasks, conversation, watching TV, listening to music	10–20 fc (108–215 lx)
Easy reading, sewing, knitting, house cleaning	20–30 fc (215–323 lx)
Reading newspapers, kitchen & laundry work, keyboarding	30–50 fc (323–538 lx)
Prolonged reading, machine sewing, hobbies, homework	50–70 fc (538–753 lx)
Prolonged detailed tasks such as fine sewing, reading fine print, drafting	70–200 fc (753–2,153 lx)

© Cengage Learning 2014

Specific Lighting. Specific lighting provides light to do a specific task, such as reading, applying makeup, shaving, or watching television. A ceiling-mounted light directly over a kitchen sink, under-cabinet lighting in a kitchen, and wall-mounted lights over bathroom sinks are examples of specific task lighting. Each type of light prevents shadows from affecting the specific work area. Other specific lighting includes recessed or wall-mounted fixtures, track lighting, and freestanding lamps. Figure 13.8 shows the use of recessed fixtures that provide light to each of the kitchen work areas.

Decorative Lighting. Decorative lighting, or mood lighting, helps create a specific atmosphere. Adjustable spot and recessed lights with partial covers are often used to cast light on art, photos, unique wall textures, or other architectural features. Figure 13.9 shows how lighting can highlight a photo over a fireplace.

Light Distribution

No matter which of the three roles the lighting fixture is designed to meet, light disperses throughout a room in one of the following five methods. Each method is shown in Figure 13.10.

- Direct lighting allows for casting light directly from a source such as a ceiling light.
- Indirect lighting reflects light off of a ceiling or wall surface and then into a room.

Courtesy BOWA Builders, Inc. Bob Narod, photographer

FIGURE 13.7 General lighting provides for the overall illumination at a comfortable level for the entire room. The overhead and recessed fixtures provide the general lighting for this dining room.

Courtesy Brent Roland, Roland Builder, Inc.

FIGURE 13.8 Specific lighting provides lighting to do a task in a specific work area. The lighting in this kitchen is arranged so that a shadow will never be cast on any work area.

FIGURE 13.9 Decorative lighting is used to create a specific atmosphere. Here light from a recessed ceiling light is directed onto the art hung over the mantle.

- Semi-direct lighting fixtures direct most of the light downward while still allowing some light to go upward.
- Semi-indirect fixtures reflect most of their light off the ceiling but cast some of it downward as direct light.
- Diffused light is spread evenly over a room through a translucent shade or globe.

Wall- and ceiling-mounted fixtures provide direct or diffused light for general lighting. Under-cabinet fixtures, wall-mounted, and recessed fixtures provide direct or diffused light for lighting specific tasks. Fixtures that provide indirect, semi-direct, and semi-indirect light are also used for decorative lighting.

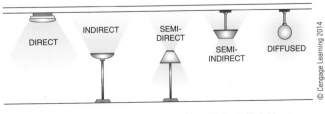

FIGURE 13.10 Five methods are used to distribute light in a room. Each of these methods can be used to meet general, specific, and decorative lighting needs.

FIGURE 13.11 The placement and type of lighting fixtures can greatly affect the appearance and livability of a residence.

Lighting Fixture Types

As seen in Figure 13.11, the selection and placement of lighting fixtures can dramatically affect the appearance and livability of a home. For a home built to appeal to a wide variety of potential buyers, the design team, and interior designer, the contractor, or the homeowner may select the fixtures prior to purchasing the home. The budget, market conditions, and timeline for the project will influence who selects the light fixtures. On a custom home, usually the architect, interior designer, or a lighting specialist works closely with the owner to select each type of fixture. Choices are generally divided into ceiling, wall, and exterior fixtures.

Ceiling Fixtures. Ceiling fixtures range from a surface-mounted fixture available at a local outlet store for $30 to a $15,000 chandelier available from a high-end lighting manufacturer. Figure 13.12 shows common types of ceiling fixtures, including surface-mounted and recessed fixtures, fluorescent light panels, and tract lighting. Surface-mounted fixtures include chandeliers as well as adjustable, pendant, and reel fixtures. Recessed lights include rectangular fixtures, which are typically used in hallways or closets, and round fixtures referred to as can lights. Can lights can be fully recessed or partially exposed. Placing a movable cover over a can fixture allows light to be focused in a specific direction. This type of light is referred to as an eyeball fixture and is often used for decorative purposes.

Another common type of ceiling lighting is *soffit* lighting, which places the fixture behind a translucent panel and directs the light source downward through the panel. Soffit fixtures can be surface- or flush-mounted and are often used in utility and sewing rooms as well as kitchens. Job-built soffit lighting can be installed between the joists or trusses and covered with plastic or glass panels that come in 24" (600 mm) modules, providing illumination to large areas of a room. An under-cabinet soffit can be added over a kitchen work area by extending the front face

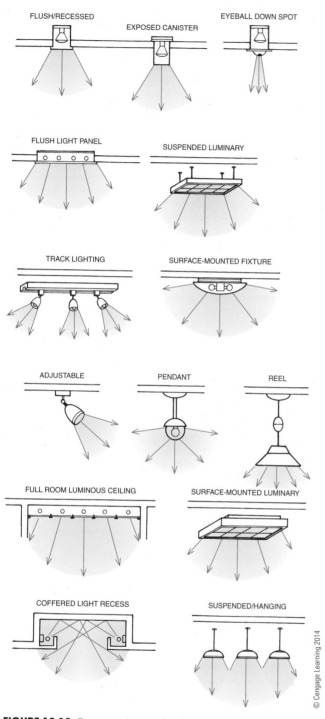

FIGURE 13.12 Common types of ceiling-mounted fixtures.

FIGURE 13.13 Lights hidden behind the front face of the upper cabinet provide direct lighting below the cabinet and indirect decorative lighting above the cabinet.

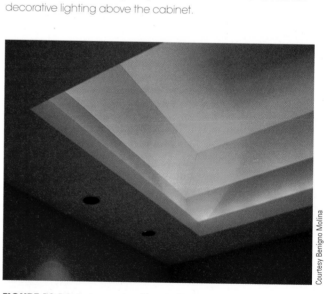

FIGURE 13.14 A stepped ceiling soffit provides a distinctive finish to this ceiling.

of the cabinet to hide the lighting fixture. Figure 13.13 shows an example of lights mounted above and below the upper cabinets to provide both specific and decorative light. Cornice lighting places the fixture near the edge of a wall and hides the light behind trim. Light can be directed either up or down depending on the placement of the trim. Figure 13.14 shows an example of stepped cornice lighting directed toward the ceiling. Both soffit and cornice lighting can produce direct or indirect lighting, and both hide the fixture so the trim controls the direction of the light.

Wall Fixtures. Wall fixtures similar to those in Figure 13.15 fill the need for general and specific lighting. Depending on the room in which they are used, wall-mounted lights connected to a dimmer switch are also used to provide decorative lighting. Wall-mounted fixtures are usually classed as a globe, sconce, canister, spots, and lanterns, which provide diffused, indirect, semi-direct, or semi-indirect lighting

FIGURE 13.15 Wall fixtures are used to provide general and specific lighting needs. If only a ceiling-mounted light were used, work at the sink would be done in shadow. The wall-mounted light will allow any task preformed at the sink or counter to be shadow-free.

Wall-mounted globe lights provide diffused light through some type of shade or translucent cover. A wall sconce directs light either up or down, depending on the shape of the sconce, and provides indirect lighting. Figure 13.16 shows wall sconces lighting a home theater. Canister lighting provides direct, indirect, or diffused light depending on the material that is used for the canister. If the can is made of a solid material, light is emitted from its top and bottom. If the canister is a translucent canister, it provides diffused, direct, and indirect lighting. Wall-mounted spotlights are adjustable to provide decorative lighting using

FIGURE 13.16 This home theater uses wall sconces to provide defused light. Using a dimmer allows the level of light to be adjusted for comfortable viewing.

direct and indirect methods. A lantern fixture resembles an antique candleholder that has been mounted on a wall. Lantern-type fixtures are often placed by exterior doors to provide direct lighting for safe access to the home.

Fixtures can also be mounted on a wall and hidden behind decorative trim to provide indirect lighting. This type of lighting, referred to as cove lighting, places trim in front of and below the fixture to reflect light upward, toward the ceiling. Valance lighting places trim in front of the fixture to reflect light upward, toward the ceiling, and allows direct lighting below the fixture. Figure 13.17 shows the use of cornice lighting placed behind the crown molding of a bedroom.

Exterior Fixtures. Wall-, ceiling-, and post-mounted lights, as well as ground fixtures similar to those in Figure 13.18, are used to accent the exterior of a structure and enhance

FIGURE 13.17 Cornice lighting placed behind the crown molding adds to the atmosphere of the room.

FIGURE 13.18 Wall, ceiling, and ground fixtures are used to accent the structure and enhance the exterior living and landscaping areas.

the exterior living and landscaping areas. Exterior lights can be installed to meet several needs. Recessed fixtures mounted in the eaves provide accent lighting to specific areas of a home. Wall-mounted fixtures provide direct or indirect general and decorative lighting for exterior areas. Connecting wall-mounted spots to a motion detector can help provide security. Installing recessed floor-mounted lights in walkways or decks can facilitate nighttime use. Lighting fixtures mounted on posts or columns or ground-mounted fixtures help light walkways and driveways or accent landscaping. Interior wall switches mounted near doors leading to decks or patios or photovoltaic controls can help control exterior lighting.

Exterior lighting attached to the structure is always shown on the electrical drawings. Depending on the project, exterior lighting for landscaping may or may not be shown on the drawings. At a minimum, the switches to control exterior lighting should be represented on the electrical plans. The location of fixtures that are not attached to the structure can be shown on a site plan or on landscaping drawings, depending on who will do the work.

Guidelines for Placing Lighting Fixtures

Use the following guidelines to place light fixtures on an electrical plan:

- Place lights in relation to their use based on general, specific, or decorative needs.

- Every entry should have at least one wall- or ceiling-mounted fixture controlled by three-way switches. Provide one switch near the entry door and one switch as you leave the entry area. Depending on the size of the foyer, additional ceiling- or wall-mounted lighting may be required.

- Use switch-controlled receptacles to provide lighting centered in the living and family rooms.

- Ceiling-mounted lights are rarely provided in living rooms for general lighting purposes, but recessed ceiling or wall lights are often provided for accent lighting.

- Use a switch-controlled centrally located overhead light in the dining room, kitchen, office, study, nooks, and baths. Also provide lighting in built-in units or in front of hutches and cabinets.

- Use ceiling- or wall-mounted lights over stairwells. Lights are required by the IRC to illuminate landings at each end of the stair. Show the fixtures on the upper and lower levels and represent three-way switches at each end of the stair.

- Use wall-mounted or recessed ceiling lights in hallways.

- Use a combination of wall-mounted, recessed ceiling, and switched duplex outlets for bedside lamps in a master bedroom.

- Use ceiling-mounted fixtures in children's bedrooms. A bedroom may have a recessed ceiling light in front of a wardrobe closet.

- Provide ceiling-mounted lights centered over the seating areas in bay windows.

- Provide a light over each kitchen sink.

- Provide a ceiling-mounted fixture for general bathroom lighting and a light above each vanity sink and mirror. In a large bathroom, place a waterproof, recessed light above a shower or tub. Lamps, hanging fixtures, track lighting, pendants, or ceiling-mounted fans that connect to a power cord can't be located in a zone that is 36" (900 mm) horizontally, or 8' (2400 mm) vertically above the rim of a bathtub or a shower stall threshold.

- Provide surface-mounted or recessed incandescent fixtures with lights that are completely enclosed in closets or any alcove or pantry that requires light. Lights must be a minimum of 12" (300 mm) above the nearest point of storage. This distance can be reduced to 6" (1250 mm) if fluorescent lights are used.

- Each enclosed bath or laundry room must have an exhaust fan or an openable window. If no window is provided, a fan with a minimum rating of 50 ft³ per minute (cfm) (0.024 m³/s) intermittent or 20 cfm (0.009 m³/s) continuous must be provided. In kitchens without windows, a minimum rating of 100 cfm (0.047 m³/s) intermittent or 25 cfm (0.012 m³/s) continuous must be provided.

- Place lights and receptacles in garages or shops in relation to their use.

- Place exterior lights to illuminate walks, drives, patios, decks, and other high-use areas.

Outlet Selection and Placement

The placement of electrical receptacles to connect appliances to the house wiring system should be planned based on the type of outlets to be used, NEC requirements, energy efficiency, and commonsense guidelines based on normal usage.

Types of Outlets

Although the terms outlet and receptacle may be used interchangeably, the NEC defines an **outlet** as the location in the circuit where electrical devices are connected. The NEC defines a **receptacle** as the device in the outlet box where the electrical component is actually attached.

No matter the term used in your area, the two major types of receptacles are 240- and 120-volt. Older designations of these voltages were 220/110 connections. The official voltage for residential appliances is 125/250V based on the National Electrical Manufacturers Association©.

240-Volt Receptacles. Large electrical appliances—such as furnace, water heater, spa, clothes dryer, oven, and range—require 240-volt receptacles. Each outlet is placed on an independent circuit for one specific appliance. A key consideration for 240-volt receptacles is the size in amps of the circuit that powers the appliance. A dryer is generally placed on a 30-amp circuit, and a range may be placed on either a 30- or 50-amp circuit depending on the manufacturer's recommendations. These receptacles may be similar to those in Figure 13.19, although each appliance except the dryer is usually hard-wired directly to the circuit. Each of these appliances is also available as gas-powered. When a gas unit is used, a dedicated 120-volt circuit is provided to the appliance to power blowers, timers, lights, or other components of the unit. Although gas ovens are available, electric ovens tend to be more popular because of their convection and self-cleaning features.

120-Volt Receptacles. A 120-volt receptacle is referred to as a *convenience outlet*. The standard receptacle consists of two plugs and is referred to as a duplex convenience outlet.

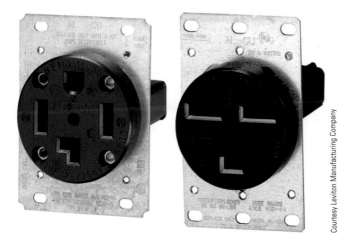

FIGURE 13.19 Fixtures such as a furnace, water heater, spa, clothes dryer, double oven, and range receive their power from 240-volt receptacles placed on an independent circuit. A key consideration for 240-volt receptacles is the size in amps of the circuit powering the appliance. A dryer is generally placed on a 30-A circuit, and a range may be placed on either a 30- or 50-A circuit depending on the manufacturer's recommendations. The range receptacle on the left is rated as 30A-250V grounding, NEMA 14-30R, with two hot connections as well as a neutral, and a grounding connection. The range receptacle on the right is rated as 30A-135/250V grounding, NEMA 14-30R, with two hot connections and a grounding connection.

Courtesy Leviton Manufacturing Company

Receptacles containing three and four plugs are also available. Common types of 120-volt convenience outlets include:

- A *half-hot receptacle*, which is a conventional outlet with one receptacle that is always hot. A second receptacle is connected to a wall switch that controls the flow of power through the receptacle. The switch will now control any fixture that is plugged into this receptacle and set in the ON position. Half-hot receptacles are used in rooms such as living rooms or bedrooms in place of a light fixture.

- *Ground fault circuit interrupter receptacles* (GFCI or GFI) are used when an appliance or fixture is to be used within 60" (1500 mm) of water. The receptacle, similar to that in Figure 13.20, disrupts the flow of electricity through the circuit with even the smallest change in current flow to protect human life. Because the receptacle trips so easily, it contains a reset button so the circuit can be restored without going all the way to the distribution panel. GFCI receptacles are generally used in bathrooms, and GFCI circuit breakers are used in kitchens, laundry rooms, garages, and for exterior fixtures and outlets. The GFCI circuit breaker is used to ensure that all lights and receptacles near the water source are protected. Exterior receptacles are required to be GFCI and waterproofed. A waterproof receptacle uses a metal or plastic cover to protect the receptacle even if it is in use.

Guidelines for Placing Outlets

The placement of 120-volt convenience outlets is based on rules established by the NEC, but energy considerations and common usage patterns will also influence placement.

Code Requirements for Placing Outlets. The placement of receptacles depends on whether a room is habitable, non-habitable, or a kitchen. *Habitable rooms* are rooms such as living rooms, dining rooms, bedrooms, dens, and family rooms. *Non-habitable rooms* include the laundry, entry, halls, and rooms intended for a specific nonliving use, such as photo labs. The electrical needs are based on specific uses for the room. Placement of receptacles for habitable rooms is based on the numbers 2, 6, and 12. For a habitable room:

- Any wall longer than 2' (600 mm) must contain an outlet. If a wall is long enough to place a nightstand or small table with a clock or other appliance, provide an outlet to service the appliance.

- An outlet must be located within 6' (1800 mm) of an opening in a wall. An opening is a total disruption

FIGURE 13.20 Any fixture or appliance that is or can be placed within 60" (1500 mm) of a water source must be powered by a GFCI circuit breaker or receptacle. The receptacle can break the supply of power in 1/40th of a second.

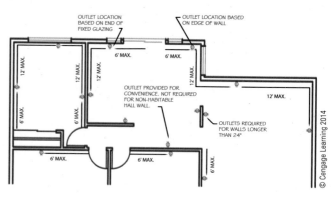

FIGURE 13.21 Outlet placements for habitable rooms are based on the 2, 6, 12 rule. Any wall longer than 2' needs a receptacle. A receptacle can't be more than 6' from the end of a wall, and no two receptacles should be more than 12' apart.

of the wall caused by a door or fireplace. This rule is based on the typical length of the cord on an appliance and not on wall corners.

- Outlets must be within 12' (3600 mm) of each other. Receptacles should be placed so that the cord is not stretched to its limits, forcing the use of an extension cord. At the other extreme, each receptacle has costs that far exceed the $3 it takes to purchase the box and the receptacle. Once the cost of the circuit, the wire, and the electrician are considered, care must be taken by the designer to limit the number of receptacles specified on an electrical plan.

Figure 13.21 shows how these minimum standards are applied to a habitable room. Kitchen receptacles require careful consideration and are not based on the numbers 2, 6, 12 for placement. Kitchen outlets are required:

- Every 4' (1200 mm) of counter space. The receptacle can be placed in the wall or in the face of the cabinet.

- Within 2' (600 mm) of a corner, end of counter, or an appliance.

- At each end of an island or peninsula.

Placement of Outlets Based on Usage

In addition to placing receptacles based on code requirements, consideration should be given to how the receptacle will be used. Use the following suggestions to improve the design when placing receptacles on the electrical plan:

- Consider furniture placement so receptacles do not become inaccessible behind large pieces of furniture.

- Place a receptacle next to or behind a desk.

- Place a receptacle near the front face of a fireplace. Specify a receptacle inside the chase for the fan motor of a zero-clearance fireplace.

- Provide at least one receptacle in the entry (foyer).

- Place a receptacle in each hallway for a vacuum.

- Provide a receptacle for each appliance, including the refrigerator, range, hood light and fan, oven, microwave, dishwasher, and trash compactor.

- Place a receptacle in a pantry for portable appliances.

- Provide an outlet on a separate circuit at an office desk where a computer will be used.

- Provide a waterproof GFCI outlet near the front door, on the front wall of a garage, and to serve each patio, balcony, and outside living area.

- Provide a waterproof GFCI outlet near the main parking areas.

- Provide a GFCI outlet on a 15- or 20-amp circuit in any crawl space.

Controlling Electrical Circuits with Switches

Switches are used to control the flow of electricity through light fixtures and receptacles. The types of switches to be used and their locations are important considerations in designing the electrical plan.

Types of Switches

The most common types of electrical switches found in a residence include single-pole, three- and four-way, dimmer, timer, photoelectric, master, low-voltage, and motion-detection switches. Examples of each of these types of switches are shown in Figure 13.22. Common uses for these switches include:

- A *single-pole switch* is used to control one or more fixtures from one location.

- *Three-way switches* are used in pairs to control one or more fixtures from two locations. Common uses include switches placed at each end of a hallway to control hall lights or switches placed at the top and bottom of a stair to control stair lighting. Three- and four-way switches are named from the number of wires required to make the circuit work, not the number of switches.

- Circuits controlled by four-way switches use three switches to control one or more fixtures from three locations. (Three switches require four wires.) Figure 13.23 shows examples of single-pole, three-way, and four-way switches.

- A *dimmer switch* allows the amount of current flowing through a fixture to be varied using a touch, slider, or rotary control. A dimmer is often used in dining

rooms, master bedrooms, home theaters, and other rooms where the need for general lighting varies.

- *Timers* are switches that allow the circuit to be regulated based on a specific amount of time. Bathroom fans, security lighting, and landscaping lighting are often controlled with timer switches.

- *Photoelectric switches* allow the circuit to be regulated based on a specific amount of natural light. When low light levels are sensed, the switch allows the flow of electricity through the circuit. The switch restricts the flow of current when high levels of light are detected. This type of switch is ideal to turn on outside lights automatically at sunset.

- *Master switches* similar to those in Figure 13.24 can be used to override all other circuits located in a structure from one location.

- *Motion-detection switches* emit an electrical beam. When a person or animal passes through it, the beam reflects back to a receiving unit in the switch. As the signal is received, it allows electricity to flow through the switch and light fixtures controlled by the switch to be activated. A motion-detector switch also contains a timer unit that interrupts the flow of electricity to the fixtures on the circuit after a specific period of time. If no additional motion is detected, the light will

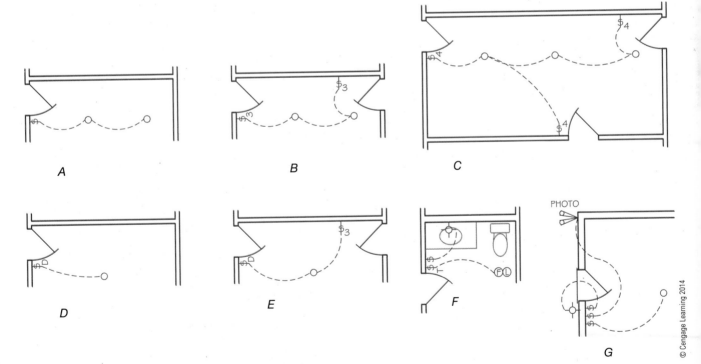

© Cengage Learning 2014

FIGURE 13.22 Common types of switches found on electrical plans. (A) A single-pole switch can be used to control one or more fixtures. (B) A three-way switch uses two switches to control one or more fixtures. (C) A four-way switch uses three switches to control one or more fixtures. (D) A dimmer switch can be used to control the amount of light produced by a fixture. (E) When a dimmer switch is used on a three-way switch, the symbol is shown by only one switch. (F) A timer switch can be used to control the length of time a circuit will remain closed. (G) Lights controlled by photovoltaic sensors turn on and off based on the amount of available natural light. A manual override is usually provided.

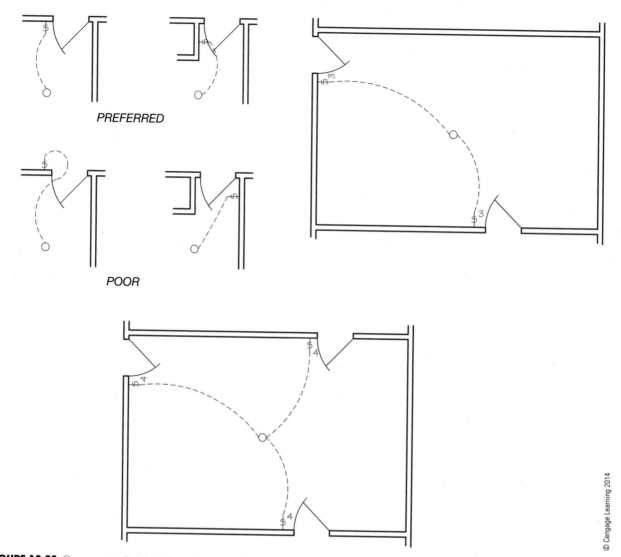

PREFERRED

POOR

FIGURE 13.23 Common switch locations. A key goal is to place a switch that controls a fixture in a dark room near a lighted area of that room. Placing a switch in a dark area will lead to accidents.

FIGURE 13.24 A master switch can be used to control multiple circuits. The Leviton Programmer provides one-touch access to up to 64 lighting scenes and remote control to over 256 devices in the home.

remain off. Continued motion reactivates the lighting fixtures controlled by the switch. Motion-detection switches can be used for interior and exterior circuits.

Switch Locations

The switch location and the number of switches in a room should be determined based on traffic patterns. The switch for a dark room must be in an area that is already in the light. Unless a fixture is controlled by a pull-cord or master switch, the following guidelines serve as aids when planning for switches:

- Every light fixture should have one or more switches to control the fixture.

- Place a switch on the interior side of the room containing the fixture or outlet to be controlled.

- Place the switch on the latch side of the door, never on the hinge side. Remember that the first 3" of wall beside a door is filled with support framing and can't be used to place a switch box (see Figure 13.23).

- Provide an adequate turning radius next to the switch for a user who might be in a wheelchair.
- Use three-way switches at the end of each hall or stairway or when the room has two means of egress. A switch by the door and another by the bed is helpful for bedrooms.
- Provide switches that control lights by the doors that lead to outside living areas. If the budget allows, provide a master control in the master bedroom for all outside lights.
- Provide a switch near the kitchen sink to control the garbage disposal. (Place it in the countertop if no walls are near the sink.)
- Provide switches to control under- and over-cabinet lighting and portable appliance compartments or an appliance garage. Place the switch in an area convenient to illuminate the work area.
- Provide switches to control exhaust fans. The kitchen exhaust fan can be in a hood with a light over the range or adjacent to the range. Locate a switch to control a fan in a utility room or small bathroom by the main access door. Fans in larger bathrooms may be located near a toilet or shower.
- Locate switches so they will not be placed within 6' (1800 mm) of a tub.
- Use switches with timers in the garage, closets, storage areas, and bathrooms to control unnecessary operation of fixtures.
- Locate switches to control garage door openers in the traffic path to the door that leads from the garage to the house.

In addition to placing switches on the plans, written specifications should be provided to specify the type and location of switches. Consider placing switches 2'-6" (750 mm) above the floor for easy use by children and people in wheelchairs. Also consider using switches that operate by touch or that are sound- or motion-activated.

DRAWING AN ELECTRICAL PLAN WITH CAD

Creating electrical drawings is a common job given to junior technicians. Because most municipalities do not require electrical drawings, it's a great drawing to allow a technician to complete as a confidence builder and to become familiar with company standards. If a mistake is made and not caught, the skill of the electrician will easily cover the mistake of the CAD technician. On a custom home, the design of the electrical plan is as critical as the design of the framing members and may be completed by an experienced CAD technician. To communicate clearly with the owner, contractor, and electrician, it's necessary to use easily recognized symbols. Most offices have symbols libraries that contain most of the symbols for completing drawings as well as a schedule similar to Figure 13.25 to explain all symbols that are likely to appear on the electrical plan. Symbols that are not part of the library can be created based on individual project requirements. Consideration must also be given to the layers that will contain the electrical information and how and when to display these layers. The final consideration will be to ensure an orderly process, so that electricity is available to all appliances and fixtures.

Common Electrical Symbols

Symbols represent the light fixtures, receptacles, and switches in the home. Common symbols are shown in Figure 13.25. Slight variations may be found with each office. Most offices provide drawing blocks that represent standard symbols. Consult the National CAD Standard for additional symbols or check the PROTO folder on the website. Use the following guidelines if you need to create additional symbols:

- Draw all electrical symbols with circles 6" (150 mm) in diameter. These circles may be slightly larger if text must be placed within them.
- Make sure all text for switches is 6" (150 mm) high and is created using simple block lettering. Do not use an architectural font that matches the general text font.
- Text used for supplementing a symbol such as WP or GFCI may be reduced, depending on space requirements and office practice. Text smaller than 4" (100 mm) high is difficult to read when a drawing is plotted at a scale of 1/4" = 1'-0".
- Place the switch symbol perpendicular to the wall, using an orientation that allows someone to read the symbol when looking from the right side or bottom of the sheet (see Figure 13.26).
- Use a thin dashed arc or spline curve to connect the switch and the fixtures the switch controls (see Figure 13.22). Figure 13.26 shows preferred methods of connecting switches to a fixture.
- When a specific location for a fixture or receptacle is required, use a local note or a dimension to locate the fixture. Figure 13.27 shows common locations for bathroom symbols and Figure 13.28 shows common locations of kitchen fixtures.

Going Green

Reducing Energy Requirements

It is far easier to make a house sustainable by reducing energy needs than it is to get off the grid. If the home's energy requirements can be reduced, then using alternative energy sources to meet the electrical needs becomes far more feasible than generating your own electricity. A first step to taking a home off the grid is to reduce the need for electricity. The designer can help by specifying efficient lighting fixtures, switches, appliances, and fixtures that meet the ENERGY STAR standards.

Energy-Saving Light Bulbs

Although the owner has final control of the type of bulbs used for the lighting fixtures, the designer can specify energy-efficient bulbs while initially equipping the home for occupancy. Fluorescent light bulbs and compact fluorescent light bulbs (CFL bulbs) can generate more light per watt of electricity than standard incandescent bulbs, and they waste far less energy through radiated heat. A drawback to using CFL bulbs is that they contain mercury, which requires special disposal requirements. LED light bulbs are extremely efficient and long lasting, but their initial cost is very high compared to other types of bulbs. Halogen light bulbs are simply regular incandescent bulbs that are designed to make its light production more energy efficient. They do become extremely hot and can pose fire hazards, so it's good to restrict their use and not place them near any loose-hanging fabrics or upholstery.

Dimmer Switches

Dimmer switches can help reduce the energy demands of each room. These switches are among the easiest to use and most effective ways to save electricity. They allow users to increase or decrease the amount of light emitted from a fixture by using an external control. Common types of dimmer switches include:

- **Touch dimmers.** Typically used with lamps, touch dimmers increase or decrease the brightness of a light source by touching either the light itself or its shade or casing.
- **Remote dimmer switches.** To control a room's main lights, remote dimmer switches mount on walls and usually have circular knobs for increasing or decreasing the light intensity.
- **Slide dimmers.** A slide dimmer is similar to a remote dimmer switch in purpose. Instead of a knob, it has a vertically shifting switch which can be raised to increase light intensity or lowered to decrease it.
- **Automatic dimmers.** Automatic switches sense the amount of natural and ambient light in a room and automatically set the dimmer to a supplementary level. The brightness of the light controlled by the dimmer switch depends on how much light is already in the room.

ENERGY STAR

Any home three stories or less can earn the ENERGY STAR label if it meets EPA's guidelines, including single-family, attached, and low-rise multi-family homes, as

(Continued)

well as systems-built homes such as SIP, ICF, or modular construction, log homes, and concrete homes. ENERGY STAR qualified homes can include a variety of energy-efficient features that contribute to improved home quality and home-owner comfort, and to lower energy demand and reduced air pollution such as:

- **Effective insulation.** Properly installed and inspected insulation in floors, walls, and attics ensures even temperatures throughout the house, reduced energy use, and increased comfort. See Chapter 15 for more information.
- **High-performance windows.** Energy-efficient windows employ advanced technologies, such as protective coatings and improved frames, to help keep heat in during winter and out during summer. These windows also block damaging ultraviolet sunlight that can discolor carpets and furnishings.
- **Tight construction and ducts.** Sealing holes and cracks in the home's exterior envelope and in heating and cooling duct systems helps reduce drafts, moisture, dust, pollen, and noise. A tightly sealed home improves comfort and indoor air quality while reducing utility and maintenance.
- **Efficient heating and cooling equipment.** In addition to using less energy to operate, energy-efficient heating and cooling systems can be quieter, reduce indoor humidity, and improve the overall comfort of the home. When properly installed into a tightly sealed home, this equipment won't have to work so hard to heat and cool the home.

Construction Methods for Energy Efficiency

The final stage of planning before starting the electrical drawings is to consider options that will make the entire system as efficient as possible. Careful planning contributes to energy savings for the homeowner at little additional cost. Increase the energy efficiency of a home by:

- Placing receptacles in interior walls rather than in exterior walls while maintaining code-required distances. Receptacles in an exterior wall eliminate or compress the insulation and reduce its insulating value. Specify receptacle gasket covers to help eliminate air infiltration in cold climates.
- In cold climates, specifying that wires run in the bottom 2" (50 mm) of the wall cavity if electrical wiring must be in an exterior wall. When wires are run at the normal height, the wall insulation will be compacted. Place a notch in the studs prior to framing the wall.
- Specifying sealing and caulking of all holes for electrical wiring in the top and bottom plates.
- Specifying caulking around all light and convenience outlets.
- Selecting energy-efficient appliances, such as a self-heating dishwasher or a high-insulation water heater.
- Using energy-saving fluorescent lighting fixtures where practical.
- Fully insulating above and around recessed lighting fixtures.
- Specifying that all recessed lights are IC (insulation cover) rated to help reduce heat loss.
- Specifying that all fans and other systems exhausting air from the building include backdraft or automatic dampers to limit air leakage.
- Providing a timer switch to control all exhaust fans to prevent unnecessary usage.

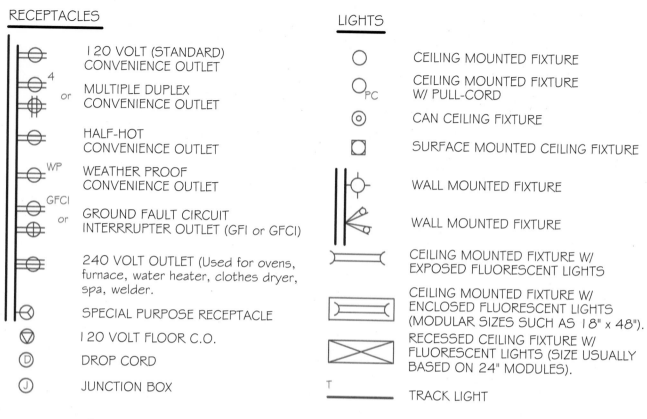

RECEPTACLES

	120 VOLT (STANDARD) CONVENIENCE OUTLET
	MULTIPLE DUPLEX CONVENIENCE OUTLET
	HALF-HOT CONVENIENCE OUTLET
	WEATHER PROOF CONVENIENCE OUTLET
	GROUND FAULT CIRCUIT INTERRRUPTER OUTLET (GFI or GFCI)
	240 VOLT OUTLET (Used for ovens, furnace, water heater, clothes dryer, spa, welder.
	SPECIAL PURPOSE RECEPTACLE
	120 VOLT FLOOR C.O.
	DROP CORD
	JUNCTION BOX

LIGHTS

	CEILING MOUNTED FIXTURE
	CEILING MOUNTED FIXTURE W/ PULL-CORD
	CAN CEILING FIXTURE
	SURFACE MOUNTED CEILING FIXTURE
	WALL MOUNTED FIXTURE
	WALL MOUNTED FIXTURE
	CEILING MOUNTED FIXTURE W/ EXPOSED FLUORESCENT LIGHTS
	CEILING MOUNTED FIXTURE W/ ENCLOSED FLUORESCENT LIGHTS (MODULAR SIZES SUCH AS 18" x 48").
	RECESSED CEILING FIXTURE W/ FLUORESCENT LIGHTS (SIZE USUALLY BASED ON 24" MODULES).
	TRACK LIGHT

SWITCHES

	SINGLE POLE SWITCH
	THREE-WAY SWITCH
	FOUR-WAY SWITCH
	DIMMER SWITCH
	SWITCH W/ TIMER

GENERAL SYMBOLS

	BELL /BUZZER
	CABLE OR SATELLITE
	CARBON MONOXIDE DETECTOR
	CIRCUIT BREAKER
	CHIME
	CLOCK
	FAN
	FAN W/ LIGHT & FAN
	GARAGE DOOR OPENER
	GENERATOR
	INTERCOM MASTER
	INTERCOM SLAVE
	PHONE
	SMOKE DETECTOR
	SURROUND SOUND SPEAKER
	VACUUM

FIGURE 13.25 Common electrical fixtures, receptacles, and switches.

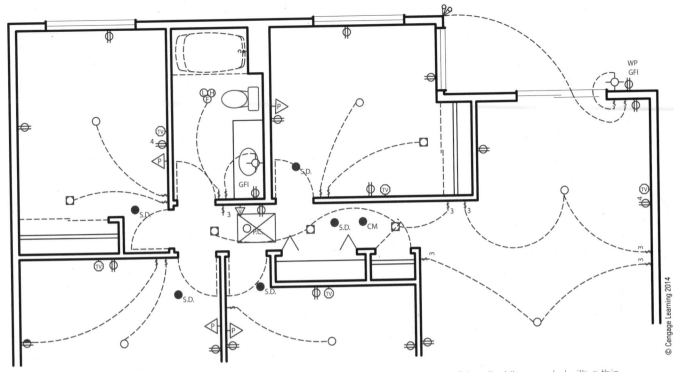

FIGURE 13.26 Switches should be placed perpendicular to the wall and connected to the fixture that they control with a thin dashed arc. Notice that only one switch, supplied by the manufacturer, controls the light/heat/fan unit.

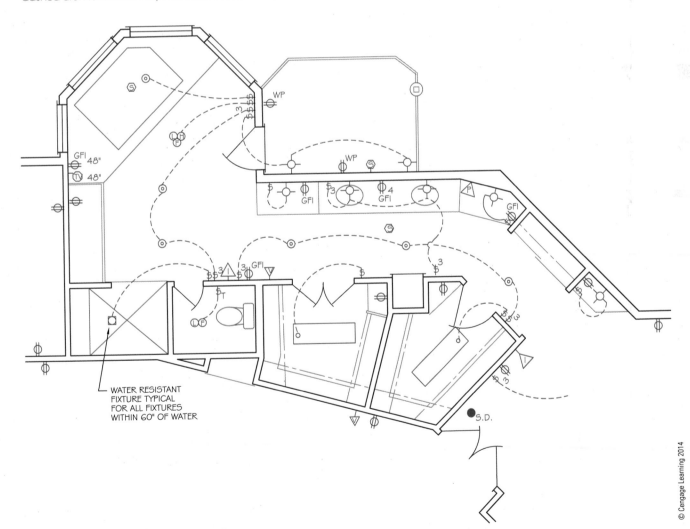

WATER RESISTANT
FIXTURE TYPICAL
FOR ALL FIXTURES
WITHIN 60" OF WATER

FIGURE 13.27 Representing common symbols in a bathroom. All fixtures and receptacles must be labeled as GFCI, or a note must be provided to indicate the use of a GFCI circuit for all bathroom fixtures within 60" of water.

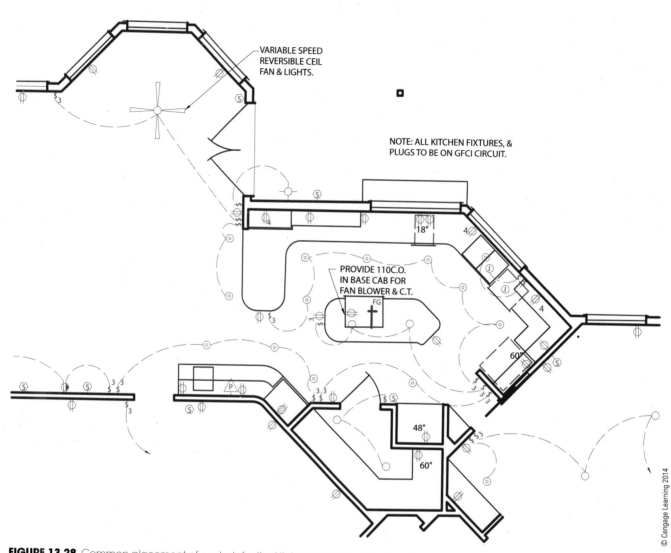

VARIABLE SPEED
REVERSIBLE CEIL
FAN & LIGHTS.

NOTE: ALL KITCHEN FIXTURES, &
PLUGS TO BE ON GFCI CIRCUIT.

PROVIDE 110C.O.
IN BASE CAB FOR
FAN BLOWER & C.T.

18"

60"

48"

60"

© Cengage Learning 2014

FIGURE 13.28 Common placement of symbols for the kitchen area. Careful planning is required to light each work area of the kitchen. Consideration must also be given to traffic flow in the kitchen and from the kitchen to related rooms.

Preparing the Drawing Base

The electrical information for a simple project may be placed on the floor plan with all the other symbols, information, and dimensions, as shown in Figure 13.29. On a custom home or complicated set of drawings, the electrical plan is drawn as a separate plan. In this case, the layers containing the base floor plan information—including the *WALLS, DOOR, GLAZ, CASE, STRS, CHIM, PATT, APPL,* and *PLMB*—should be displayed and used as a base for the electrical plan. Before placing symbols on the electrical drawings, create layers to separate the electrical information from the information on the floor plan. Layers for the electrical information should start with a prefix of *ELEC*. Name layers containing electrical information with a modifier listed in Appendix E on the website. As with any other drawing, create layers as needed to ensure that only layers that will be used are added to the drawing.

Creating a Separate Electrical Plan

Step 1. Freeze all information directly related to the floor plan. Your base drawing should display the walls, doors, windows, stairs, cabinets, and the fireplace. Basic room titles are optional but if displayed do not include room sizes. A base drawing for the residence that is in Chapter 12 is shown in Figure 13.30. Use the following steps as a guide. The order is not as important as proceeding in an orderly manner. Some technicians prefer to insert all lights and then all receptacles. If you prefer a different order or going room by room, that works too. The goal is to provide for all of the needs of the family. Use the checklist from Appendix D on the website when your drawing is complete to evaluate your success at meeting the goal.

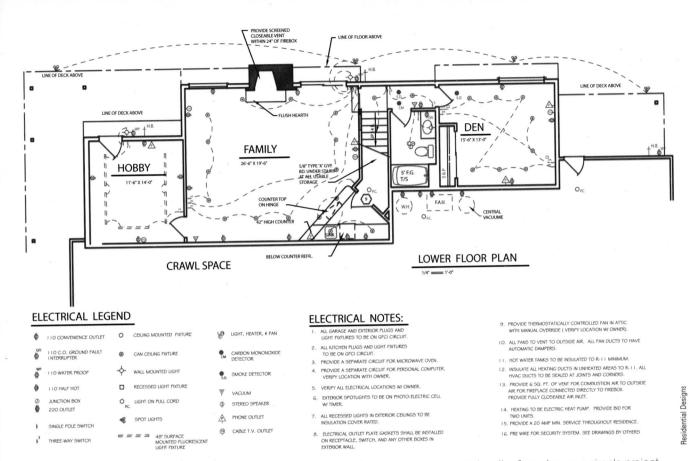

FIGURE 13.29 Electrical information can be combined with other information and displayed on the floor plan on a simple project. This is the lower level of the home in Chapter 13. Figure 13.36 shows the completed upper floor electrical plan for the same home.

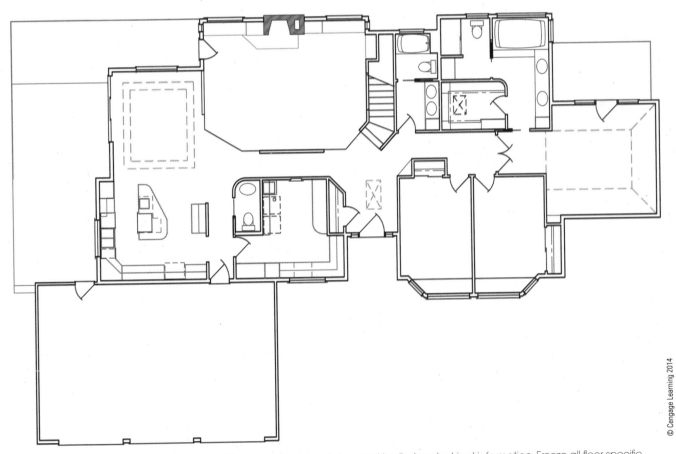

FIGURE 13.30 Use the floor plan as a base if a separate plan is to be used to display electrical information. Freeze all floor-specific information and display the walls, windows, doors, cabinets, appliances, plumbing, stairs, and fireplace. Room names are optional based on company policy.

Placing Lighting Fixtures

Place the items described in the following steps on the *ELEC SYMB* layer.

Step 2. Place a light fixture on the interior side of the door.

Step 3. Place a light fixture on the exterior side of each exterior door, including the garage door. Provide lights as necessary to ensure a well-lit walkway from the driveway to the front door.

Step 4. Place a light fixture in the entry. Proceed from the entry through each hallway and place fixtures as needed for general lighting needs.

Step 5. Start at the front door and mentally walk through the residence. Place a light fixture in each room to meet the general, specific, and decorative needs in keeping with the budget of the homeowner. Lights placed in the centers of rooms can be easily placed using the OBJECT TRACKING feature of AutoCAD. Their locations can also be determined by eye, since the electrician will have the final say on their location. You may find it easier to keep coming back to the front door and inserting blocks to represent each type of fixture. Using this method, you can place all ceiling-mounted fixtures, all wall fixtures, and all fluorescent fixtures and then all "can" fixtures until all lighting needs have been met.

Placing Outlets

Step 6. Start at the front door and place receptacles in the entry.

Step 7. Place necessary receptacles in each hallway.

Step 8. Place receptacles in all habitable rooms to meet the 2, 6, 12 rule.

Step 9. Place receptacles for all non-habitable rooms based on usage and the location of specific appliances.

Step 10. Place necessary half-hot receptacles.

Step 11. Place all receptacles for the kitchen based on the location of appliances and usage.

Step 12. Place GFCI receptacles in each bathroom based on usage and code restrictions.

Step 13. Place GFCI outlets in the garage and waterproof receptacles to provide for all exterior living areas.

Step 14. Place 240-volt receptacles for the furnace, water heater, spa, clothes dryer, oven, range, and specialty equipment in the garage or utility room.

Step 15. Place specialty waterproof GFCI receptacles for landscaping, pools, and spas.

Placing Switches

Step 16. Start at the front door and mentally walk through the home placing all single-pole switches.

Step 17. Place all required 3- and 4-way switches.

Step 18. Place the dashed control lines from each switch to the fixture or receptacle to be controlled on the *ELEC POWR* layer.

Place the items described in the following steps on the *ELEC ANNO* layer.

Step 19. Provide an electrical legend to identify all symbols on the drawing. Use the legend on the website and modify it to match your project.

Step 20. Place all notes required to explain any special construction for electrical needs. Place a drawing title and scale below the drawings and complete text in the title block to describe the drawing contents.

Figure 13.31 shows an electrical plan including the placement of lights, receptacles, and switches.

Placing Electrical Specialty Equipment and Fixtures

Place specialty equipment on the electrical drawings once all lighting fixtures, receptacles, and switches are represented. This includes the placement of smoke detectors, telephones, television jacks for cable or satellite lines, speakers for surround-sound systems and intercoms, inlets for built-in vacuum systems, security systems, and home automation. Add symbols to represent these materials to the *ELEC SYMB* layer.

Placing Smoke Alarms

Methods of representing smoke alarms are shown in Figure 13.25. Smoke alarms are generally shown on the electrical plan along with the symbols for other electrical equipment because of the need to be connected to the primary power supply. Back-up power must also be supplied by battery. Key location requirements for smoke alarms include:

- At the start of every hall that serves a bedroom.
- In each sleeping room near the entry door.
- On every floor, including the basement for multilevel homes.
- Over the stair leading to the upper level.

Review Chapter 5 or the local codes for additional requirements that affect placement of smoke alarms. They are generally shown on electrical plans along with the symbols for other electrical equipment. Indicate the type

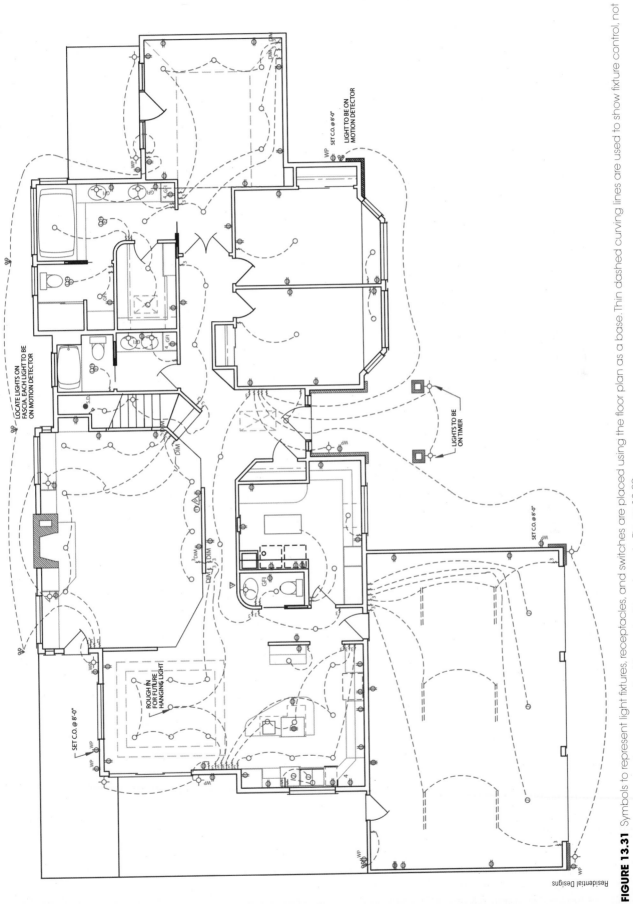

LOCATE LIGHTS ON
FASCIA. EACH LIGHT TO BE
ON MOTION DETECTOR

SET C.O. @ 8'-0"

LIGHT TO BE ON
MOTION DETECTOR

LIGHTS TO BE
ON TIMER

SET C.O. @ 8'-0"

ROUGH IN
FOR FUTURE
HANGING LIGHT

SET C.O. @ 8'-0"

FIGURE 13.31 Symbols to represent light fixtures, receptacles, and switches are placed using the floor plan as a base. Thin dashed curving lines are used to show fixture control, not circuit layout. Notes to specify specific needs of the project are shown in Figure 13.29.

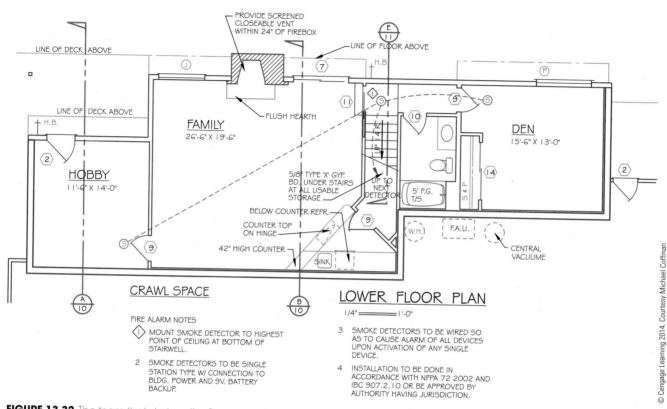

FIGURE 13.32 The team that designs the fire suppression system may plan the location of the smoke detectors. The layout for the lower floor's smoke detectors was completed by the consultants who designed the fire suppression system shown in Chapter 14.

of smoke alarm in the electrical general notes. Occasionally the team that designs the fire suppression system also plans the location of the smoke detectors. Figure 13.32 shows an example of the smoke detector layout for the lower floor. Figure 13.36 also shows the placement of the smoke alarms.

Placing Carbon Monoxide Alarms

Carbon monoxide alarms are required for all new home construction that have fuel-fired appliances. They are also to be installed in homes with attached garages. Place the alarms outside of each sleeping area in the immediate vicinity of the bedrooms. Represent the carbon monoxide alarm on the electrical plan with a symbol similar to a smoke detector using the letters CM beside the symbol. See Figure 13.25.

Representing Telephones

Even in an age of wireless communication, portable and cell phones, the location of telephone jacks should be given some consideration. There is usually a phone jack in the kitchen, each bedroom, laundry room, family room, and office. There should also be one near the entertainment center or by computer workstations unless a wireless system provides service to the TV or computer. Telephone jacks should be rough-wired for future installation in children's bedrooms. Represent telephone jacks using the

symbol from Figure 13.25 and place them near seating and work areas. Place a jack near the bed location in each bedroom and on each side of where the bed will likely be in the master bedroom.

Television, Stereo, and Intercom Systems

Include the wiring for television, stereo sound systems, and home intercoms into the project design so electrical needs for these items can be pre-wired before the walls are covered with sheetrock. Symbols for each system can be found in Figure 13.25. Using an antenna, cable, or satellite will determine the necessary television wiring for installation. Although the service provider generally determines the location and runs the required cables, planning the placement for service jacks will aid the owner. Provide TV jacks in high-usage rooms such as the living, family, and recreation rooms, as well as the kitchen, laundry, master bedroom, and master bathroom. Children's rooms are also typically pre-wired for future access.

Stereo installations can be wired separately throughout the home or in association with the cable television. A central intercom system similar to that in Figure 13.33 contains a radio, CD player, and MP3 player. In addition to delivering sound, most systems can also be used for two-way communication and room monitoring or serve as speakers for door chimes or driveway gate monitors. If installing an intercom, represent a master station and each

Courtesy Broan-NuTone Image Library Administrator

FIGURE 13.33 A central intercom system can deliver music from a radio, CD, or MP3 player as well as providing controls for two-way communication, room monitoring, door chime amplification, and gate monitors.

slave speaker on the electrical drawings. Locate the intercom master in a central location such as a kitchen desk area or in the family room near a major traffic pattern. Slave speakers are usually located near a doorway for each room, including the garage and major outside living areas.

For a custom home, the television is most likely wired for the addition of a surround-sound system. If representing this system on the electrical drawings, the designer should work closely with a media consultant to help plan the locations of sound equipment. Figure 13.34 shows four common layouts for home theaters with surround sound. Individual speakers for the surround-sound system must be distinguished from intercom speakers. The height above the floor must be given for each wall-mounted speaker, and ceiling-mounted speakers may need dimensions to mark their locations. In addition to planning the speaker locations, pay attention to the number and location of receptacles for the equipment in an entertainment center. If specifications on the floor and electrical plans must be supplemented in details and interior elevations, put a note on the electrical plan to alert the electrician to additional sources of information. Figure 13.35 shows the electrical plan for a simple entertainment center above a gas fireplace.

Built-in Vacuum System

A built-in vacuum system uses a central power unit with individual inlet valves located throughout the home. The central unit is usually located in a garage, basement, or utility room. Wall inlet valves are installed in various locations throughout the home and connected to the power unit through tubing that runs through the wall and floor framing. Plugging a portable hose into a wall inlet activates the system. The dirt, dust, animal dander, and allergens are

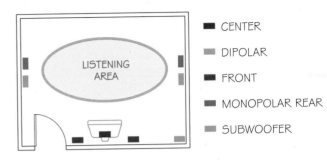

■ CENTER
■ DIPOLAR
■ FRONT
■ MONOPOLAR REAR
■ SUBWOOFER

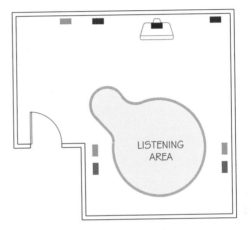

LARGE LISTENING AREA

L-SHAPED ROOM

ELONGATED ROOM

SMALL LISTENING AREA

FIGURE 13.34 Four common layouts for home theater surround-sound systems.

© Cengage Learning 2014

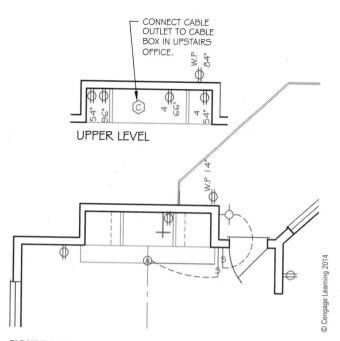

FIGURE 13.35 The electrical plan for a simple entertainment center that will be above a gas fireplace. The number of receptacles and their heights above the floor must be specified to receive adequate service for all equipment.

then carried out of the room and into the main power unit, where all of the debris is deposited into the canister. The central unit, introduced in Figure 10.49, should be shown on both the floor and electrical plans. Individual inlet valves are shown only on the electrical plan, as seen in Figure 13.26.

As a general guideline, install one inlet valve for every 600 sq ft of a home. Household cleaning needs, the number of stories, and convenience will also have an impact on the number of necessary inlets. Strategically place inlet valves to reach all areas of the home. Unless it's necessary to reach the tops of drapes or ledges, two hose lengths is the maximum distance that should separate two inlet valves. Assume a hose length of 25' (7500 mm). Locate the first inlet valve at a point the farthest distance from the power unit. From this location, additional valve locations can be selected that allow a hose to reach all rooms. Remember, walls and furniture can shorten the distance serviced by a valve in some areas, so be sure to locate inlets with furniture and walls in mind. Figure 13.36 shows the complete electrical drawings for the home drawn in Chapter 12. Figure 13.37 shows the complete plan for the lower level. Use the checklist from Appendix D to evaluate your work.

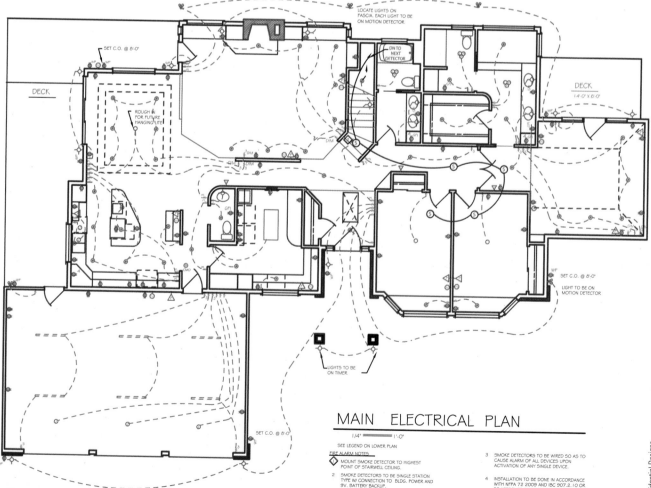

MAIN ELECTRICAL PLAN

1/4" = 1'-0"

SEE LEGEND ON LOWER PLAN

FIRE ALARM NOTES

1. MOUNT SMOKE DETECTOR TO HIGHEST POINT OF STAIRWELL CEILING.

2. SMOKE DETECTORS TO BE SINGLE STATION TYPE W/ CONNECTION TO BLDG. POWER AND 9V. BATTERY BACKUP.

3. SMOKE DETECTORS TO BE WIRED SO AS TO CAUSE ALARM OF ALL DEVICES UPON ACTIVATION OF ANY SINGLE DEVICE.

4. INSTALLATION TO BE DONE IN ACCORDANCE WITH NFPA 72 2009 AND IBC 907.2.10 OR BE APPROVED BY AUTHORITY HAVING JURISDICTION.

FIGURE 13.36 The completed electrical plan containing all fixtures, receptacles, switches, and specialty equipment.

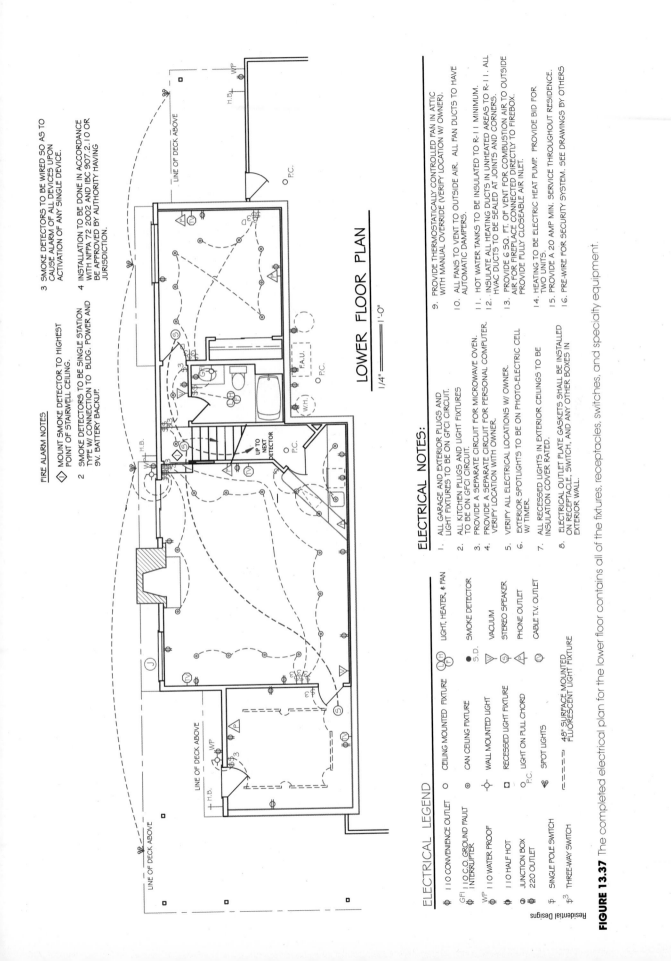

FIGURE 13.37 The completed electrical plan for the lower floor contains all of the fixtures, receptacles, switches, and specialty equipment.

Security Systems

Home security for a custom home involves more than providing exterior security lighting. Provisions are often made for internal video monitoring, perimeter surveillance, moisture detection, burglary, fire, carbon monoxide, and medical alert monitoring. Each type of system can be an internal system or one connected to a monitoring station. Monitoring can be provided by a private security or health care provider or linked directly to a public police or fire department. The home may even include a separate room to provide security from the forces of nature or from intruders. To meet any of these security needs, design the system in cooperation with a security expert for the best possible installation needed by the owner. When providing a secure room, consult with a structural engineer to help plan additional reinforcing and structural features.

Home Wiring and Automation

Some custom homes are built with automation systems to control and operate mechanical devices that regulate the heating, air conditioning, landscape sprinkler systems, lighting, and security systems. It's possible to link these systems to a personal computer to allow the user to set and monitor a variety of electrical circuits throughout the home. To make efficient use of home computers, consider structured wiring systems for Internet access during the planning of the electrical system. Structured wiring systems allow high-speed voice, data lines, and video cables wired to a central service location. These wires and cables optimize the speed and quality of various communication signals coming in and out of the residence by dedicating a line from each electrical outlet, telephone jack, or computer port back to the central service location. The central service location allows the wires to be connected as needed for a network configuration or for dedicated wiring from the outside.

High-quality structured wiring systems use network connectors and parallel circuits to maintain a strong electrical signal. A parallel circuit is an electrical circuit that contains two or more paths for the electricity or signal to flow from a common source. Structured wiring systems allow the use of a fax, multiline telephone, and computer at the same time. Additional applications include a digital satellite system (DSS), digital broadcast system (DBS), stereo audio, and closed-circuit security systems.

The product supplier or the design team may do the design and drawing of the home automation system.

FIGURE 13.38 The automation center for a home theater. Cables from the home computer are routed through the hub and then to each piece of equipment to be controlled.

© Cengage Learning 2014

Electrical symbols and specific notes are placed on the floor and electrical plans. The automation center for a home theater is shown in Figure 13.38 Cables from the home computer are routed through the hub and then to each fixture to be controlled.

> ### NOTE:
> Keep in mind that electrical fixtures and controls have changed and will continue to change rapidly. Appliances and fixtures that just a few years ago required wiring, are now controlled by wireless systems. Although the signal may be sent through a wireless interface, an electrical supply is still required to the appliance.

Additional Resources

Use the following websites as resources to help keep you current with changes in electrical plan-related materials.

Address	Company or Organization
www.acousticalsolutions.com	Acoustical Solutions, Inc.
www.alternative-heating-info.com	Alternative Heating
www.avenvironments.com	A/V Environments
www.beamvac.com	Beam Central Vacuum Systems
www.broan.com	Broan® (Bath Fans)
www.cedia.net	Custom Electronic Design & Installation Association®
www.hometheather.com	Home Theater Magazine
www.infinitepower.org	Infinite Power of Texas (introduction to Photovoltaic Systems)
www.leviton.com	Leviton® (lighting controls)
www.lucent.com	Alcatel-Lucent® (wiring systems)
www.nutone.com	NuTone, Inc.® (central cleaning systems, intercoms)
www.onqtech.com	Legrand (On-Q Home Wiring Systems)
www.pv-systems.org	PV Systems (photovoltaic systems)
www.solarcity.com	SolarCity® (photovoltaic systems)
www.thesolarguide.com	The Solar Guide
www.squared.com	Schneider Electric® (SquareD electrical systems)
www.windpoweringamerica.gov	Wind Powering America Program, U.S. Department of Energy
www.seco.cpa.state.tx.us	State Energy Conservation Office
www.windandsolar.com	Wind Solar Hydro (wind and solar information)

Electrical Plans Test

Follow these instructions to access and complete an electronic copy of the Chapter 13 Electrical Plans Test.

1. Go to cengagebrain.com
2. Enter the email address and password you used to register for the site (see Preface for full instructions).
3. Select the website from the **My Course & Materials** area of your home page. Select the chapter you want from the pull-down menu at the top of the page. Choose the resources for that chapter from the menu on the left.
4. Type your name, the chapter number, and the date at the top of the sheet.
5. Answer the following questions with short, complete statements using a word processor.

NOTE:

The answers to some questions may not be contained in this chapter and will require you to do additional research using the Internet. Use your favorite search engine to search for specific professional companies, or general categories of information.

Questions

13.1. What is the maximum allowable distance between duplex convenience outlets in a living room?

13.2. What is the maximum allowable distance a duplex convenience outlet can be installed from a corner in a kitchen?

13.3. Describe at least four energy-efficient considerations related to electrical design.

13.4. Draw the proper floor plan symbol for:
a. 120 duplex convenience outlet
b. 240-volt outlet
c. Circuit breaker panel
d. Speakers for surround-sound system
e. Ceiling-mounted light fixture
f. Wall-mounted light fixture
g. Three-way switch
h. Simplified fluorescent light fixture
i. Bathroom fan, heat, and light fixture

13.5. Explain where to place a switch in a bedroom as it relates to the door.

13.6. What is a GFCI duplex convenience outlet?

13.7. How many amps are typically provided for a residential distribution box?

13.8. Define a junction box as it relates to electrical wiring.

13.9. What voltages are normally delivered to a residence?

13.10. What level of lighting should be provided to an area intended for reading?

13.11. What size circuit breaker should be provided for an electric range with six burners?

13.12. List four code requirements for the spacing of receptacles in a kitchen.

13.13. What size circuit breaker should be provided for a gas dryer?

13.14. Define structured wiring systems.

13.15. List four locations that require smoke detectors.

13.16. After completing your electrical plan, research with a representative of the local utility company the electrical demands and the cost of electricity for the home you designed in Chapter 12.

13.17. Visit the website of your local utility company and research energy programs available in your area. Incorporate as many of the energy saving tips that are suitable for your project. Write a report on incentives and programs available to new homebuilders.

13.18. Use the Internet to research innovative developments and trends in home electronics. Show the necessary electrical fixtures on your plan for equipment that is suitable for your project.

13.19. After making an appointment, contact a local supplier and installer of photovoltaic systems to research the cost of installing a photovoltaic system for the home you started in Chapter 12. In addition to the start-up cost, research the savings that could be expected in a year if a system is installed versus the cost of supplying power through the local utility company.

13.20. After making an appointment, contact a local supplier and installer of wind powered turbines to research the cost of installing a wind powered system for the home you started in Chapter 12. In addition to the start-up cost, research the savings that could be expected in a year if a system is installed versus the cost of supplying power through the local utility company.

Drawing Problems

13.1 Convert each symbol in the website\Drawing Blocks\FLOOR BLOCKS\ELECTRICAL\ ELEC SYMB to a drawing block. Assign all drawing objects to appropriate layers. Provide appropriate insertion points and names to easily identify each block.

13.2 Draw a floor plan representation of the following items assuming plotting at a scale of 1/4" = 1'-0".
   a. A room with two means of access with appropriate switches controlling three ceiling-mounted lighting fixtures.
   b. A room with three means of access with appropriate switches to control one ceiling-mounted lighting fixture.
   c. A room with three single-pole switches that control three different light fixtures.
   d. A single-pole switch that controls two half-hot convenience outlets.

13.3 Draw a small bathroom layout with a tub/shower, water closet, and vanity with two lavatories. Provide lighting fixtures, receptacles, and switches to control fixtures as needed.

13.4 Draw a U-shaped kitchen with a double sink, dishwasher, gas range, warming drawer, built-in espresso machine, double oven with a separate microwave oven, and a wall-mounted television connected to a satellite receiver. Provide the necessary notes and symbols to make the kitchen legal and functional.

13.5 Use the drawing of the house that you started in Chapter 12 to do one of the following as directed by your instructor: Insert the electrical notes and symbols from the Website\DRAWING BLOCKS\FLOOR BLOCKS\ELECT and edit them to meet the needs of your project. Use a legend to explain each symbol used on the electrical portion of your drawing.
   a. Add the needed information to meet local codes and the demands of the general public on the floor plan that was started in Chapter 12.
   b. Use the floor plan started in Chapter 12 as a base and draw an electrical plan to meet the local codes and the demands of the general public. Freeze all unnecessary floor information and create an electrical plan that includes:
   • all electrical fixtures, plugs, and switches.
   • a distribution box, doorbell and chime, a maximum of five phone jacks, four TV jacks, and three waterproof receptacles.
   • a wall-mounted light by each exterior door.
   c. Use the floor plan started in Chapter 12 as a base and draw an electrical plan to meet local code requirements and the demands of a specific family. Freeze all unnecessary floor information and create an electrical plan that includes:
   • the location of all electrical fixtures, plugs, and switches to meet code and general, specific, and decorative lighting needs.
   • a meter, distribution box, doorbell and chime, a minimum of five phone jacks, four TV jacks, and three waterproof receptacles. Provide a wall-mounted light by each exterior door, an intercom system with slave units in each room, surround sound in the family room, and a built-in vacuum system.

Project Planning

After reviewing the drawing criteria for this project on the student website, either verbally or in a written memo, demonstrate to your client (your instructor) your understanding of the project, and list the amount of time you expect the drawing to take and any resources you require to complete it. Respond verbally to any questions your client might have of you, and let them know when the project will be complete. Ask for clarification of any questions you have regarding the drawing criteria. If you plan to present your project preview verbally, be prepared with your questions written down so that you can ask relevant questions in a professional manner and be prepared to take notes regarding comments from the client.

Once you have the criteria and the direction needed to begin the project, make a plan to get it done. Using the guidelines presented in this chapter, include the minimum contents as well as an estimate of the time you require to complete each aspect of the drawing:

Research

Major steps to complete the drawing

Applicable codes that will apply to this drawing

Applicable local requirements that apply to the drawing

Adjusting drawing templates to set plotting standards, text heights, dimensions, and linetypes

Completing all required annotation and dimensioning

Evaluation based on the minimum standards for electrical plans located on the website

Track the amount of time

Compare the estimated completion time for each aspect of the project with the actual required time.

Use the appropriate checklist from Appendix D of the student website prior to submitting your drawing to your instructor.

Chapter 14
Plumbing Systems

The plumbing system involves the delivery of fresh water and the control and discharge of all liquids, solids, and gases from the residence. The design team does not complete the plumbing drawings for residential drawings. For most municipalities, even the plumbing contractor may not be required to complete drawings. Instead of drawings, the application for a plumbing permit requires a listing of the number of fixtures being installed. Fees charged for the permit are based on the size and complexity of the plumbing work to be done. Some municipalities base the plumbing fees on the required number of fixtures or the number of feet of water and sewer lines or the number of rain drains. Some municipalities require a one-line diagram showing pipe sizes for fresh- and wastewater lines.

The architectural team places plumbing-related information on the site plan, floor plan, and occasionally on the foundation plan. But the plumbing contractor completes plans that show pipe sizes and locations. The site plan shows the locations of the water meter, water and gas supply lines, and sewer lines that connect the home to the sewer lateral. If there is a private sewer disposal system, the site plan must also include the septic tank and drain field. Drains connected to the roof downspouts and foundation drain lines are shown on the foundation plan for most custom homes.

Most plumbing information is placed on the floor plan, which shows symbols that represent fixtures such as sinks, toilets, bidets, tubs, and the water heater.

Drawings showing how the system works are not drawn by the architectural team. This fact, however, does not free the CAD technician from having to understand the drawings that the plumbing and fire safety contractors create. Figure 14.1 shows a simple one-line schematic drawing that a plumber might draw to explain a layout. You must also understand how each system works. This requires an understanding of delivery methods, fresh- and wastewater systems, fire suppression systems, and other systems for eliminating waste gas. Most importantly, you need to understand how work by the plumber affects other structural portions of the home that you are responsible for drawing.

Key Terms

Branch lines	Fitting	Lateral	Potable
Drain	Gray water	Main	Riser
Effluent	Hose bibb	Manifold	Sanitary sewer

Soil line   Storm sewer   Vent stack   Water closet

Stack line   Valve

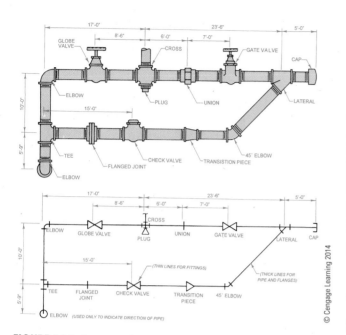

FIGURE 14.1 A comparison of an orthographic drawing and a one-line schematic drawing. For a residence, someone working for the plumbing contractor will provide any needed one-line diagrams to obtain a building permit.

DELIVERY AND REMOVAL MATERIALS

The pipe material and its size affects the design of the plumbing system and can affect the framing system. The pipes used in the plumbing system may be made of plastic, copper, galvanized steel, or cast iron, depending on the usage. The usage and material affects the pipe size to be used. The type of pipe to be used for specific parts of the plumbing system is often specified when the plans for a custom home are prepared. This can be done by placing general plumbing notes on the floor plan, on a separate page with specifications, or in a separate document containing all written specifications for the project (see Chapter 33).

Common Materials

The common types of pipes referred to by the IRC include the main, branch, and risers. The **main** is the water supply line that extends from the water meter into the home to deliver potable (drinkable) water. **Branch lines** are feeder lines that branch off the main line to supply fixture groups in the home. A **riser** is a water supply pipe that extends vertically one or more stories to carry water to fixtures. The IRC defines a fixture as a unit for containing and discharging water. Common fixtures found in a residence include sinks, lavatories, showers, tubs, toilets (**water closets**),

FIGURE 14.2 Copper lines have been used for years in residential plumbing systems to deliver fresh water.

bidets, spas, and **hose bibbs**. The IRC allows the use of copper, plastic, steel, and cast-iron pipes to service fixtures.

Copper Piping

Copper lines similar to those in Figure 14.2 have been a popular choice for delivering hot and cold-water in homes for more than 50 years. Copper pipes provide a durable material to distribute water and are quickly assembled by the use of soldered joints and **fittings**. Because of the expense and the use of other materials, in many areas copper is used for only the main supply line and for a **manifold** (see Figure 14.3). Smaller manifolds may also be provided at the ends of branch lines to feed each fixture group. Copper pipes, once a popular choice for branch and riser lines, have been replaced in many areas of the country by flexible or rigid plastic pipes inside the structure.

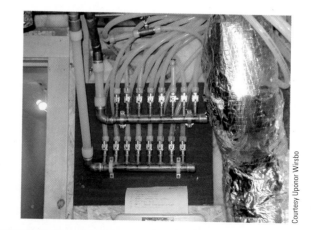

FIGURE 14.3 A manifold is a distribution center between the main, branch, and riser lines. Smaller manifolds are used at the end of feeder lines to distribute water to each fixture.

© Cengage Learning 2014. Courtesy Megan Jefferis

FIGURE 14.4 Plastic polyethylene tubing is used to deliver fresh water throughout the interior of the home that is remodeled in Chapter 33.

Plastic Pipes

Plastic pipes have glued joints and fittings and are used for fresh water, wastewater, and vent pipes. Plastic piping includes the use of cross-linked polyethylene (PEX), polyvinyl chloride (PVC), post-chlorinated polyvinyl chloride (CPVC), polybutylene (PB), and acrylonitrile-butadiene-styrene (ABS).

Most new homes use plastic polyethylene tubing, similar to the piping shown in Figure 14.4, to deliver fresh water throughout the interior of the home. Plastic tubing, known as PEX or Wirsbo (also a specific brand name), has been used in homes for more than 30 years. PEX is a flexible, expandable plastic that can easily be run through framing. Rather than having glued joints, PEX joints are heated and expanded to fit over fittings. Once the tubing cools, a watertight seal is formed, providing a system that withstands high pressure and freezing. If the tube freezes, it returns to its original size when it thaws.

PVC pipe is used throughout residential construction for below- and above-ground uses. Common uses for PVC include water mains, fresh- and wastewater lines, drain and waste-vent lines, and irrigation lines. The components of a PVC piping system are manufactured in a

variety of colors to help identify the application. A common color scheme (although not universal) is:

- White: Drain, waste, and vent, along with some low-pressure applications.
- White, blue, and dark gray: cold-water piping.
- Green: sewer service.
- Dark gray: high-pressure applications.

This color scheme has an exception in that much of the white PVC pipe is dual-rated for DWV (drain/waste/vent) and pressure applications.

CPVC is a corrosion-resistant plastic piping. Potable water applications include cold-water services from wells or water mains up to the building as well as hot- and cold-water distribution piping within buildings. Because it is corrosion-resistant, it maintains water purity even under severe conditions.

Polybutylene or PB piping is a form of plastic resin for use in the manufacture of water-supply piping. It is popular because of the low material cost and ease of installation. PB piping may fail if oxidants such as chlorine in the water supply react with the piping, causing it to become brittle. As the system becomes weak, it may fail, causing damage to the structure and personal property. Although the IRC still approves PB piping, its popularity has decreased.

ABS pipes and fittings are for use throughout the waste and vent systems for in- or above-ground applications. They may be used outdoors if the pipe contains pigments to shield it against ultraviolet radiation, or jurisdictions may require the pipes to be painted with water-base latex paint for outdoor use. ABS is preferable to cast iron, which corrodes, causing pipes to block. ABS pipes do not corrode.

Steel Pipe

Flexible steel pipe with a coat of varnish for protection delivers natural gas or propane to a fixture such as a water heater, furnace, or fireplace. Steel pipe is joined by threaded joints and fittings or grooved joints.

Cast-Iron Pipe

Although often replaced by ABS, contractors in some areas still use cast-iron pipe to carry solid and liquid waste from the structure to the local sewer system. Cast-iron pipe may also be used for the piping in the drain system throughout the structure to help reduce the noise of water flow. It is more expensive than plastic pipe, but quiet piping may be worth the price for many clients.

Pipe Sizes

In addition to pipe material, the pipe size is also important. The IRC requires a minimum water main diameter of 3/4" (20 mm), but diameters of 1" or 1 1/2" (25 or 38 mm) are

TABLE 14.1 Minimum Pipe Sizes

FIXTURE	WATER SUPPLY SIZE	MINIMUM TRAP AND DRAIN SIZE	MINIMUM VENT SIZE
Bidet	3/8"	1 1/2"	1 1/4"
Clothes Washer	1/2"	1 1/2"	1 1/4"
Dishwasher	3/8"	1 1/2"	1 1/4"
Kitchen Sink	1/2"	1 1/2"	1 1/4"
Laundry Sink	1/2"	1 1/2"	1 1/4"
Lavatory	3/8"	1 1/4"	1 1/4"
Shower	1/2"	2"	1 1/4"
Tub	1/2"	1 1/2"	1 1/4"
Water Closet	3/8"	3"	2"
Water Heater	3/4"	–	4"

© Cengage Learning 2014

more common. The plumber determines the size of residential branches and risers based on:

- IRC requirements for the total load on the pipe.
- The psi available to the home.
- The amount of water needed at the fixture.
- The height of the riser.
- The length of the pipe.
- The flow pressure needed at the farthest point from the source.

The IRC requires a minimum diameter of 3/8" (10 mm) for individual feeder lines from branch lines. See Table 14.1 for other common sizes. The manufacturers of spas and other fixtures often dictate the use of larger supply lines. When a larger size is required, the size of the supply line should be specified in the general notes on the floor plan. Supply lines are not allowed to be longer than 60' (18 000 mm). Although the plumber must know this to install the system, the design team must consider these guidelines in specifying fixtures on the floor plan. General notes on the floor plan also list minimum sizes.

FRESH-WATER SYSTEMS

The fresh-water supply system consists of a network of pipes similar to that seen in Figure 14.5, which deliver fresh water using pressure throughout the residence. The IRC uses the term *potable* to refer to water free of impurities and suitable for drinking. The term main describes the primary water delivery line to the residence. Water is brought from a public supply main or from a private well

through a building main. If using public water, the main contains a utility company *valve*, a meter, and a building main valve. The main also routes the water to the water heater or to branch lines. In many locations, the main connects water to a filtering system to filter, soften, and purify water before it is dispersed throughout the house.

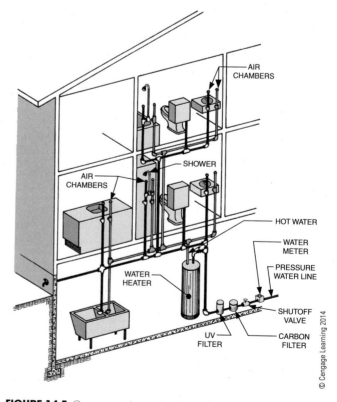

FIGURE 14.5 Common elements of the fresh-water delivery system include the main, branch, and feeder lines and the air chambers. Air chambers are pipe extensions placed by each fixture that are used to eliminate noises caused by pipe vibration when taps are opened and closed.

© Cengage Learning 2014

FIGURE 14.6 When the home is on a private water system or water pressure is low, the main water line often leads to a storage tank. For this home, water is then sent to a filtering system.

FIGURE 14.7 Plastic lines are used throughout the home to deliver fresh water. Blue indicates cold-water lines and red the hot-water lines.

The IRC requires a minimum 40 psi (276 kPa) and a maximum of 80 psi (551 kPa) for water entering the home. Water pressure exceeding 80 psi requires the installation of an approved pressure-reducing valve on the main or riser at the connection to the water-service pipe. For homes with poor water pressure or those on private wells, pressurized storage tanks are available to store water in sufficient supply for appliances and fixtures. Figure 14.6 shows the use of a storage tank and filters. Hose bibbs, exterior sprinkler systems, a fire-suppression system, and other fixtures that do not require purification are connected to the water main before the water supply line enters the filtering system. After filtering, water is pushed by pressure into the cold-water branch lines and the hot-water main. The cold-water line branches to each fixture. The hot-water line passes through the water heater and then on to fixtures that require hot water. Because water in the hot and cold lines is under pressure, pipes can run in any direction. Hot-water branch lines are normally located 6" (150 mm) from and parallel to cold-water lines. Hot-water lines are placed on the left side of cold-water lines and may even be color-coded, like the lines in Figure 14.7. As the line reaches the termination point for a fixture, a shutoff valve must be provided.

Hot-Water Systems

Common methods to provide heated water to a system include hot-water storage, tanks, tankless heating systems, and continuous loop systems.

Hot-Water Tanks

Hot-water storage systems have been the traditional method to heat water since people got tired of using

buckets to boil water over an open fire. A water heater is a storage tank that heats water and keeps it warm. These systems are typically powered by gas or electricity, with gas units providing a much cheaper fuel source. Water heaters are available in a variety of sizes, including 30-, 40-, 50-, 65-, and 80-gallon (115-, 150-, 190-, 250-, and 300-liter) tanks. Special applications may require ordering larger-capacity tanks. The size should be selected based on the size of the family and the appliance load to be served (showers, dishwashers, and washing machines). Common guidelines to size a water heater include:

Number of Baths	Number of Bedrooms	WATER HEATER SIZE (GALLONS)*	
		Gas	Electric
1 to 1	2	30	30
	3	30	40
2 to 2 1/2	2	30	40
	3	40	50
	4	40	50
	5	50	66
3 to 3 1/2	3	40	50
	4	50	66
	5	50	66
	6	50	80

*Some spas are larger than a typical tub and require a higher-capacity water heater to provide an adequate supply of hot water.

The method of heating the water and the location of the tank affects what must be specified on the floor plan.

Common specifications on the floor plan in the form of general notes may include:

- Gas-fired water heaters should be placed on a platform so the flame source is at least 18" (450 mm) above floor level.

- A water heater in a living area must be placed over a 1 1/2" (38 mm) deep × 24-gauge overflow tray with a 3/4" (19 mm) diameter drain.

- Fuel-fired water heaters must not be installed in a room used as a storage closet. Other regulated areas within the living space include:

- A bedroom or bathroom containing a water heater that is not a direct-vent model. Such a water heater must be installed in a sealed enclosure so combustion air is not taken from the living area.

- When a water heater is in an attic or crawl space and the access is in the closet of a sleeping room or bathroom, the access must have a minimum opening size of 30 × 22" (750 × 550 mm).

- Attic passageways serving the water heater or other mechanical equipment must not exceed 20' (6000 mm) in length and must not be less than 24" (600 mm) wide.

Going Green

Energy-Efficient Methods of Heating Water

In addition to using natural gas or propane rather than electricity to fuel the water heater, three methods are available to increase the efficiency of the hot-water delivery system. These systems, which also offer LEED points, include tankless hot-water systems, circulating hot-water systems, and solar hot-water systems.

Tankless Hot-Water Systems

Tankless hot-water systems provide continuous hot water when the tap is on. Rather than storing hot water and keeping it hot until it is needed, tankless systems generate hot water on demand, and depending on the model, they can deliver between 200 and 500 gallons (760 and 1900 liters) of hot water per hour on demand. This feature results in savings of time, money, and space over a traditional water heater. An average tankless water heater is approximately 20 × 14 × 6" (500 × 350 × 150 mm). See Figure 14.8.

Tankless water heaters start to operate as soon as the hot-water tap at a fixture is opened. The heater detects the flow of water and a computer in the unit automatically ignites the burner. Water flows over a heat exchanger in the unit

FIGURE 14.8 A tankless water system provides continuous hot water once a tap is turned on.

© Jupiterimages/Comstock Images/Getty Images

(Continued)

and, within approximately 5 seconds, is heated to the preset temperature. The unit continues to provide hot water until the water tap is closed. With the tap closed, the heating unit automatically shuts down until it's needed again. It is extremely important that the design team size a tankless water-heater system to meet the needs of the family. If operating multiple fixtures simultaneously, the demand may exceed the ability of the heater to supply hot water at the desired temperature.

Circulating Hot-Water Systems

Hot-water recirculation is the process of constantly moving water through a continuous loop in a hot-water pipe. Loops form between the water heater and groups of appliances so there is no wait for the water to warm up. Circulating systems use a small motor located by the water heater to keep hot water moving through a loop formed between the water tank and each group fixture. The system loop conserves water by providing hot water as soon as the hot-water tap is turned on. Figure 14.9 shows the concept of a circulating system.

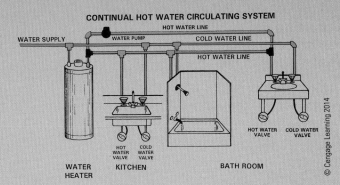

© Cengage Learning 2014

FIGURE 14.9 A continual hot-water circulating system keeps water moving between the hot-water supply and each fixture on the loop.

Heat Pump Water Heaters

In addition to heating and cooling a home (see Chapter 15), a heat pump can heat water in either a stand-alone water heating system or a combination water heating and space conditioning system. A heat pump water heater system uses electricity to move heat from one place to another. To heat water, a heat pump works like a refrigerator in reverse. A refrigerator pulls heat from inside its insulated box and releases it into the surrounding room. A heat pump water heater pulls heat from the surrounding air and moves it into a storage tank to heat water.

Heat pump water heaters require installation in locations that remain in the 40°–90°F (4.4°–32.2°C) range year-round and provide at least 1,000 cubic feet (28.3 cubic meters) of air space around the water heater. Cool exhaust air can be exhausted into the living area or outdoors. The ideal location for a heat pump water heater is in a space with excess heat, such as a furnace room. Heat pump water heaters do not operate efficiently in a cold space. They tend to cool the spaces they are in.

Heat pump systems that combine heating, cooling, and water heating are also available. These combination systems pull their heat into the building envelope from the outdoor air in the winter and from the indoor air in the summer. Because they remove heat from the air, any type of air-source heat pump system works more efficiently in a warm climate.

Solar Hot Water

A solar water-heating system uses the energy it captures from the sun to heat water. Solar energy is collected by water that passes through a panel system and into

(Continued)

a hot-water storage tank that is separate from the standard water heater. Once collected, heated water is dispersed to the domestic hot-water system or to a swimming pool. Solar panels may be located on a roof, a wall, or on a ground-level frame. Figure 14.10 shows a roof-mounted application of solar collectors. Solar systems vary in efficiency but generally preheat water before entering the water heater. The number of south-facing collectors needed to provide hot water to a structure depends on the size of the structure and the volume of water needed.

A conventional central heating pump forces water through a coiled pipe in the solar panel, where it is heated by the sun. The heated water then flows down and through a second coil in the hot-water cylinder. Hot water passing through this coil heats the water in the cylinder. A pump then returns the water to the solar panels. If the system is roof-mounted, solar panels are specified on the roof plan; the storage tank and any required pumps are specified on the floor and electrical plans.

FIGURE 14.10 Solar heating can be used in most areas of the country to either heat or preheat water for a residence.

© Cengage Learning 2014

- A solid floor must be provided to access the unit when placed in an attic, as well as a level service platform 30 × 30" (750 × 750 mm) wide on all sides of the unit that might require service.
- Strap water heaters to the walls of the structure.
- When a water heater is located in a garage, a concrete-filled steel pipe embedded in concrete must be placed in front of the unit to protect it from impact.

WASTEWATER AND VENTING SYSTEMS

The drainage system moves water and other waste from the plumbing system to the main sewer line. The main sewer line then *drains* into a public system or to a private waste system. The vent system prevents vacuum blocks in the drainage system to allow a continuous flow of air through the wastewater system to vent gases and odors out of the house. In addition to the drainage system, plan the venting system when drawing the floor plan.

Waste Discharge System

The waste discharge system takes water from the fixture drains and moves it to the disposal source. See Figure 14.11. Waste lines ranging in size from 1 1/2 to 4" (38 to 100 mm) remove gray water and sewage from the residence. *Soil lines* are empty until waste is flushed through the system. Because the waste system is a non-pressurized gravity-flow system, waste lines are larger than the water supply lines. Common sizes of waste lines are shown in Table 14.1. In addition to the size difference, drainage pipes must have a minimum slope of 1/4" per foot (6/25 mm).

Branch and Stack Lines

Two common types of soil lines include branches and stacks. Branches are the nearly horizontal lines that carry waste from each fixture to the stacks. The *stack lines* are the vertical drain lines that carry waste from the home to the sewer main. Stack lines range in size from 3 to 4" (75 to 100 mm) in diameter, increasing in size as the distance from the fixture increases. The portion of the soil stack above the highest branch intersection is a vent stack. Some vent stacks are separate and parallel to the soil stack. *Vent stacks* are dry pipes

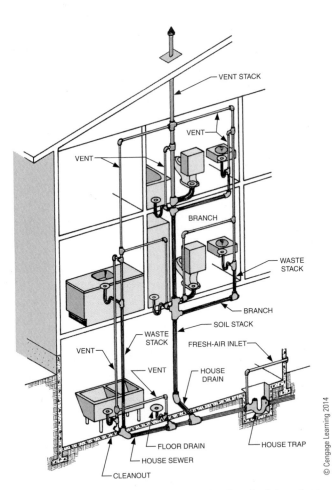

VENT STACK

VENT

VENT

VENT

BRANCH

WASTE
STACK

BRANCH

SOIL STACK

WASTE
STACK

FRESH-AIR INLET

VENT

VENT

HOUSE
DRAIN

HOUSE TRAP

FLOOR DRAIN

HOUSE SEWER

CLEANOUT

© Cengage Learning 2014

FIGURE 14.11 The flow of all wastewater begins at a fixture, then runs through a trap into a branch line, and finally into the main sewer line. Once the line extends past the exterior walls of the residence, a cleanout is provided in the main sewer line to allow access for cleaning. The main then extends to the municipal sewer lateral serving the construction site.

that extend through the roof a minimum of 6" (150 mm) or 6" (150 mm) above the anticipated snow accumulation point, whichever is greater, to provide ventilation for the discharge system. The vent stack is not to be located within 48" (1200 mm) beneath any door, openable window or other air intake opening of the building, or an adjacent building. The vent also must be 10" (3000 mm) horizontally from these air intake openings in the buildings unless the opening is 36" (900 mm) above the stack Vent stacks permit sewer gases to escape to outside air and equalize the air pressure in the system. Examples of each are shown in Figure 14.11.

The flow of all wastewater begins at a fixture. Each fixture contains a fixture trap to prevent the backflow of sewer gas from the branch lines. With the exception of toilet traps, which are built into the fixture, fixture traps are exposed for easy maintenance. A total-system house trap is provided in the main sewer line once the line extends past an exterior wall of the residence. In addition to the trap, there is a cleanout in the main sewer line and in each drain line for sinks.

Sewage Disposal

Once the main sewer line leaves the home it connects either to the public sewer system or to a private disposal system. Each type of system must be represented on the site plan. For a home on a public system, only the main waste line is represented. Homes with private disposal systems require the location of the septic tank and drain field, as well as the relation of each to a well or other bodies of water. See Section 2 for site plan information requirements.

Public Sewers

Each municipality provides sewer service to residences. Many cities also extend service to all but the most rural residents. Where available, **sanitary sewers** are located under the street or in an easement next to the construction site. Most cities have a separate **storm sewer** system to dispose of groundwater, rainwater, surface water, or other nonpolluting waste. Sewer line locations and depths are available at the public works department of the governing body. The municipality generally is responsible for placing the lateral that connects each building parcel to the public system. A **lateral** is an underground branch line that extends from the sewer line to the edge of the street or to the property line. The plumbing contractor is responsible for locating the existing lateral and connecting the house to the public system.

Private Sewage Systems

A private septic system consists of a storage tank and an absorption field. Solid and liquid waste enters the septic tank for storage and decomposition into sludge. Liquid material, or **effluent**, flows from the tank outlet and disperses into a drain field. These lines are sometimes referred to as leach lines.

When the solid waste decomposes, it also dissipates into the soil absorption field. Chemicals are added to the system periodically to aid in the decomposition of solid waste. Septic tanks must also have solids pumped from the tank so that the system does not become overloaded. The leach lines are PVC perforated pipes laid in a coarse gravel bed approximately 12" (300 mm) below the grade level. See Figure 14.12. Fields are arranged in a variety of shapes and patterns depending on the site contour and restrictions, such as buildings or tree locations.

During the design process, the characteristics of the soil must be verified by a percolation test suitable for a septic system. To size the drain field, a soils engineer determines the rate at which water percolates through the soil. The better water passes through the soil, the less drain lines are required to drain liquid from the septic tank. The size of the tank and the length of the drain lines

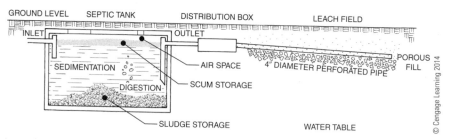

FIGURE 14.12 The major components of a private septic system include the septic tank, distribution box, and leach lines.

also depend on the number of occupants, bathrooms, and the topography of the site.

Local codes specify the minimum distance between the drainage field and bodies of water, wells, roadways, rights-of-way, buildings, and property lines. Common restrictions on the location of the drainage field include:

- Drains lines must be located under paved areas or uphill from a well or water supply.

- Drain fields may be placed no closer than 5' (1500 mm) from a water-table level.

- Regardless of location, soil under the field must be porous enough to absorb the effluent.

- The drain field should be at least 100' (30 m) from a water well, but this distance should be verified with local codes.

Going Green

Gray Water

While the term *white water* refers to water suitable for drinking, *black water* refers to water that is discharged from a toilet or a kitchen sink. Water from the kitchen sink is considered black water because it may become contaminated by soiled diapers or food waste products. **Gray water** is wastewater captured using separate drain lines from other waste lines for bathtubs, showers, lavatories, clothes washing machines, and laundry sinks. The IRC allows gray water to be reused on-site for landscape irrigation. As seen in Figure 14.13a, drain lines containing gray water run through an approved filter to a storage tank and do not connect to the main sewer line. Lines from the storage tank can then be connected to yard sprinkler systems or for other uses of nonpotable water. Because gray water is not disinfected, it could be contaminated. Although laws governing the use of gray water vary, common guidelines to avoid potential hazards include:

- Gray water is not potable water.
- Do not use gray water directly on anything that may be eaten.
- Gray water should not be sprayed or allowed to puddle or run off property.
- Do not recirculate gray water from the kitchen sink or water that comes in contact with soiled diapers, meat, or poultry.
- The permeability of the soil where the fluid is to be discharged must be determined by percolation or permeability evaluation.

(Continued)

Under special circumstances, the 2012 IRC allows using gray water to flush toilets and urinals. The layout for such as system can be seen in Figure 14.13b. Some of the main requirements for using water from these sources include:

- Use a blue or green food-grade vegetable dye to color the gray water before supplying it to the fixtures.
- Identify distribution piping and reservoirs as containing nonpotable water.
- Size reservoirs to limit the holding time of gray water to a maximum of 24 hours. The system must be designed according to equations from the IRC for determining the gallons-per-day per occupant number and the type of fixtures connected to the gray water system.

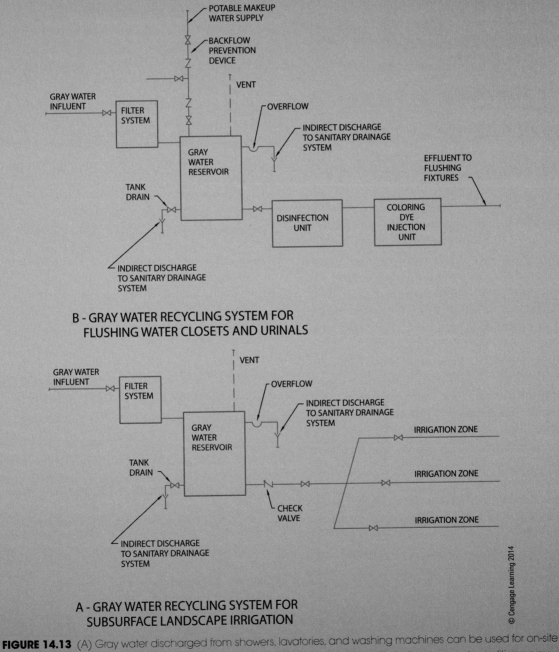

B - GRAY WATER RECYCLING SYSTEM FOR FLUSHING WATER CLOSETS AND URINALS

A - GRAY WATER RECYCLING SYSTEM FOR SUBSURFACE LANDSCAPE IRRIGATION

© Cengage Learning 2014

FIGURE 14.13 (A) Gray water discharged from showers, lavatories, and washing machines can be used for on-site subsurface landscape irrigation using the IRC approved system shown here (B) Under approved conditions, gray water can be filtered and reused for flushing of toilets and urinals. Based on Figure P3009.1(2) of the 2012 International Residential Code.

FIRE-SUPPRESSION SYSTEMS

Many municipalities require fire-suppression systems for homes that are approximately 4000 sq ft in area and larger. The exact size is based on the location of the home in relation to fire hydrants and the municipal water pressure at the hydrant. The method of fire suppression may also be dependent on the home insurance carrier and fire marshal. Suppression systems may range from the installation of a private fire hydrant connected to the public system, a pump connected to a swimming pool, or a fire sprinkler system. If you build in an area governed by the Life Safety Code®, as of January 2006, this code requires all homes to have sprinklers. The 2012 IRC uses the NFPA 13D as its standard. If your building department has adopted the 2012 IRC, all new homes, regardless of size, must now have sprinkler systems.

Home Fire Sprinklers

Fire sprinklers are most effective during the fire's initial flame growth stage. A properly selected sprinkler detects the fire's heat, initiates an alarm, and begins suppression within seconds after flames appear. Studies by the **Fire Suppression System Association** show that in most instances, sprinklers control fire advancement within a few minutes of their activation. Reducing the advancement of flames results in significantly less damage than would be the case without sprinklers.

If you're thinking less damage from fire, more damage from water, you have bought into a widely held myth about sprinklers. In a home fire sprinkler system, a network of piping filled with water under pressure is installed behind the walls and ceilings, and individual sprinklers are placed along the piping to protect the areas beneath them. The sprinklers work independently. When the temperature from a fire reaches approximately 130 to 150 degrees, the sprinkler closest to the flame automatically opens and sprays water over the area, providing plenty of time for a family to escape unharmed from the fire.

The 2012 IRC requires the installation of sprinklers to provide protection to all areas of a home. Review Chapter 5 for placement requirements and limitations. Figure 14.14 shows examples of the rough installation as well as the finished fixture. Water is always in the piping, so the sprinkler system is always available for delivery. If fire breaks out, the air temperature above the fire rises to a degree that is high enough to activate the sprinkler. The sprinkler sprays water over the flames at a rate of between 10 and 25 gallons (38 and 95 liters) per minute. Only the sprinkler nearest the fire is activated. Smoke does not activate sprinklers. Figure 14.15 shows the sprinkler plan for the upper level of the home drawn in Chapter 12.

FIGURE 14.14 A network of piping filled with water under pressure is installed behind the walls and ceilings, and individual sprinklers are placed along the piping to protect the areas beneath them. The top photo shows plastic supply and branch lines merging at a sprinkler head. The bottom photo shows a sprinkler head in the finished ceiling.

THE EFFECTS OF THE PLUMBING SYSTEM ON THE FRAMING SYSTEM

You've been introduced to the basic components of the fresh- and wastewater systems and told repeatedly that the architectural team usually doesn't have to worry about the required drawings. You do need to plan for how the plumbing affects the design of the floor plan, where lines can be placed, and how the placement of plumbing lines affect framing members.

Room Design

Chapters 6 and 11 introduce how plumbing affects the layout of the floor plan. Design elements that must be considered include:

- Notes on the floor or plumbing plan for:
  - Keeping plumbing lines from exterior walls whenever possible.

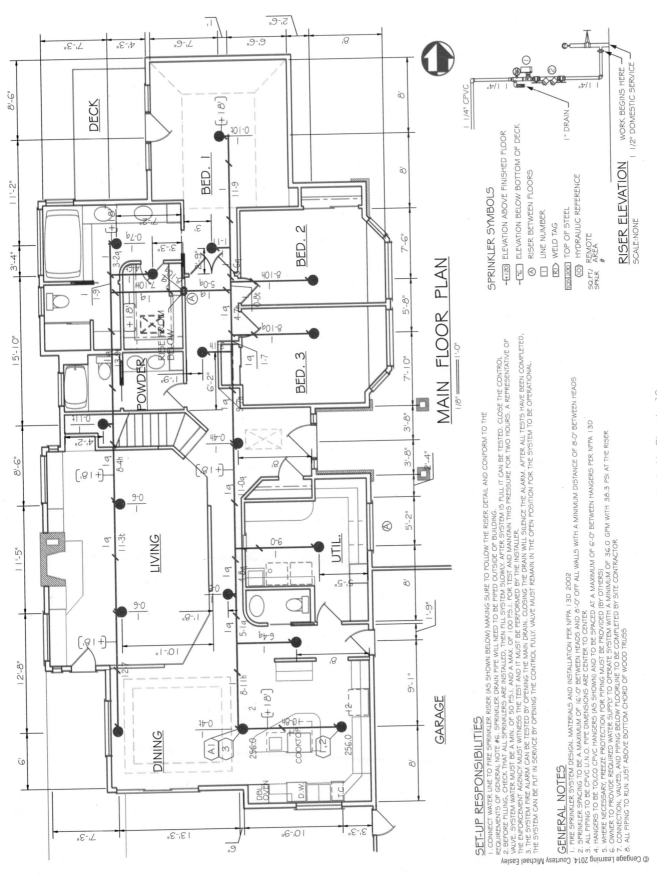

FIGURE 14.15 The upper level of the fire-suppression drawings for the home started in Chapter 12.

- Installing all fresh-water lines in heated spaces or insulating each line if placed in an unheated space.
- Caulking plumbing lines for all penetrations in walls, floors, and ceilings.
- Note: see related notes in the Placing Plumbing in Wood Framing section at the end of this chapter for placement on the plumbing and framing plan.
- In cold climates, locate the water heater in a heated space.
- Keep bathroom plumbing away from bedroom walls. If plumbing must be placed in a bedroom wall, use insulated water pipes, cast-iron drain lines, or wall insulation to control noise.
- When possible, place plumbing fixtures back to back to save materials and labor costs.
- In designing a two-story structure, it is economical to place plumbing fixtures one above the other. If the functional design of the floor plan does not allow for such economies, arrange plumbing fixtures to share stack and vent lines.
- Locate the laundry room next to a bath or other plumbing trees.
- Never use pocket doors where the pocket is behind a plumbing fixture. Always verify the placement of fresh-water, vent, and drain lines by inserting a fixture symbol on the floor plan.

- Carefully plan for the placement of vent lines when there is a window in the wall behind a plumbing fixture.

Perhaps the biggest design consideration involves the placement of bathrooms in a multilevel structure. Multi-level designs can present problems for the placement of drain and waste lines. Fresh-water lines are small enough that their placement is not a problem. Because of the drain line's large size and need to slope, the depth of the floor joists dictate how far it can run before it connects with the riser. Most designers consider it tacky to place a riser in the middle of a family room on the lower floor. Exposed drainpipes are a great place to hang coats, but they have little other appeal. Carefully plan the placement of lower walls to hide drain lines on the floor below the fixture. Equally important is to plan the placement of vent lines on floor levels above the fixture. Figure 14.16 shows the rough plumbing for a vanity with two sinks. You don't have to draw the pipes on the floor plan, but you must plan for them. Figure 14.17 shows the drawings provided by the plumbing contractor for the home started in Chapter 12.

Planning Below-Slab Work

When a concrete slab is used for the lower floor system, great care must be taken to locate plumbing when the foundation plan is drawn. Figure 14.18 shows the rough plumbing for back-to-back bathrooms in a concrete slab.

© Cengage Learning 2014

FIGURE 14.16 In planning a residence, the design team must consider where the rough plumbing will be placed. Space above the fixture for vent lines and below the fixture for drain lines must be carefully planned.

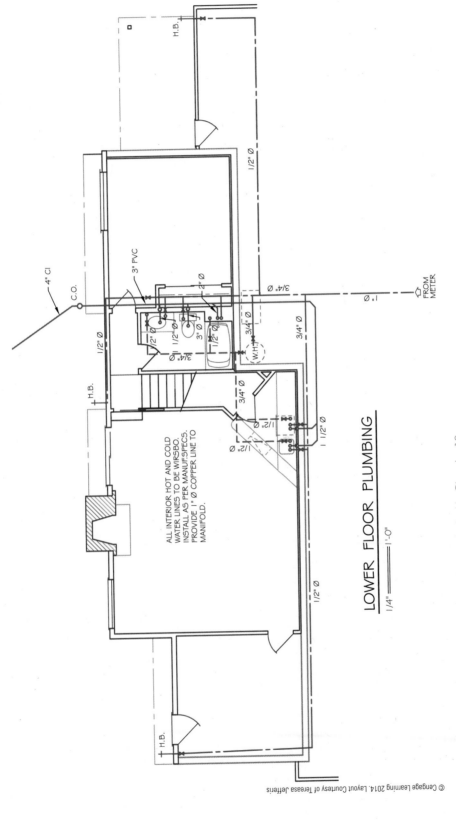

LOWER FLOOR PLUMBING
1/4" = 1'-0"

ALL INTERIOR HOT AND COLD
WATER LINES TO BE WIRSBO.
INSTALL AS PER MANUF.SPECS.
PROVIDE 1" Ø COPPER LINE TO
MANIFOLD.

4" CI
C.O.
3" PVC
H.B.
FROM METER
W.H.

FIGURE 14.17 The fresh- and wastewater layout for the home started in Chapter 12.

FIGURE 14.18 If plumbing will be placed in a concrete slab, the foundation plan will need to accurately dimension the location of all plumbing fixtures and drawings.

Stacks that intersect with house sewer lines under the slab must be dimensioned accurately to ensure alignment of the stack pipe with the partition location.

When plumbing is in an exterior wall, you must also consider how drain lines are affected at the intersection of the wall, floor, and concrete stem walls. With a joist floor system, the depth of the joist usually provides enough depth to run pipes in the interior side of the stem wall. With a post-and-beam floor, the concrete must be notched. Figure 14.19 shows a notch in the stem wall to allow placement of the drainpipe. Poor planning by the design team often requires adjustments by the plumber at the job site.

Placement of plumbing over a concrete retaining wall is even more critical. If the plumbing is in a nonhabitable room, the pipes can be left exposed. If the pipes enter habitable space, place furring over the retaining wall to hide the plumbing. Normally 1× or 2× (25× or 50×)

thick fur strips are necessary to hide the concrete basement walls. The furring thickness is often increased to 4" (100 mm) if waste pipes must be hidden.

Placing Plumbing in Wood Framing

A home with a wood floor system allows the plumber ample space to run fresh- and wastewater lines. Lines are often placed in the cavity formed between joists. When lines must run perpendicular to the floor joists, care must be taken so drilled holes do not weaken the joists. The IRC requires the following limits on notches in sawn joists and beams:

- The notch depth must not exceed 1/6 of the joist depth.
- The notch length must not be longer than 1/3 the depth of the member being notched.
- Do not place the notch in the middle third of a joist span.
- Notches placed at the end of a joist must not exceed 1/4 of the joist depth.
- The tension side of a member 4" (100 mm) or wider in thickness must not be notched except at the ends of the joists.
- Holes bored into joists must not exceed 1/3 of the joist depth.
- Holes must not be within 2" (50 mm) of the top or bottom of the joists.
- Place holes a minimum of 2" (50 mm) apart from other holes and notches.

Although plumbers are usually aware of these requirements, add these notes on the framing plan to ensure quality construction. Figure 14.20 shows the results of plumbing notches that were made by an uninformed plumber.

Wood walls hide most vent and drain lines, but walls hiding the vent lines for toilets need special attention. Plumbing walls that hide toilet vents are usually framed with 2 × 6 (50 × 150) studs to hide plumbing for toilets on the lower level of multilevel structures. Pipes for toilets in a single-level home and other plumbing fixtures can be placed in a 2 × 4 stud wall, but 2 × 6 studs are also used to aid plumbers.

READING PLUMBING DRAWINGS

Although designers and CAD technicians rarely are required to create residential plumbing drawings, the ability to recognize common symbols used on plumbing drawings will aid you in your career advancement. Figure 14.21 shows

FIGURE 14.19 The architectural team must plan how lines can be placed where walls intersect the concrete stem walls.

FIGURE 14.20 The location of notches and holes in joists is highly regulated by the IRC. Notes to specify notches and holes should be placed on the framing plan.

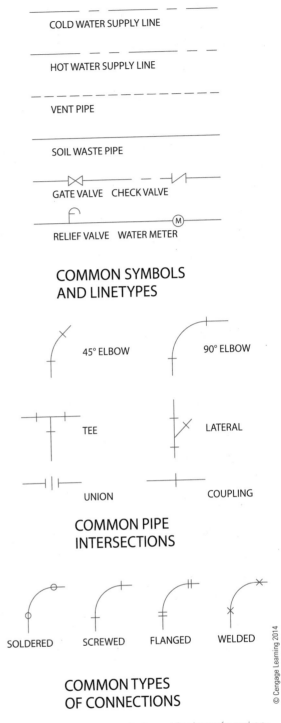

COLD WATER SUPPLY LINE

HOT WATER SUPPLY LINE

VENT PIPE

SOIL WASTE PIPE

GATE VALVE   CHECK VALVE

RELIEF VALVE   WATER METER

COMMON SYMBOLS AND LINETYPES

45° ELBOW   90° ELBOW

TEE   LATERAL

UNION   COUPLING

COMMON PIPE INTERSECTIONS

SOLDERED   SCREWED   FLANGED   WELDED

COMMON TYPES OF CONNECTIONS

typical plumbing symbols that are often represented on residential plumbing drawings. Figure 14.22 shows how these symbols may appear in the fresh-water drawings for the home used throughout this textbook. If a project calls for plumbing drawings, start them in a similar manner that was used to start the electrical plan in Chapter 13. Freeze all information directly related to the floor plan and only display the walls, doors, windows, stairs, cabinets, plumbing fixtures, and the fireplace. The base drawing for the residence started in Chapter 12 is shown in Figure 12.31. The National CAD Standards recommends using following layers for CAD displaying plumbing information:

FIGURE 14.21 Common symbols and linetypes found on residential plumbing drawings.

PLUMBING DISCIPLINE DESIGNATORS	
Designator	**Description**
P	Plumbing
PD	Plumbing Demolition
PP	Plumbing Piping
PQ	Plumbing Equipment

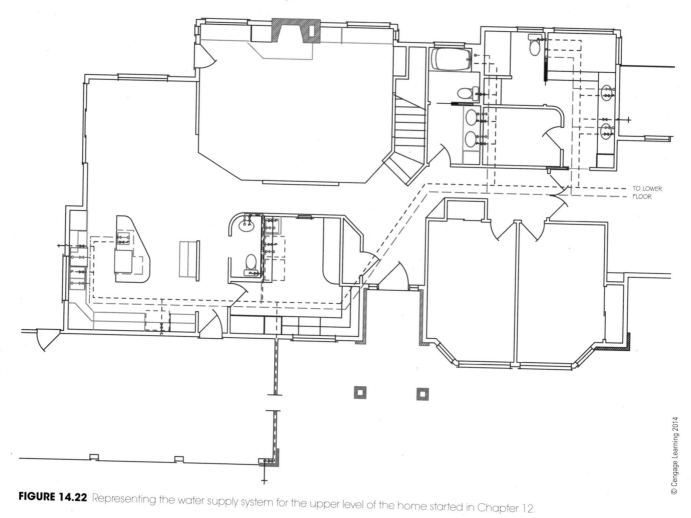

TO LOWER
FLOOR

© Cengage Learning 2014

FIGURE 14.22 Representing the water supply system for the upper level of the home started in Chapter 12.

PLUMBING LAYER LIST

Layer Name	Description
P FLOR	Floor
P FLOR-ANNO	Annotation
P FLOR-PENE	Floor penetrations
P FLOR-SYMB	Fixture symbols
P SSWR	Sanitary sewer
P SSWR-ANNO	Sanitary sewer annotation
P SSWR-EQPM	Sanitary sewer equipment
P SSWR-FIXT	Sanitary sewer: fixtures
P SSWR-FLDR	Sanitary sewer: floor drains
P SSWR-PIPE	Sanitary sewer: piping
P SSWR-RISR	Sanitary sewer: risers
P SSWR-VENT	Sanitary sewer: vents

Note: Reference the National CAD Standard for a complete list of plumbing discipline designators and layer names.

© Cengage Learning 2014

Additional Resources

Use the following websites as resources to help you keep current with changes in plumbing materials.

Address	Company or Organization
www.allaroundthehouse.com	All Around The House™
www.americanstandard.com	American Standard
www.aquaglass.com	Aqua Glass® (bathing fixtures)
www.energystar.com	ENERGY STAR
www.energystar.gov	ENERGY STAR
www.fssa.net	Fire Suppression System Association
www.polybutylene.com	Polybutylene Plumbing (general information regarding polybutylene piping)
www.graywatersystems.com	Gray Water Systems
www.homedepot.com	The Home Depot
www.homefiresprinkler.org	Home Fire Sprinkler Coalition
www.kohler.com	Kohler Co.
www.lowes.com	Lowe's (home improvement)
www.nfpa.org	National Fire Protection Association
www.nibco.com	NIBCO® (Flow Control)
www.graywater.net	Oasis Design®
www.energysavers.gov	U.S. Department of Energy (Energy Savers)
www.usfa.fema.gov	U.S. Fire Administration (FEMA)
www.wagner-solar.com/en	Wagner & Co. (European Solar Thermal Industry Federation)

Plumbing Systems Test

Follow these instructions to access and complete an electronic copy of the Chapter 14 Plumbing Systems Test:

1. Go to cengagebrain.com
2. Enter the email address and password you used to register for the site (see Preface for full instructions).
3. Select the website from the **My Course & Materials** area of your home page. Select the chapter you want from the pull-down menu at the top of the page. Choose the resources for that chapter from the menu on the left.
4. Type your name, the chapter number, and the date at the top of the sheet.
5. Answer the following questions with short, complete statements using a word processor.

> ## NOTE:
>
> *The answers to some questions may not be contained in this chapter and will require you to do additional research using the Internet. Use your favorite search engine to search for specific professional companies or general categories of information.*

Questions

14.1. What plumbing drawings are required to get a plumbing permit?

14.2. Visit the website of your local building department and determine the requirements for residential fire sprinklers.

14.3. List the maximum length and rise for a residential supply line based on the IRC.

14.4. List three different types of pipes described by the IRC.

14.5. A gas-fired water heater will be placed in a pantry by the kitchen. List any requirements for this location based on your local building codes.

14.6. Explain the difference and the relationship of drain and vent pipes.

14.7. Determine the physical size and output of the smallest and largest Takagai tankless water heater.

14.8. List a minimum of four requirements to place a water heater in an attic based on the IRC.

14.9. What is the minimum water main size allowed by the IRC?

14.10. List at least four factors that influence the sizing of water-supply pipes.

14.11. Check with your local building department to find the permit requirements to install a solar hot-water system.

14.12. Verify with your local water bureau to learn the expected water and sewer rates for the home you designed in Chapter 12 if a family of four owned the home.

14.13. Visit the website for your local water bureau and obtain their recommendations for making a home more water efficient. Write specifications or alter your floor plan to make it comply with your findings.

14.14. After scheduling an appointment, visit a plumbing contractor to find out the estimated cost of plumbing your home using traditional practices and compare the cost of providing a gray water system. Write a report on your findings.

14.15. After scheduling an appointment, visit a company that designs and installs home sprinkler systems. Get an estimate of the cost of installing a system.

Drawing Problems

14.1   Based on the requirements in Chapter 5, use a copy of your floor plan and create a base drawing similar to the base plan created for the electrical plan. Use the base drawing to draw a fire sprinkler plan. Verify requirements with your local building department.

14.2   Using the examples in this chapter and information from the building department, complete the application for a plumbing permit.

14.3   Using the examples in this chapter and information from the building department, complete a one-line drawing for the fresh-water system of the home you started in Chapter 12.

14.4   Using the examples in this chapter and information from the building department, complete a one-line drawing for the waste-water system of the home you started in Chapter 12.

14.5   Use the Internet to research available options for water heaters suitable for the home you started in Chapter 12. As a minimum, compare standard units, on-demand units, and solar units plus any new developments in water heating. Select and specify a suitable unit based on initial cost, yearly service cost, and water capacity output rates.

Chapter 15
Comfort Control Systems

Comfort control requires more than just delivering air at a comfortable temperature. True comfort includes providing clean, fresh, odorless air at the correct temperature and humidity. The demands of comfort control are met with a heating system, a cooling system, air filters, and humidifiers. The type of system and the requirements of the building department dictate whether drawings are needed to obtain a mechanical permit. If drawings must be provided, the mechanical contractor who installs the system usually completes them, showing any required climate-control equipment. As with the plumbing drawings, even though the architectural team does not supply them, you must understand their contents to effectively complete the architectural drawings.

Climate-control plans show the system and the equipment used to maintain temperature, moisture, and the exchange and purification of the air supply. Mechanical systems control air temperature, movement, pollutants, humidity, and odors. Heating, ventilating, and air-conditioning systems, also known as HVAC, include a wide variety of devices and delivery systems shown on the HVAC drawings. The most common types of systems for bringing comfort control to a building are forced-air, hydronics, radiant, steam, active solar, and passive solar systems.

Key Terms

Active solar system

Air-to-air heat exchanger

British thermal unit (BTU)

Conduction

Convection

Dehumidifier

Design heat loss

Diffuser

Direct gain

Ducts

Forced-air system

Geothermal reservoirs

Gravity system

Greenhouse effect

Heat gain

Heat loss

Heat pump

Humidifer

Hydronic system

Indirect gain

Infiltration

Insulation

Latent heat gain

Mass walls

One-pipe heating system

Passive solar system

Plenum

Radiant heat

R-value

Sensible heat gain

Series-loop system

Solar orientation

Solarium

Steam-heating unit

Thermal conductivity

Thermal mass

Thermostat

Trombe wall

Two-pipe heating system

U-value

Winter inside design
temperature

Winter outside design
temperature

Zoned heating
system

PRINCIPLES OF HEAT TRANSFER

A key element to understanding HVAC drawings is to understand the basics of creating and transferring heat from one object to another. Heat inside a building is created not only by natural solar heat gained through roofs, windows, and walls but also by heat-producing equipment such as computers, television sets, and ovens. The occupants of a room also raise its temperature.

Methods of Heat Transfer

Whether it is inside or outside a structure, heat always travels from a warm surface or area to a cooler surface or area. Heat travels by radiation, convection, and conduction. *Radiant heat* travels in waves through the atmosphere in the same manner as light. All materials constantly radiate heat because molecules at their surfaces are constantly moving. Radiant heat travels from a heated surface to the cooler air surrounding the heated surface. An example of radiant heat is a burning coal on a barbecue: long after the glow of the flame dies, the coal still radiates heat.

Convection transfers heat by moving molecules from one place to another. Heat travels from a heated surface to the molecules of liquids or gases surrounding that surface. Convection occurs when heat transfers from a heated surface to a fluid moving over the heated surface or when molecules in a fluid transfer from one heated molecule to another. *Hydronic systems* pass heated liquid through tubes buried in the floor. These tubes pass heat from the liquid to the concrete floor and then through radiation to the surrounding air. The heated air rises and cool air moves in to take its place, causing a convective current.

Each material that is struck by the sun's radiation absorbs some solar radiation. As a material absorbs this radiation, heat is conducted between its molecules. The denser the material, the better the conduction rate. *Conduction* carries heat through indirect contact between hot and cold molecules. Placing a steel poker into a fire is an example of conduction: left in the fire, the poker absorbs heat and becomes hot. Many solar applications depend on heat absorbed into dense materials and radiated back into the room as the air around the surface cools. This principle also works in reverse. Materials with tiny air pockets will not transfer heat well. The use of materials such as insulation, with thousands of tiny air pockets, slows the transfer of heat from heated to cold surfaces.

Heat Measurement

The standard unit of measurement for heat production or loss is the *British thermal unit (BTU)*. The metric unit of heat measurement is joules (J). BTUs are converted to joules by multiplying the BTU value by 1055. *Thermal conductivity* is the measure of the amount of heat that flows from one face of a material to the opposite face. Materials that transfer heat easily are known as conductors. Materials that resist the

CONCRETE/MASONRY R-RATING	
4" Brick	0.44
1" Stone	0.08
1" Stucco	0.20
1" Poured concrete	0.08
8" Concrete block	1.04 (hollow)
8" Concrete block	1.93 (filled)
WOOD	
1" Soft wood	1.25
1" Hardwoods	0.91
1" Plywood	1.25
1" Poured concrete	0.08
5/8" Particle board	0.82
1" Wood fiberboard	1.93
SIDING	
Aluminum siding	0.61
Beveled wood	0.81
Building paper	0.06
Vinyl siding	1.00
Wood shingles	0.87
INSULATION	
1" Glass fiber batt	3.13
1" Blown cellulose	3.40
1" Expanded polystyrene	3.85
1" Expanded polyurethane	6.64
1" Extruded polystyrene	4.92 (Styrofoam blue board)
ROOFING	
Built-up	0.33
Fiberglass shingles	0.44
Slate roofing	0.05
Wood shingles	0.94

transfer of heat are known as insulators. The effectiveness of a material to resist heat transfer is indicated as its R-value. Thermal resistance is the reciprocal of thermal conductivity.

R-Values and U-Values

The **R-value** of a material provides a uniform method to rate the resistance of heat flow through it. The higher the R-value, the greater the ability of a material to resist heat transfer to another material. Most major building materials have been tested and assigned an R-value. Common R-values include those shown in table on previous page.

When building materials are combined in layers, the sum of their R-values becomes the total R-value for the component. Figure 15.1 shows the R-value for a 2 × 6 (50 × 100) stud wall.

The **U-value** is the reciprocal (1/R) of the R-value and indicates the combined thermal conductivity of all materials in a structure, including air spaces. The U-value is the amount of heat conducted in one hour through a 1-sq-ft area for each Fahrenheit degree of difference in temperature between inside and outside air. High R-values and low U-values indicate greater efficiency. Because different climates and seasons require different R-value levels to maintain the desired indoor temperature, R-values must be chosen for the average low temperature of a geographic area. Table 15.1 provides examples of the required R-values to maintain various temperatures.

Windows and doors account for the greatest heat loss in cold climates. The door surface and core material greatly affect R- and U-values. Two common materials for exterior doors include:

- Solid core wood   R = 2.3   U = 0.43
- Metal with urethane core   R = 13.5   U = 0.07

Heat flows through windows in both directions through radiation, convection, and conduction. Windows with a sealed space between double layers of glazing greatly reduce heat loss. Filling the air space between the glazing with argon or krypton gas further reduces heat loss. Low-E glass has a transparent coating that acts as a thermal mirror to increase the insulating value. The coating reflects heat energy, which is invisible solar radiation, but allows the transmission of visible light. Most codes now require low-E glazing because of its increased efficiency. These measures increase R-values and decrease U-values. Table 15.2 compares R- and U-values for various glass products.

Doors and windows lose heat by air **infiltration**—the flow of air through poorly sealed building intersections. The proper use of caulking and insulation greatly reduce infiltration and increase energy efficiency. The DRAWING BLOCKS\FLOOR BLOCKS\NOTES folder of the student website contains common caulking and insulation notes that can be added to a set of plans. These notes can be inserted on the floor plan, on a sheet containing all general notes, or on any sheet that space allows. If these notes are not located on the floor plan, be sure to list them in the title block and on a table of contents on the title sheet. Edit the standard notes to meet code and climate requirements for your area.

Insulation

The IRC refers to the exterior of a home as the building envelope. The insulation, outer walls, ceiling, doors, windows, and floors work together to control airflow in and out of the structure, repel moisture, and prevent heat loss or gain.

A high-performance envelope maintains a consistent temperature even under extremely hot or cold conditions. **Insulation** is any material used to slow the transfer of heat. It improves the home envelope to make homes more comfortable and energy-efficient. Without insulation a HVAC system must work harder to overcome the loss of treated air through the walls, floors, and ceilings. Figure 15.2 shows where to apply insulation and caulking to a home. Determining how much insulation to use in a home depends on the IRC or other applicable codes, the climate, energy cost, and personal desires of the homeowner. Moderate zones of the country require the following minimum values:

Ceilings	R-30 through 38
Wood walls	R-13 through 20
Floors	R-13 through 19
Basement walls	R-0 through 13
Mass walls	R-3/4 through 8/13

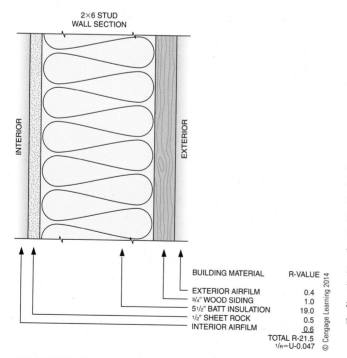

BUILDING MATERIAL	R-VALUE
EXTERIOR AIRFILM	0.4
3/4" WOOD SIDING	1.0
5 1/2" BATT INSULATION	19.0
1/2" SHEET ROCK	0.5
INTERIOR AIRFILM	0.6
	TOTAL R-21.5
	1/R = U-0.047

© Cengage Learning 2014

FIGURE 15.1 When building materials are combined, the sum of their R-values becomes the total R-value for the component. The combined R-value for a 2 × 6 (50 × 100) stud wall is 21.5 with a U-value of .047.

TABLE 15.1 Required R-values Needed to Maintain Various Indoor Temperatures Based on the Outdoor Temperature

	INDOOR SURFACE TEMPERATURE				
Outdoor Temp	**Cool 60°F**	**Fair 64°F**	**Medium 66°F**	**Warm 68°F**	**Min for Floor**
+30°F	R-2.3	R-3.4	R-5.1	R-10.0	R-1.7
+20°F	R-2.8	R-4.2	R-6.4	R-12.5	R-2.2
+10°F	R-3.4	R-5.1	R-7.8	R-14.5	R-2.6
0°F	R-3.9	R-6.0	R-9.2	R-17.0	R-3.0
−10°F	R-4.4	R-6.8	R-10.1	R-20.0	R-3.4
−20°F	R-5.1	R-7.8	R-11.3	R-23.0	R-3.9
−30°F	R-5.7	R-8.4	R-12.8	R-25.0	R-4.4
−40°F	R-6.4	R-10.2	R-14.5	R-28.0	R-4.8

© Cengage Learning 2014

> ## NOTE:
>
> *Review Chapter 5 for IRC required insulation minimums. See Figure 5.18 (IRC Table R402.1.1)® for the insulation requirements of specific climate zones. Also see Chapter 22 of this text for air barrier requirements.*

For **mass walls**, the second value applies when over half of the insulation is on the interior of the mass wall. Because of such wide differences in climates throughout the country, individual building codes determine specific needs.

Types of Insulation

Common insulation materials include fiberglass, rock wool, cellulose, urethane foam, and recycled cotton. Insulation is available in the form of blanket, loose fill, rigid board, and expanding spray foam.

Batts and Blanket Insulation. The common form of batts and blanket insulation is roll insulation made of fiberglass fibers produced in widths suitable to place between standard framing members. The thickness of the insulation determines its R-value. Batts and blankets are available with or without vapor-retarded facings. Figure 15.3 shows the application of batt insulation.

Loose-Fill Insulation. Loose-fill insulation consists of fibers or granules primarily made from cellulose, fiberglass, rock wool, or cotton materials. Loose-fill insulation is blown into areas and cavities, as shown in Figure 15.4. For use in attics, blown-in insulation allows the material to fill in empty cavities. A disadvantage of using loose-fill

TABLE 15.2 Comparative R- and U-values for Various Glass Products

	U-FACTOR		R-VALUE	
Material	**Cold Climate (Winter)**	**Warm Climate (Summer)**	**Cold Climate (Winter)**	**Warm Climate (Summer)**
SINGLE GLASS	1.13	1.06	0.88	0.94
INSULATED GLASS				
1/4″ Air space	0.65	0.61	1.54	1.64
1/2″ Air space	0.58	0.56	1.72	1.79
STORM WINDOWS				
1″–4″ Air space	0.56	0.54	1.79	1.85
LOW EMITTANCE				
1/2″ Air space	0.32	0.38	3.13	2.63
ε = .20 ε = .60	0.43	0.51	2.33	1.96
GLASS BLOCK				
6″ × 6″ × 4″	0.60	0.57	1.67	1.76
12″ × 12″ × 4″	0.52	0.50	1.92	2.00

© Cengage Learning 2014

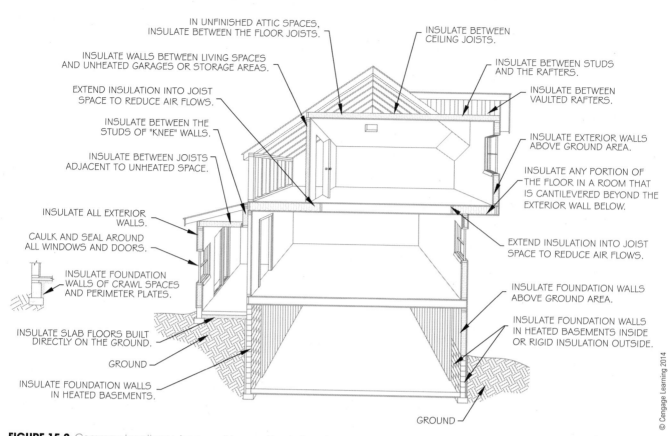

IN UNFINISHED ATTIC SPACES, INSULATE BETWEEN THE FLOOR JOISTS.

INSULATE WALLS BETWEEN LIVING SPACES AND UNHEATED GARAGES OR STORAGE AREAS.

EXTEND INSULATION INTO JOIST SPACE TO REDUCE AIR FLOWS.

INSULATE BETWEEN THE STUDS OF "KNEE" WALLS.

INSULATE BETWEEN JOISTS ADJACENT TO UNHEATED SPACE.

INSULATE ALL EXTERIOR WALLS.

CAULK AND SEAL AROUND ALL WINDOWS AND DOORS.

INSULATE FOUNDATION WALLS OF CRAWL SPACES AND PERIMETER PLATES.

INSULATE SLAB FLOORS BUILT DIRECTLY ON THE GROUND.

GROUND

INSULATE FOUNDATION WALLS IN HEATED BASEMENTS.

INSULATE BETWEEN CEILING JOISTS.

INSULATE BETWEEN STUDS AND THE RAFTERS.

INSULATE BETWEEN VAULTED RAFTERS.

INSULATE EXTERIOR WALLS ABOVE GROUND AREA.

INSULATE ANY PORTION OF THE FLOOR IN A ROOM THAT IS CANTILEVERED BEYOND THE EXTERIOR WALL BELOW.

EXTEND INSULATION INTO JOIST SPACE TO REDUCE AIR FLOWS.

INSULATE FOUNDATION WALLS ABOVE GROUND AREA.

INSULATE FOUNDATION WALLS IN HEATED BASEMENTS INSIDE OR RIGID INSULATION OUTSIDE.

GROUND

© Cengage Learning 2014

FIGURE 15.2 Common locations where caulking and insulation should be applied. It is up to the architectural team to specify the location and each type of caulking and insulation.

insulation is that it settles over time, leaving uninsulated areas at the tops of the cavities.

Rigid Insulation. Rigid insulation is made from plastic foams and is formed into sheets. The thickness varies based on the desired R-value. Rigid foam insulation primarily insulates foundation walls and footings and vaulted ceilings as an overlay to roof decking. When insulating foundation walls, use a protective layer of concrete board on exposed exterior areas. Figure 15.5 shows a detail that describes the use of rigid insulation for a foundation application. See Chapter 27 for additional review of foundation insulation.

Spray-in-Place Foam Insulation. Thin layers of polyurethane spray-in foam insulation provide the highest R-value per inch of current insulation materials. With a value of R-7 per inch, the material is sprayed into an open cavity and hard-to-access areas, where it expands up to 100 times its original liquid volume, filling the cavity and any existing cracks. Excess foam is trimmed away when it hardens (see Figure 15.6).

Courtesy CertainTeed Corporation

FIGURE 15.3 Batt insulation is applied in most new homes because of its ease of installation and low cost.

Courtesy CertainTeed Corporation

FIGURE 15.4 Blown-in insulation is a popular choice for open attic spaces, but it tends to compress over time.

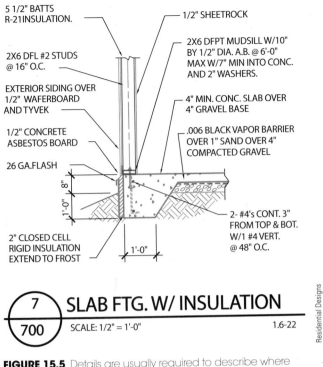

5 1/2" BATTS
R-21INSULATION.

2X6 DFL #2 STUDS
@ 16" O.C.

EXTERIOR SIDING OVER
1/2" WAFERBOARD
AND TYVEK

1/2" CONCRETE
ASBESTOS BOARD

26 GA.FLASH

2" CLOSED CELL
RIGID INSULATION
EXTEND TO FROST

1/2" SHEETROCK

2X6 DFPT MUDSILL W/10"
BY 1/2" DIA. A.B. @ 6'-0"
MAX W/7" MIN INTO CONC.
AND 2" WASHERS.

4" MIN. CONC. SLAB OVER
4" GRAVEL BASE

.006 BLACK VAPOR BARRIER
OVER 1" SAND OVER 4"
COMPACTED GRAVEL

2- #4's CONT. 3"
FROM TOP & BOT.
W/1 #4 VERT.
@ 48" O.C.

7 / 700   SLAB FTG. W/ INSULATION
SCALE: 1/2" = 1'-0"   1.6-22

Residential Designs

FIGURE 15.5 Details are usually required to describe where the insulation will be placed and how it will be protected from damage.

Examining Heat Loss

Studies show that an average home loses its heat in the following methods:

- 25 percent heat loss through the roof.
- 15 percent heat loss through the floor.
- 25 percent heat loss through openings.
- 35 percent heat loss through uninsulated walls.

Determining the exact amount of heat loss for a home is the job of the designer or heating contractor. The person responsible for the design depends on the complexity of the plan, who the home is designed for, and average contrast between the inside and outside temperature conditions. For a stock home or a spec home, the HVAC contractor typically determines the heat loss for a home. For a custom home, the architect or designer will typically do a preliminary design analysis with the heating contractor.

To determine the heat loss for a home, it's important to understand some basic principles of heat flow. Heat travels through the walls, windows, and ceilings of the building envelope to the outside by conduction. Cold air leaks into the house and warm air leaks out through infiltration. There is a continuous movement of heat from the inside to the outside, which is measured in units called BTUs. The speed of the movement of heat through the building envelope is called the **heat loss** and is measured in BTUs per hour (BTUH).

Courtesy Icynene® Insulation System

FIGURE 15.6 Spray-in foam insulation provides the highest R-value per inch of all current insulation materials.

The determination of heat loss starts with the **winter inside design temperature**, which is the desired temperature of the structure. This temperature is usually around 72° in the winter. If it is 72° inside the house and 42° outside, then the 30°-temperature differential will cause a certain number of BTUs to leave the house each hour. For this example, assume that the heat loss of this house at 42° is 20,000 BTUH. This means that your heating system must produce 20,000 BTUs per hour to keep the house at 72°, when it is 42° outside. If it is even colder outside than in the house, the heat loss is higher. Other factors affecting heat loss include:

- The area of the building envelope. The smaller the building envelope, the lower the heat loss in comparison to a larger home.
- Thermal resistance. Increasing the insulation or the R-value to the building envelope slows heat loss.
- Air tightness. Sealing cracks around doors and windows as well as penetrations in the envelope for electrical, plumbing, and heating ducts reduces infiltration.

When selecting a heating system and determining heat loss, the average outdoor winter temperature, referred to as the *winter outside design temperature,* must be known. The average depends on where you live and how cold the winters are. The local building department provides this information or it can be obtained from Appendix D of the 2012 International Plumbing Code (IPC). This is the temperature, say 10° for instance, at which only 2.5 percent of the time is colder than 10°. The heat loss of the house, when calculated with the winter outside design temperature, is called the *design heat loss*.

Examining Heat Gain

Heat gain consists of heat gained by conduction through the building envelope from warm outside air coming in, and cool inside air leaking out. Common sources of heat gain include:

- Moisture gained by infiltration. Humid outside air coming in, dryer inside air passing through the building envelope.
- Radiation from the sun. Either direct or indirect, radiation from the sun comes in through windows, glass doors, and skylights.
- Building occupants.
- Heat given off by appliances.

The heat gain associated with the temperature of the air is called the *sensible heat gain*. It includes two types of heat gain:

- Water in the air that leaks in due to infiltration.
- Water that evaporates from the skin of the occupants as well as the moisture in their breath, called *latent heat gain*.

Adding the sensible gain to the latent gain provides the total heat gain. The total heat gain compared to the outside summer design conditions determines the cooling requirements for a structure. The summer design condition consists of the summer design temperature and summer moisture content. Both of these measurements are available from the local building department, although many computer programs for determining heat loss and gain contain the summer and winter design conditions. The daily range is a measurement of how the temperature varies during the day. A high daily range means temperatures start cool in the morning, turn hot in midday, and cool down at night. A high daily range results in a lower heat gain than a low daily range where it starts out hot and stays hot all day.

An additional unit of measurement for describing the cooling capacity of air conditioners is *ton*. One ton is equal to 12,000 BTUH, and is derived from the number of BTUs absorbed by a ton of ice melting in 24 hours. If you have a heat gain of 50,000 BTUH, then you must remove 50,000 BTUH to keep the house at the desired indoor design temperature. To equal the mountain of ice needed each day requires a 4.2-ton (50,000/12,000) air conditioner.

Sizing Air Conditioners and Furnaces

Most HVAC software programs provide the summer and winter outside design temperatures required for determining the heat loss and heat gain of the house. By determining and entering the areas for the walls, ceilings, floors, and openings, the type and thickness of insulation, and the types of glazing, software programs will determine the design heat loss of the home in BTUs. If you determine that the design heat loss is 55,000 BTUH, that assumes that the outdoor winter design temperature remains constant throughout the winter. Since this is not true, most HVAC contractors recommend adding and additional 15 percent to the required BTUs to compensate for the output necessary on colder days. Having this safety factor requires a heating unit with an output of 63,250 BTUH. Be cautious in adding the safety factor. Although some contractors may recommend adding up to 25 percent of the original recommended BTU, remember the initial cost of the furnace and its operating cost increase as the BTU output is increased. If the software you're using takes into account the average winter temperature range, adding in the safety factor will not be necessary.

When sizing an air conditioner, remember that the air conditioner's function goes beyond just lowering the inside temperature; it's also expected to lower the humidity in the structure. The design goal is to match the required cooling load of the house closely to total cooling capacity of the air conditioner. When the air conditioner is operating, the warm air is blown over a coil used to cool the air. As the air is cooled, humidity in the air is condensed into to water, and is routed to a drain. If it is too large, the air conditioner will cool the air quickly, and the thermostat will shut the system off when the desired temperature is reached. If the air conditioner drops the temperature too quickly, it does not have time to remove the humidity. Even though the desired temperature is achieved, the excess humidity remaining in the air will make the home feel hotter than it is. To match ability to cool and remove the humidity from the air inside the building envelope, no safety factor is added to the required minimum calculated BTU size.

HEATING SYSTEMS

While there are a variety of conventional methods for producing heat, including forced-air, hot-water, steam, electrical, heat-pump, and solar systems, drafters must also consider how to distribute heat. Heat is usually circulated throughout a residence by *ducts*, tubes, *plenums*, pipes, or wires. Round, square, or rectangular ducts move both heated and cooled air. Typically ducts are made from sheet metal, flexible foil-covered fiberglass, and the wood of the framing system. Copper pipes carry hot water or steam to radiators within each room. Flexible plastic tubes are buried in concrete slabs to circulate heated water to warm the concrete. *Radiant heating* systems rely on electrical resistance wires embedded in ceilings or floors or connected to floor or wall convection units.

Before considering any HVAC systems, you must understand the symbols used by mechanical contractors to represent HVAC components. Figure 15.7 shows common symbols used on HVAC drawings. Understanding these symbols will give you a better understanding of the drawings completed by the mechanical contractor and help you coordinate the architectural drawings with the mechanical drawings. These symbols show the location and type of equipment. Arrows show the movement of hot air, cold air, and water. HVAC symbols are available in the DesignCenter of AutoCAD or from third-party vendors to improve productivity. Custom CAD programs are also available to aid in completing HVAC drawings.

Forced-Warm-Air Furnace Units

Warm-air furnace units operate using either gravity or forced air. Locate the furnace for a *gravity system* below the lowest level in the structure that will be heated. *Forced-air systems* heat air in a central furnace and then use a fan to force air through ducts to distribute the heated air to *diffusers* throughout the residence. Forced-air units are represented and labeled FAU on the floor and electrical plans, but the ducts and diffusers do not appear on either plan. If a mechanical plan is drawn, represent the unit and the ducting. The complexity of the system dictates whether a drawing is necessary with the construction documents. If drawings are not provided, the installer must work with drawings or sketches that the mechanical contractor creates. Figure 15.8 shows the drawings for the forced-air system for the home that was started in Chapter 12. The advantages of using a forced-air unit are that air-cooling systems can use the same ductwork and filters and dehumidifiers can be built into the system for heating and cooling cycles.

Residential furnaces produce heat by burning fuel oil, natural gas, or by using electric heating coils. If heat comes from burning fuel oil or natural gas, the combustion takes place inside a combustion chamber. Air absorbs heat from the outer surface of the chamber. The combustion gases are vented through a chimney or metal ducting that extends through the roof. When a furnace is powered by electricity, cool air is heated as it passes over the heating coils. Electric furnaces do not require exterior venting.

In the heating cycle, the system forces heated air to ducts that lead to floor outlets. Heat outlets are usually placed in front of windows in outside walls. There should be at least one outlet for each 15′ (4500 mm) of exterior wall space. Where heating ducts also serve an air-conditioning system, the locations of the inside air handlers, exhaust hoses, and outside compressor units must be represented. Ceiling locations are preferred for cooling, but separate duct systems are rarely used for heating and cooling.

In addition to the distribution ductwork, forced-air systems use a second set of ducts to bring return air to the furnace to be warmed. A home with an open layout does not require return ducts. Instead, return air moves directly to the return side of a furnace. Forced-air distribution ducts connect to a *plenum* chamber—an enclosed space located between the furnace and distribution ducts. The plenum is larger than any duct and slows the flow of air through the ducts.

The location, size, and BTU capacity of each duct is shown on an HVAC plan. Each duct is represented by outlining the position of the ducts and providing a notation such as 6/18 (150/450) to represent a duct 6 × 18″ (150 × 450 mm).

NAME	ABBREV	SYMBOL	NAME	ABBREV	SYMBOL
DUCT SIZE & FLOW SELECTION	DCT/FD	10″ × 15″	HEAT REGISTER	R	R
DUCT SIZE CHANGE	DCT/SC		THERMOSTAT	T	T
DUCT LOWERING	DCT/LW	D	RADIATOR	RAD	RAD
DUCT RISING	DCT/RS	R	CONVECTOR	CONV	CONV
DUCT RETURN	DCT/RT		ROOM AIR CONDITIONER	RAC	RAC
DUCT SUPPLY	DCT SUP	S	HEATING PLANT FURNACE	HT PLT FUR	FURN
CEILING-DUCT OUTLET	CLG DCT OUT		FUEL-OIL TANK	FOT	OIL
WARM-AIR SUPPLY	WA SUP	WA	HUMIDISTAT	H	H
SECOND-FLOOR SUPPLY	2nd FL SUP		HEAT PUMP	HP	HP
COLD AIR RETURN	CA RET	CA	THERMOMETER	T	T
SECOND-FLOOR RETURN	2 FL RET		PUMP	P	
GAS OUTLET	G OUT	G	GAGE	GA	
HEAT OUTLET	HT OUT		FORCED CONVECTION	FRC CONV	

FIGURE 15.7 Common climate-control symbols found on HVAC drawings.

© Cengage Learning 2014

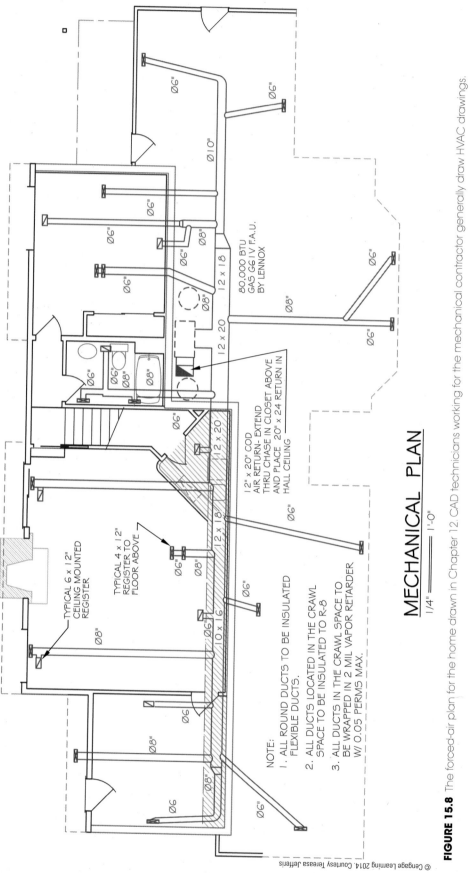

MECHANICAL PLAN
1/4" = 1'-0"

80,000 BTU
GAS G6 IV F.A.U.
BY LENNOX

12" x 20" COD
AIR RETURN- EXTEND
THRU CHASE IN CLOSET ABOVE
AND PLACE 20" x 24 RETURN IN
HALL CEILING

TYPICAL 6 x 12"
CEILING MOUNTED
REGISTER

TYPICAL 4 x 12"
REGISTER TO
FLOOR ABOVE

NOTE:
1. ALL ROUND DUCTS TO BE INSULATED
   FLEXIBLE DUCTS.

2. ALL DUCTS LOCATED IN THE CRAWL
   SPACE TO BE INSULATED TO R-8

3. ALL DUCTS IN THE CRAWL SPACE TO
   BE WRAPPED IN 2 MIL VAPOR RETARDER
   W/ 0.05 PERMS MAX.

FIGURE 15.8 The forced-air plan for the home drawn in Chapter 12. CAD technicians working for the mechanical contractor generally draw HVAC drawings.

A single number by a duct represents its diameter. Other notations that might be shown by a duct include:

WA: warm air
RA: return air (cold air)
CFM: cubic feet per minute

The sizes of all registers are also listed on the drawing. Because vertical ducts pass through the plane of projection, diagonal lines indicate the location of vertical ducts. HVAC plans also show the locations of all control devices, outlets, pipes, and heating and cooling units.

Locating Ductwork

Although you will not be drawing the HVAC plan, the architectural team must plan for the location of each duct. And while you don't plan the sizes of the ducts, you do plan the spaces available for them. Review Chapter 11 for a discussion of where and how to locate a duct or chase on the drawings that the architectural team creates.

Wood Plenum System

Instead of ducts, a plenum system may be used to distribute heat throughout a single-level residence. Plenum systems are based on a simple concept that has been in use since the Romans: The entire crawl space is sealed and used to distribute treated air through floor registers in rooms above it. This type of system requires the sealing and insulating of foundation walls. The fan on the forced-air units maintains slight air pressure in the plenum. This ensures a uniform distribution of conditioned air throughout the residence.

Zone-Control Systems

An electric *zoned heating system* offers much greater flexibility than a central heating system. A zoned heating system requires one heater and one thermostat per room. The heaters in unoccupied rooms remain off. Common types of zone heaters include baseboard and wall-mounted units with fans. Baseboard units have electric heating elements that cause a convection current as the air around the unit is heated. The heated air rises into the room and replaces cooler air that falls to the floor. Baseboard heaters should be placed on exterior walls under or next to windows or other openings. These units project a few inches into the room at floor level.

Fan heaters are mounted in a wall recess. A resistance heater is used to generate heat, and a fan circulates the heat into the room. The location of baseboard and wall-mounted heaters and their thermostats are shown on the electrical plan. Avoid placing the heaters in exterior walls to avoid reducing the insulation. Wall and baseboard units should be placed on the electrical plan, along with each

thermostat. Figure 15.9 shows an example of baseboard heaters in the home from Chapter 12.

Hydronic Units

Hydronic systems provide even heat in a residence by circulating hot water to radiators, finned tubes, or convectors. These systems use a gas- or oil-fired boiler to heat fresh water, which is circulated around a combustion chamber, where it absorbs heat. A pump then circulates water heated to temperatures ranging between 150°F and 180°F throughout the system. When heat is needed, a thermostat starts the circulator, which supplies hot water to the room convectors. Although these systems are efficient for heating, they do not provide air filtration or circulation and are not compatible with cooling systems that use air ducts.

Baseboard Heaters

The most common and effective type of hydronic heater is a baseboard unit. These units provide most of their heat through convection, with a small amount of heat produced through radiation. Some hydronic system units eliminate the need for a separate water-heating unit by also providing hot water for the fresh hot-water supply and for home heating. Common types of residential hot-water systems include the series-loop system, the one-pipe system, the two-pipe system, and the radiant system.

Common conductors for each system include baseboards and radiators. Baseboard units are generally placed along exterior walls. Radiators are typically made of cast iron or decorative aluminum and provide more mass for heating than any other type of heating device. Heat comes predominately through convection. Drawings for each system resemble those shown in Figure 15.9. The locations of the delivery tubes are not shown.

Series-Loop Systems. The *series-loop system* shown in Figure 15.10 is a continuous loop of pipes containing hot water. Hot water flows continually from the boiler through conductors and then back to the boiler for reheating. The heat in a series-loop system cannot be controlled except at the source of the loop. The entire loop is either conducting heat or is turned off.

One-Pipe Systems. *One-pipe heating systems* circulate heated water through a continuous pipe loop. Individual radiators connect to the circulating loop using a bypass loop. This system allows control of individual heating units by valves at the radiator. Once the water routes through a heating unit, it goes back to the main loop, through other heating units on the basis of demand, and then back to the boiler for reheating. Figure 15.11 shows an example of a one-pipe system.

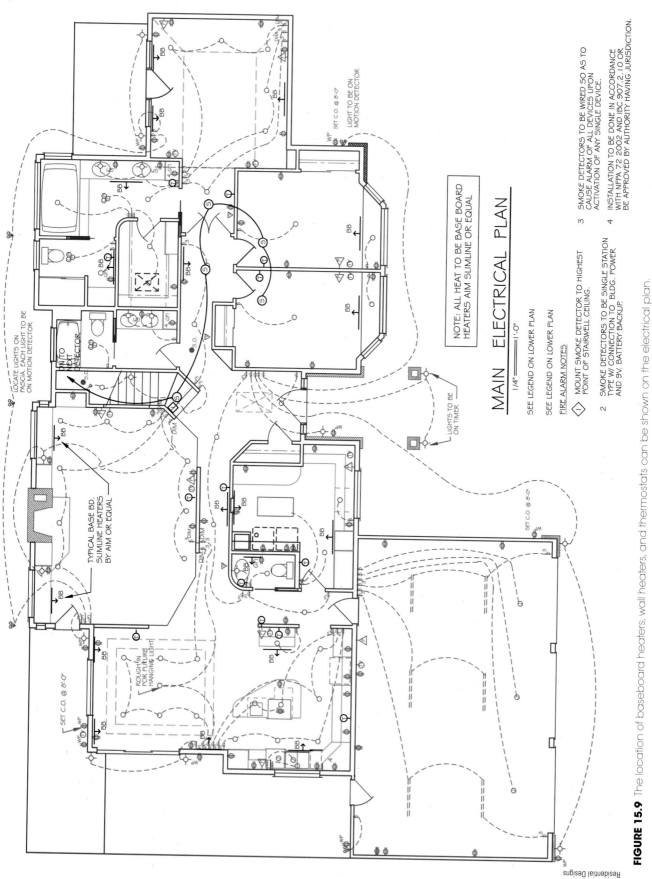

NOTE: ALL HEAT TO BE BASE BOARD HEATERS AIM SLIMLINE OR EQUAL

MAIN ELECTRICAL PLAN
1/4" = 1'-0"

SEE LEGEND ON LOWER PLAN

SEE LEGEND ON LOWER PLAN

FIRE ALARM NOTES

1. MOUNT SMOKE DETECTOR TO HIGHEST POINT OF STAIRWELL CEILING.

2. SMOKE DETECTORS TO BE SINGLE STATION TYPE W/ CONNECTION TO BLDG. POWER AND 9V. BATTERY BACKUP.

3. SMOKE DETECTORS TO BE WIRED SO AS TO CAUSE ALARM OF ALL DEVICES UPON ACTIVATION OF ANY SINGLE DEVICE.

4. INSTALLATION TO BE DONE IN ACCORDANCE WITH NFPA 72 2002 AND IBC 907.2.10 OR BE APPROVED BY AUTHORITY HAVING JURISDICTION.

LOCATE LIGHTS ON FASCIA. EACH LIGHT TO BE ON MOTION DETECTOR

TYPICAL BASE BD. SLIMLINE HEATERS BY AIM OR EQUAL

LIGHT TO BE ON MOTION DETECTOR

LIGHTS TO BE ON TIMER

ROUGH IN FOR FUTURE HANGING LIGHT

SET C.O. @ 8'-0"

Residential Designs

FIGURE 15.9 The location of baseboard heaters, wall heaters, and thermostats can be shown on the electrical plan.

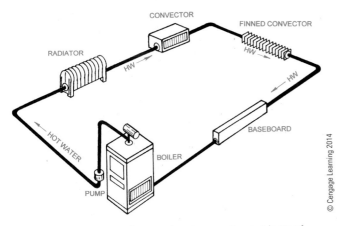

FIGURE 15.10 The series-loop system is a continuous loop of pipes that circulates hot water to heating units. Hot water flows continually from the boiler through conductors and then back to the boiler for reheating.

Two-Pipe Systems.

A *Two-pipe heating system* uses two parallel pipes to route water through the heating system. One pipe forms a loop for supplying heated water to each convector, allowing each heating unit to be used as needed. The heating loop circulates water to each heating unit and routes unused water back to the boiler to maintain the water temperature. Once water passes through a conductor rather than routing back into the heated line, it exits the heater into the second pipe of the system. The parallel pipe routes cooled water back to the boiler rather than to the next conductor. Figure 15.12 shows an example of a two-pipe heating system.

Radiant Systems.

Radiant heating systems were first used by the Romans to provide heat to floors. Radiant heating distributes hot water through a series of continual tubes in the floor system, turning the whole floor system into a radiator. Tubes can also be placed in ceilings and walls to

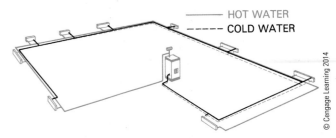

FIGURE 15.12 Two-pipe hydronic systems use one set of pipes to deliver heat to each heater and another set of pipes to return cooled water to the boiler.

provide supplemental heating in colder climates when the floor system cannot match the heat loss of a room. Tubing is generally only in the lower 42″ (1050 mm) of a wall to avoid interference with window framing and possible punctures when objects are hung on the wall. Figure 15.13 shows an example of wall-mounted tubing.

A radiant floor system consists of a heating unit that warms the water and pipes laid on a concrete base that is then covered by a concrete slab. Heating can be provided by gas, oil, electricity, geothermal heat, wood, or pellet-burning boilers. The hot pipes conduct heat to the surface where convection currents take over. The system can be divided into zones so that heat can be provided to rooms as desired. Figure 15.14 shows a radiant hot-water system prepared for the pouring of the concrete slab.

Steam Units

A *steam-heating unit* uses a boiler to make steam that is transported through pipes to radiators and baseboard heaters, producing heat through convection. After passing the heating unit, the steam condenses to water and returns to the boiler for reheating to steam. Although steam-heating

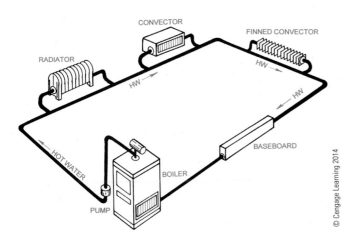

FIGURE 15.11 One-pipe heating systems circulate heated water through a continuous pipe loop. Individual heaters are connected to the circulating loop using a bypass that allows each heater to be controlled.

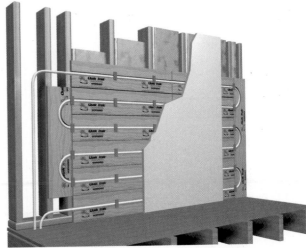

FIGURE 15.13 Radiant tubes can also be placed in ceilings and walls to provide supplemental heating in colder climates when the floor system cannot match the heat loss of a room.

FIGURE 15.14 Radiant tubes laid in preparation for the pouring of a concrete slab. The tubes will circulate heated water through the concrete. The concrete floor will then act as a radiator. Notice that the individual lines in the upper right corner lead to different zones, which will allow individual control of each zone.

systems function on water vapor rather than hot water, drawings for steam systems are identical to those prepared for hot-water systems. Steam-heated radiators are most likely found on larger multifamily projects in cold climates and in remodeling projects involving older homes.

Electric Resistance Heat

Electric heat produces a clean heat by passing an electrical current through resistance wires. The heat is usually radiated using similar methods as those used for radiant floor heat or through fan-blown methods. Resistance wires can be placed in panel heaters installed in a wall or ceiling, in baseboard heating units, or in plaster for heating the walls, ceilings, or floors. Although electric heat requires no storage of fuel and no ductwork, a ventilation- and humidity-control system should be included with electric heating systems because they provide no air circulation and cause the air in the home to become dry.

Separate plans are usually not drawn for electric heat systems, but annotation should be placed on the floor, electrical, or reflective ceiling plans to explain that ceiling-mounted electric heat is to be provided. The locations of the power supply and thermostats should also be shown on the electrical plan.

COOLING SYSTEMS

Because heat transfers only from warm objects to cooler objects, buildings must be cooled by removing heat. To cool a building, warm air is carried away from rooms to an air-conditioning unit where a filter removes dust and other impurities. A cooling coil containing refrigerant absorbs heat from the air passing around it. Then the blower that pulls the warm air from the rooms pushes cooled air back to the rooms, using the same ducts and outlets used with the heating systems.

The size of air-conditioning equipment is rated in BTU. A 2000-sq-ft home can be comfortably cooled with a central air-conditioning unit of 24,000 to 36,000 BTU. Larger homes may require 60,000 or more BTU, depending on the components specified. Drawings of combined systems use the same duct patterns and outlets used for the heating unit.

Heat-Pump Systems

A ***heat-pump*** is a forced-air central heating and cooling system that operates using a compressor and a circulating refrigerant system. Heat is extracted from outside air and pumped inside the residence. The cycle reverses in the summer and the unit operates as an air conditioner. In this mode, the heat is extracted from the inside air and pumped outside. On the cooling cycle, the heat pump also acts as a dehumidifier. Figure 15.15 shows how a heat pump works. Heat pumps may not be as efficient in some areas of the

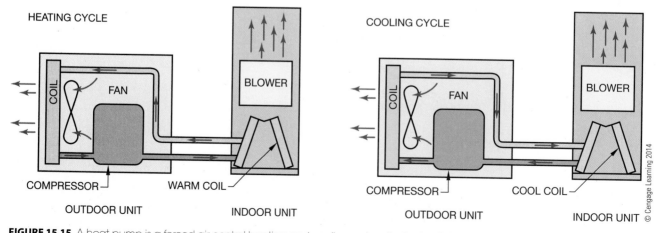

FIGURE 15.15 A heat pump is a forced-air central heating and cooling system that extracts heat from outside air and pumps the air to the inside of the residence. In the summer the cycle is reversed and the unit operates as an air conditioner.

country as in other areas because of annual low or high temperatures. Verify the product efficiency with local vendors.

Residential heat pumps vary in size from two to five tons. During minimal demand, the more efficient three-ton phase is used; the five-ton phase is operable during peak demand. In planning the size of the unit, assume that each ton of the rating will remove approximately 12,000 BTUH of heat. The total heat-pump system uses an outside compressor, an inside blower to circulate air, a backup heating coil, and a complete duct system. All but the duct system is shown on the floor and electrical plans which the mechanical contractor will place on the HVAC plan. Show and specify the concrete pad on the foundation plan. Place the unit in a shady location where the noise will not cause a problem. Place the compressor on a fiberglass or concrete slab that provides approximately

Going Green

Geothermal Heat-Pumps

The word geothermal comes from the Greek words *geo* (earth) and *thermo* (heat) to describe heat from within the earth. This renewable energy source that is constantly being produced inside the earth can be recovered as steam or hot water and used to heat structures or generate electricity. Most **geothermal reservoirs** are deep underground with no visible clues showing above ground. Occasionally geothermal energy sometimes finds its way to the surface in the form of volcanoes, hot springs, or geysers. In the United States, most of the visible geothermal resources are found in the western states.

Geothermal energy is typically used in heat pump systems to heat homes. Geothermal heat pumps are similar to ordinary heat pumps, but instead of using heat found in outside air, they rely on the heat below the surface of the earth to provide heating, air-conditioning, and hot water. Despite large swings in the air temperature, the soil temperature below the frost line remains at a relatively constant temperature. Although the temperatures vary according to latitude, below the frost line temperatures usually range from 55 degrees to 75 degrees Fahrenheit. It's the constant soil temperature that is the principle behind geothermal heat pumps. In the winter, they move the heat from below ground into a structure and in the summer, they pull the heat from the building envelope and discharge it into the ground. In addition to home heating and cooling, the system can be adjusted to heat water that circulates in the regular water heater tank. During the summer, heat is taken from the house to heat the water. In the winter, the geothermal system can supplement the cost of heating water. Geothermal heat-pumps collect the natural heat from below the earth's surface through a series of underground pipes, called a loop. Horizontal loops are often buried about ten feet (3000 mm) deep. Vertical loop depths may range from 100 to 400 feet (30 000 to 120 000 mm) deep. A horizontal underground loop is typically made of high-density polyethylene or copper. A vertical loop is typically polyethylene. The fluid in the loop is water or an environmentally safe antifreeze solution that circulates through the pipes in a closed system. The fluid circulates through the loop and carries the heat to the house. There, an electrically driven compressor and a heat exchanger concentrate the heated fluid and release it inside the home at a higher temperature. Ductwork distributes the heat to different rooms.

6″ (150 mm) on all sides of the compressor. To avoid transmitting vibrations from the compressor into the residence, make sure the slab that is not attached to the home.

IMPROVING AIR QUALITY IN THE HOME

In addition to heating and cooing the residence, some means must be provided to control each system, including ventilation, filtration, and humidity control.

Thermostatic Controls

A *thermostat* is an automatic mechanism to control the amount of air treatment provided by a heating or cooling system. Once a desired temperature range is achieved, thermostatic controls keep buildings temperatures constant by turning the climate-control system on or off.

The type of system for controlling the air temperature determines the number of thermostats required. Central heating and cooling systems usually require only one thermostat for each unit servicing the structure. For zoned heating or cooling units, thermostats must be placed to control each zone; alternatively, a central thermostat to control each room may be placed in a convenient location. Systems using electrical heating and some water systems require that rooms be thermostatically controlled.

The location of thermostats is shown on the electrical plans with a thermostat symbol (see Figure 15.9). Place annotation on the electrical plan to specify that the thermostats are between 36 and 48″ (900 to 1200 mm) above the floor level. Since thermostats are sensitive to heat and cold, they should be located on interior walls, away from sources of heat or cold such as fireplaces or windows. A location near the center of the residence and close to a return air duct is an ideal location because the temperate air entering the air return will cause only minor temperature variation at the thermostat. Also ensure a location that is free from drafts caused by an exterior door, direct sunlight from windows, or heat from a heat register. Avoid locations by stairwells to prevent convective air currents between floors and vibrations caused by traffic on the stairs.

Heat Recovery and Ventilation

In addition to the air temperature, comfort control requires providing well-ventilated clean air. One of the drawbacks of new construction is that many architects and designers spend much of their design time focusing on how to minimize air infiltration, so they overlook the need for proper ventilation. The tighter homes become because of super insulation, air wraps, and caulking at every point of entry,

the more important good ventilation becomes to keep fresh air circulating and to remove pollutants. Ventilation also plays an important role in keeping the interior air humidity balanced. Air in a residence must be in constant circulation to reduce the risk of allergies, which can develop from exposure to the chemicals used in many building materials. Poor ventilation causes common problems, such as:

- Structural damage as well as health problems due to high interior humidity levels. In addition to natural humidity from the atmosphere, steam from showers, cooking, and the home's occupants can produce as much as one gallon (3.8 liters) of water vapor per day.

- Eye irritation and respiratory problems from formaldehyde found in carpets, furniture, the glue used in plywood, particle board, and some insulation products.

- Deadly carbon monoxide gas. Due to incomplete combustion in gas-fired or wood-burning appliances, carbon monoxide can be trapped in a residence.

- Serious health risks such as cancer due to the buildup of radon, a naturally occurring radioactive gas. Chapter 26 introduces specific methods to control the buildup of radon by venting the crawl space.

Blowers built into the heating and cooling units provide interior air movement. Ceiling fans and exhaust fans remove steam and odors from kitchens and bathrooms. Roof vents with power ventilators reduce the buildup of heat in the attic and circulate air in attics and crawl spaces. Including crawl space ventilation helps remove excessive moist air from this space before it enters the living space. Section 7 introduces requirements for crawl space ventilation for various types of foundation systems as well as ventilation systems to remove radon.

Exhaust System Requirements

The information required for the exhaust system must appear throughout the construction documents. The following are some general IRC requirements that need to be considered during the design process. Unless noted otherwise, place these specifications in general notes on the floor plan.

- Vent range hoods to the outside by a single-wall, galvanized stainless steel or copper duct. This duct must have a smooth inner surface, be substantially airtight, and have a backdraft damper.

- Cabinets supporting the range hood must not be closer than 24″ (600 mm) to the cooking surface (Show the minimum height on the cabinet elevations.) Clothes dryer vents must be:

  - Independent of all other systems.

  - Directly vented to carry the moisture outside.

- Made of rigid metal 0.016″ (0.406 mm) thick with a smooth inside, joints running in the direction of the airflow, and equipped with a backdraft damper.
- No longer than 25′ (7500 mm) from the dryer to the wall or roof vent if the is duct 4″ (100 mm) in diameter. The total length must be reduced by 2′-6″ (750 mm) for each 45° bend.
- Made with a total length that is reduced by 5′ (1500 mm) for each 90° bend.

Air-to-Air Heat Exchangers

An ***air-to-air heat exchanger*** is a heat recovery and ventilation device that pulls polluted air from within the building envelope and transfers the heat by pulling fresh air into the house. A heat exchanger does not produce heat but moves it from one air stream to another. The two streams of air never come in contact with each other, thus preventing the indoor pollutants in the stale air from being added back into the fresh air.

Air Filtration

Moving air throughout a home does not ensure that the home will have a supply of fresh air. To create clean air, airborne pollutants such as dust mites, pollen, bacteria, mold spores, and mildew must constantly be removed from the air inside the residence. For many, these pollutants are just minor irritants. For inhabitants with allergies, they can be the source of ongoing health problems. Each heating or cooling system that relies on ducts to move the treated air can be equipped with air filters. Filters filled with fiberglass or charcoal remove approximately 15 percent of the household pollutants. Electronic filters remove approximately 80 percent of the household impurities, but they also dry the air and cause a buildup of static electricity. Electrostatic filters with ionizing wires trap more than 99 percent of household impurities. To further purify the air, ozonators may be attached to the ductwork. An ozonator adds low levels of electronically charged oxygen to the air supply.

Humidity Control

Moisture in the air is referred to as humidity. The proper amount of moisture in the air is important for good climate-control as well as the control of common household allergens. Some heating devices, such as forced-air systems, dry the air. Heating systems that use hot water generally add moisture to the interior of the home. The use of vapor barriers in the walls, ceiling, and foundation can help limit the buildup of excessive moisture within the building envelope.

Two electronic devices are also available to control humidity: a ***humidifier*** to increase the humidity levels of the interior air and a ***dehumidifier*** to remove excessive moisture from the building envelope. Either of these units can be added individually to a home or to any comfort control system that uses ductwork.

Going Green

Solar Heating Systems

Solar heating and cooling involves using the sun's energy to provide heat and convective currents within a home. ***Passive solar systems*** operate without the use of special mechanical or electronic devices. Passive systems use the structure and orientation of the residence to maximize energy from the sun. They are easy to incorporate into home construction and many of the basic design considerations have become common features of good design based on green and ENERGY STAR programs. Active solar systems incorporate mechanical devices to provide power, heat, and hot water for a home.

No matter the type of system, solar heating and cooling includes the four basic steps of collecting, storing, distributing, and controlling the collected solar radiation. Both passive and active systems are still popular means to heat homes,

(Continued)

but their use is decreasing with the incorporation of other green and ENERGY STAR building advances. Due to the expense of active systems, they are not examined in this text.

Solar Design Basics

Not all of the sun's energy directed toward earth strikes its surface. As much as 35 percent of the sun's energy is reflected back into space by our atmosphere. As much as 15 percent of the remaining energy is scattered and reflected by water vapor, dust, and other particles in the air. The distance through the atmosphere through which the remaining radiation must pass and the angle it travels in relation to the earth's surface, determine how effective the remaining energy is. When the sun is directly overhead, radiation travels through the least amount of atmosphere to reach the earth's surface. During the early hours after sunrise or the later stages of the afternoon, when the sun is closer to the horizon, the radiation passes through more of the atmosphere. Figure 15.16 illustrates this elementary but important concept. The more atmosphere the radiation must pass through, the lower the amount of energy available at the surface of the earth.

The seasonal position of the earth in relation to the sun is a second major consideration affecting the available amount of solar radiation. Because of the earth's tilt and rotation, the amount of atmosphere the solar radiation must pass through varies throughout the year. The earth orbits the sun in an elliptical path and rotates once a day on an axis that extends through the north and south poles. The axis is tilted at 23.47° from vertical of the plane of the earth's orbit around the sun. The constant tilt of Earth's axis produces the seasonal variations in weather. The northern hemisphere is tilted away from the sun during winter, decreasing the hours of available sunlight and increasing the atmosphere through which radiation must pass. For those in the southern hemisphere, the situation is reversed; they experience summer while we experience winter. During the summer, the situation is again reversed. The northern axis of the earth is tilted toward the sun, the length of available daylight increases, and the available radiation from the sun is closer to perpendicular to the earth's surface. As the sun's rays move closer to perpendicular to the surface of the earth, the amount of radiation from the sun increases. This may be third-grade science, but it's important to know if a residence is to be made to work efficiently.

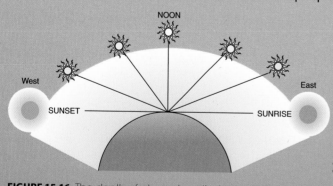

FIGURE 15.16 The depth of atmosphere that solar radiation must pass through and its angle in relation to the earth's surface determines how concentrated the energy will be. When the sun is directly overhead, radiation travels through the least amount of atmosphere to reach the surface of the earth. During the early hours after sunrise or the later hours of the afternoon, when the sun is closer to the horizon, the radiation must pass through a greater depth of atmosphere.

© Cengage Learning 2014

Solar Orientation

Chapter 8 introduces the importance of the home's orientation in taking advantage of solar heating. A rectangular home with its long surface facing south is ideal to maximize solar gain. Although facing due south is

(Continued)

the ideal, the south side of the home may be rotated up to 30° to the east or west and still receive 90 percent of the available radiation. Equally important to the orientation of the home is the angle of the window surfaces to the sun's rays. Windows perpendicular to the angle of the sun's rays intercept 100 percent of the rays. This is why many solar homes shown in magazines and on television have windows on an angle rather than in the normal vertical position. As the angle of the glass decreases from being perpendicular to the rays of the sun, so does the absorption. Glass tilted 25° to the angle of the sun can still achieve 90 percent of the sun's radiation. Tables are available on the Internet and through books to determine the angle of the sun at various latitudes at different times of the year. For instance, at 45° north latitude, the sun's angle is 21° above the horizon on January 21; it is 69° above the horizon during the summer. Armed with this information, a simple section can be drawn of a proposed project to determine roof overhangs that block the sun as well as the depth that the sun will enter a home during the winter (see Figure 15.17). In addition to the atmospheric relationship of the sun to the earth's surface, two other principles of solar physics are used in passive solar planning: 1) the greenhouse effect and 2) the natural law of rising warm air.

Greenhouse Effect

The trapping of heat in the atmosphere is known as the **greenhouse effect**. Glass allows virtually all solar radiation striking its surface to pass through to the cool side of the glass. Once the sunlight is transmitted through the glass and absorbed by materials on the interior side, thermal energy radiated by these materials will not pass back out through the glass until the outside air is cooler than the glass. If, during the summer, you've gotten into a car with its windows rolled up, you experienced the greenhouse effect. Although the greenhouse effect can be dangerous to someone left in a sealed automobile, it is very useful in a residence. Heat from the sun that enters through windows can be stored in some type of thermal mass. The heat is released when the home cools to provide heating when the sun's energy is not available.

A **thermal mass** is any material that absorbs heat from the sun and later radiates the heat back into the air. Walls, floors, and masonry features function as a thermal mass in a building designed for maximum solar effectiveness. The concrete floor of a home, even if covered with carpet or wood, acts as a thermal mass. Masonry or stone veneer on an interior wall or a masonry chimney are all examples of common areas that provide thermal mass in a residence. These items and other materials exposed to the sun's radiation serve both for storage and distribution in a

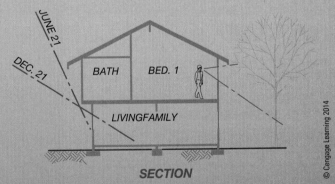

SECTION

FIGURE 15.17 A simple section can be used to project the winter and summer sun angles into the residence. The goal is to have the greatest penetration during the winter and the smallest penetration during the summer.

© Cengage Learning 2014

(Continued)

FIGURE 15.18 A greenhouse can be used to collect solar heat.

Courtesy Velux®-America, Inc.

FIGURE 15.19 Any room with south-facing glass can be used as a solarium. An efficient collector will also have areas of high thermal mass to store heat as well as openable windows to remove heat during the cooling cycle.

Courtesy BOWA Builders, Inc. Greg Hadley, photographer.

passive solar system. Storing and dissipating the trapped heat to either lower or raise the temperature of a building as needed is a key element of passive solar design. If the budget, the terrain, and the orientation of the house allow, a greenhouse can be attached to the south side of a residence to further increase the solar gain. Don't become trapped by the thought of a green house. A greenhouse or solarium does not have to be a room totally surrounded by glass, as shown in Figure 15.18. Although this is an attractive room, it does not fit in with many historic styles of houses. Figure 15.19 shows a room that blends with the entire design of the residence and also collects solar radiation effectively. A *solarium* used as a family room, nook, or enclosed deck also doubles as a solar collector.

Convective Air Loops

Heated air always rises. Passive solar homes take advantage of this fact and introduce heat at the lower levels of the home. Natural convection circulates the air through the structure. Placing cold air returns in the ceiling is an excellent method of recirculating heated air by a forced-air heating system. Using slow-moving ceiling fans is a less expensive method to accomplish a similar effect. Reversible fans can force heated air to the floor level during heating cycles. The fan direction can be reversed to accelerate the rise of heated air during the cooling cycle.

Homes with large amounts of south-facing glass risk overheating

(Continued)

during the summer. In addition to collecting heat, a home must be able to release heat during the cooling cycle. The room in Figure 15.19 has upper windows that open to release the hot air that accumulates at the ceiling. Openable windows on the north face of the home also create a convective current from south to north through the residence. Openable skylights, such as those in Figure 15.20, allow for natural venting of the heated air from the kitchen. When the kitchen is in use, it becomes a heat producer. The skylights allow for venting the hot air without activating the home cooling system. During the heating cycle, the skylights produce a negative effect on heat gain. Although most skylights are double-glazed and contain low-E glass, a protective shade that can be drawn across the opening further reduces heat loss. In placing skylights on a roof plan, remember that skylights on the south, east, and west sides of the roof will have some heat gain. Skylights on the north face of the roof gain heat only during the latest part of the summer, when the sun is at its highest point above the horizon.

Passive Solar Methods

Passive solar heating and cooling methods rely on basic principles of physics to help control the home environment. The direct- and indirect-gain methods take advantage of solar radiation to provide heat and to block the sun's heat when the home is in the cooling cycle.

Direct-Gain Method

Direct gain is the simplest approach to passive solar heat gain. Using the direct-gain method, the inside of a building is directly heated by the sun's rays as they pass through large areas of south-facing glass (see Figure 15.21). Once the sun's rays enter the residence, they are absorbed by each thermal mass. As the room cools throughout the evening, the stored heat in the thermal mass radiates back into the room. Water has the highest capacity to retain heat, but steel, aluminum, concrete, masonry, and rock also make excellent thermal storage materials. Wood and similar porous materials are ineffective in retaining heat.

Indirect-Gain Method

The **indirect-gain** method places a thermal mass between the sun

FIGURE 15.20 Openable skylights allow heated air to be vented, providing a convective current in the home.

Courtesy Velux® America, Inc.

(Continued)

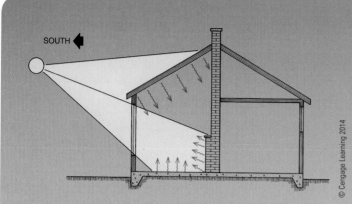

FIGURE 15.21 Passive solar heating depends on trapping collected heat in a thermal mass. The denser the mass, the longer the heat will be stored before being released back into the room.

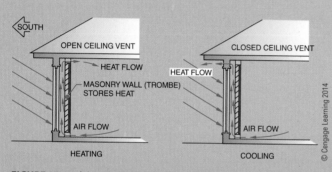

FIGURE 15.22 A trombe wall uses dense materials such as masonry or water containers to store heat. Heat is stored in the wall and then radiated into the living areas.

and the interior of the residence. With indirect solar gain, light passes through glass and strikes the thermal mass and then radiates into the living space. The most common method of implementing indirect gain is to use a trombe wall. A ***trombe wall*** uses dense materials such as masonry or water containers to store heat (see Figure 15.22). The space between the glass and the wall generates very high temperatures in addition to heating the wall. This air is drawn by convection or the use of mechanical fans into the residence to increase the amount of heat that reaches the living space. An obvious drawback to this system is that it limits visibility on the south side of the home.

Active Solar Methods

Planning for ***active solar systems*** requires knowledge of both mechanical systems and thermal principles. Active solar systems use mechanical devices to drive the components needed for solar heating or cooling. This includes devices and facilities to collect, store, distribute, and control heat. Active solar systems operate more effectively when they are combined with passive solar features. The most frequent use of active systems is to heat hot water for the fresh-water system or for heating pool and spa water. Active systems are most effective when combined with passive solar design features. Mechanical consulting firms generally design and draw active systems.

Additional Resources

Use the following websites as resources to help you keep current with changes with HVAC systems.

Address	Company or Organization
www.ase.org	The Alliance to Save Energy
www.ashrae.org	American Society of Heating, Refrigerating and Air-Conditioning Engineers, Inc.
www.ases.org	American Solar Energy Society

www.basf.com	BASF – The Chemical Company
www.arcat.com	ARCAT© (building product information)
www.buildingscience.com	Building Science Corporation
www.carrier.com	Carrier
www.certainteed.com	CertainTeed
www.consumerenergycenter.org	Consumer Energy Center
www.dap.com	Dap®
www.earthadvantage.com	Earth Advantage Institute©
www.energystar.gov	ENERGY STAR
www.eeba.org	Energy & Environmental Building Alliance
www.geothermal.marin.org	Geothermal Education Office
www.geo-energy.org	Geothermal Energy Association
www.pprbd.org/plancheck/heat	Heat Loss Calculations for Residential Construction
www.hvaccomputer.com	HVAC Computer Systems, Ltd.
www.radiantbarrier.com	Innovative Insulation Inc.
www.insulate.org	Insulation Contractors of America
www.jm.com	Johns Manville (insulation)
www.lennox.com	Lennox
www.naima.org	North American Insulation Manufacturers Association
www.insulation.owenscorning.com	Owens Corning®
www.powerfromthesun.net	Solar Concepts
www.seia.org	Solar Energy Industries Association®
www.sprayfoam.org	Spray Polyurethane Foam Alliance
www.thermafiber.com	Thermafiber, Inc.® (insulation)
www.trane.com	Trane®
www.doe.gov	U.S. Department of Energy
www.energysavers.gov	U.S. Department of Energy, Energy Savers
www.eere.energy.gov/geothermal	U.S. Department of Energy, Geothermal Technologies Program
www.usgbc.org	U.S. Green Building Council
www.wisehomedesign.com	Wise Home Design

Comfort Control Systems Test

Follow these instructions to access and complete an electronic copy of the Chapter 15 Comfort Control Systems Test:

1. Go to cengagebrain.com
2. Enter the email address and password you used to register for the site (see Preface for full instructions).
3. Select the website from the **My Course & Materials** area of your home page. Select the chapter you want from the pull-down menu at the top of the page. Choose the resources for that chapter from the menu on the left.
4. Type your name, the chapter number, and the date at the top of the sheet.
5. Answer the following questions with short, complete statements using a word processor.

➤ **NOTE:**

The answers to some questions may not be contained in this chapter and will require you to do additional research using the Internet. Use your favorite search engine to search for specific professional companies or general categories of information.

Questions

15.1. Describe and explain the units of heat measurement.

15.2. Describe the four major steps of solar heating and cooling.

15.3. List two advantages and two disadvantages of a zonal heat system as compared with central forced-air heating.

15.4. Describe the difference between a heat pump and a forced-air heating system.

15.5. Describe four factors that influence placement of a thermostat.

15.6. Describe and explain systems that contribute to a healthy interior environment.

15.7. Describe the function of an air-to-air heat exchanger.

15.8. What is a plenum?

15.9. Define combustion air.

15.10. List passive solar design features that can easily be included in a residence.

15.11. Use the table in Chapter 5 to determine your climate zone and then determine the required insulation values for stem wall, basement walls, floors, wood walls, and ceilings for your area.

15.12. Verify with your local building department website or use Appendix D of the IPC to determine the outdoor winter design temperature of your area.

15.13. Research ten of the most common building materials in your area and list their R-values.

15.14. What are two major problems that an air-conditioning system must overcome?

15.15. Research the type of heating and cooling systems that several major local builders install in their new homes. Discuss the reasons for choosing the system they typically install including cost and efficiency.

15.16. After setting up an appointment, discuss with a local HVAC contractor any special framing requirements that must be made to accommodate the HVAC system they typically install.

15.17. Research the feasibility of using passive solar heating in your area. Incorporate your findings into the home that you started in Chapter 12.

15.18. List three factors that affect the rate of heat loss of a home:

15.19. List four common sources of heat gain.

15.20. Using the Internet, search for software suitable for calculating heat loss for a residence.

Section 4

Roof Plans

Chapter 16
Roof Plan Components

The design of the roof must be considered long before the roof plan is drawn. The architect or designer will typically design the basic shape of the roof as the floor plan and elevations are drawn at the preliminary design stage. At this stage, the designer plans only the general shape and type of roofing material to be used, not the entire structural system for the roof. By examining the structure in Figure 16.1, you can see the impact of the roof design on the structure. Often the roof can present a larger visible surface area than the walls. In addition to aesthetic considerations, the roof can also be used to provide rigidity in a structure when wall areas are filled with glass. To ensure that the roof will meet the designer's criteria, a roof plan is usually drawn by the CAD technician to provide construction information. In order to draw the roof plan, knowledge of the types of roof plans, common roof terms, common roof shapes, and common roof materials is required.

Key Terms

A-frame	Eave	Hip	Single-ply roof
Barge rafter	Elastomeric	Mansard	Slate shingles
Boxed eave	Fascia	Overhang	Soffit
Built-up roofing	Flashing	Pitch	Solar reflectance
Composition shingles	Gable	Rake	Square
Cool roof	Gable end wall	Ridge	Sustainable roof
Cornice	Gambrel	Roof framing plan	Thermal emittance
Dormer	Green roof	Roof plan	Underlayment
Dutch hip	Half-hip	Sheathing	Valley

FIGURE 16.1 The shape of the roof can play an important role in the design of the structure.

TYPES OF ROOF DRAWINGS

The plan that is drawn of the roof area may be either a roof plan or a roof framing plan. For some types of roofs, a roof drainage plan may also be drawn. Roof framing plans are discussed in Chapter 25.

Roof Plans

A **_roof plan_** is used to show the shape of the roof. Materials such as the roofing material, vents and their location, and the type of underlayment are also typically specified on the roof plan, as seen in Figure 16.2. Roof plans are often drawn at a scale smaller than the scale used for the floor plan. A scale of 1/8" = 1'-0" or 1/16" = 1'-0" (1:100 or 1:200) is commonly used for a roof plan. A roof plan is usually displayed on the same sheet as the exterior elevations.

Roof Framing Plans

Roof framing plans are required for complicated residential roof shapes. A roof framing plan shows the size and direction of the construction members required to frame the roof. Figure 16.3 shows an example of a roof framing plan. On very complex projects, every framing member is shown, as seen in Figure 16.4. Framing plans are discussed further in Chapter 25.

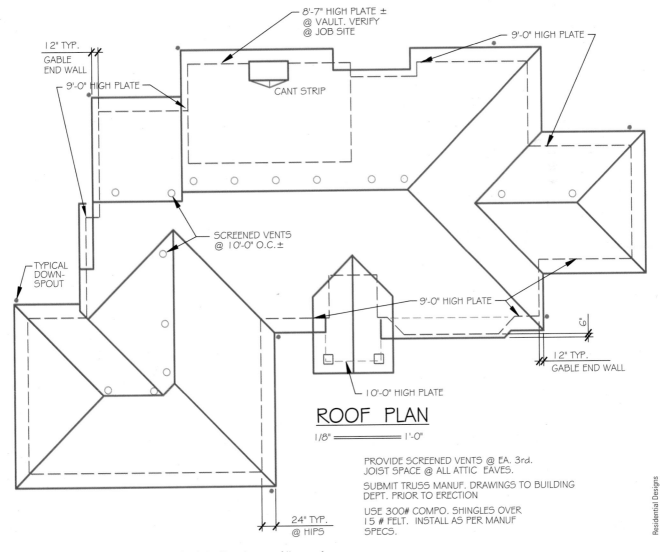

FIGURE 16.2 A roof plan is drawn to show the shape of the roof.

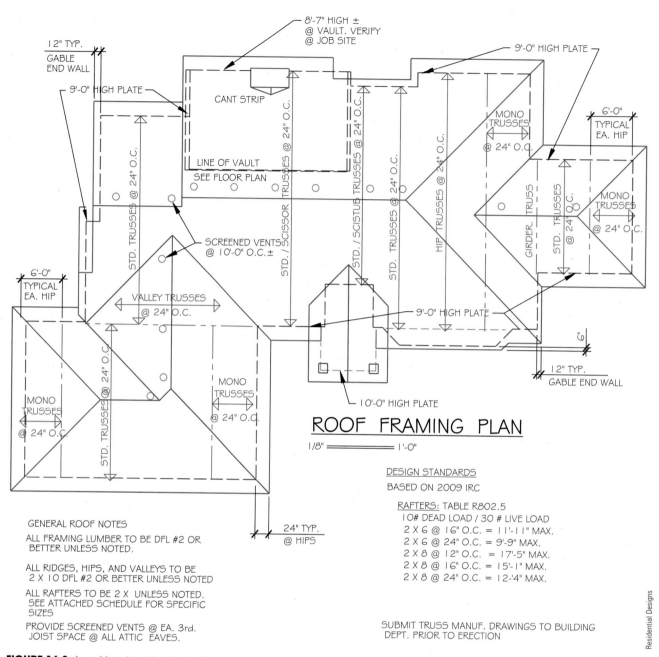

FIGURE 16.3 A roof framing plan is used to show the framing members for the roof.

COMMON ROOF TERMS

You must understand several terms that represent common roof components before completing a roof plan or roof framing plan. These terms include *ridge, roof pitch, overhang, eave, soffit, cornice,* and *fascia.* Several of these terms are used interchangeably. The portions of the roof that these terms represent are shown in Figure 16.5.

Ridge

The term **ridge** is used in several ways that relate to the roof framing methods. Some of these terms include *ridge*

board, ridge block, ridge beam, and *ridge brace.* Each of these terms is discussed in Chapters 17 and 21 as roof framing methods are explored. A ridge is a horizontal intersection between two or more roof planes, and it represents the highest point of a roof. In drawing a roof plan, the ridge is centered between the two walls that support a roof if the following two conditions are met:

- The support walls must be of equal height.
- The angle (pitch) of the roof planes must be equal.

If wall heights or roof angles are unequal, the ridge location will be altered, as seen in Figure 16.6.

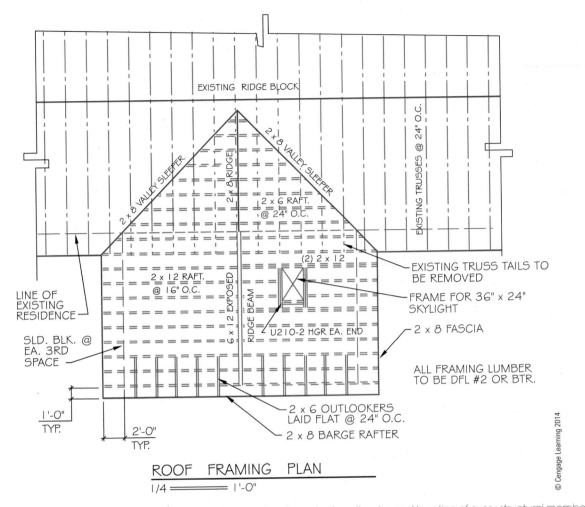

FIGURE 16.4 For complicated roofs, a roof framing plan may be drawn to show the size and location of every structural member.

Overhang

The *overhang* is the portion of the roof that extends past the walls. The overhang provides shade for wall openings and it provides protection to the walls from weather. The historical style of the home, the amount of shade and protection desired, and the pitch of the roof influence the size of the overhang.

Roof Pitch

Roof *pitch* describes the angle of the roof that compares the horizontal run and the vertical rise. Roof pitch is measured in the field with a framer's square, using inches as the unit of measurement. As a CAD technician, you can determine the rise and run using inches, feet, millimeters, meters, or any other equal units. The roof pitch is not represented on the roof drawings, but the intersections that result from various roof pitches must be represented. It is also necessary to understand the effects of pitch on the size of the overhang. The roof slope, shown when the elevations and sections are drawn, is discussed in Chapters 17, 19, 22 and 30.

In order to plot the intersection between two roof surfaces correctly, it is necessary to understand how various roof pitches are drawn. Figure 16.7 shows how the roof pitch can be visualized. This method of using the rise and run can be used to determine any roof pitch. The roof pitch can also be drawn if you know the angle that represents the desired pitch. For example, knowing that a 4/12 roof pitch equals 18 1/2° allows the correct angle to be entered without having to plot the layout. Table 16.1 shows angles for common roof pitches.

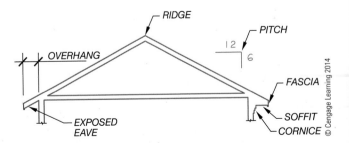

FIGURE 16.5 Common roof terms associated with roof drawings include ridge, roof pitch, overhang, eave, soffit, cornice, and fascia.

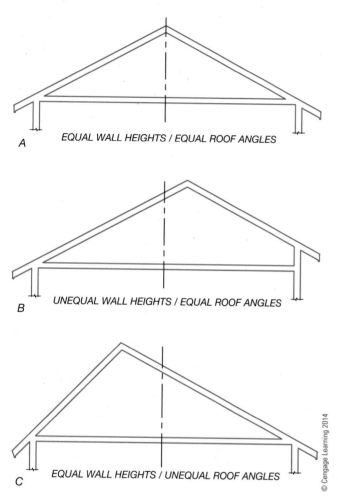

FIGURE 16.6 Three options for determining the ridge location. (A) If the walls supporting the roof are the same height and the angles of the roof planes are equal, the ridge will be centered between the support walls. (B) If the height of one of the two support walls is altered, the ridge location will be altered. (C) If the angles of the roof planes are not the same, the ridge will no longer be centered between the support walls.

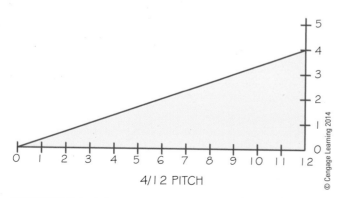

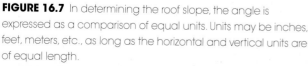

FIGURE 16.7 In determining the roof slope, the angle is expressed as a comparison of equal units. Units may be inches, feet, meters, etc., as long as the horizontal and vertical units are of equal length.

TABLE 16.1 Common Roof Pitches and Angles

COMMON ANGLES FOR DRAWING ROOF PITCHES

ROOF PITCH	ANGLE
1/12	4°–30'
2/12	9°–30'
3/12	15°–0'
4/12	18°–30'
5/12	22°–30'
6/12	26°–30'
7/12	30°–0'
8/12	33°–45'
9/12	37°–0'
10/12	40°–0'
11/12	42°–30'
12/12	45°–0'

Angles shown are approximate and are to be used for drawing purposes only.

Roof pitches can be considered as very slight, slight, moderate, or dramatic slopes.

- Roofs with a pitch of less than 2/12 are considered to have slight slopes. A very slight-sloping roof is not practical for deflecting rain and snow, but in arid parts of the world, slope is less important. The development of more durable roofing materials has allowed flat roofs to become common on modern, International-style homes, and many townhouses.

- Roofs with a pitch between 2/12 to 4/12 are considered to have gradual slopes. Low, gently pitched roofs are characteristic of Mediterranean and Italianate-style homes and many twentieth-century styles, such as Craftsman-, Bungalow-, Prairie-, and Ranch-style homes.

- Roofs built with a pitch between 4/12 and 7/12 have moderate roof slopes. Any style of home can have a moderate roof pitch.

- Steep roof slopes are roofs that have an 8/12 pitch or greater. Steep gable roofs are common on Gothic-, Greek Revival-, Tudor-, Cape Cod-, French Manor-, Colonial-, and Farmhouse-style homes.

Sun Angle and Overhang Size

The size of the overhang varies depending on the pitch of the roof and the amount of shade desired. As seen in Figure 16.8, the steeper the roof pitch, the smaller the over-hang that is required to shade an area. If you are drawing

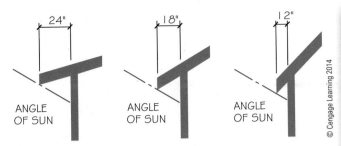

FIGURE 16.8 The steeper the roof pitch, the more shadow will be cast. Typically the overhang is decreased as the pitch is increased.

© Cengage Learning 2014

LATITUDE (IN DEGREES)	F
26	5.6 to 11.1
32	4.0 to 6.3
36	3.0 to 4.5
40	2.5 to 3.4
44	2.0 to 2.7
48	1.7 to 2.2
52	1.5 to 1.8
56	1.3 to 1.5

© Cengage Learning 2014

a home for a southern location, an overhang large enough to protect glazing from direct sunlight is usually desirable. In northern areas, the overhang is usually restricted to maximize the amount of sunlight received during the winter months. Figure 16.9 compares the effect of an overhang at different times of the year. Another important consideration regarding the size of the overhang is how it will affect the view from windows. As the angle of the roof is increased, the size of the overhang may need to be decreased so that the eave will not extend into the line of sight from a window. The designer will need to base the size of the overhang on the roof pitch so that the view is not hindered. The required length of an overhang can be determined using the following formula:

$$OH = WH / F$$

where OH is the overhang length and WH is the window height. F is a factor that takes into account the north latitude and whether or not you desire full shading at noon on June 21 or August 1.

The F factor with the highest value for your north latitude will provide full shading at noon on June 21. The lower of the two F factors will provide full shading on

August 1. These calculations assume that the structure is facing due south. If the structure is situated 15° east or west of true south, the overhang will need to be extended by 10 percent to ensure proper shading.

Eaves and Rakes

The *eave* is the horizontal edge of a roof that overhangs the exterior wall. The eave area can be open or enclosed. When the eave is left exposed, the rafter or truss tails (the ends of the members) are visible and require painting or other protection from the elements (see the upper portion of Figure 16.10). Plywood on top of the rafter or truss tails that is exposed to the elements at the eave must be rated for weather exposure. When the rafter or truss tails are enclosed, interior grade ply or OSB can be used. Chapter 21 explores eave framing. A *rake* is the sloped end portion of a roof that forms at the gable end wall where the roof intersects the wall. It is the equivalent of an inclined eave.

Boxed and Soffited Eaves

A *boxed eave* is an eave with a covering applied directly to the bottom side of the rafter or truss tails. A *soffit* is the enclosed area below the overhang that is used to protect the rafter or truss tails from the elements (see the lower portion of Figure 16.10). By enclosing the eave area, future maintenance cost can be reduced. Figure 16.11 shows examples of flat and arched soffits.

Cornice

A *cornice* is an ornamental molding or combination of two or more moldings located at the top of an exterior wall just below a roof. Cornice molding is used on many homes in order to match a particular historic style such as Federal or Greek revival. Figure 16.12 shows the use of cornice molding. Figure 16.13 shows an example of a cornice detail completed by a CAD technician.

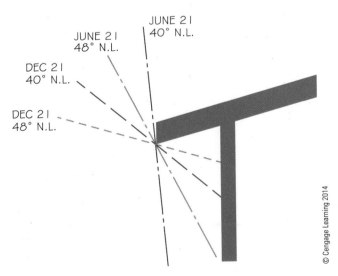

FIGURE 16.9 The overhang blocks different amounts of sunlight at different times of the year. Notice the difference in the sun's angles at 40° and 48° north latitude.

© Cengage Learning 2014

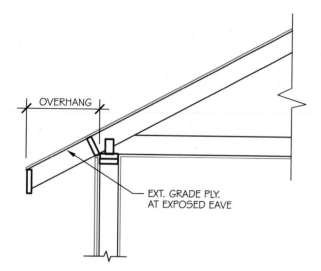

EXPOSED EAVES

OVERHANG

EXT. GRADE PLY.
AT EXPOSED EAVE

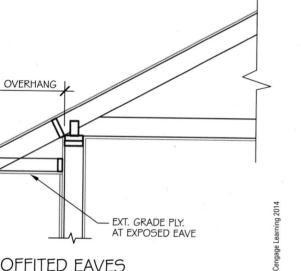

OVERHANG

EXT. GRADE PLY.
AT EXPOSED EAVE

SOFFITED EAVES

© Cengage Learning 2014

FIGURE 16.10 The ends of a rafter or truss can be either exposed to the elements or enclosed.

Fascias and Barge Rafters

The *fascia* is the trim placed at the end of the truss or rafter tails. The fascia serves to hide the ends of the roof-framing members and provides a mounting service for the gutters. A fascia runs parallel to the ridge and remains parallel to the floor level. The fascia can be seen in Figures 16.10 and 16.13. When the fascia is placed parallel to the rafters or trusses, it is referred to as a *barge rafter.* A barge rafter is the inclined trim that hangs from the projecting edge of a roof rake (see Figure 16.14). Depending on your area of the country, a barge may also be referred to as a verge board, gable rafter, or gable board.

Courtesy APA—The Engineered Wood Association®

FIGURE 16.11 A soffit is used to enclose the underside of the roof overhang. Flat soffits can be seen on either side of the curved entry soffit.

© Cengage Learning 2014

FIGURE 16.12 A cornice is the decorative molding placed at the top of an exterior wall just below a roof.

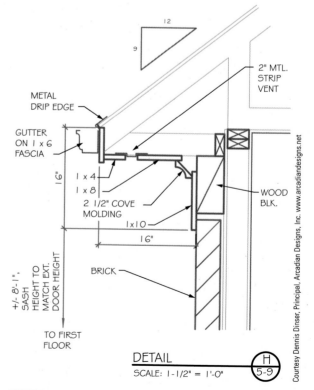

METAL
DRIP EDGE

GUTTER
ON 1 x 6
FASCIA

16"

1 x 4
1 x 8
2 1/2" COVE
MOLDING

1 x 10

16"

BRICK

+/- 8'-1"
SASH
HEIGHT TO
MATCH EXT.
DOOR HEIGHT

TO FIRST
FLOOR

2" MTL.
STRIP
VENT

WOOD
BLK.

DETAIL
SCALE: 1-1/2" = 1'-0"

H
5-9

Courtesy Dennis Dinser, Principal, Arcadian Designs, Inc. www.arcadiandesigns.net

FIGURE 16.13 A cornice detail completed by a CAD technician.

© Cengage Learning 2014

FIGURE 16.14 The fascia is the horizontal trim placed at the end of the truss or rafter tails. A barge rafter is the inclined trim that hangs from the projecting edge of a roof.

COMMON ROOF SHAPES

By changing the roof pitch or adding additional planes, the designer can change the shape of the roof. Common roof shapes include flat, shed, gable, A-frame, gambrel, hip, half-hip, Dutch hip, and mansard. Including a dormer for a window in the roof also affects roof shape. See Chapter 22 for a complete discussion of roof framing terms.

Flat Roofs

The flat roof seen on the home in Figure 16.15 is a very common style in areas with little rain or snow and is specific to several home styles. Modern, International, Southwestern, Pueblo, and some Spanish home styles usually have low-sloped roofs. The flat roof is economical to construct because ceiling joists are eliminated and rafters are used to support both the roof and ceiling loads.

photobank.ch/Shutterstock.com

FIGURE 16.15 Flat roofs with a minimum pitch of .25/12 are used in many areas with minimal amounts of rainfall.

Figure 16.16 shows the materials commonly used to frame a flat roof. Figure 16.17 shows how a flat roof could be represented on the roof plan. What is referred to as a flat roof must have a minimum pitch of 1/4" per foot (2 percent slope) to help prevent water from ponding on the roof. As water flows to the edge, a metal diverter is usually placed at the eave to prevent dripping at walkways. A flat roof will often have a parapet, or false wall, surrounding the perimeter of the roof.

Shed Roofs

The shed roof, as seen in Figure 16.18, offers the simplicity and economical construction methods of a flat roof but does not have the drainage problems associated with a flat roof. Figure 16.19 shows construction methods for shed roofs. The shed roof may be constructed at any pitch. The roofing material and aesthetic considerations are the only factors limiting the pitch. Drawn in plan view, the shed roof will resemble the flat roof, as seen in Figure 16.20.

Gable Roofs

A *gable* roof is one of the most common roof types in residential construction. As seen in Figure 16.21, it uses two shed roofs that meet to form a ridge between the support walls. Figure 16.22 shows the construction of a gable roof system. The gable can be constructed at any pitch, with the choice of pitch limited only by the roofing material and the effect desired. A gable roof is often used on designs seeking a traditional appearance and formal balance. Figure 16.23 shows how a gable roof is typically represented in plan view. Many plans use two or more gables at 90° angles to each other. The intersections of gable surfaces are called either hips or valleys. A *hip* is an exterior corner formed by two intersecting roof planes. A *valley* is an interior roof intersection. Each term is explored further in Chapters 17 and 21. An additional term associated with gable roofs is gable end wall. A *gable end wall* is the wall perpendicular to the ridge. This type of wall is not specified on the roof plan, but the overhang for a gable end wall is often smaller than the overhang parallel to the ridge. The valley and hip are represented on the roof plan and their size is specified on the roof framing plan.

A-Frame Roofs

A-frame is a method of framing walls as well as a system of framing roofs. An A-frame structure uses rafters to form its supporting walls, as shown in Figure 16.24. The structure gets its name from the letter "A," which is formed by the roof and floor systems (see Figure 16.25). The roof

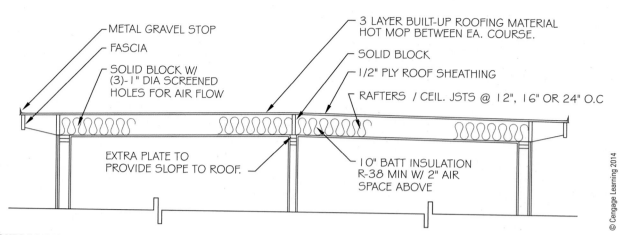

- METAL GRAVEL STOP
- FASCIA
- SOLID BLOCK W/ (3)-1" DIA SCREENED HOLES FOR AIR FLOW
- EXTRA PLATE TO PROVIDE SLOPE TO ROOF.
- 3 LAYER BUILT-UP ROOFING MATERIAL HOT MOP BETWEEN EA. COURSE.
- SOLID BLOCK
- 1/2" PLY ROOF SHEATHING
- RAFTERS / CEIL. JSTS @ 12", 16" OR 24" O.C
- 10" BATT INSULATION R-38 MIN W/ 2" AIR SPACE ABOVE

FIGURE 16.16 Common construction components of a flat roof.

© Cengage Learning 2014

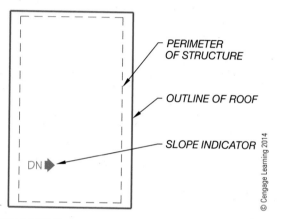

- PERIMETER OF STRUCTURE
- OUTLINE OF ROOF
- SLOPE INDICATOR

DN ▶

© Cengage Learning 2014

FIGURE 16.17 Flat roof in plan view.

Courtesy Reward Wall Systems, photo by Nicole Werner

FIGURE 16.18 Many contemporary homes combine shed roofs to create a pleasing design.

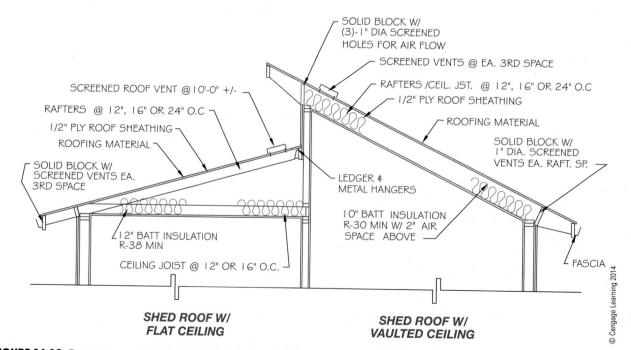

- SOLID BLOCK W/ (3)-1" DIA SCREENED HOLES FOR AIR FLOW
- SCREENED VENTS @ EA. 3RD SPACE
- RAFTERS /CEIL. JST. @ 12", 16" OR 24" O.C
- 1/2" PLY ROOF SHEATHING
- ROOFING MATERIAL
- SOLID BLOCK W/ 1" DIA. SCREENED VENTS EA. RAFT. SP.
- SCREENED ROOF VENT @ 10'-0" +/-
- RAFTERS @ 12", 16" OR 24" O.C
- 1/2" PLY ROOF SHEATHING
- ROOFING MATERIAL
- SOLID BLOCK W/ SCREENED VENTS EA. 3RD SPACE
- LEDGER & METAL HANGERS
- 10" BATT INSULATION R-30 MIN W/ 2" AIR SPACE ABOVE
- 12" BATT INSULATION R-38 MIN
- CEILING JOIST @ 12" OR 16" O.C.
- FASCIA

SHED ROOF W/ FLAT CEILING

SHED ROOF W/ VAULTED CEILING

© Cengage Learning 2014

FIGURE 16.19 Common construction components of shed roofs.

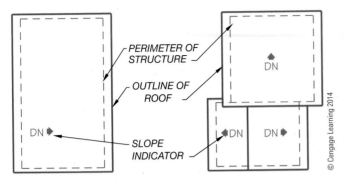

FIGURE 16.20 Representing shed roof shapes in plan view.

FIGURE 16.21 A gable roof is composed of two intersecting planes that form a ridge between them.

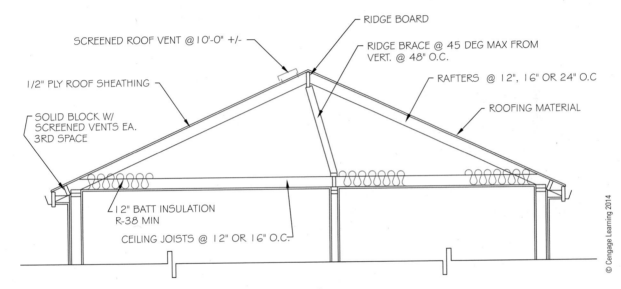

FIGURE 16.22 Common construction components of a gable roof.

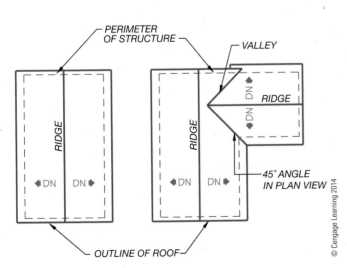

FIGURE 16.23 A gable roof in plan view. Overhangs, ridges, valleys, and hips must be represented in relation to the exterior walls of the roof plans.

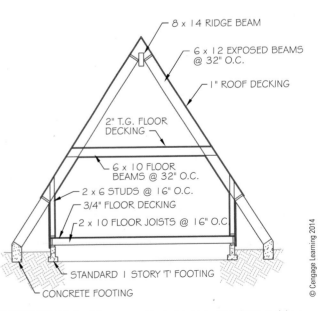

FIGURE 16.24 An A-frame roof is similar to a very steep gable roof but framed with different framing methods. Common components of A-frame construction typically include large roof beams that extend from the ridge to the foundation so that roof loads go directly into the foundation and not into exterior walls.

FIGURE 16.25 An A-frame uses a steep roof to form the walls of the upper level.

FIGURE 16.26 A gambrel roof, which is comprised of four planes, is a common feature of the Dutch Colonial style.

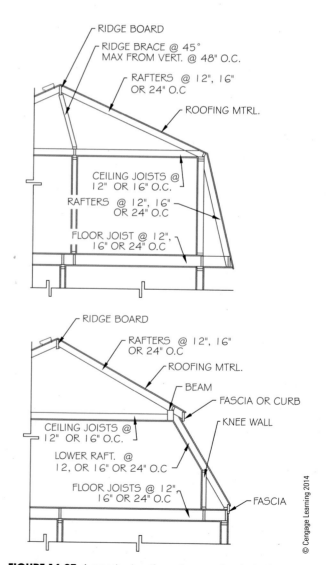

FIGURE 16.27 A gambrel roof can be constructed with or without a fascia or curb between the upper and lower roofs.

plan for an A-frame is very similar to the plan for a gable roof. However, the framing materials are usually quite different. An A-frame is represented on the roof plan using the same methods used to represent a gable roof.

Gambrel Roofs

A gambrel roof is shown in Figure 16.26. The ***gambrel*** roof is a traditional shape that dates back to the Colonial period. Figure 16.27 shows construction methods for a gambrel roof. The lower level is covered with a steep roof surface, which connects into the upper roof system with a moderate pitch. By covering the lower level with roofing material rather than siding, the structure is made to appear shorter than it actually is. This roof system can also reduce the cost of siding materials by using less expensive roofing materials. Figure 16.28 shows a plan view of a gambrel roof.

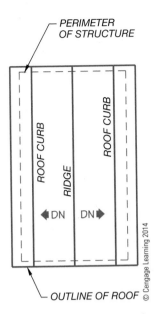

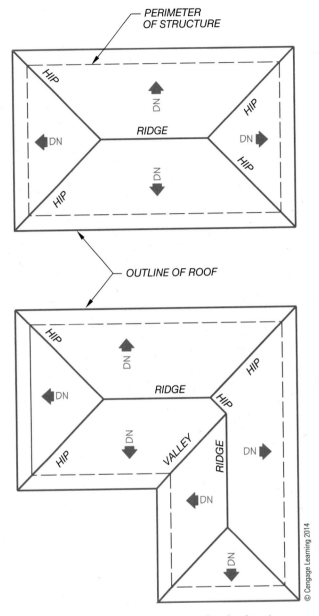

FIGURE 16.28 Each plane of a gambrel roof, as well as any hips or valleys that result from intersecting roofs, must be represented in plan view.

Hip Roofs

The hip roof, illustrated in Figure 16.29, is a traditional shape that has a minimum of four surfaces instead of two. Because a hip roof has no gable end walls, it can be used to help eliminate some of the roof mass and create a structure with a smaller appearance. The inclined intersection between surfaces is called a hip. If built on a square structure, the hips will come together to form a point. If a hip roof is built on a rectangular structure, the hips will form two points with a ridge spanning the distance between them. When hips are placed over an L- or T-shaped structure, an interior intersection will be formed; this is called a valley. The valley of a hip roof is the same as the valley of a gable roof. Hips and valleys are shown in plan view in Figure 16.30. The elements of a hip roof that must be

FIGURE 16.30 Representing hips and valleys in plan view.

represented include the ridge, overhangs, valleys, and hips. The ridge for a hip roof is located in the same manner as the ridge for a gable. The overhangs for a hip roof are generally of uniform size. The hips and valleys can be easily drawn if you remember three simple rules:

- Hips and valleys will always pass through the corner of two intersecting walls.

- Hips and valleys will always be represented on the plan view using an angle that is equal to half the angle of the intersecting walls. Generally this will mean that hips and valleys will be drawn at a 45° angle.

- Three lines will always be required to represent the intersections of hips, valleys, ridges, or overhangs on a roof plan.

FIGURE 16.29 A hip roof is made of four or more intersecting planes.

FIGURE 16.31 A roof with a half-hip places the hip at the top of the roof and then uses a partial gable end wall to terminate the lower portion of the roof.

Half-Hip

The term **half-hip** describes two alternative methods of framing a hip roof. One alternative method is to form the hip at the top of the roof and then terminate the hip at a gable end wall similar to the roof in Figure 16.31. The size of the hip will depend on the spacing of the framing members, but generally the hip will be three or four spaces wide. A second method of altering a hip roof is to remove one or more corners of the hip. This alteration is often done on an irregularly shaped structure to allow more light into what would have been a covered porch. Figure 16.32 shows how to represent each hip shape on a roof plan.

Dutch Hip Roofs

The **Dutch hip** roof is a combination of a hip and a gable roof (see Figure 16.33). The center section of the roof is framed using a method similar to that for a gable roof. The ends of the roof are framed with a partial hip that blends into the gable. A small wall (gable end wall) is formed between the hip and the gable roofs, as seen in Figure 16.34. On the roof plan, the shape, distance, and wall location must be shown, as in the plan in Figure 16.35.

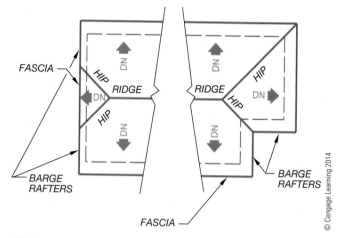

FIGURE 16.32 Representing a half-hip and a notched hip on roof drawings.

Mansard Roofs

The **mansard** roof has angled walls on all four sides of the structure to enclose the upper floor. A mansard roof can also be used as a parapet wall to hide mechanical equipment on the roof or to help hide the height of the upper level of a structure. An example is shown in Figure 16.36. Mansard roofs can be constructed in many different ways. Figure 16.37 shows two common methods of constructing a mansard roof. The roof plan for a mansard roof will resemble the plan shown in Figure 16.38.

Dormers

A **dormer** is an opening framed in the roof to allow for window placement. Figure 16.39 shows a dormer that has been added to provide light and ventilation to rooms in what would have been attic space. The dormer width can vary in size from the width required to place one window to the entire width of the structure. Figure 16.40 shows alternative dormer shapes. Dormers are used most frequently on traditional roofs such as the gable or hip. Figure 16.41 shows one of the many ways in which dormers can be constructed. Dormers are usually shown on the roof plan, as in Figure 16.42.

FIGURE 16.33 A Dutch hip is a combination of a hip roof for the lower portion of the roof and a gable roof for the upper portion of the roof.

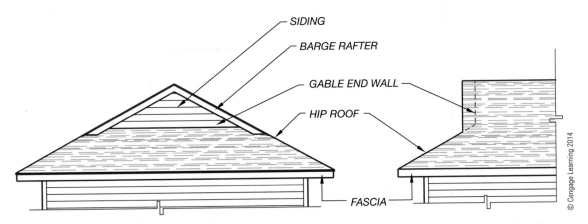

SIDING

BARGE RAFTER

GABLE END WALL

HIP ROOF

FASCIA

FIGURE 16.34 A wall is formed between the hip and the gable roof of a Dutch hip roof. The dashed line is used for reference only and can be omitted when drawing the elevations.

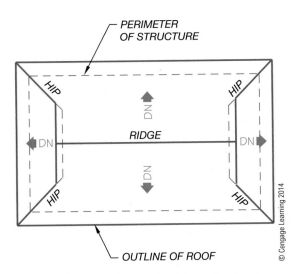

PERIMETER
OF STRUCTURE

HIP

HIP

DN

RIDGE

DN

DN

HIP

HIP

OUTLINE OF ROOF

FIGURE 16.35 Representing a Dutch hip roof in plan view.

FIGURE 16.36 Mansard roofs are used to help disguise the height of a structure.

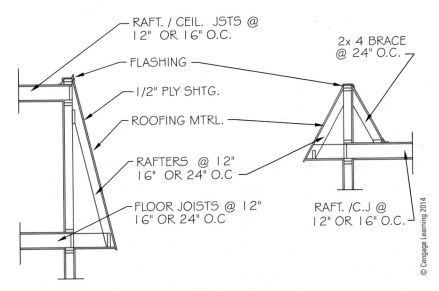

RAFT. / CEIL. JSTS @ 12" OR 16" O.C.

FLASHING

1/2" PLY SHTG.

ROOFING MTRL.

RAFTERS @ 12" 16" OR 24" O.C

FLOOR JOISTS @ 12" 16" OR 24" O.C

2x 4 BRACE @ 24" O.C.

RAFT. /C.J @ 12" OR 16" O.C.

FIGURE 16.37 Common methods of constructing a mansard roof.

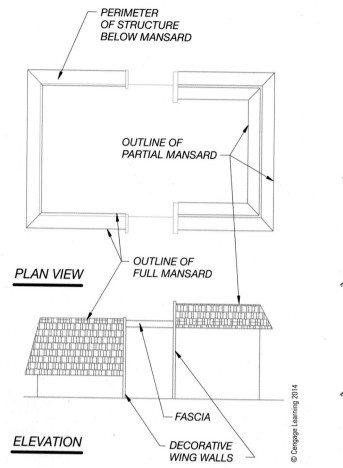

FIGURE 16.38 Representing a mansard roof in plan view.

ROOF MATERIALS

The material used on the roof depends on the pitch, exterior style, cost of the structure, and the weather. Common roofing materials include built-up roofing, shingles, clay and cement tiles, and metal panels. In ordering or specifying these materials, the term *square* is used. This term describes an area of roofing that covers 100 sq ft (9.3 m²). The drafter will need to be aware of the weight per square

FIGURE 16.39 Dormers allow windows to be added to attic areas.

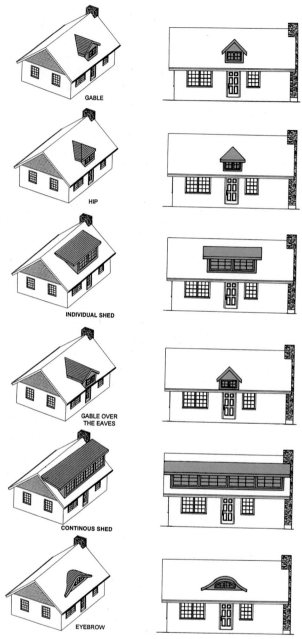

FIGURE 16.40 The width of a dormer can vary depending on the needs of the design. A typical dormer is based on the width of a window, but the dormer can extend to the full width of the structure.

and the required pitch as the plan is being drawn. The weight of the roofing material will affect the size of the framing members all the way down to the foundation level. The material also will affect the required pitch and the appearance that results from the selected pitch.

Underlayment

A term common to all of the roofing materials that will be explored in the following section is *underlayment*. The IRC and other local codes typically use the term **underlayment**

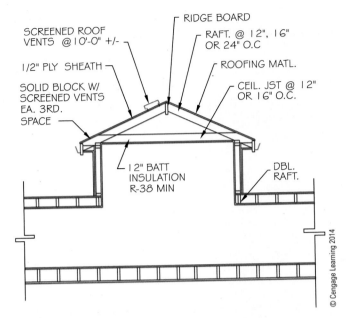

FIGURE 16.41 Typical components of dormer construction.

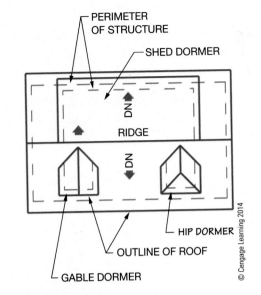

FIGURE 16.42 Dormers in plan view.

Going Green

Green Roofing

The term **green roof** is generally used to describe a roof system consisting of some type of vegetation growing in soil, planted over a waterproof membrane. Layers of a green roof, from top to bottom, typically include:

- Vegetation in the growing medium.
- Filter membrane.
- Drainage layer.
- Waterproofing layer.
- Support panel.
- Thermal insulation.
- Vapor-control layer.
- Structural support system.

This type of roof system first become popular in many municipal buildings, industrial facilities, offices, and other commercial property. Green roofs are now used for storm-water management and energy savings, as well as aesthetic benefits in residential construction. Other benefits of a green roof system include:

- Economic benefits achieved through longer material life span of the roof resulting in decreased maintenance and savings in replacement costs and heating and cooling costs.
- Insulation from sound waves produced by machinery, traffic, or airplanes. Green roofs insulate for sound by absorbing, reflecting, or deflecting. The

(Continued)

substrate tends to block lower sound frequencies and the plants block higher frequencies.

Although popular, this green roof system is not the only type of sustainable roof system available. Two other categories of roofing—cool roofs and sustainable roofs—also are available to the design team to gain LEED credits.

Cool Roofs

A **cool roof** is a roof that features light colors and highly reflective materials. It can be something as simple as finishing the roof by painting it with a coating of light-colored water sealant or more high tech when covered with special light-colored, reflective membranes that reflect heat from the roof surface. In the same way that white clothing helps keep you cool in the summertime, white roofs reflect sunlight and heat. Most dark roofs absorb 90 percent or more of the incoming solar energy. A dark-colored roof can reach temperatures higher than 150°F (66°C) when it's warm and sunny. High roof temperatures increase the heat flow into the building, causing the air-conditioning system to work harder and use more energy. A light-colored roof absorbs less than 50 percent of the solar energy, reducing the roof temperature and decreasing air-conditioning energy use. Controlling the temperature gain through roof color will reduce the demand for air conditioning during hot weather but will increase the need for heating during colder weather.

When determining the effectiveness of a cool roof, solar reflectance and thermal emittance are the two key material properties that affect a roof's temperature. **Solar reflectance** is measured on a scale of 0 to 1. The value measures the amount of sunlight that a surface reflects. Sunlight that is not reflected is absorbed by the structure as heat. If a surface reflects 55 percent of sunlight, it has a solar reflectance of 0.55. Most dark roof materials reflect 5 to 20 percent of sunlight, while light-colored roof materials typically reflect 55 to 90 percent. Solar reflectance has the biggest effect on keeping your roof cool in the summer

Thermal emittance describes how efficiently a surface cools itself by emitting thermal radiation. Thermal emittance is also measured on a scale of 0 to 1, with a value of 1 representing an efficient emitter. Most non-metallic surfaces have high thermal emittance that helps them cool down. Metal surfaces have low thermal emittance, which helps them stay warm.

Sustainable Roofing

Although not as flashy as a garden roof, the roof structure can be just as green if produced and installed to meet certain criteria. To be considered a **sustainable roof**, the system must meet the five E's of design that include energy, environment, endurance, economics, and engineering.

© Cengage Learning 2014

(Continued)

- **Energy.** High-performance roofing materials can be a powerful asset in reducing energy consumption and forming an energy-efficient roof. When used with appropriate insulation on low-sloped or flat roofs, high-emissivity products can:
  - Reduce building energy consumption by up to 40 percent.
  - Improve insulation performance to reduce winter heat loss and summer heat gain.
  - Preserve the efficiency of rooftop air conditioning and potentially reduce HVAC capacity requirements.
  - Decrease the effects of urban heat islands and related urban air pollution.
- **Environment.** A roof system generally is considered to be friendly to the environment if it is designed, constructed, maintained, rehabilitated, and demolished with an emphasis throughout its life cycle on using natural resources efficiently and preserving the global environment. This would include roofing materials that are produced, applied, and reused following methods that comply with LEED guidelines.
- **Endurance.** The amount of time a product can be used before being replaced is a key feature in its LEED certification. Endurance for a roofing component is measured in terms of reliability, water absorption, wind and fire resistance, maintenance, and repair. No matter how green a roof is, it still has to protect the building for years in all types of weather.
- **Economics.** While some types of roofing may have lower initial costs, the true cost of a roofing system is measured over its total life cycle and must be considered to gain LEED credits. The true cost of a roof includes maintenance and repair costs, energy savings, and tear-off and disposal costs.
- **Engineering.** Smart engineering and design is the key to what the Department of Energy refers to as whole-building design. All subsystems in the structure must be integrated to work effectively together throughout the life of the structure. From the selection of raw materials, the manufacturing process, job-site delivery, installation, and the life cycle of the product in the residence, to the recycling of the product, planning and design are key ingredients in ensuring a cool roofing system.

As you work with the design team to meet these goals, key elements shown on a roof plan include the finish roofing materials, skylights, drainage systems, and mechanical equipment. Use of each of these products earns LEED credits primarily from the Materials and Resources division. Information to be shown on the roof plan includes credits primarily from CSI Section 07—Thermal and moisture protection. Specific areas to research include:

- 07 31 13 – Asphalt shingles.
- 07 31 16 – Metal shingles.
- 07 31 19 – Mineral fiber cement shingles.
- 07 31 26 – Slate shingles.
- 07 31 29 – Wood shingles and shakes.
- 07 31 33 – Plastic and rubber shingles.
- 07 32 13 – Clay roof tiles.
- 07 34 00 – Building integrated photovoltaic roofing.
- 07 41 00 – Roof panels.

to describe the water-resistant membrane that is placed on top of the roof sheathing and below the finished roofing material. In some areas of the country, the term *underlayment* refers to the material that goes on top of the rafters or trusses to support the finished roofing material, but this material is more widely known as roof **sheathing.**

Most roofing materials require the use of 15-lb felt as the underlayment, but the size and overlap requirements vary based on the roofing material and the pitch of the roof. In addition to these two common factors, the IRC has added new requirements for underlayment based on wind speed. Specific requirements still vary based on materials, but where basic wind speeds equal or exceed 120 mph (43 m/s), new code requirements state that underlayment comply with ASTM© D226 Type II, ASTM 4369 Type IV, or ASTM D6757. The CAD technician can meet this requirement by placing a general note on the roof plan stating that the underlayment must meet one of these three minimum standards. A second requirement to note on the plans for underlayment that will be applied in high-wind areas is how the underlayment will be attached. Specifically, the underlayment must be attached to the sheathing with metal or plastic cap nails with a minimum head diameter of 1" (25 mm) and a minimum 32-gauge thickness, and a minimum 12-gauge shank that has a minimum length able to penetrate the roof sheathing or at least able to penetrate 3/4" (19 mm) into the roof sheathing. The underlayment also must be fastened to the sheathing using these nails placed in a grid pattern of 12" (305 mm) between side laps, and a 6" spacing at the side laps of the underlayment. The nailing for concrete or clay tiles, slate or slate-type shingles, metal shingles, and mineral-surfaced roll roofing is reduced to 4" (102 mm) at the underlayment side laps. If you are designing a project in a high-wind area, these minimum standards should be verified with the building department that will provide the building permit.

Single-ply Roofs

Single-ply roofs are a popular choice for low-sloped roofs. This roofing system can be applied as a thin liquid or sheet made from ethylene propylene diene monomer (EPDM), which is an **elastomeric** or synthetic rubber material. Polyvinyl chloride (PVC), chlorosulfonated polyethylene (CSPE), and polymer-modified bitumens are also used. These materials are designed to be applied to roof decks with a minimum pitch of 1/4/12. In liquid form, these materials can be applied directly to the roof decking with a roller or sprayer to conform to irregular-shaped roofs.

Single-sheet roofs are rolled out and bonded together to form one large sheet. The sheet can be bonded to the roof deck by mechanical fasteners. Some applications are not attached to the roof deck, but are held in place by gravel material that is placed over the roofing material to provide ballast. A typical specification for a single-ply roof would specify the material, the application method, and the aggregate size. A typical specification would resemble:

> APPLY TWO COATS OF ACU-SHIELD ELASTOMERIC ROOF COATING BY ADVANCED COATING SYSTEMS INSTALLED AS PER THE MANUFACTURER'S SPECIFICATIONS FOR STORING, HANDLING, PREPARING THE ROOF DECK, AND INSTALLING EACH COAT.

Built-Up Roofing

Built-up roofing of felt and asphalt is used on low-sloped roofs that have a minimum pitch of 1/4/12. When the roof has a low pitch, water will either pond or drain very slowly. Built-up roofing is used because it has no seams, and this prevents water from leaking into a structure. On a residence, a built-up roof often consists of three alternate layers of felt and hot asphalt placed over solid roof decking, similar to that shown in Figure 16.43. The decking is usually plywood or OSB. Gravel is often used as a finishing layer to help cover the felt. On roofs with a pitch over 2/12, coarse rocks 2 or 3" (50 or 75 mm) in diameter are used to protect the roof and for appearance. When built-up roofs are specified on the roof plan, the note should include the number of layers, the material to be used, and the size of the finishing material. A typical note would be:

> 3-LAYER BUILT-UP ROOF WITH HOT ASPHALTIC EMULSION BTWN. LAYERS WITH 1/4" (6 mm) PEA GRAVEL

Other roofing materials suitable for low-sloped (1/4/12 minimum pitch) roofs and typical specifications that might be included on a low-sloped roof include:

- Modified bitumen: MODIFIED BITUMEN SHEET ROOFING BY JOHNS MANVILLE OR EQUAL OVER LAYERS OF

Courtesy CertainTeed Corporation

FIGURE 16.43 Built-up roofing of felt and asphalt is used on flat or low-sloped roofs below a 3/12 pitch.

UNDERLAYMENT PER ASTM D226 TYPE I CEMENTED TOGETHER

- Single-ply thermoplastic: THERMOPLASTIC SINGLE-PLY ROOF SYSTEM BY SARNAFIL OR EQUAL INSTALLED PER ASTM D4434
- Sprayed polyurethane foam: SPF ROOFING BY MAINLAND INDUSTRIAL COATINGS, INC., APPLIED PER ASTM 1029
- Liquid applied coating: GREENSEAL LIQUID WATERPROOFING MEMBRANE OR EQUAL INSTALLED PER MANUF. SPECS

Each material can be applied to a roof with minimum pitch of ¼/12. Mineral-surface roll roofing can be used on roofs with a minimum pitch of 1/12. The extent of the note that is placed on the drawings will vary depending on the use of complete specifications. When specifications are provided, the notes on the drawings to specify materials will be kept generic.

Shingles

Asphalt, fiberglass, wood, and metal are the most typical types of shingles used as roofing materials. Most building codes and manufacturers require a minimum roof pitch of 4/12 with an underlayment of one layer of 15-lb felt. Asphalt and fiberglass shingles can be laid on roofs as low as 2/12 if two layers of 15-lb felt are laid under the shingles and if the shingles are sealed. Figure 16.44 shows fiberglass shingles being installed.

Asphalt and Fiberglass Shingles

Asphalt and fiberglass are similar in appearance and application. Both types of shingles come in a variety of colors and patterns. Also known as ***composition shingles,***

FIGURE 16.44 Composition shingles being installed over 15-lb felt and metal edge flashing.

FIGURE 16.45 Composition or three-tab shingles are a common roofing material on high-sloped roofs.

they are typically made of fiberglass backing and covered with asphalt and a filler with a coating of finely crushed particles of stone. The asphalt waterproofs the shingle and the filler provides fire protection. The standard shingle is a three-tab rectangular strip weighing 235-lb per square. The upper portion of the strip is coated with self-sealing adhesive and covered by the next row of shingles. The lower portion of a three-tab shingle is divided into three flaps that are exposed to the weather (see Figure 16.45).

Composition shingles are also available in random widths and thicknesses to give the appearance of cedar shakes. These shingles weigh approximately 300-lb per square based on the shingle style and manufacturer (see Figure 16.46). Both types of shingles styles can be used in a variety of conditions on roofs having a minimum slope of 2/12. When used on roof pitches between 2/12 and 4/12, a minimum of two layers of 15-lb felt are required. For roofs having a pitch of 4/12 or greater, only one layer of 15-lb felt is required. The lifetime guarantees for shingles varies from 20 to 40 years.

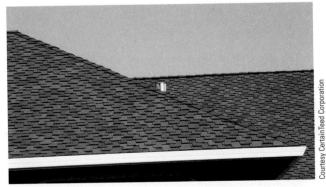

FIGURE 16.46 Laminated composition shingles with a weight of 300-lb per square or greater are made with tabs of random width and length.

NOTE:

In an effort to meet the goal of zero carbon building standards that are being developed, many roofing manufacturers are researching the feasibility of harnessing solar energy through solar roof shingles. Solar roofing shingles conventionally have been used to deploy photovoltaic cells that transform the sun's energy into electricity. Modern solar shingles have the photovoltaic elements integrated into their design, making them virtually unnoticeable, allowing aesthetically appealing homes to be energy efficient. Dow Solar has become a leader in the development of solar roofing shingles that generate electricity. A typical specification for solar shingles would be:

DOW POWERHOUSE SOLAR SHINGLES™ INSTALLED OVER ELK VERSASHIELD™ UNDERLAYMENT AND 15/32 (11.9 MM) PLY ROOF SHEATHING. USE A MINIMUM 4/12 PITCH AND FASTEN PER MANUF SPECS

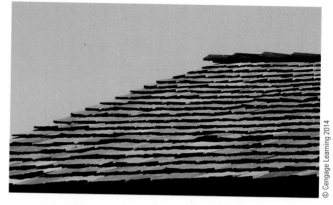

FIGURE 16.47 Cedar shakes are a rustic but elegant roofing material.

Drawings typically specify shingles in note form, listing the material, the weight, and the underlayment. The note may also specify color and manufacturer. This information is often omitted in residential construction to allow the contractor to purchase a suitable brand at the best cost. A typical call-out would be:

- 235# COMPOSITION SHINGLES OVER 15# FELT

- 300# COMPOSITION SHINGLES OVER 15# FELT

- GEORGIAN BRICK 425# COMPOSITION SHINGLES OVER 15# FELT BY CERTAINTEED LAID W/ 8" EXPOSURE

- ARCHITECT 80 CLASS "A" FIBERGLASS SHINGLES WITH 5 5/8" EXPOSURE OVER 15# FELT UNDERLAYMENT

Wood Shingles and Shakes

Wood can also be used for shakes and shingles, but its use may be restricted in areas of high fire danger. Wood shakes are thicker than shingles and are also more irregular in texture (see Figure 16.47). Wood shingles must be installed on roofs having a pitch of at least 3/12 using a base layer of 15-lb felt. An additional layer of 15-lb × 18" (457 mm) wide felt is also placed between each course of shingles. Wood shakes and shingles can be installed over solid or spaced sheathing. The weather, material availability, and labor practices affect the type of underlayment used, and this will be further discussed in Chapter 22.

Depending on the area of the country, shakes and shingles are usually made of cedar, redwood, or cypress. They are also produced in various lengths. When shakes or shingles are specified on the roof plan, the note should usually include the thickness, the material, the exposure, the underlayment, and the type of sheathing. A typical specification for wood shakes would be:

MED. CEDAR SHAKES OVER 15# FELT W/15# × 18" WIDE FELT BETWEEN EACH COURSE. LAY WITH 10 1/2" EXPOSURE

Metal Shingles

Metal is sometimes used for roof shingles on roofs with a 3/12 or greater pitch. Metal shingles are available in a variety of shapes and colors and provide a durable, fire-resistant roofing material. They also offer energy savings and exceptional durability under extreme weather conditions. Metal shingles similar to those shown in Figure 16.48 are usually installed using the same precautions applied to asphalt shingles. Metal is typically specified on the roof plan in a note listing the manufacturer, type of shingle, and underlayment. A typical specification for metal shingles would be:

FIGURE 16.48 Metal roof shingles are both durable and fire-resistant.

.004 THICK × 12" × 60" ALUMINUM CEDAR RED OXFORD SHINGLES BY AMERICAN METAL ROOF INSTALLED OVER 30# FELT AND 1/2" OSB.

Slate Shingles

Slate roofs offer beauty, strength, durability, fire resistance, water resistance, minimal maintenance, and long-term value. Many structures throughout Europe have slate roofs that have remained intact for hundreds of years. *Slate shingles* are made from ancient metamorphic rock that was formed out of the sediment at the bottom of prehistoric oceans and rivers and pressurized into its fine-grain rocky nature. Its main mineral ingredients are quartz, chlorite, mica, and calcite.

Based on IRC requirements, slate shingles can be used on roofs with solid sheathing that have a minimum pitch of 4/12 or greater. Slate shingles are typically specified on the roof plan using a note listing the thickness, width, length, weight per square, manufacturer, color, type of shingle, and underlayment. A typical specification for slate shingles would be:

> 1/4" × 12, 14, & 16" STAGGERED WIDTHS × 24" LONG (800#/SQ) VERMONT SPLENDOR BLEND SLATE SHINGLES BY EVERGREEN SLATE COMPANY W/ 10 1/2" EXPOSURE ROOFING INSTALLED OVER 30# FELT AND 7/16" APPROVED OSB.

Slate-type Shingles

Slate-type shingles are manufactured in a variety of colors and textures. Most simulated slate shingles are made from recycled materials and have an expected 50-year life cycle. Synthetic slate shingles are made from a wide range of materials depending on the manufacturer. Common materials used to make synthetic slate shingles include recycled rubber or plastic products, steel-reinforced rubber, polypropylene blends, and slate and clay particles reinforced with fiberglass and bonded with resin. Synthetic slate tiles fall between slate and fiberglass shingles in cost and weight. Imitation slate roofs can weigh as little as 200-lb per square to as much as 600-lb per square. Manufacturers of synthetic slate shingles estimate the life span at 40 to 60 years for their products.

Simulated slate shingles must be installed over solid roof sheathing on roofs with a minimum roof pitch of 4/12. They are typically specified on the roof plan using a note listing the width, length, exposure, weight per square, manufacturer, color, type of shingle, and underlayment. A typical specification for slate shingles would be:

> 6" × 18" COLONIAL GRAY COMPOSITE SLATE SHINGLE (225 #/SQ) W/ 6" EXPOSURE BY CERTAINTEED INSTALLED OVER 30# FELT & 3/8" APA APPD. PLY OR 7/16" OSB MINIMUM.

FIGURE 16.49a Tile is an excellent choice of roofing material because of its durability.

© Cengage Learning 2014

Clay and Cement Tiles

Clay and cement tiles are often used for homes on the high end of the price scale or where the risk of fire is extreme. Although tile may cost twice as much as the better grades of asphalt shingle, it offers a lifetime guarantee. Roofing tile is available in a variety of colors, materials, and patterns (see Figure 16.49a, b).

Roof tiles are manufactured in both curved and flat shapes. Curved tiles are often called Spanish tiles and come in a variety of shapes and colors. Flat or bar tiles are also produced in many colors and shapes. Tiles are installed on roofs having a pitch of 2½/12 or greater. When installed on roofs having a pitch between 2½/12 and 4/12, tiles must be installed over a double layer of 15-lb felt. Tiles can be placed over either spaced or solid sheathing. If solid sheathing is used, wood strips are generally added on top of the sheathing to support the tiles. Figure 16.49c shows the use of furring strips applied over building felt and solid sheathing.

When specifying tile, special precautions must be taken with the design of the structure. Tile roofs weigh between 850 and 1000-lb per square. These weights

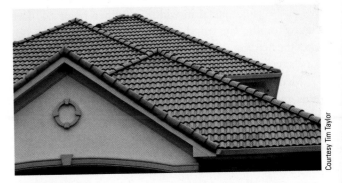

FIGURE 16.49b Tile patterns are available in many styles and colors.

Courtesy Tim Taylor

FIGURE 16.49c Furring strips and hip flashing installed in preparation for installing tile roofing.

FIGURE 16.50 Metal is often selected for its durability and pleasing appearance.

require rafters, headers, and other supporting members to be larger than normally required for other types of roofing material. Tiles are generally specified on the roof plan in a note, which lists the manufacturer, style, color, weight, fastening method, and underlayment. A typical note on the roof plan might be:

MONIER BURNT TERRA COTTA MISSION'S ROOF TILE OVER 15# FELT AND 1 × 3 SKIP SHEATHING. USE A 3" MINIMUM HEAD LAP AND INSTALL AS PER MANUF. SPECS

Seamed Metal Panels

Metal roofing panels often provide savings because of the speed and ease of installation. Metal roof panels provide a water- and fireproof material that comes with a warranty for a protected period that can range from 20 to 50 years. Lapped, non-soldered metal roofing panels with lap sealant can be laid on a roof with a pitch of 1/2/12 or greater. Non-soldered seam metal roofing panels without a lap sealant are required to be laid on a pitch of 3/12 or greater. Standing seam metal roof systems can be laid on a roof with a pitch of 1/4/12 or greater. Panels are typically produced in either 22- or 24-gauge metal in widths of either 18 or 24" (see Figure 16.50). The length of the panel can be specified to meet the needs of the roof in lengths up to 40'. Metal roofing panels typically weigh between 50- and 100-lb per square.

Metal roofs are manufactured in many colors and patterns and can be used to blend with almost any material. Steel, stainless steel, aluminum, copper, and zinc alloys are typically used for metal roofing. Steel panels are heavier and more durable than other metals but they must have a protective coating to inhibit rust and corrosion. A baked-on acrylic coating typically provides both color and weather protection. Stainless steel does not rust or corrode, but it is more expen-

sive than steel. Stainless steel weathers to a natural matte-gray finish. Aluminum is extremely lightweight and does not rust. Finish coatings are similar to those used for steel. Copper has been used for centuries as a roofing material. Copper roofs weather to a blue-green color and do not rust. In specifying metal roofing on the roof plan, the note should include the manufacturer, pattern, material, underlayment, and trim and flashing. A typical note would be:

24 GA. × 16" WIDE MEDALLION-LOK STANDING SEAM PANEL SYSTEM BY MCELROY METAL INSTALLED OVER 15# FELT AS PER MANUF. SPECS

Metal Flashing

In addition to using metal as a roof covering, metal is often used as a flashing as well. *Flashing* can be found at all levels of a structure. It is material used to protect intersections and joints from moisture intrusion. Roof flashing is an underlayment used to protect joints in the roof. Major joints that must be protected include hips, valleys, and ridges. Special shingles similar to those in Figure 16.51 that are specifically made for these applications usually protect hips and ridges. Valleys may be protected by either extra building paper or by metal flashing in high wind and snow areas. Figure 16.52 shows the use of metal flashing to protect a valley. Metal flashing is also used to protect openings in the roof for chimneys and skylights and to protect the fascia/roofing intersection. Flashing is not shown on the roof plan, but the location and type of flashing is specified in general roof notes.

ROOF VENTILATION AND ACCESS

The size of the attic space must be considered as the roof plan is drawn. The attic is the space formed between the

FIGURE 16.51 Special shingles are manufactured to protect the ridge and hip intersections. In addition to the ridge cap shingles, a continuous ridge vent also protects this roof.

Courtesy CertainTeed Corporation

FIGURE 16.52 Flashing is used to protect valley intersections and also at roof projections such as skylights and chimneys.

© Cengage Learning 2014. Courtesy Michael Jefferis

- In climate zones 6, 7, and 8 if a vapor retarder is provided on the warm-in-winter side of the attic floor.
- At least 40 percent and not more than 50 percent of the required vents are placed in the upper half of the roof area and no more than 36" (914 mm) below the ridge.

The method used to provide the required vents varies throughout the country. Vents may be placed in the gable end walls near the ridge (see Figure 16.51). This allows the roof surface to remain vent-free. In some areas, a continuous vent is placed in the eaves, or a vent may be placed in each third rafter space. Vents placed near the ridge should be located on planes that are not visible to the line of sight on entering the residence. These vents are normally placed at approximately 10' (3000 mm) intervals, but the exact spacing will vary based on the size of the vent and the size of the attic space. In areas subject to high winds or snow pack, ridge vents can allow wind-driven moisture to enter the attic. Continuous vents can also be used at the ridge to eliminate the need to place holes in the roof (see Figure 16.51). Because of their lower profile, moisture is less likely to be driven into the attic through continuous ridge vents.

Attic Access

Consideration must also be given to how to get into the attic space if the space has an area of 30 sq ft (2.8 m²) or greater and a height of 30" (760 mm) or greater. The actual opening into the attic is usually shown on the floor plan, but its location must be considered when the roof plan is being drawn. The IRC requires the minimum size of the access opening to be 22 × 30" (560 × 760 mm) with 30" (760 mm) minimum headroom. If a heating unit is mounted in the attic, the minimum access opening must be large enough to remove the appliance (DUH!). While planning the roof shape, the drafter must find a suitable location for the attic access that meets both code and aesthetic requirements. Code requires the access to be located in a hallway or other accessible location. The access should be placed where it can easily be reached but not where it will dominate a space visually. Avoid placing the access in areas such as the garage; areas with high moisture content, such as bathrooms and utility rooms; or in bedrooms that will be used by young children. A walk-in closet is an excellent location for the access, but it should be placed in an area that does not require the movement of stored material. Hallways provide an area to place an access that is easily accessible but not a focal point of the structure. Avoid placing the access in the garage if the one-hour fire rating between the house and the garage will be compromised.

ceiling and the roofing. The attic space must be provided with vents that are covered with 1/8" (3.2 mm) screen mesh unless the code official deems it not required due to climatic conditions. These vents must have an area equal to 1/150 of the attic area. This area can be reduced to 1/300 of the attic area if one of the following conditions are met:

Additional Resources

The following websites can be used as a resource to help you keep current with changes in roof materials.

Address	Company or Organization
www.asphaltroofing.org	Asphalt Roofing Manufacturers Association
www.calredwood.org	California Redwood Association©
www.cedarbureau.org	Cedar Shake & Shingle Bureau
www.certainteed.org	CertainTeed Corporation (asphalt shingles)
www.davinciroofscapes.com	DaVinci Roofscapes
www.ecostar.carlisle.com	EcoStar Roofing©
www.energysealcoatings.com	Energy Seal Coatings
www.gaf.com	GAF Corporation (asphalt shingles)
www/luxuryhousingtrends.com	Green Roofing Materials
www.greenroof solutions.com	Green Roof Solutions
www.jm.com	Johns Manville (roofing)
www.lpcorp.com	Louisiana Pacific® (radiant roof barriers)
www.ludowici.com	Ludowici Roof Tile™
www.mca-tile.com	MCA®, Inc. (tile roofing)
www.malarkey-rfg.com	Malarkey Corporation (high-wind asphalt shingles)
www.mcelroymetal.com	McElroy Metal
www.metalconstruction.org	Metal Construction Association
www.metalroofing.com	Metal Roofing Alliance
www.monier.com	Monier Lifetile Concrete Roofing
www.nahbgreen.org	National Green Building Program
www.ncra.net	National Roofing Contractors Association
www.owenscorning.com	Owens-Corning Corporation (asphalt shingles)
www.pabcoroofing.com	Pabco® Roofing Products
www.therrci.org	Reflective Roof Coating Institute
www.riei.org	Roofing Industry Educational Institute
www.spri.org	Single Ply Roofing Institute
www.stone-slate.com	Slate/Select Inc.
www.solatube.com	Solatube® (skylights)
www.sprayfoam.org	Spray Polyurethane Foam Alliance
www.truslate.com	TruSlate® from GAF
www.velux.com	Velux® (skylights)
www.vinylbydesign.com	Vinyl By Design (roofing membranes)
www.zappone.com	Zappone Manufacturing (copper shingles)

Roof Plan Components Test

Follow these instructions to access and complete an electronic copy of the Chapter 16 Roof Plan Components Test:

1. Go to cengagebrain.com
2. Enter the email address and password you used to register for the site (see Preface for full instructions).
3. Select the website from the **My Course & Materials** area of your home page. Select the chapter you want from the pull-down menu at the top of the page. Choose the resources for that chapter from the menu on the left.
4. Type your name, the chapter number, and the date at the top of the sheet.
5. Answer the following questions with short, complete statements using a word processor.

NOTE:

The answers to some questions may not be contained in this chapter and will require you to do additional research using the Internet. Use your favorite search engine to search for specific professional companies or general categories of information.

Questions

16.1. List and describe two different types of roof plans.

16.2. In describing roof pitch, what do the numbers 4/12 represent?

16.3. What angle represents a 6/12 pitch?

16.4. What is a barge rafter?

16.5. What are two advantages of using a flat roof?

16.6. What is the major disadvantage of using a flat roof?

16.7. List three traditional roof shapes.

16.8. Sketch and define the difference between a hip and a Dutch hip roof.

16.9. What are the two uses for a mansard roof?

16.10. List two common weights for asphalt or fiberglass shingles.

16.11. What are two common shapes of clay roof tiles?

16.12. What advantage do metal roofing panels have over other roofing materials?

16.13. What is the minimum headroom required at the attic access?

16.14. What is the minimum size of an attic access opening?

16.15. What type of roof is both a roof system and a framing system?

16.16. Use the Internet to determine common materials for the waterproofing layer or the growing medium for a green roof.

16.17. Use the Internet to research cool-roof materials that do not have to be a light color, and explain how these products work.

16.18. Verify the assumed basic wind speed for your area, and describe the affects of the wind speed on how the underlayment and roofing materials must be attached.

16.19. What five qualities do roofing products need to demonstrate to be considered friendly to the environment?

16.20. Use the Internet to find five companies that provide and install green roofing products in your area. After making an appointment, contact one of these companies to determine special heating or cooling problems that may be encountered, and how the problems can be overcome in your area.

Section 5
Elevations

Chapter 18

Introduction to Elevations

Elevations are an essential part of the design and drawing process. They are a group of drawings that show the exterior of a building. To communicate clearly, the technician must carefully plan the number, type, and scale to be used to complete the drawings. Skill is also necessary to represent materials accurately without spending unnecessary drawing time.

Key Terms

Exterior insulation
    and finishing
    system (EIFS)

Quoins

CAD Commands and Tools

In addition to basic drawing, editing, text, and dimensioning commands, the following AutoCAD commands and tools are concepts that you should be familiar with to successfully understand and complete the CAD skills referenced in this chapter.

ARRAY	HATCH	LTSCALE	STRETCH
BLOCK	INSERT	MIRROR	

PLANNING ELEVATIONS

An elevation is an orthographic drawing that shows one side of a building. In true orthographic projection, the elevations are displayed as shown in Figure 18.1a. The true projection is typically modified, as shown in Figure 18.1b, to ease viewing. No matter how elevations are displayed, it is important to realize that between each elevation projection and the plan view is an imaginary 90° fold line. An imaginary 90° fold line also exists between elevations in Figure 18.1b. Elevations are drawn to show exterior shapes and finishes as well as the vertical relationships of the building levels. By using the elevations, sections, and floor plans, the exterior shape of a building can be determined.

Required Elevations

Typically, there are four elevations that show the features of a building. On a simple building, only three elevations are needed, as shown in Figure 18.2. When drawing a building with an irregular shape, parts of it may be hidden. An elevation of each surface should be drawn, as shown in Figure 18.3. If a building has walls that are not at 90° to each other, a true orthographic drawing may be confusing. In the orthographic projection, part of the elevation is distorted, as shown in Figure 18.4. Elevations of this building type are usually expanded so a separate elevation of each face is drawn. Figure 18.5 shows the layout for a residence with an irregular shape.

Types of Elevations

Elevations can be drawn as either presentation drawings or working drawings. Each type of elevation displays different types of information to people associated with the different steps in the design and construction phases.

Presentation Elevations

Chapter 2 introduces presentation drawings and Chapter 34 covers them in depth. Presentation drawings similar to Figure 18.6 are part of the initial design process and may

range from sketches to detailed drawings intended to help the owner and lending institution understand the basic design concepts.

Because the front elevation is drawn as part of the preliminary design process, it is often drawn using rendering methods. Common elements that can be added to a rendered elevation include shade, landscaping, people, and automobiles. Each of these items can be added to a drawing using blocks developed by third-party vendors. Text and dimensions are generic and kept to a minimum. While there must be enough information to explain the project, complete annotation is not added until the working drawings are started.

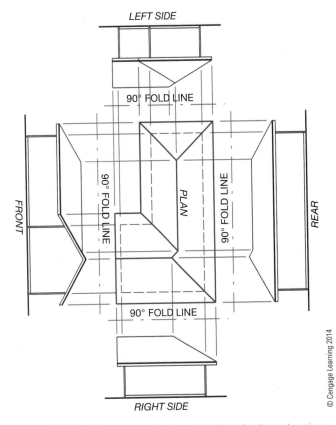

FIGURE 18.1a Elevations are orthographic projections showing each side of a structure.

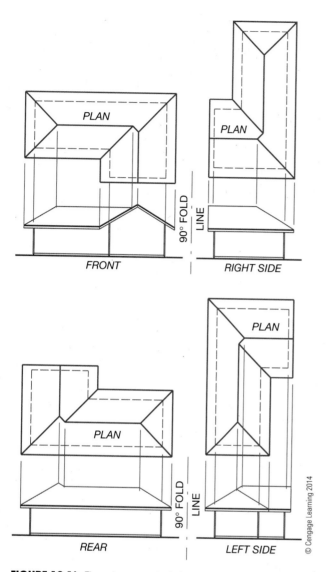

FIGURE 18.1b The placement of elevations is usually altered to ease viewing. Group elevations so that a 90° rotation exists between views.

Working Elevations

Working elevations are part of the construction drawings that provide information to the building team. They include information on roofing, siding, openings, chimneys, land shape, and sometimes even the depth of footings, as shown in Figure 18.7. Although the preliminary elevation serves as a drawing base, the layers containing the artistic material are often frozen to provide better clarity to the building team. Information should be added to each note that clearly explains the application of each material. Because the front elevation is drawn to please the owner during the preliminary process, it will generally show all materials. The working elevations are drawn to communicate with the building team and will generally show just enough material to represent the material to be applied. Figure 18.8 shows an example of a working elevation. The floor plans and elevations provide the information the contractor needs to determine surface areas. Once surface areas are known, exact quantities of material can be determined. The heating contractor also uses the elevations if heat loss calculations need to be completed. The elevations are used to determine the surface area of walls and wall openings for the required heat-loss formulas.

Elevation Scales

Draw elevations at full scale in model space. This allows them to project directly from the floor plans. They are generally plotted in paper space at the same scale as the floor plan. For most plans, this means plotting at a scale of 1/4" = 1'-0", with two elevations placed on a sheet. Some floor plans for multifamily projects may be laid out at a scale of 1/16" = 1'-0" or even as small as 1/32" = 1'-0". When using a scale of 1/8" = 1'-0" or less, there is generally little detail in the drawings. Depending on the complexity of the project or the amount of space on a page, the front elevation may be drawn at 1/4" = 1'-0" and the balance of the elevations at a smaller scale. If the side, rear, side elevations are plotted at a different scale from the front elevation, the scale must be clearly indicated below each drawings.

Elevation Placement

It is usually the CAD technician's responsibility to plan the layout for drawing the elevations. The layout will depend on the scale, the size of the drawing sheet, and the number of drawings required. Because of size limitations, the elevations are not usually laid out in the true orthographic projection of front, side, rear, side. A common method of layout for four elevations is seen in Figure 18.9. This layout places a side elevation by both the front and rear elevations

FIGURE 18.2 Elevations are used to show the exterior shape and material of a building. For a simple structure, only three views may be required.

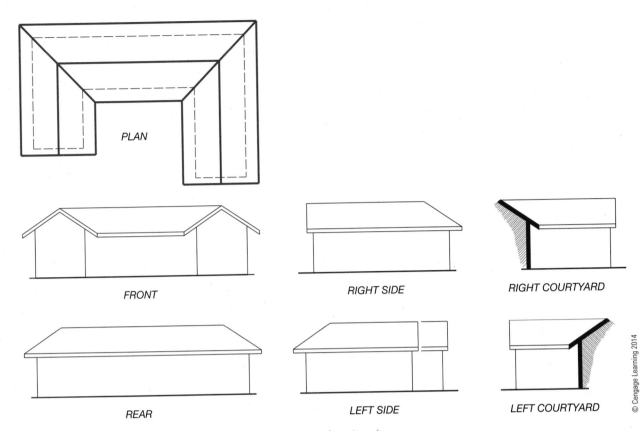

PLAN

FRONT

RIGHT SIDE

RIGHT COURTYARD

REAR

LEFT SIDE

LEFT COURTYARD

© Cengage Learning 2014

FIGURE 18.3 Plans of irregular shapes often require an elevation of each surface.

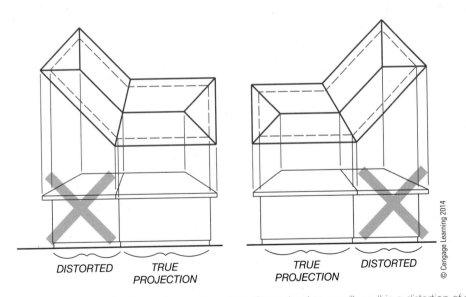

DISTORTED   TRUE PROJECTION

TRUE PROJECTION   DISTORTED

© Cengage Learning 2014

FIGURE 18.4 Using true orthographic projection methods with a plan of irregular shapes will result in a distortion of part of the view.

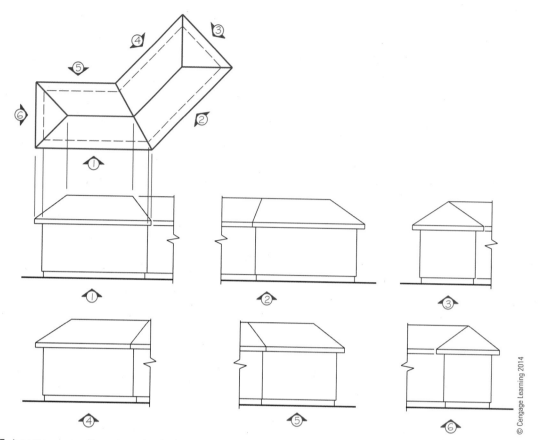

© Cengage Learning 2014

FIGURE 18.5 A common practice when drawing an irregularly shaped structure is to draw an elevation of each surface. Each elevation is then given a reference number to tie the elevation to the floor plan.

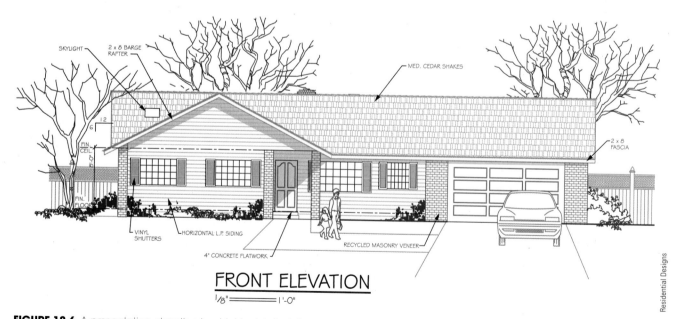

SKYLIGHT

2 x 8 BARGE RAFTER

MED. CEDAR SHAKES

2 x 8 FASCIA

FIN. CEIL.

FIN. FLOOR

VINYL SHUTTERS

HORIZONTAL L.P. SIDING

4" CONCRETE FLATWORK

RECYCLED MASONRY VENEER

FRONT ELEVATION
1/8" = 1'-0"

Residential Designs

FIGURE 18.6 A presentation elevation is a highly detailed drawing used to show the exterior shapes and material to be used. Shades, shadows, and landscaping are usually added to enhance the drawing.

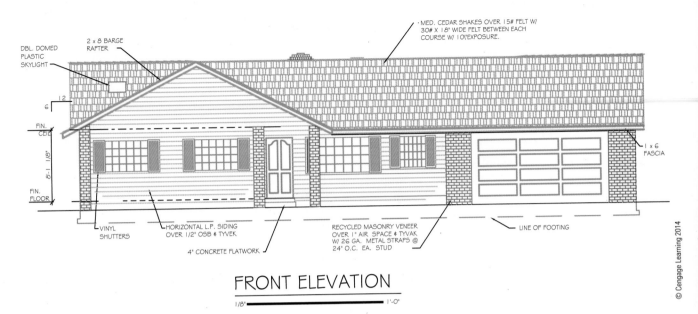

FRONT ELEVATION

FIGURE 18.7 Working elevations contain less finish detail but still show the shape of a structure accurately and include specifications for all materials to be provided.

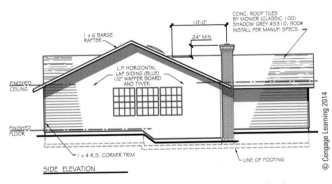

SIDE ELEVATION

FIGURE 18.8 The side and rear elevations are typically drawn with less detail than the front elevation.

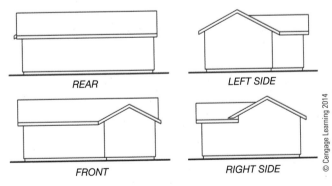

REAR   LEFT SIDE

FRONT   RIGHT SIDE

FIGURE 18.9 A common method of elevation layout is to place a side elevation beside both the front and the rear elevations. This allows for heights to be transferred directly from one view to the other.

to project true vertical heights from one view to another. This layout method also allows a 90° fold line to be maintained between the two views that are side by side. If the drawing paper is not long enough for this placement, use the layout shown in Figure 18.10. This arrangement is often

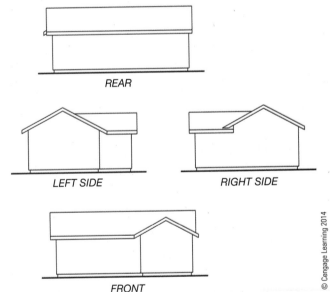

REAR

LEFT SIDE   RIGHT SIDE

FRONT

FIGURE 18.10 An alternative elevation arrangement is to place the two shortest elevations side by side.

used when the elevations are placed next to the floor plan to conserve space. Chapter 19 offers aids for the drawing setup regardless of how they will be displayed for plotting.

Elevation Identification

The method for naming the elevations depends on the client, and whether the elevations are being developed for a specific site. The three common methods include:

- If the drawings are for a spec house when a specific site is not known, titles such as FRONT, SIDE, REAR, and SIDE generally appear below each elevation.

- If a specific site is known, the elevations are often named for their relationship to the north arrow on the floor plan. If the front wall on the floor plan faces south, instead of being labeled FRONT ELEVATION, this elevation is labeled SOUTH ELEVATION. The remaining elevations are then named EAST, NORTH, and WEST.
- Irregularly shaped homes are often numbered rather than labeled. A number symbol is typically placed on the floor plan to identify each elevation plane, and the corresponding number is placed below each elevation. Figure 18.5 shows examples of elevation number symbols for the floor and elevations. A small non-scaled floor plan is often placed on the sheet containing the elevations to aid in referencing the elevation to the structure.

REPRESENTING SURFACE MATERIALS IN ELEVATION

The materials that are used to protect the building from the weather must be shown on the elevations. This information is considered in four categories: roofing, wall coverings, doors, and windows. Additional considerations include rails, shutters, eave vents, and chimneys. Many third-party architectural programs have a variety of elevation symbols representing doors, windows, and other common materials.

Creating and Saving CAD Drawing Blocks

If the program you are using does not contain architectural blocks, they can easily created using the examples found throughout this chapter. Each of the materials, including doors, windows, and rails, can be drawn, saved, and reused.

Once a symbol such as door has been created, the location where it is saved in should be given careful consideration. Creating a folder titled PROTO or BLOCKS will make an excellent storage area for keeping symbols. Be sure to subdivide the folder for each drawing so that you can easily find the desired symbol. Subfolders such as FLOOR, ELECTRICAL, and EXTELEV help provide organization to your storage system. If you plan on creating large quantities of symbols, use titles such as ROOF, WALL, and LANDSCAPING to further subdivide your drawing elements. A sample title for a tree, for example, might read PROTOS/EXTELEV/LANDSCAPING/TREE/OAK. Taking the time to get organized as you create symbols will greatly decrease the amount of time you spend looking for a symbol to insert into a drawing.

Roofing Materials

Several common materials protect a roof from the elements. Among the most popular are asphalt shingles, wood shakes and shingles, clay and concrete tiles, metal sheets, and built-up roofing materials, which were introduced in Chapter 16. It is important to have an idea of what each material looks like so that it can be drawn in a realistic style. It is also important to remember that the elevations are meant for the framing crew. The framer's job is not made easier by seeing every shingle drawn or other techniques appearing on presentation drawings and renderings. Materials must be represented clearly and quickly on the elevations.

Shingles

Asphalt, fiberglass, and metal shingles come in many colors and patterns. Asphalt shingles are typically drawn using the method seen in Figure 18.11. When these are placed using AutoCAD, use the AR-RROOF hatch pattern to represent shingles. Use a scale that places the lines in the pattern about 1/16 to 1/8" (1.5 to 3 mm) apart.

Wood Shakes and Shingles

Figure 18.12 shows a roof protected with wood shakes. Other materials such as Masonite simulate wood shakes. Shakes, Masonite, slate, and synthetic slate each creates

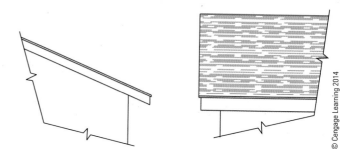

FIGURE 18.11 The AR-RROOF hatch pattern of AutoCAD can be used to represent composition shingles.

FIGURE 18.12 Wood shakes and shingles have much more texture than asphalt shingles.

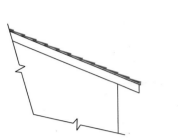

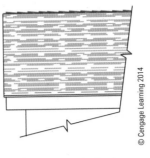

FIGURE 18.13 Shakes and shingles can be represented using AR-RROOF or AR-RSKE. Notice that an inclined line is added to the eave and to the ridge to represent the contour of the roofing material.

a jagged surface at the ridge and the edge. These types of materials are often represented using the AR-RROOF hatch pattern. Represent the edge of the shingles on the barge rafter using a thick line placed about 2° less than the rake of the roof. Lines representing shingles will resemble Figure 18.13.

Tile

Concrete, clay, or a lightweight simulated tile material presents a rugged surface at the ridge and edge as well as many shadows throughout the roof. Figure 18.14a shows flat tiles. Figure 18.14b shows a roof with Spanish tile. If blocks are not available from third-party vendors, create one to represent a small area of the tiles. The block can then be inserted to fill the desired area. Draw flat tiles as shown in Figure 18.15 or represent Spanish tiles as shown in Figure 18.16.

Metal

Draw metal shingles in a manner similar to asphalt shingles. Seamed metal roofs are also a popular form of metal for residential roofing. Figure 18.17 shows an example of metal

FIGURE 18.14b Curved or Spanish tiles are a traditional roofing material of Spanish and Mediterranean style homes.

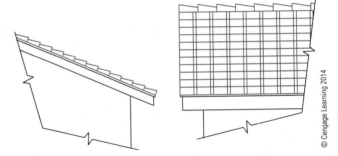

FIGURE 18.15 Representations of tile may require a hatch pattern to be created if a pattern from third-party software is not available.

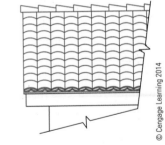

FIGURE 18.16 Representing Spanish tiles.

FIGURE 18.14a Flat tiles are used in many parts of the country because of their low maintenance, durability, and resistance to the forces of nature.

FIGURE 18.17 Standing metal seamed roofs are often used for homes in rural settings because of their resistance to fires.

© Cengage Learning 2014

Courtesy Benigno Molina

panel roof sheathing. Draw metal panels with a series of vertical lines to represent the panel seams. Space the seams between 12 and 18" (300 and 450 mm) on the drawings, specifying the exact spacing in a note.

Built-up Roofs

Because of the low pitch and the lack of surface texture, built-up roofs are usually outlined and left blank. Occasionally a built-up roof will be covered with 2 or 3" (50 or 75 mm) diameter rock. Figure 18.18 shows the drawing technique for this roof.

Skylights

Skylights may be made of either flat glass or domed plastic and come in a variety of shapes and styles. Depending on the pitch of the roof, skylights may or may not be drawn. On very low-pitched roofs, a skylight may be unrecognizable. On roofs over 3/12 pitch, the shape of the skylight can usually be drawn without creating confusion. Unless the roof is very steep, a rectangular skylight will appear almost square. The flatter the roof, the more distortion there will be in the size of the skylight. Figure 18.19 shows common methods of drawing both flat-glass and domed skylights.

Wall Coverings

Exterior wall coverings are usually made of wood, wood substitutes, masonry, metal, plaster, or stucco. Each has its own distinctive look in elevation.

Wood

Wood siding can be installed in large sheets or in individual pieces. Plywood sheets are a popular wood siding because of their low cost and ease of installation. Individual pieces of wood provide an attractive finish but usually cost more than plywood. This higher cost results from differences in material and the labor to install each individual piece.

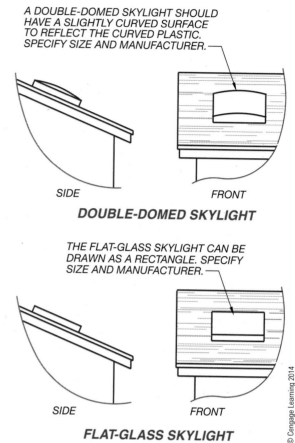

A DOUBLE-DOMED SKYLIGHT SHOULD HAVE A SLIGHTLY CURVED SURFACE TO REFLECT THE CURVED PLASTIC. SPECIFY SIZE AND MANUFACTURER.

SIDE   FRONT

DOUBLE-DOMED SKYLIGHT

THE FLAT-GLASS SKYLIGHT CAN BE DRAWN AS A RECTANGLE. SPECIFY SIZE AND MANUFACTURER.

SIDE   FRONT

FLAT-GLASS SKYLIGHT

© Cengage Learning 2014

FIGURE 18.19 Representing domed and flat-glass skylights on elevations.

Plywood. Plywood siding can have many textures, finishes, and patterns. Textures and finishes are not shown on the elevations but may be specified in a general note. Patterns in the plywood are usually shown and include T1-11 (Figure 18.20), board on board (Figure 18.21), board and batten (Figure 18.22), and plain or rough-cut plywood. Figure 18.23 shows methods for drawing each type of siding.

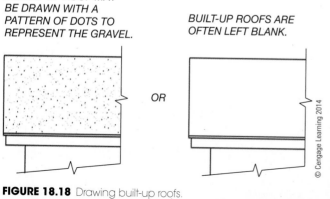
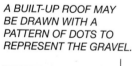
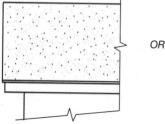

A BUILT-UP ROOF MAY BE DRAWN WITH A PATTERN OF DOTS TO REPRESENT THE GRAVEL.

BUILT-UP ROOFS ARE OFTEN LEFT BLANK.

OR

© Cengage Learning 2014

FIGURE 18.18 Drawing built-up roofs.

Courtesy Tim Taylor

FIGURE 18.20 T1-11 plywood is a common siding.

FIGURE 18.21 Redwood board-on-board siding is used to protect this home from the elements.

FIGURE 18.22 Batt-on-board siding is used to highlight the horizontal siding of this home.

FIGURE 18.24 Vertical siding is a common natural material for protecting a structure from the elements.

Lumber Siding. Lumber siding comes in several types and can be laid in many patterns. Common lumber for siding is cedar, redwood, pine, fir, spruce, and hemlock. Common styles of lumber siding are tongue and groove, bevel, and channel. Various types of wood siding appear in Figures 18.24 through 18.26. Figure 18.27 shows common shapes of wood siding. Each of these materials can be installed vertically, horizontally, diagonally, or laid to match the rake of the roof. The material and type of siding must be specified in a general note on the elevations. The pattern in which the siding is to be installed must be shown on the elevations as in Figure 18.28. The type of siding and the position in which it is laid affects how the siding appears at a corner. Figure 18.29 shows two common methods of corner treatment.

Wood shingles similar to Figure 18.30 can be installed individually or in panels. Figure 18.31 shows how to represent shingles using the AR-RSHKE hatch pattern.

Alternative Wood Siding Materials

Hardboard, fiber cement, aluminum, and vinyl siding can be produced to resemble lumber siding. Figure 18.32 shows a home finished with hardboard siding. Hardboard siding is generally installed in large sheets similar to plywood but often has more detail than plywood or lumber siding. It

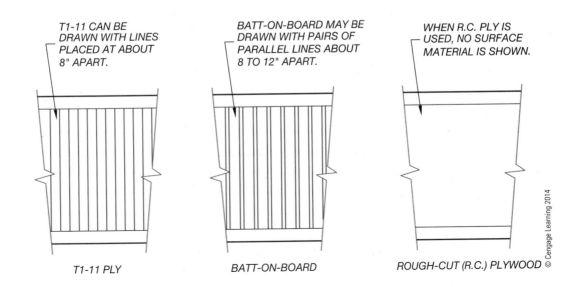

T1-11 CAN BE DRAWN WITH LINES PLACED AT ABOUT 8" APART.

BATT-ON-BOARD MAY BE DRAWN WITH PAIRS OF PARALLEL LINES ABOUT 8 TO 12" APART.

WHEN R.C. PLY IS USED, NO SURFACE MATERIAL IS SHOWN.

T1-11 PLY

BATT-ON-BOARD

ROUGH-CUT (R.C.) PLYWOOD

FIGURE 18.23 Drawing plywood siding in elevation.

Courtesy California Redwood Association

FIGURE 18.25 Beveled redwood siding is used on this home to create a pleasing blend of the home with the site.

Courtesy California Redwood Association

FIGURE 18.26 Finger-jointed redwood siding is used to create the lower walls of this project.

is drawn using the same methods used for drawing lumber sidings. Each of the major national wood distributors has also developed siding products made from wood by-products that resemble individual pieces of beveled siding. Strands of wood created during the milling process are saturated with a water-resistant resin binder and compressed under extreme heat and pressure. The exterior surface typically has an embossed finish to resemble the natural surface of cedar. Most engineered lap sidings are primed to provide protection from moisture prior to installation.

Fiber cement siding products are a common wood substitute because of their durability. Engineered to be resistant to moisture, cold, insects, salt air, and fire, fiber cement products such as DuraPress® by ABTCO and Hardieplank® by James Hardie are being used in many areas of the country as an alternative to wood and plaster products. Available in widths of 6 1/2, 7 1/2, and 9 1/2" (165, 190, and 240 mm) or 4' × 8' (100 × 200 mm) sheets, fiber cement products can reproduce smooth or textured wood patterns as well as cedar plywood panels and stucco. Products are installed in much the same way as their wood counterparts. Figure 18.33 shows an example of fiber cement bevel siding. Aluminum and vinyl sidings also resemble lumber siding in appearance, as shown in Figure

18.34. Aluminum and vinyl sidings are drawn similarly to their lumber counterpart.

Masonry

Masonry finishes include the materials of brick, concrete block, and stone. Brick is used on many homes, like the one in Figure 18.35, because of its beauty and durability. It comes in a variety of sizes, patterns, and textures. In drawing elevations, represent the pattern of the bricks on the drawing and the material and texture in the written specifications. A common method for drawing bricks is shown in Figure 18.36. The horizontal brick was drawn using the BRICK hatch pattern. The BRSTONE pattern can also be used. Notice, in Figure 18.36a, that two rows of decorative brick add interest to the wall. These vertical bricks were drawn using the LINE and ARRAY commands. Figure 18.36b shows the use of quoins with the brick. *Quoins* made from granite blocks were originally used to reinforce the corners of masonry walls. Many modern homes with brick, plaster, or stucco exteriors use decorative quoins to enhance the exterior styles. Modern quoins are typically

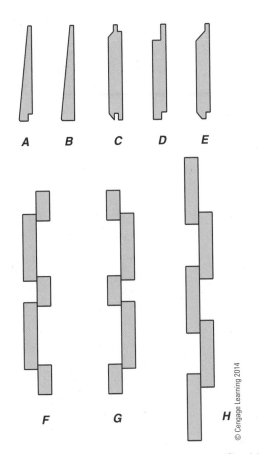

FIGURE 18.27 Common types of siding: (A) bevel; (B) rabbeted; (C) tongue and groove; (D) channel shiplap; (E) V shiplap; (F, G, H) these types can have a variety of appearances, depending on the width of the boards and battens being used.

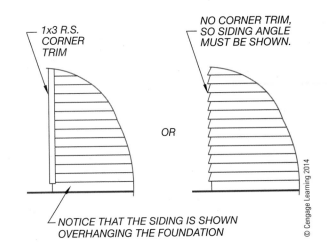

FIGURE 18.29 Common methods of corner treatment.

FIGURE 18.30 Shingles are often used as a siding material to provide a casual or rustic finish.

made of brick, or built-up plaster. Figure 18.36b shows how to represent quoins.

Although bricks are not usually drawn exactly to scale, the proportions of the brick must be maintained. Because the LTSCALE factor does not control the hatch pattern, it helps to draw a line that is the approximate length of a brick, and then match the line size while inserting the pattern.

Concrete block is often used as a weather-resistant material for above- and below-grade construction. Figure 18.37 shows examples of two types of concrete block forming above-ground walls. Show the size, pattern, and texture on

VERTICAL   HORIZONTAL LAP   DIAGONAL

FIGURE 18.28 Representing siding in elevation.

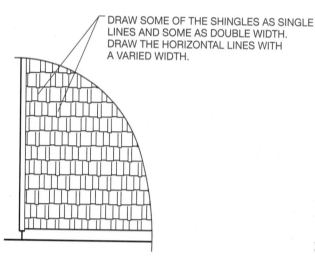

DRAW SOME OF THE SHINGLES AS SINGLE LINES AND SOME AS DOUBLE WIDTH. DRAW THE HORIZONTAL LINES WITH A VARIED WIDTH.

© Cengage Learning 2014

FIGURE 18.31 The AutoCAD AR-RSHKE hatch pattern can be used to represent shingle siding.

© Cengage Learning 2014

FIGURE 18.32 Hardboard can be used as a siding material if precautions are taken to protect against moisture.

© ABT Building Products

FIGURE 18.33 Fiber cement siding provides excellent protection from moisture, insects, and other natural elements.

© ABT Building Products

FIGURE 18.34 Vinyl and aluminum sidings are manufactured to resemble their wood counterparts.

the elevation when drawing concrete blocks. Figure 18.38 shows an example of simplified concrete blocks placed with the AR-B16 hatch pattern. If the AR-B16C pattern is used, the grout lines will be represented. Draw a line 16" (400 mm) long and use it as a guide to set the scale of the hatch pattern during insertion.

Stone is often used to provide a charming, traditional style that is extremely weather-resistant. Figure 18.39 shows an example of stone used to accent a home. Stone or rock finishes also come in a wide variety of sizes and shapes and are laid in a variety of patterns. Stone or rock may be natural or artificial. Both appear the same when drawn in elevation. Represent rounded stone using the GRAVEL pattern from AutoCAD. If a pattern is not available

through third-party vendors, be careful to represent the irregular shape, as shown in Figure 18.40.

Metal

Although primarily a roofing material, metal can be used as an attractive wall covering. Drawing metal in elevation uses a method similar to drawing lumber siding.

FIGURE 18.35 Brick is used in many traditional designs because of its elegant appearance and resistance to natural forces.

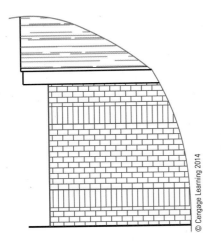

FIGURE 18.36a Representing brick in elevation with a soldier course added to the top and bottom of the wall for decoration.

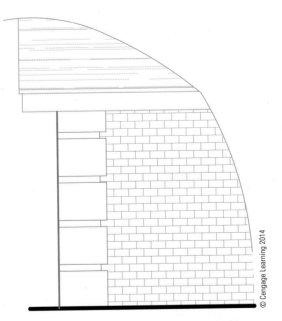

FIGURE 18.36b Representing brick with decorative stone quoins added to the corners to mimic historic uses of brick construction.

FIGURE 18.37 Concrete block is used in many areas to provide a long-lasting, energy-efficient building material.

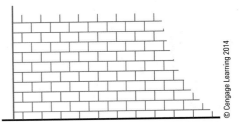

FIGURE 18.38 Representing 8" × 8" × 16" concrete blocks in elevation.

Plaster or Stucco

Although primarily used in areas with little rainfall, plaster or stucco can be found throughout the country. Figure 18.41 shows an example of a wall with a stucco cover. Represent stucco as shown in Figure 18.42a using the AR-SAND hatch pattern. Similar in appearance to stucco or plaster are *exterior insulation and finishing systems (EIFS)*. This type of weather protection is installed over a rigid insulation board that is used as a base for a fiberglass-reinforced base coat. A weather-resistant, colored finish coat is then applied by trowel to seal the structure. Add shapes made of insulation board wherever three-dimensional details are desired. Figure 18.42b shows an example of representing EIFS with raised trim.

FIGURE 18.39 Stone is used on homes in many traditional styles.

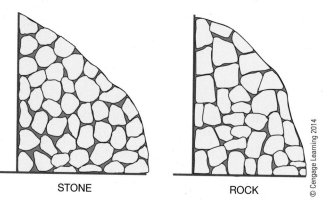

STONE   ROCK

FIGURE 18.40 Stone is used in a variety of shapes and patterns.

FIGURE 18.41 Stucco and plaster can be installed in many different patterns and colors to provide a durable finish. EIFS offers the look of stucco while providing added insulation and durability.

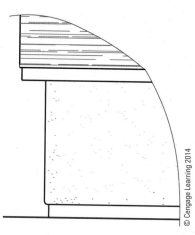

FIGURE 18.42a Representing stucco, plaster, and EIFS in elevation that is installed with no corner bead so that a rounded edge is produced. Notes are used to explain which product will be applied.

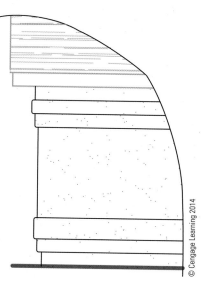

FIGURE 18.42b Stucco, plaster, and EIFS are often represented with raised areas to provide added texture to the wall.

Doors

Draw doors to resemble the type of door specified in the door schedule, but be careful not to try to reproduce an exact likeness of a door. This is especially true of entry and garage doors, which have decorative patterns on them. It is important to show this pattern, but do not spend time trying to reproduce the exact pattern. Since the door is manufactured, you'll be wasting your time drawing details that add nothing to the plan. Figure 18.43 shows the layout of a raised-panel door, and Figure 18.44 shows how to represent other common types of doors.

When using AutoCAD, draw doors using the steps described in Figure 18.43. When the drawing is complete, save it as a block for future insertion. Place the drawing in a file with a title such as PROTO/EXTELEV/

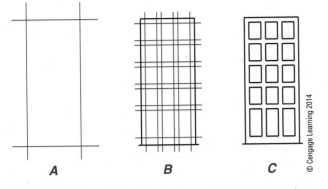

FIGURE 18.43 Layout steps for drawing a block to represent a raised-panel door.

DOOR/RP for future reference. An insertion point must be specified as a block is created. The midpoint of the sill will prove to be an excellent insertion point. The doors from Figure 18.44 can be found on the student website in the SUPPLEMENTAL DRAWING MATERIAL folder.

Windows

The same precautions about drawing needless details for doors should be taken in drawing windows. Care must be given to the frame material. Wooden frames are wider than metal frames. When starting the elevations in the preliminary stages of design, the drafter may not know what type of frames will be used. In this case, the drafter should draw the windows in the most typical usage for the area. Figure 18.45 shows the layout steps for a vinyl or aluminum sliding window. Figure 18.46 shows how to represent other common types of windows.

When drawing windows using AutoCAD, use the steps described in Figure 18.45. When creating your own blocks,

assign a width of 1. With a width of 1, an X factor representing the desired width can be assigned as the block is inserted into the elevation. An insertion point must be specified as a block before saving the block. The midpoint of the top of the window will prove to be an excellent insertion point. When the drawing is complete, save it as a block in a file with a title such as PROTO/EXTELEV WINDOW for future reference. The windows from Figure 18.46 are on the website in the SUPPLEMENTAL DRAWING MATERIAL folder.

Rails

Simple rails can be solid, to match the wall material, or open. Open rails can be made of wood or wrought iron. Vertical rails must be no more than 4" (100 mm) clear and are often made from 2 × 2 (50 × 50) material. Place verticals using the ARRAY command. Rails are often built using a 2 × 6 (50 × 150) and can be drawn as shown in Figure 18.47. The entire railing should be represented on the front elevation. On the remaining elevations, only a portion of a rail may be drawn as shown in Figure 18.48, with the line representing the limits of the rail. More decorative railings similar to Figure 18.49 may be required to match a specific historic style. Use the MIRROR command once one side of a baluster has been drawn. Place the balusters using the ARRAY or COPY command. When a section of the rail drawing is complete, save it as a block in a file with a title such as PROTO/EXTELEV/RAILS for future reference. The rail from Figure 18.49 is on the website in the SUPPLEMENTAL DRAWING MATERIAL folder.

Shutters

Shutters are sometimes used as part of the exterior design to match specific historic styles and must be shown on the

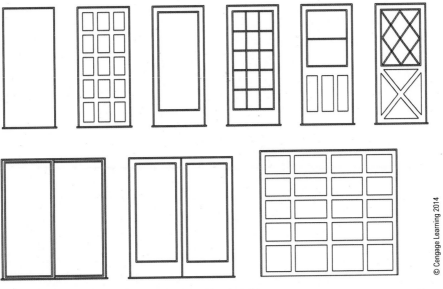

FIGURE 18.44 Common door blocks that can be represented in elevation.

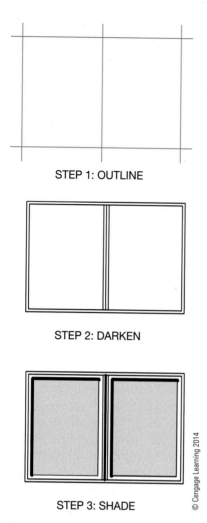

FIGURE 18.45 Layout steps for creating a block to represent a sliding window.

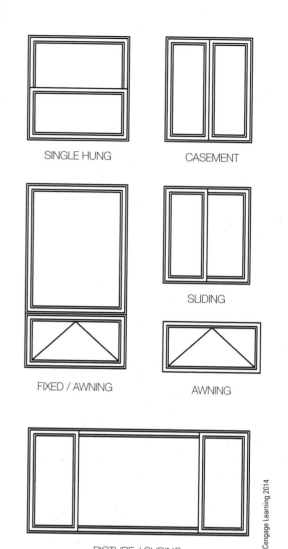

FIGURE 18.46 Representing common window shapes on elevations. A block with a width of 1 can be created for each style of window. When inserted into the drawing the X factor can be adjusted to meet the required width. The depth can be adjusted by altering the Y scale factor or by using the STRETCH command.

elevations. Figure 18.50 shows a typical shutter and how it can be drawn. When using AutoCAD, place the individual slats of the shutter using the COPY or ARRAY commands. Spacing for the outer frame and the louvers was represented in Figure 18.50 using a 1 1/2" (38 mm) offset. When a shutter is complete, save the drawing as a block in a file with a title such as PROTO/EXTELEV/SHUTTER for future reference. The shutter from Figure 18.50 is on the website in the SUPPLEMENTAL DRAWING MATERIAL folder. The width of the shutter can be adjusted using the STRETCH command. The shutter length can be reduced by erasing unneeded slats, and then using the STRETCH command to shorten the exterior frame. The shutter length can be extended by using the STRETCH command to extend the frame length, and then using the COPY or ARRAY command to add the necessary slats.

Gable End Wall Vents

Drawing eave vents is similar to drawing shutters. Figure 18.51 shows common methods of drawing attic vents for

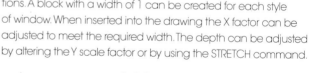
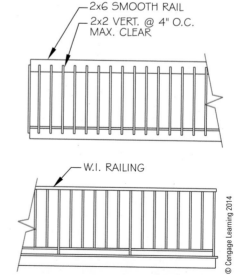

FIGURE 18.47 Common railings include wood railings made with 2 × 2 (50 × 50) verticals or wrought iron railings.

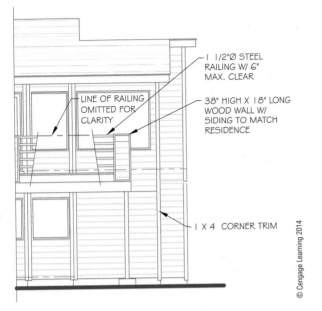

1 1/2"Ø STEEL
RAILING W/ 6"
MAX. CLEAR

LINE OF RAILING
OMITTED FOR
CLARITY

38" HIGH X 18" LONG
WOOD WALL W/
SIDING TO MATCH
RESIDENCE

1 X 4 CORNER TRIM

© Cengage Learning 2014

FIGURE 18.48 Railings can often be omitted to allow objects that lie beyond the rail to be seen. Use a center or phantom line to represent the limits of the rails that have been omitted.

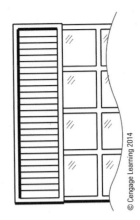

© Cengage Learning 2014

FIGURE 18.50 Creating a block to represent a shutter for use in exterior elevations.

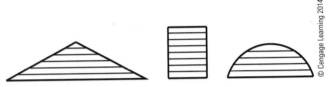

© Cengage Learning 2014

FIGURE 18.51 Common blocks for representing attic vents on gable end walls in elevations.

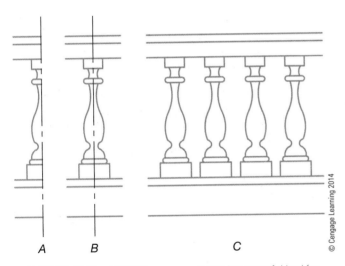

© Cengage Learning 2014

FIGURE 18.49 The MIRROR command can be a useful tool for creating decorative railings. (A) Half of the baluster is drawn. (B) One full baluster created. (C) Multiple balusters are created using the COPY command.

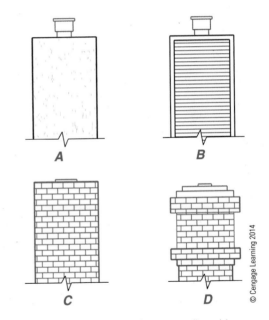

© Cengage Learning 2014

FIGURE 18.52 Common blocks for representing chimneys include (A) stucco chase with metal cap; (B) horizontal wood siding with metal cap; (C) common brick; (D) decorative masonry.

a gable end wall. When the drawing is complete, save it as a block in a file with a title such as PROTO/EXTELEV VENT for future reference. The vents from Figure 18.51 are on the website in the SUPPLEMENTAL DRAWING MATERIAL folder.

Chimney

There are several different methods for representing a chimney. Figure 18.52 shows examples of the wood and masonry chimneys on the website in the SUPPLEMENTAL DRAWING MATERIAL folder.

Going Green

Exterior Building Materials

Nearly every manufacturer of key elements shown on the exterior elevations including exterior wall finishing materials, roof materials, windows, doors, and skylights have introduced features to increase the environmental friendliness of their products. These include, but are not limited to, changes in the manufacturing process to remove harmful chemicals, increasing the amount of recycled materials in the products, and increasing the reuse of the product once its useful life has been achieved.

These products primarily earn LEED credits from the Materials and Resources division. Information shown on the exterior elevations includes credits from the following categories:

- *Resource reuse.* Reusing materials that are salvaged from previous building sites. Common materials for reuse include concrete and wood siding.
- *Recycled content.* Using recycled materials or materials that contain a high amount of recycled materials.
- *Local/regional materials.* Using materials that are produced near the construction site to minimize damage to the environment from transportation-related factors. This allows for the use of a product even though the product may not typically be considered "green."
- *Rapidly renewable materials.* Using biobased, biocomposites, and biofirers.
- *Certified wood.* Using materials such as lumber products originating in certified forests.

Additional Resources

Use the following websites as resources to help you keep current with changes in roofing and exterior siding materials.

Address	Company or Organization
www.abtco.com	Abtco Vinyl Siding (hardboard and vinyl siding products)
www.alsco.com	Alsco Inc. (vinyl and aluminum siding)
www.alside.com	Alside (vinyl siding, windows, trim)
www.ambrico.com	Ambrico American Brick Company
www.apawood.org	APA – The Engineered Wood Association
www.culturedstone.com	BORAL Cultured Stone®
www.brickinfo.org	The Brick Industry Association©
www.cwc.ca	Canadian Wood Council
www.canamould.com	Canamould™ Extrusions Inc. (exterior moldings)
www.caststone.org	Cast Stone Institute®
www.cedarbureau.org	Cedar Shake & Shingle Bureau

www.cemplank.com	Cemboard (fiber-cement siding)
www.vinylsiding.com	CertainTeed Corporation
www.eifsfacts.com	EIFS Industry Members Association
www.fabral.com	Fabral Metal Wall and Roof Systems
www.gp.com	Georgia-Pacific© (siding)
www.jameshardie.com	James Hardie Building Products, Inc.
www.alcoahomes.com	Mastic Home Exteriors (aluminum and vinyl siding products)
www.napcobuildingmaterials.com	NAPCO Building Specialties
www.norandex.com	Norandex (vinyl siding)
www.owenscorning.com	Owens Corning
www.reynoldsbp.com	Reynolds Building Products
www.senergybasf.com	Senergy Inc. (EIFS)
www.shakertown.com	Shakertown (cedar shingles)
www.vinylinfo.org	The Vinyl Institute
www.wrcla.org	Western Red Cedar Lumber Association

Introduction to Elevations Test

Follow these instructions to access and complete an electronic copy of the Chapter 18 Introduction to Elevations Test:

1. Go to cengagebrain.com
2. Enter the email address and password you used to register for the site (see Preface for full instructions).
3. Select the website from the **My Course & Materials** area of your home page. Select the chapter you want from the pull-down menu at the top of the page. Choose the resources for that chapter from the menu on the left.
4. Type your name, the chapter number, and the date at the top of the sheet.
5. Answer the following questions with short, complete statements using a word processor.

NOTE:

The answers to some questions may not be contained in this chapter and will require you to do additional research using the Internet. Use your favorite search engine to search for specific professional companies or general categories of information.

Questions

18.1. Under what circumstances is a technician required to draw only three elevations?

18.2. When are more than four elevations required?

18.3. What are the goals of the exterior elevations?

18.4. What is the most common scale for plotting elevations?

18.5. Would an elevation plotted at a scale of 1/16" = 1' = 0" require the same methods to represent finishing materials as an elevation that will be plotted at a larger scale?

18.6. Describe methods for transferring the heights of one elevation to another.

18.7. Describe two different methods of showing concrete tile roofs.

18.8. What are the two major types of wood siding?

18.9. How do you express the texture of wood when drawing a home with plywood siding?

18.10. Sketch the pattern most typically used for brickwork.

18.11. What problems are likely to be encountered when drawing stone?

18.12. Sketch the way wood shingles appear when one is looking at the gable end of a roof.

18.13. Give the major consideration for drawing doors in elevation.

18.14. What are the most common materials used for rails?

18.15. How should the pattern be expressed in drawing stucco?

18.16. Use the Internet to research three siding manufacturers and find information regarding changes that have be made in the production of their products to make them more sustainable.

18.17. Use the Internet to research a suitable EIFS specification for applying the product in the weather conditions for your area.

18.18. Use the Internet to determine the requirements for installing brick veneer as an exterior siding according to the local building code.

18.19. Use the Internet to determine specific requirements related to the number of exterior elevations required when applying for a building permit at your local building department.

18.20. Use the Internet to research specific requirements of your local building department related to applying three roofing materials common to your area based on local wind conditions.

Section 6
Framing Methods and Plans

Chapter 21
Framing Methods

More so than any other drawing, the structural drawings—the framing plans, sections and details, and foundation plan—require a thorough understanding of the materials and process of construction. A CAD technician can successfully complete the architectural drawings with minimal understanding of the structural processes involved. However, to work on drawings that will show how a structure is assembled, the technician must understand basic construction principles and materials.

Wood, steel, masonry, and concrete are the most common materials used in the construction of homes. Each material has its own green properties and methods of achieving LEED credits. With each material, the CAD technician can use several different framing methods to assemble the components.

Key Terms

Advanced framing techniques

Balloon framing

Bond

Bond beam

Cement

Concrete form masonry units

Concrete masonry units

Engineered lumber

Expanded polystyrene forms

Fire cut

Flashing

Forest Stewardship Council

Grout

Insulated concrete forms

Laminated strand lumber

Laminated veneer lumber

Modular home

Mortar

Parapet wall

Platform framing

Plywood

Post-and-beam framing

Rebar

Reinforcing

Sheathing

Structural insulated panels

Subfloor

Timber framing

Tongue-and-groove

Veneer

Volatile organic compounds

Weep hole

Wythe

CAD Commands and Tools

No new CAD commands are introduced in this chapter.

WOOD FRAMING METHODS

Wood is the most widely used material for the framing of houses, apartments, and condominiums. Common wood framing methods include:

- Balloon framing.
- Western platform framing.
- Post-and-beam framing.
- Timber.

Although not often used for new structures other than framing gable end walls, the CAD technician needs to understand balloon framing methods when completing renovations on existing structures. Several variations of platform framing can improve green building methods and increase energy efficiency. Each of these methods has many green properties that lead to LEED credits in the categories of Energy and Atmosphere and Material and Resources. Common credits gained by the use of wood framing methods include recycled content, building resource, rapidly renewable materials, and certified wood products. Division 6 of the CSI classifications covers wood framing methods. Components for each system will be introduced in Chapter 22.

Balloon Framing

Although **balloon framing** is not widely used except for gable end walls, understanding this system will prove helpful if an older home is being renovated or remodeled. With **balloon** or eastern framing, the exterior studs run from the top of the foundation to the top of the highest level, as shown in Figure 21.1. This is one of the benefits of the system. Wood has a tendency to shrink as the moisture content decreases, and it shrinks more in width than in length. Because the wall members are continuous from foundation to roof, fewer horizontal members are used, resulting in less shrinkage. Brick veneer or stucco is often applied to the exterior face of the wall, and the minimal shrinkage of the balloon system helps to keep the exterior finish from cracking.

Figure 21.1b shows the use of balloon framing methods for making a gable end wall. Because of the long pieces of lumber needed, a two-story structure is the maximum that can easily be built using balloon framing. Floor framing at the midlevel is supported by a ledger set into the studs. Structural members are usually spaced at 12, 16, or 24" (300, 400, or 600 mm) on center (o.c.). Although the length of the stud gives the building stability, it also caused the demise of the system. The major flaw with balloon framing is the danger of fire. A fire starting in the lower level can quickly race through the cavities formed in the wall or floor systems of the building. Blocking or smoke-activated dampers are now required by building codes at all levels to resist the spread of fire.

Platform Framing

Platform framing or western platform framing is the most common framing system now in use. The system is named for the platform created by each floor as the building is being framed. The framing crew is able to use the floor as a platform to assemble the walls for that level and then tilt them into position (see Figure 21.2). Platform framing grew out of the need for fireblocks in the balloon framing system. The fireblocks that had been inserted individually between the studs in balloon framing became continuous members placed over the studs to form a solid bearing surface for the floor or roof system (see Figure 21.3).

Building with the Platform System

Once the foundation is in place, the framing crew sets the girders and the floor members. Figure 21.4 shows a foundation with the floor joists set in place. The major components of platform construction are shown in Figure 21.5. Sawn floor joists ranging in size from 2 × 6 through 2 × 14 (50 × 150 to 50 × 350) can be used, depending on the distance they are required to span. If engineered joists are used, 9 1/2 and 11 7/8" (240 and 300 mm) are common depths. Chapter 22 explores the use of engineered joists. Once the joists are in place, **plywood** or OSB floor sheathing ranging in thickness from 15/32, 19/32, or 23/32" (12, 15, or 18 mm) is installed over the floor joists.

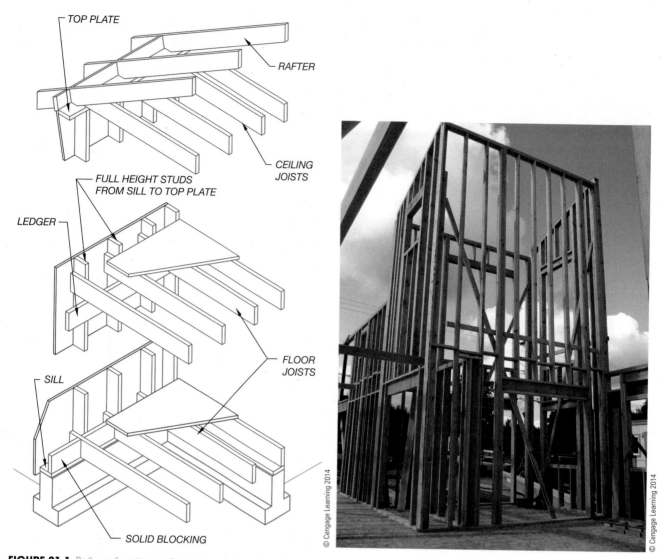

TOP PLATE

RAFTER

CEILING JOISTS

FULL HEIGHT STUDS FROM SILL TO TOP PLATE

LEDGER

FLOOR JOISTS

SILL

SOLID BLOCKING

FIGURE 21.1 Balloon framing wall members extend from the foundation to the roof level in one continuous piece.

FIGURE 21.2 Western platform framing allows the framers to use the floor to construct the walls that will support the next level. Once completed, walls can be tilted into position and the next level can be started.

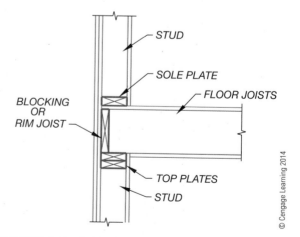

STUD

SOLE PLATE

FLOOR JOISTS

BLOCKING OR RIM JOIST

TOP PLATES

STUD

FIGURE 21.3 The fireblocks of the balloon system gave way to continuous supports (top plates) at each floor and ceiling level. Blocking is placed between each floor joist to stop the joists from rolling over.

FIGURE 21.4 A western platform floor system is constructed with floor joists resting on a pressure treated sill. Floor joists are typically placed at 16" (400 mm) o.c.

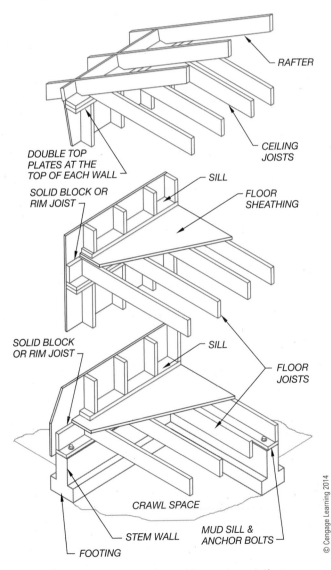

RAFTER

CEILING JOISTS

DOUBLE TOP PLATES AT THE TOP OF EACH WALL

SOLID BLOCK OR RIM JOIST

SILL

FLOOR SHEATHING

SOLID BLOCK OR RIM JOIST

SILL

FLOOR JOISTS

CRAWL SPACE

STEM WALL

MUD SILL & ANCHOR BOLTS

FOOTING

FIGURE 21.5 Structural members of the western platform framing system.

The sheathing, referred to as ***subfloor***, usually has a ***tongue-and-groove*** (T&G) pattern in the edge to help minimize floor squeaking. Gluing the plywood to the supporting members in addition to the normal nailing also helps eliminate squeaks. Occasionally T&G lumber 1 × 4 or 1 × 6 (25 × 100 or 25 × 150 mm) will be laid diagonally to the floor joists to form the floor system, but OSB and plywood are primarily used because they can be installed quickly. Figure 21.6 shows the plywood being installed over the floor joists.

With the floor in place, the walls are constructed using the floor as a clean, flat layout surface. Walls are typically built flat on the floor using a bottom plate, studs, and two top plates. With the walls squared, ***sheathing*** can be nailed to the exterior face of the wall, and then the wall is tilted up into place. When all of the bearing walls are in place, the next level can be started. As in the balloon system, studs are typically placed at 12, 16, or 24" (300, 400, or 600 mm), with 16" (400 mm) o.c. being the most common spacing. Although in theory, the height of a structure is limitless with the platform framing method, the IRC does not allow studs for each level to be taller than 10' (3000 mm)—or 12' (6000 mm) under special conditions presented in Chapter 25—and it does not allow a wood-framed residence to be more than three stories above grade. The height restriction is due to the combustible nature of wood and the resulting risk of fire, and the risk of lateral failure from high winds and earthquakes. Energy-efficient methods of platform framing will be presented later in this chapter.

Post-and-Beam Framing

Post-and-beam framing places framing members at greater distances apart than platform methods do. In residential

FIGURE 21.6 Platform floors are constructed using 1/2, 5/8, or 3/4" (12.5, 15.5, or 18.5 mm) thick floor sheathing nailed over the floor joists.

construction, posts and beams are usually spaced at 48" (1200 mm) o.c. Although this system uses less lumber than other methods, it requires larger members. Sizes vary depending on the span, but beams 4 or 6" (100 or 150 mm) wide are typically used. The subfloor and roofing over the beams are usually 2 × 6, 2 × 8, or 1 1/8 (50 × 150, 50 × 200, or 28) T&G plywood. Figure 21.7 shows typical construction members of post-and-beam construction. Post-and-beam construction can offer great savings in both lumber and nonstructural materials. Savings result from careful planning of the locations of the posts and the doors and windows that will be located between them. Savings also result from having the building conform to the modular dimensions of the material being used. Although an entire home can be framed with post-and-beam or timber methods, many contractors use the post-and-beam system for supporting the lower floor (when no basement is required) and then use conventional framing methods for the walls and upper levels, as seen in Figure 21.8. Figure 21.9 shows the beams of a post-and-beam floor system.

Timber Construction

Although *timber framing* has been used for more than 2000 years, the system has not been widely used for the last 100 years. The development of balloon framing methods

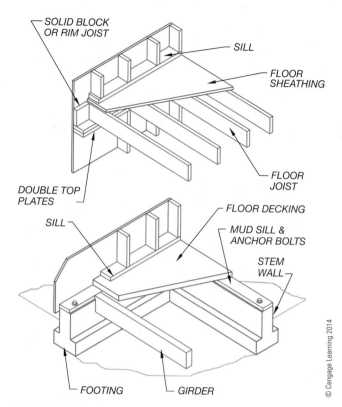

FIGURE 21.8 Post-and-beam construction (lower floor) is often mixed with platform construction for upper floors and roof framing.

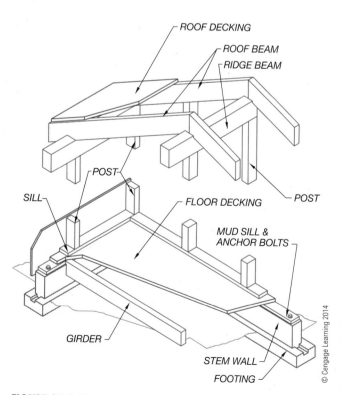

FIGURE 21.7 Structural members of a post-and-beam framing system. In residential construction, structural members are usually placed at 48" (1200 mm) o.c.

FIGURE 21.9 Beam placement for a post-and-beam floor system.

FIGURE 21.10 The use of exposed timbers throughout the residence creates a warm, cozy feeling.

© Cengage Learning 2014. Courtesy Sara Jefferis

with its smaller materials greatly reduced the desire for timber methods. Many homeowners are now returning to timber framing methods for the warmth and coziness timber homes tend to create. Figure 21.10 shows the roof of a home with timber framing set in place.

The length and availability of lumber affect the size of the frame. Although custom sizes are available for added cost, many mills no longer stock timbers longer than 16' (4900 mm). If laminated timbers are used, spans will not be a consideration. The method for lifting the timbers into place may also affect the size of the frame. Beams often are lifted into place by brute force, by winch, by forklift, or by crane. The method of joining the beams at joints affects the frame size. Figure 21.11 shows common timber components.

FIGURE 21.11 Typical components of a timber framed home.

© John Burke/Photolibrary/Getty Images

ENERGY-EFFICIENT FRAMING METHODS

In addition to the use of common wood framing methods that can be used to gain LEED credits, additional methods and materials are available to increase the sustainability of a structure. These include the use of:

- Energy-efficient platform framing.
- Engineered lumber and materials.
- Structural engineered panels.
- Steel framing.
- Concrete masonry units.
- Concrete form masonry units.
- Solid masonry construction.
- Insulated concrete form construction.
- Modular framing methods.

Energy-Efficient Platform Framing

Typically, exterior walls have been framed with 2 × 4 (50 × 100) studs at 16" (400 mm) spacing. The IRC allows framers to substitute 2 × 6 (50 × 150) studs at 24" (600 mm) spacing to allow for added insulation in the wall cavity. Many traditional framing practices have been altered to allow for greater energy savings. These framing practices are referred to as ***advanced framing techniques*** (AFTs).

AFT systems eliminate nonstructural wood from the building shell and replace it with insulation. Wood has an average resistive value for heat loss of R-1 per inch of wood compared with R-3.5 through R-8.3 per inch of insulation. Reducing the amount of wood in the shell increases the energy efficiency of the structure. Advanced framing methods include 24" (600 mm) stud spacing, insulated corners, insulation in exterior walls behind partition intersections, and insulated headers. Many municipalities limit advanced framing methods to one-level construction. For a multilevel residence, advanced methods can be used on the upper level, and the spacing can be altered to 16" (400 mm) for the lower floor.

The R-value of the insulation added to corners, wall intersections, and headers must equal the R-value of the surrounding wall. Figure 21.12 shows examples of framing intersections using advanced framing techniques. Figure 21.13 shows examples of how insulated headers can be framed. Advanced framing methods also affect how the roof will intersect the walls. Figure 21.14 compares standard roof and wall intersections with those of advanced methods.

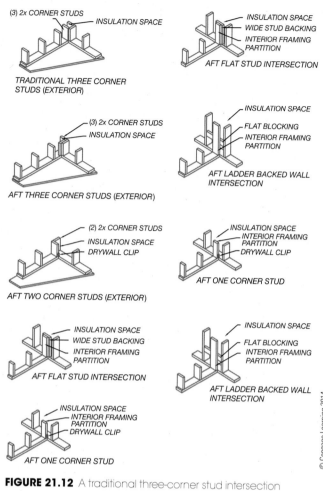

FIGURE 21.12 A traditional three-corner stud intersection compared with advanced framing options. Reducing the amount of lumber used at wall intersections reduces the framing cost and allows added insulation to be used.

Engineered Lumber Framing

In addition to using advanced framing techniques, engineered materials affect both the framing method and the impact the framing system will have on the environment. ***Engineered lumber*** products are made from fast-growing tree species grown on tree farms specifically for use in structural materials. Depending on the product, engineered building products are made from sawdust, wood scraps, small pieces of lumber, or whole pieces of sawn lumber joined by adhesives applied under heat and pressure. Common engineered products found throughout a residence include laminated veneered lumber, oriented strand board, engineered studs, I-joists, and laminated beams. Production of engineered framing products provides efficient use of each log that enters the mill; predictable, superior structural quality; and reduced construction waste at the job site. Figure 21.15 shows a platform floor system constructed of engineered lumber.

Engineered lumber for framing consists of ***laminated veneer lumber*** (LVL) and ***laminated strand lumber*** (LSL). This lumber is made by combining small pieces of second-growth trees to create wood that is free of knots and splits. LSL is created by assembling small sections of wood approximately 12" (300 mm) long into larger members. LVL is created by stacking thin veneers of wood peeled from a log and cutting them into lumber-sized members. Framing members can also be created using small pieces of lumber that would have been scrapped and joining them together with finger joints and adhesive. Once joined with finger joints, this lumber will be as strong as a standard

© Cengage Learning 2014

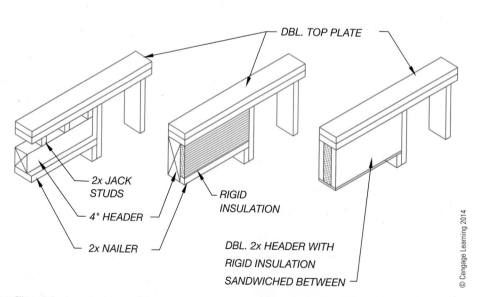

FIGURE 21.13 A traditional 4 × header in a wall framed with 2 × 6 studs. With advanced framing methods, rigid insulation placed behind or between headers increases the insulation value of a header from R-4 to R-11.

© Cengage Learning 2014

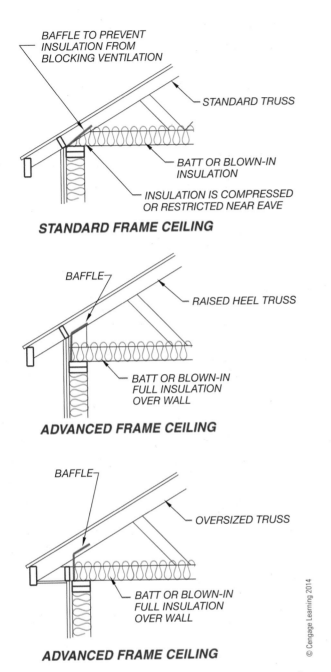

STANDARD FRAME CEILING

BAFFLE TO PREVENT INSULATION FROM BLOCKING VENTILATION

STANDARD TRUSS

BATT OR BLOWN-IN INSULATION

INSULATION IS COMPRESSED OR RESTRICTED NEAR EAVE

ADVANCED FRAME CEILING

BAFFLE

RAISED HEEL TRUSS

BATT OR BLOWN-IN FULL INSULATION OVER WALL

ADVANCED FRAME CEILING

BAFFLE

OVERSIZED TRUSS

BATT OR BLOWN-IN FULL INSULATION OVER WALL

© Cengage Learning 2014

FIGURE 21.14 By altering the bearing point of a truss or rafter, the ceiling insulation can be carried to the outer edge of the exterior wall, thus reducing heat loss.

FIGURE 21.15 Engineered lumber used for the floor joists, rim joist, and mudsill.

Courtesy Brent Roland, Roland Builder, Inc.

of structural board with an adhesive to form a single solid pane. Typically, expanded polystyrene (EPS) foam is used as the insulation material, and oriented strand board (OSB) is used for the outer shell of the panel. By using OSB made from fast-growing trees, SIPs are an environmentally friendly product suitable for wall, floor, and roof construction. ESP panels are also available with a steel structural framework with no OSB facing, or panels can be shipped with 1/2" (13 mm) gypsum board preinstalled over the OSB panel. Panels that use structural gypsum board as the interior face are also available. Figure 21.16 shows a SIP being prepared for installation.

The EPS used to fill the SIP offers increased R-values over a wood wall of similar size with batt insulation. Although values differ somewhat for each manufacturer,

piece of lumber of the same grade. Engineered materials and how they are used in the construction industry are explored in Chapter 22.

Structural Insulated Panels

Structural insulated panels (SIPs) are an economical method of energy-efficient construction used in many parts of the country. SIPs are composed of a continuous core of rigid foam insulation laminated between two layers

FIGURE 21.16 Structural insulated panels are made with a continuous core of rigid foam insulation that is laminated between two layers of OSB. Panels are joined to each other with tongue-and-groove seams.

Courtesy Insulspan®

an R-value of 4.35 per inch of EPS is common. In addition to the increased R-value, because the panels do not contain studs, the SIPs do not create a thermal bridge from the exterior face to the interior face. At the edges of panels, joint techniques allow the insulation to be virtually continuous. In addition to the insulation value, SIPs are environmentally friendly. Although the foam core is made from a nonrenewable resource, it does offer a very efficient use of the resource. One quart of an oil-based product is expanded to create approximately 40 quarts of foam panel filler. SIPs also offer increased construction savings by combining framing, sheathing, and insulation procedures into one step during construction. Panels can be made in sizes ranging from 4 through 24' (1200 through 7300 mm) long and 8' (2400 mm) high, depending on the manufacturer and design requirements. SIPs can be precut and custom-fabricated for use on the most elaborately shaped structures. Figure 21.17 shows an example of SIPs used to form the walls of a home. Door and window openings can be precut during assembly or cut at the job site. A chase is typically installed in the panels to allow for electrical wiring.

Steel Framing

Steel framing has become increasingly competitive with wood framing techniques in residential construction. Lower energy costs, greater strength, and insurance considerations are helping steel framing companies make inroads into residential markets. Because exterior steel walls are wider, insulation of R-30 can be used in them. Steel framing also has excellent properties for resisting stress from snow, wind, and seismic forces. They are consistent in their shape; will not warp, split, crack, or rot; and are resistant to termite and fire damage.

Steel offers several earth-friendly benefits as a construction material and its use can earn LEED credits in several categories of the Materials and Resources division. Standard steel used for construction contains approximately 50 percent recycled metal and it is 100 percent recyclable. Steel can be reused if the building is altered or remodeled, or it can be recycled after the life of the structure. Although steel requires large amounts of energy in the initial manufacturing process, the recycled content value exceeds the goals of LEED. Because steel is very conductive, steel framing increases the risk of thermal bridging through the exterior walls. This conductivity can be overcome by using insulated exterior sheathing. Many residential steel structures incorporate techniques similar to western platform construction methods (see Figure 21.18), using steel studs, steel joists, and open-web steel trusses. Each of these will be explored further in Chapter 22.

Concrete Masonry Construction

Concrete masonry units (CMUs) are a durable, economical building material that provides excellent structural and insulation values. The material is energy-efficient because the mass of concrete blocks acts as a reservoir to trap and store heat from the sun, so that interiors stay cooler longer. Information related to CMUs can be found in Division 04 22 of the CSI classifications. LEED credits are typically gained in several categories of the Energy and Atmosphere and Materials and Resources division.

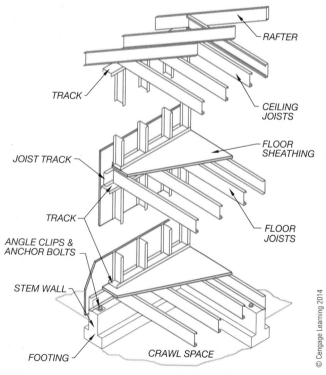

FIGURE 21.18 Structural members of a western platform framing system composed of steel members.

© Cengage Learning 2014

Courtesy Insulspan®

FIGURE 21.17 SIPs can be used for walls and roofs. Openings can be formed at the factory or cut into the panel at the job site.

Concrete blocks are used primarily in warmer climates, from Florida to southern California, as an above-ground building material. Advanced manufacturing processes create CMUs that are insulated and waterproofed, which allows the blocks to be used in all climate zones. Water repellants can be mixed into the blocks as they are produced, additional sealants and *flashing* can be applied at the job site, cement-based paints can be used as the exterior finish, or the blocks can be covered with exterior insulation and finishing system (EIFS) or stucco. Waterproof wood furring strips are normally attached to the interior side of the block to support gypsum board. Insulation can be applied to either face of the block wall at the job site or to the cavity as the block is manufactured. Cavity insulation can include placing foam into the cavities that will not require *reinforcing* and *grout*. Blocks can also be created with the insulation injected into the concrete mix as the block is formed at the plant. Mortarless dry-stacked blocks also may be used. Blocks set in this method are typically held together by a coat of bonding *cement* placed on the inside and outside of the blocks.

Classifications of Concrete Blocks

Four classifications used to define concrete blocks for construction include:

- Hollow load-bearing (ASTM C 90).
- Solid load-bearing (ASTM C 145).
- Non-load-bearing blocks (ASTM C 129), which are either solid or hollow blocks.

Solid blocks must be 75 percent solid material in any cross-sectional plane. Blocks are also classed by their weight as normal, medium, and lightweight. The weight of the block is affected by the type of aggregate used to form the unit. Normal aggregates such as crushed rock and gravel produce a block weight of between 40 and 50 lb (18 and 23 kg) for a block 8 × 8 × 16" (200 × 200 × 400 mm). Lightweight aggregates include coal cinders, shale, clay, volcanic cinders, pumice, and vermiculite. Using a lightweight aggregate will produce approximately a 50 percent savings in weight.

Modular Block Sizes

CMUs come in a wide variety of patterns and shapes.

- The most common size is 8 × 8 × 16" (200 × 200 × 400 mm).
- Nominal block widths are 4, 6, 8, 10, and 12" (100, 150, 200, 250, and 300 mm).
- Lengths include 6, 8, 12, 16, and 24" (150, 200, 300, 400, and 600 mm).

Each dimension of a concrete block is actually 3/8" (10 mm) smaller to allow for a *mortar* joint. Although the project manager is responsible for the design and size of the structure, each member of the team needs to be aware of the modular principles of concrete block construction. Lengths of walls, locations of openings in a wall, and heights of walls and openings must be based on the modular size of the block. Failure to maintain the modular layout can result in a tremendous increase in the cost of labor to cut and lay the blocks. To minimize cutting and labor cost, a concrete block structure should be kept to its modular size. For the standard 8 × 8 × 16" (200 × 200 × 400 mm) CMU:

- Structures that are an even number of feet long should have dimensions that end in 0" or 8". For instance, structures that are 24'-0" or 32'-8" are modular.
- Dimensions for walls that are an odd number of feet should end with 4". Walls that are 3'-4", 9'-4", and 15'-4" are modular, but a wall that is 15'-8" will require blocks to be cut.

Common CMU Shapes and Wall Reinforcement

Concrete blocks come in a variety of shapes, as shown in Figure 21.19. These shapes allow for the placement of steel reinforcement bars, but steel reinforcing mesh can also be used. Chapter 26 provides further information on concrete reinforcement. Reinforcing is typically required at

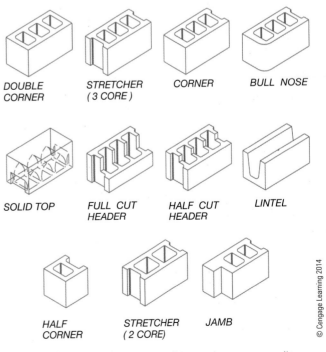

DOUBLE CORNER   STRETCHER (3 CORE)   CORNER   BULL NOSE

SOLID TOP   FULL CUT HEADER   HALF CUT HEADER   LINTEL

HALF CORNER   STRETCHER (2 CORE)   JAMB

FIGURE 21.19 Common shapes of concrete masonry units.

© Cengage Learning 2014

approximately 48" (1200 mm) o.c. vertically. Horizontal reinforcement is approximately 16" (400 mm) o.c., but the exact spacing depends on possible seismic or wind stresses to be resisted. Reinforcement is typically specified on the framing plan and also shown in a cross section and detail. Figure 21.20 shows components of CMU construction.

Masonry Representation

Concrete blocks are represented in plan view as shown in Figure 21.21. Type, size, and reinforcement are specified on the plan views, with bold lines to represent the edges of the masonry. Thin lines for hatching are placed at a 45° angle to the edge of the wall. The size and location of concrete block walls must be dimensioned on the floor plan. For walls, concrete block is dimensioned from edge to edge. Openings in the wall are also located by dimensioning to the edge. Masonry is also shown in sections and details, but the scale of the drawing will affect the drawing method. At scales under 1/2" = 1'-0", the wall is typically drawn just as in plan view. At larger scales, details typically reflect the cells of the block. Figure 21.22 shows methods of representing concrete blocks in cross section.

Steel Reinforcement of Masonry Walls

Masonry units are excellent at resisting forces from compression but very weak at resisting forces in tension. Steel is excellent at resisting forces of tension but tends to buckle under forces of compression. The combination of these two materials forms an excellent unit for resisting great

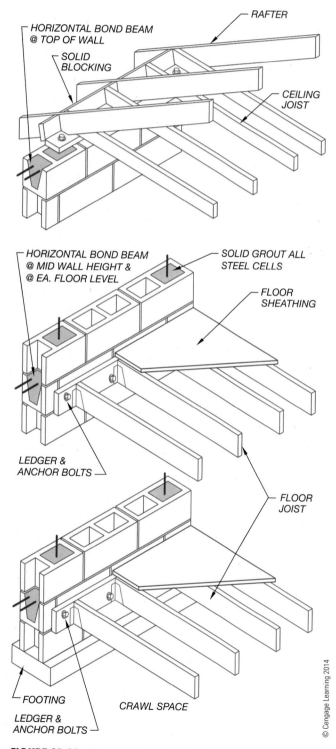

FIGURE 21.20 Components of concrete masonry construction.

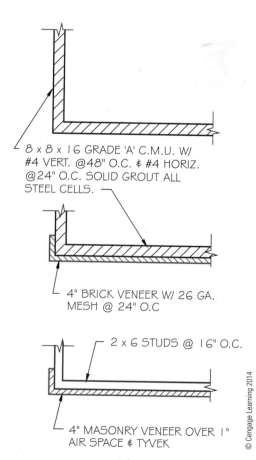

8 x 8 x 16 GRADE 'A' C.M.U. W/ #4 VERT. @48" O.C. & #4 HORIZ. @24" O.C. SOLID GROUT ALL STEEL CELLS.

4" BRICK VENEER W/ 26 GA. MESH @ 24" O.C

2 x 6 STUDS @ 16" O.C.

4" MASONRY VENEER OVER 1" AIR SPACE & TYVEK

FIGURE 21.21 Representing masonry products in plan view.

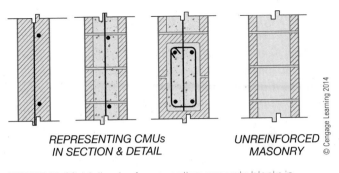

REPRESENTING CMUs
IN SECTION & DETAIL

UNREINFORCED
MASONRY

© Cengage Learning 2014

FIGURE 21.22 Methods of representing concrete blocks in sections and details.

TABLE 21.1 Rebar Sizes

BAR SIZE	METRIC BAR SIZE	DIAMETER IN INCHES, NOMINAL
# 3	# 10	0.375 – 3/8"
# 4	# 13	0.500 – 1/2"
# 5	# 16	0.625 – 5/8"
# 6	# 19	0.750 – 3/4"
# 7	# 22	0.875 – 7/8"
# 8	# 25	1.000 – 1"
# 9	# 29	1.128 – 1 1/8"
# 10	# 32	1.270 – 1 1/4"
# 11	# 36	1.410 – 1 3/8"
# 14	# 43	1.693 – 1 3/4"
# 18	# 57	2.257 – 2 1/4"

© Cengage Learning 2014

loads from lateral and vertical forces. Reinforced masonry structures are stable because the masonry, steel, grout, and mortar bond together effectively. Loads that create tension on the masonry are effectively transferred to the steel. If the steel is carefully placed, the forces will result in tension on the steel and will be safely resisted.

Reinforcing Bars

Steel reinforcing bars, called **rebar**, are used to reinforce masonry walls. The IRC sets specific guidelines for the size and spacing of rebar based on the seismic zone of the construction site. Reinforcement is specified by the engineer throughout the calculations and sketches and must be represented accurately by the CAD technician. Steel rebar may be smooth, but most rebar used for reinforcing masonry walls is deformed so that the concrete will bond more effectively with the bar and not allow slippage as the wall flexes under pressure. Deformations consist of small ribs that are placed around the surface of the bar. Deformed bars range in size from 3/8 through 2 1/4" diameter. Inch sizes do not readily convert to metric sizes. Bars are referenced on plans by a number rather than a size. A number represents the size of the steel in approximately 1/8" increments. Table 21.1 lists common rebar sizes.

Steel Placement

Wall reinforcing is held in place by filling each masonry cell containing steel with grout. The placement of steel varies with each application, but steel reinforcement is typically placed on the side of the wall that is in tension. Because a wall will receive pressure from each side, masonry wall construction usually has the steel centered in the wall cavity. For partial height retaining walls, steel is placed near the soil side of the wall. For full-height retaining walls anchored at the top and bottom, the steel is placed near the side that is opposite the soil. The location of steel in relation to the edge of the wall must be specified in the wall details. Retaining walls will be explored further in Sections 7 and 8 of this text.

Vertical Reinforcing. Vertical reinforcement is required by the IRC in walls at 48" (1200 mm) o.c. with a maximum spacing of 24" (600 mm) if stacked bond masonry is used. The exact spacing depends on the seismic or wind loads to be resisted and is designed by the engineer for each specific use. The IRC also requires a vertical piece of steel to be placed within 16" from each end of a wall. Additional vertical reinforcing is usually required at the edges of openings in walls to serve the same function as a post in wood construction. For small loads, two vertical bars in the same cell may be sufficient. As loads increase, the size of the vertical bond and the number of bars used will increase. Horizontal ties are normally added when four or more vertical bars are required to keep the bars from separating. Figure 21.23 shows an example of a reinforced door jamb.

Horizontal Reinforcing. Horizontal reinforcement is placed approximately 16" (400 mm) o.c., but the exact spacing depends on the seismic or wind loads to be resisted and is designed by the engineer for each specific use. In addition to the horizontal steel required by the building code, extra steel is placed at the midpoint of a wall between each floor level (see Figure 21.20). Generally two bars are placed at the midpoint of each wall level, forming a reinforced area referred to as a **bond beam**. Extra reinforcing is also added where a floor or roof level intersects the wall. A 16"-deep bond beam with two pieces of steel at the top and bottom is a standard method of constructing the bond beam at floor and roof levels. An 8"-deep bond beam with two pieces of steel is also placed at the top of concrete block **parapet walls**. Another common location for a

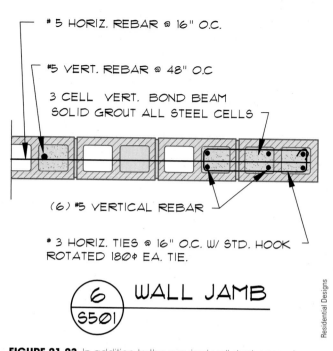

#5 HORIZ. REBAR @ 16" O.C.

#5 VERT. REBAR @ 48" O.C

3 CELL VERT. BOND BEAM
SOLID GROUT ALL STEEL CELLS

(6) #5 VERTICAL REBAR

#3 HORIZ. TIES @ 16" O.C. W/ STD. HOOK
ROTATED 180ɸ EA. TIE.

⬭ 6 / S501 — WALL JAMB

FIGURE 21.23 In addition to the required wall steel, concrete block beside wall openings requires special reinforcement. Vertical reinforcing placed beside the opening is held in place by horizontal ties.

bond beam is over the openings for doors and windows. Figure 21.24 shows a detail representing the reinforcing required over a door opening. The engineer will specify the exact depth, quantity of rebar, and ties based on the load to be supported and the span of the bond beam.

Rebar Representation

The quantity of bars, the bar size by number, the direction that the steel runs, and the steel grade will need to

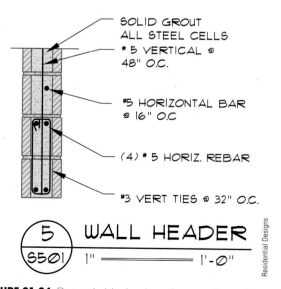

SOLID GROUT
ALL STEEL CELLS

#5 VERTICAL @
48" O.C.

#5 HORIZONTAL BAR
@ 16" O.C

(4) #5 HORIZ. REBAR

#3 VERT TIES @ 32" O.C.

⬭ 5 / S501 — WALL HEADER
1" ══════ 1'-0"

FIGURE 21.24 Concrete blocks placed over wall openings require special reinforcement. Above an opening, horizontal steel is held together with vertical ties.

be specified on the drawings. Common grades associated with residential construction are 40, 50, 60, and 75. On drawings such as the framing plan, walls will be drawn, but the steel is not drawn. Steel specifications are generally included in the wall reference, as in Figure 21.21. When shown in section or detail, steel is represented by a bold line, which can be solid or dashed depending on office practice. A solid circle represents steel when it is shown in end view. In detail, steel is often drawn at an exaggerated size so that it can be clearly seen. It should not be so small that it blends with the hatch pattern used for the grout, or so large that it is the first thing seen in the detail. Figures 21.22 and 21.23 shows how to represent steel in detail.

Locating Steel. Dimensions will be required to show the location of the steel from the edge of the concrete. The engineer may provide a note in the calculations such as:

(7)- #5 HORIZ. @ 3" UP/DN

Although this note could be placed on the drawings exactly as is, a better method would be to use dimensions to specify the distance from the top and bottom of the concrete. The quantity and size of the steel are located in the detail, but the locations are placed using separate dimensions. Although this requires slightly more work on the part of the CAD technician, the more visual specifications will be less likely to be overlooked or misunderstood. Depending on the engineer and the type of stress to be placed on the masonry, the location may be given from edge of concrete to edge of steel or from edge of concrete to center of steel. To distinguish the edge of steel location, the term *clear* or CLR is added to the dimension. In addition to the information placed in the details, steel will also be referenced in the written specifications. The written specifications will detail the grade and strength requirements for general areas of the structure such as walls, floors, columns, and retaining walls.

Concrete Form Masonry Units

Concrete form masonry unit (CFMU) construction is a hybrid design that blends unit masonry construction and cast-in-place concrete construction into an efficient, single-process, composite wall system. CFMU walls have the outer appearance of conventional CMU surfaces and are installed using traditional methods. After a CFMU wall is laid to its desired height, the interior cavity is filled with concrete grout and reinforcing. The end result is a cost-effective, one-operation "sandwich wall" that has all the aesthetic possibilities of masonry and the strength of cast-in-place concrete, with superior performance characteristics.

Residential Designs

Solid Masonry Construction

The use of brick as a construction material for the building envelope can contribute greatly to the LEED sustainability properties, for which a building gains credits in the Energy and Atmosphere and Materials and Resources divisions. Unlike most construction materials, properly installed brick can last for centuries. Because of the thermal mass associated with brick construction, temperature swings within a structure are reduced. This can help reduce the size of the HVAC system required, which will help save on energy costs. The large mass also will help with sound-proofing a structure. When the structure has completed its usefulness, the building can be dismantled and the materials recycled. Information regarding bricks and mortar can be found in Division 4 of the CSI classifications.

Brick Positions and Patterns

One of the most popular features of brick is the wide variety of positions and patterns in which it can be placed. These patterns are achieved by placing the bricks in various positions relative to each other. The position in which the brick is placed will alter what it is called. Figure 21.25 shows the names of common brick positions. Bricks can be placed in various positions to form a variety of bonds and patterns. A **bond** is the connecting of two wythes to form

stability within the wall. The pattern is the arrangement of the bricks within one **wythe**, which is a vertical section of a wall that is one brick thick. The Flemish and English bonds in Figure 21.26 are the most common methods of bonding two wythes. The Flemish bond consists of alternating

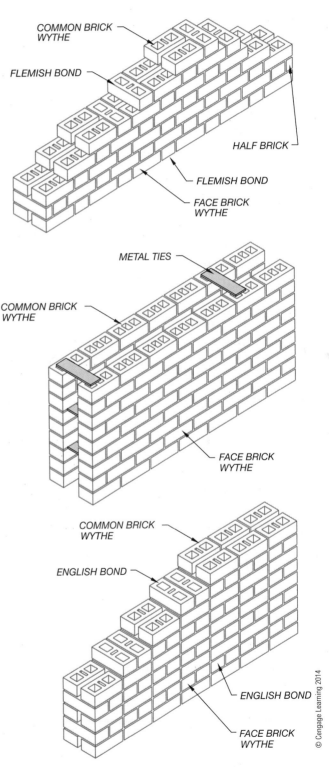

FIGURE 21.26 Brick walls can be strengthened by metal ties or bricks connecting the wythes. The most common types of brick bonds are the Flemish and English.

HEADER COURSE

SAILOR COURSE

ROWLOCK COURSE

STRETCHER COURSE

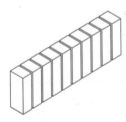

SOLDIER COURSE

SHINER COURSE

FIGURE 21.25 The position in which a brick is placed alters the name of the unit.

© Cengage Learning 2014

headers and stretchers in every course. A course of brick is one row in height. An English bond consists of alternating courses of headers and stretchers. The headers span between the wythes to keep the wall from separating.

Masonry walls must be reinforced using methods similar to those used with concrete blocks. The loads to be supported and the stress from wind and seismic loads determine the size and spacing of the rebar to be used and are established by the architect or engineer. If a masonry wall is to be used to support a floor, a space one wythe wide will be left to support the joist. Joists are usually required to be strapped to the wall so that the wall and floor will move together under lateral stress. The end of the joist must be cut on an angle, called a *fire cut*. If the floor joist is damaged by fire, the fire cut will allow the floor joist to fall out of the wall without destroying the wall. When a roof framing system is to be supported on masonry, a pressure-treated plate is usually bolted to the brick. This is similar to how a plate is attached to a concrete foundation.

Because brick is very porous and absorbs moisture easily, the end of the joist must be protected from absorbing moisture from the masonry. This is typically achieved by wrapping the end of the joist with 55# felt and setting it in a 1/2" (13 mm) air space. The interior of a masonry wall also must be protected from moisture. A layer of hot asphaltic emulsion can be applied to the inner side of the interior wythe and a furring strip attached to the wall. In addition to supporting the gypsum board or plaster, the space between the furring strips can be used to hold batt or rigid insulation.

Another method of using brick is to form a cavity between each wythe of brick. The cavity is typically 2" (50 mm) wide and creates a wall approximately 10" (250 mm) wide with masonry exposed on the exterior and interior surfaces. The air space between wythes cannot exceed 4" (100 mm) wide unless calculations for the wall ties and spacing have been provided to the building departments. The air space provides an effective barrier to moisture penetration to the interior wall. Weep holes in the lower course of the exterior wythe will allow moisture that collects to escape. A *weep hole* is an opening left in the grout to allow water to escape from the wall cavity. The IRC requires weep holes to be at least 3/16" (5 mm) in diameter at a maximum spacing of 33" (825 mm) o.c. Holes must be placed immediately above any required flashing.

Rigid insulation can be applied to the interior wythe to increase the insulation value of the air space in cold climates. Care must be taken to keep the insulation from touching the exterior wythe so that moisture is not transferred to the interior. Metal ties are typically embedded in mortar joints at approximately 24" (600 mm) o.c. maximum vertical spacing and 36" (900 mm) o.c. horizontal spacing to tie each wythe together. Adjustable wall ties placed for each

2.67 square feet (0.248 m²) of wall space, or prefabricated joint reinforcement with at least one cross wire serving 2.67 square feet (0.248 m²) of wall space, are also allowed to be used by the IRC to bond wythes together.

Masonry Veneer

A common method of using brick and stone in residential construction is as a *veneer*, or a nonstructural covering material similar to the home in Figure 21.27. Using brick as a veneer offers the charm and warmth of brick with a lower construction cost than structural brick. If brick is used as a veneer over a wood bearing wall, for example, the amount of brick required is half that of structural brick. Care must be taken to protect the wood frame from moisture in the masonry. Brick must be installed over a 1" (25 mm) and a maximum of 4 1/2" (114 mm) air space with a 15-lb layer of felt applied to the framing. The veneer is attached to the framing with 22-gauge metal ties at 24" (600 mm) o.c. along each stud or with 9-gauge wire with a hook embedded in the mortar joint. Weep holes must be provided for brick veneer just as with masonry construction. Figure 21.28 shows an example of how masonry veneer is attached to a wood-frame wall. When veneer is placed above an opening, the IRC requires the use of a 6 × 4 × 5/16" (150 × 100 × 8 mm) steel angle with the 6" (150 mm) leg of the angle placed vertically and anchored to (2)–2 × 4 (50 × 100) studs spaced at a maximum of 16" (400 mm) o.c. with (2)–7/16" (11 mm) diameter × 4" (100 mm) lag screws.

Insulated Concrete Form Construction

Originally used to form foundation walls, *insulated concrete forms* (ICFs) are now being used to provide an energy-efficient wall framing system for an entire structure. Poured concrete is placed in rigid expanded polystyrene

FIGURE 21.27 Brick veneer is often added to a home.

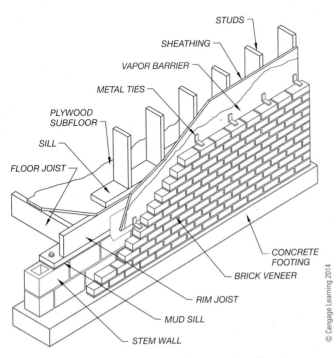

FIGURE 21.28 Brick is typically used as a non-load-bearing veneer attached to wood or concrete construction with metal ties.

STUDS

SHEATHING

VAPOR BARRIER

METAL TIES

PLYWOOD SUBFLOOR

SILL

FLOOR JOIST

CONCRETE FOOTING

BRICK VENEER

RIM JOIST

MUD SILL

STEM WALL

© Cengage Learning 2014

FIGURE 21.29 Insulated concrete forms can be easily placed. Reinforcing and concrete is then added to complete the wall.

Courtesy Carol Ventura

(EPS) forms that snap together and are left in place to create a super-insulated concrete wall system. ICFs are covered in Division 03 11 of the CSI classification. Use of ICFs generally gains LEED credits in the categories of Indoor Environmental Air Quality, Material and Resources, and Innovative Design.

Forms are placed in a pattern similar to concrete blocks or bricks and then filed with steel reinforcing and concrete (see Figure 21.29). Forms 6" and 8" (150 and 200 mm) wide × 16" (400 mm) high × 48" (1200 mm) long are available from most manufacturers. Figure 21.30 shows a typical detail of an insulated concrete form supplied by the manufacturer. This detail can be inserted into the drawings provided by the design team to explain the construction process. The concrete in the forms creates a pattern similar to post-and-beam construction. Vertical posts are created at 12" (300 mm) o.c., and horizontal beams are created at 16" (400 mm) o.c. Solid concrete webs are created between the posts and beams at the center of the forms.

Expanded polystyrene forms (EPFs) provide a stable base for attaching interior and exterior finishing materials and help to create the high energy efficiency of the system. The thermal mass of the concrete and the R-20 value of the EPF produce the energy efficiency. Depending on the width of the wall and finishing materials, the total R-value can range from R-30 to R-50. The system also excels by reducing air leakage and air infiltration into the structure. Structures constructed from ICF average 0.1 air exchange per hour (ACH), compared with 0.4 ACH for wood-framed walls. Figure 21.31 shows wall construction using ICF methods.

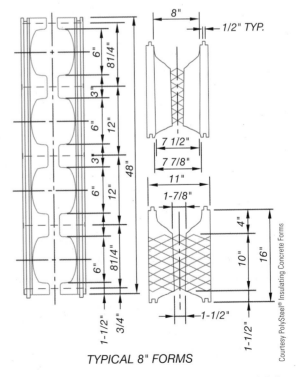

TYPICAL 8" FORMS

Courtesy PolySteel® Insulating Concrete Forms

FIGURE 21.30 The manufacturer of the ICFs provides details that can be added to the construction documents.

FIGURE 21.31 Finishing work for a wall made with insulated concrete forms is similar to poured concrete construction.

Modular Framing Methods

Many people confuse the term *modular home* with mobile or manufactured home, but this is not the case. Manufactured homes are built on a steel chassis and are built to meet codes other than the IRC. Modular homes are governed by the same codes that govern site-built homes. The difference is that modular homes are built off site.

Modular construction is a highly engineered method of constructing a building or building components in an efficient and cost-effective manner. Modular homes begin as components designed, engineered, and assembled in the controlled environment of a factory using assembly-line techniques; the home in Figure 21.32 is an example. Work is never slowed by weather, and materials are not subject to warping due to moisture absorption. A home travels to different workstations, where members of each building trade perform the required assembly. For example,

rooms that require plumbing can be assembled in a separate area and then inserted into a module. Modules can be shipped to the construction site, where they are assembled on a conventional foundation. Modules can be shipped complete or may require additional site construction, depending on the complexity of the module. Figure 21.33 shows a wall component of a modular home being delivered to the construction site.

Structures can also use preassembled components. Panelized walls—which include windows, doors, and interior and exterior finish—can be assembled in a factory but installed at the job site. Floor and roof framing members can be precut in a factory, numbered for their exact location, and then shipped for assembly at the job site. This system of construction can offer economical construction in remote areas where materials are not readily available. Figure 21.34 shows a roof module being placed for the home shown in Figure 3.44a.

FIGURE 21.33 Components ranging in size from a wall panel to a 12'-wide module of a home can be shipped to the site and then assembled.

FIGURE 21.32 Modular construction allows as much as 90% of the construction work to be completed inside an environmentally controlled factory.

FIGURE 21.34 Modular construction allows components to be constructed off site in climate-controlled conditions. Here a roof module for the home shown in Figure 3.44a is being placed.

GREEN CONSTRUCTION GOALS

The final point to be considered in this chapter is not a framing method but a building mindset. Whether it's called earth-friendly, green, ecological, or sustainable construction, the concept is to produce a structure using energy efficiently, with materials that have a low impact on the environment, and that will be healthy to live in. Environmentally friendly framing is not just a matter of selecting green materials, but these materials, once selected, must be used in a manner that will reduce the environmental impact of the home. Products that are not considered green can be used in a home, and they may still benefit the homeowner. Creating an environmentally friendly home requires the matching of materials to a specific design and site that minimizes the effect on that site. Five questions should be considered that will affect the selection of framing and finish materials to make a sustainable structure:

- Can products be selected that are made from environmentally friendly materials?
- Can products be selected because of what they do not contain?
- Will the products reduce the environmental impact during construction?
- Will the products reduce the environmental impact of operating the building?
- Will the products contribute to a safe, healthy indoor environment?

Environmentally Friendly Materials

One of the major considerations that affect framing materials is the selection of products and construction materials made from environmentally friendly components. The materials used to produce a building product and where those materials come from are key determinants in labeling a product a green building material. Points to consider in selecting building materials include products that can be salvaged or recycled, certified green products, quick-growth products, agricultural waste materials, and products that require minimal processing. Chapter 22 contains additional information about sustainable building materials.

Salvaged Products

A major goal of sustainable construction is to reuse a product whenever possible instead of producing a new one. Common salvaged materials used in buildings include bricks, millwork, framing lumber, plumbing fixtures, and period hardware. All of these materials may be found at salvage yards.

Products with Recycled Content

Recycled content is an important feature of many green products because materials are more likely to be diverted from landfills. Industrial by-products such as iron-ore slag can be used to make mineral wool insulation, fly ash can be used to make concrete, and PVC pipe scraps can be used to make shingles.

Certified Wood Products

Third-party forest certification, based on standards developed by the *Forest Stewardship Council* (FSC), will help to ensure that wood products come from well-managed forests. Wood products must go through a certification process to carry an FSC stamp. Manufactured wood products can meet the FSC certification requirements with less than 100 percent certified wood content.

Quick-Growth and Waste By-Products

The use of quick-growth products for framing materials allows old and second-growth trees to remain in the forest. Rapidly renewable materials are made from wood from tree farms with a harvest rotation of approximately 10 years. Examples are wood products such as LVL, OSB, and laminated beams. Interior finish products are also produced from agricultural crops or their waste products. Examples of green products made from agricultural crops include linoleum, form-release agents made from plant oils, natural paints, textile fabrics made from coir and jute, cork, organic cotton, wool, and sisal. Building products can also be produced from agricultural waste products made from straw (the stems left after harvesting cereal grain), rice hulls, and citrus oil. These products can be used to improve the interior environment and create an ecologically friendly structure.

Minimally Processed Products

Products that are minimally processed can be green because of low energy use and low risk of chemical release during manufacture. These can include wood products, agricultural or nonagricultural plant products, and mineral products such as natural stone and slate shingles.

Removing Materials to Become Earth-Friendly

Some building products are considered green not because of their content but because they allow material savings elsewhere or they are better alternatives to conventional products containing harmful chemicals. Chemicals that deplete the ozone, CCA wood preservative, polyvinyl chloride (PVC), and polycarbonate are products that should be avoided in a structure. Products made with

> **NOTE:**
>
> *No matter what areas of the AEC world you enter, the reduction of hazardous chemicals and the safe use of hazardous chemicals and other materials is a major concern. Every person involved in a construction project must be trained in methods of eliminating hazardous chemicals and products from the job site where possible, substituting green alternatives where possible for hazardous products, and selecting and handling hazardous chemicals and products brought to the job site.*

these chemicals may be considered earth-friendly because the product itself has significant environmental benefits. Some examples include drywall clips that allow the elimination of corner studs, engineered lumber that reduces lumber waste, the piers for a joist floor system that minimize the use of concrete compared to the post-and-beam system, and concrete pigments that eliminate the need for conventional finish flooring by letting the concrete slabs serve as the finished floor.

Reducing the Impact of Construction

Some building products produce their environmental benefits by avoiding pollution or other environmental impacts during construction. Products that reduce the impacts of new construction include various erosion-control products, foundation products that eliminate the need for excavation, and exterior stains that result in lower VOC (*volatile organic compounds*) emissions into the atmosphere. The greatest impact from construction can come from careful design that creates a home that suits the site and a foundation system that requires minimal excavation. Review Chapters 11 and 12 for methods of reducing site impact during construction.

Reducing the Impact After Construction

The ongoing environmental impact that results from operating a structure will far outweigh the impact associated with its construction. It is important during the design phase to select components that will reduce heating and cooling loads and conserve energy, select fixtures and equipment that conserve water, choose materials with exceptional durability or low-maintenance requirements, select products that prevent pollution or reduce waste, and specify products that reduce or eliminate pesticide treatments.

Reducing Energy Demands

SIPs, ICFs, autoclaved aerated concrete (AAC) blocks, and high-performance windows are examples of materials that can be used during construction to reduce HVAC loads over the life of the structure. Select other energy-consuming equipment such as water heaters, furnaces, dishwashers, refrigerators, washing machines, and dryers for their ability to conserve energy after construction. ENERGY STAR standards now rate most home appliances, and these standards have been adopted nationally. ENERGY STAR is a government-backed program designed to help consumers obtain energy efficiency. Using compact fluorescent lamps and occupancy or daylighting control equipment can save additional energy. Installing efficient equipment as the home is constructed will reduce energy needs over the life of the structure.

Renewable Energy

Equipment that uses renewable energy instead of fossil fuels and conventional electricity is highly beneficial from an environmental standpoint. Examples include solar water heaters and photovoltaic systems (see Chapter 15). Natural gas fuel cells or cells that use other fossil fuels such as a hydrogen source are considered green because emissions are lower than combustion-based equipment they replace.

Conserving Water

All toilets and showerheads are required to meet the federal water efficiency standards. Other products, such as rainwater storage systems, will also contribute to making a residence earth-friendly (see Chapter 14).

Reducing Maintenance

Products that reduce maintenance make a residence environmentally attractive because they need to be replaced less frequently, or their maintenance has very low impact. Sometimes durability is a contributing factor to the green designation but not enough to distinguish the product as green on its own. Included in this category are such products as fiber-cement siding, fiberglass windows, slate shingles, and vitrified clay waste pipes.

Preventing Pollution

Methods of controlling substances from entering the environment contribute to making a home earth-friendly. Alternative wastewater disposal systems reduce groundwater pollution by decomposing organic wastes more effectively. Porous paving products and vegetated roofing systems result in less storm water runoff and thereby reduce surface water pollution. Convenient recycling centers within the home will allow homeowners to safely store recyclables for collection. A compost system will further allow homeowners to reduce the generation of solid waste.

Eliminating Pesticide Treatments

Although they may be needed to increase livability, periodic pesticide treatments around buildings can be a significant health and environmental hazard. The use of green products such as termite barriers, borate-treated building products, and bait systems that eliminate the need for pesticide application will contribute to a sustainable structure.

Contributing to the Environment

Product selection has a significant effect on the quality of the interior environment. Green building products that help ensure a healthy interior living space can be separated into several categories including products that don't release pollutants, products that block the spread of indoor contaminants, and products that warn occupants of health hazards.

Nonpolluting Products

One of the dangers of modern construction is the ability to make a structure practically airtight. This in itself is not a problem, but the adhesives in most products can be harmful when constant air changes are not provided. Products that don't release significant pollutants into a structure contribute to an earth-friendly home. Interior products that contribute to improving the interior environment include zero- and low-VOC paints, caulks, and adhesives as well as products with very low emissions, such as non-formaldehyde manufactured wood products.

Blocking, Removing, and Warning of Contaminants

Certain materials and products are green because they prevent the contaminants from entering the interior environment. Linoleum is available that helps control microbial growth. Coated duct board is available that helps control mold growth, and products are available for blocking the entry of mold-laden air into a duct system. Other products can help remove pollutants from the shoes of people entering the residence. Each of these types of products can help provide an environmentally friendly home.

Once contaminants have entered the residence, several products are available to warn the homeowner. This would include the use of carbon monoxide (CO) detectors and lead paint test kits. Once a homeowner becomes aware of certain environmental dangers, several products are available to remove them. This would include the use of ventilation products, filters, radon mitigation equipment, and other equipment that can remove pollutants or introduce fresh air.

Going Green

Green Framing Methods

Don't be fooled by thinking that older framing methods can't be green. The home shown on the next page was built in the early seventeenth century but featured many green components that some today consider to be "new technology." This home featured double wall stone construction, south-facing glazing, and a "green roof" to protect the inhabitants from the cold New England winters. Each of the construction features presented throughout this chapter has some green features and can qualify for a wide variety of LEED credits. The very nature of wood makes it a green product. Long before it became trendy, lumber producers such as Georgia-Pacific, Louisiana-Pacific, and Weyerhaeuser® as well as lumber associations such as the APA—The Engineered Wood Association, California Redwood Association, Southern Forest Products Association®, and the Western Wood Products Association® were working to increase the efficiency and health of America's forests. These groups have worked closely with the International Code Council and their founding codes of ICBO, SBCCI, BOCA, and CABO (see Chapter 5) to ensure that products and construction methods will produce safe homes that use materials efficiently.

(Continued)

© Cengage Learning 2014

Homes framed with the traditional balloon, post-and-beam, or timber framing methods have stood safely and efficiently for more than 400 years in many parts of the country. Western platform construction is at the core of many energy-efficient homes. Simply changing the depth of the wall framing members from 4″ to 6″ (100 to 150 mm) or altering the size of the roof overhang of homes framed with western platform methods can produce tremendous benefits in heating and cooling efficiency. These methods remain the core of the home building industry and can still be used to produce a very efficient structure. In areas that are subject to high wind loads or severe seismic activity, these methods are still a preferred method of construction.

Other building methods presented in this chapter, such as masonry, concrete block, and steel-framed construction, have been popular for years but are seeing renewed interest because of advances in their production and usage. Brick homes dating back to our early settlers are highly sought after, not only for their historic value, but also because of their durability and insulative qualities.

Adobe masonry products have been used in similar methods as their brick counterparts for hundreds of years throughout the Southwest for the same reasons that make other masonry products desirable. Although not as old as masonry construction, concrete blocks are used in many areas because of the protection they provide from airborne objects, and their insulative qualities.

Steel has long been a popular building material because of its strength. Depending on manufacturing method and construction methods, even steel can be considered a green product and gain LEED credits for its efficient use of materials, its high use of recycled content, and its ability to be completely recycled when the life of the structure ends. This chapter has introduced new production methods that have enhanced the energy efficiency of each of these materials.

The balance of the construction methods presented in this chapter are not new, but they may be fairly new to home construction. Structural insulated panels have been used since the mid-twentieth century for commercial construction, but they have only recently made a major impact in the housing market. Insulated concrete foam construction has been used since the late twentieth century, but its use has skyrocketed with the current trend to green construction. Engineered lumber has been in use since the mid-twentieth century but continues to grow in popularity because of the shortage of quality-sawn lumber, its superior building qualities over sawn lumber, its efficient use of materials, and its high LEED credit value.

So if Solomon was correct when he said, "There is nothing new under the sun," why the big push toward green construction? Because we live on a planet with diminishing resources and a growing population, and we have a need to be able

(Continued)

to breathe clean air, drink clean water, and live in an environment that can sustain us. As you enter the design field, you'll be working in a business where some are content to maintain the status quo while others are hoping to save the planet. Your job will be to find balance using proven methods in new ways. The ideal methods will please your client, save materials to reduce costs to the builder and homeowner, produce a home with a low impact on the environment, be energy efficient, be recyclable, be buildable by the current workforce, and not break the bank. Welcome to the challenging world of design that awaits you.

Additional Resources

The following websites can be used as a resource to help you keep current with changes in framing materials.

Address	Company or Organization
www.concrete.org	American Concrete Institute
www.steel.org	American Iron and Steel Institute
www.alhloghomes.com	Appalachian Log Homes
www.apawood.org	APA—The Engineered Wood Association
www.betterbricks.com	Better Bricks, an initiative of the Northwest Energy Efficiency Alliance
www.bia.org	Brick Industry Association
www.buildinggreen.com	Building Green Inc.
www.building-your-green-home.com	Planning Your Dream Green Home
www.cardinalhomes.com	Cardinal Homes, Inc. (modular homes)
www.crbt.org	Center for Resourceful Building Technology
www.cmpc.org	Concrete Masonry Promotions Council
www.eere.energy.gov	DOE Integrated Building for Energy Efficiency
www.enercept.com	Enercept, Inc®. (SIPs)
www.energydesignresources.com	Energy Design Resources
www.energystar.gov	ENERGY STAR (appliance energy standards)
www.ewpa.com	Engineered Wood Products Association
www.fscus.com	Forest Stewardship Council
www.generalshale.com	General Shale Brick
www.forms.org	Insulating Concrete Forms Association
www.imiwebi.org	International Masonry Institute
www.iza.com	International Zinc Association
www.kodiaksteelhomes.com	Kodiak Steel Homes®
www.lpcorp.com	Louisiana-Pacific Corporation
www.masonrysociety.org	Masonry Society
www.metalhomes.com	Steel Framed Home Construction
www.nahbrc.org	National Association of Home Builders Research Center
www.newbuildings.org	New Buildings Institute
www.steelframingalliance.com	North American Steel Framing Alliance©
www.nudura.com	Nudura® Integrated Building Technology
www.pge.com	Pacific Energy Center

www.polysteel.com	Polysteel® Forms
www.concretehomes.com	Portland Cement Association© (concrete homes site)
www.portcement.org	Portland Cement Association
www.quadlock.com	Quad-lock® Insulated Concrete Forms
www.rasta.com	Rasta Insulated Concrete Forms
www.reddi-wall.com	Reddi-wall©
www.rewardwalls.com	Reward Wall Systems©
www.southernpine.com	Southern Pine Council
www.spacejoist.com	SpaceJoist (open web trusses)
www.ssina.com	Specialty Steel Industry of North America
www.steeljoist.org	Steel Joist Institute
www.housingzone.com	Sustainable Buildings Industry Council
www.greenbuilder.com	Sustainable Resources
www.timberpeg.com	Timberpeg® (post-and-beam homes)
www.trimjoist.com	TrimJoist Engineered Wood Products
www.usgbc.com	U.S. Green Building Council
www.wwpa.org	Western Wood Products Association
www.wbdg.org	Whole Building Design Guide

Framing Methods Test

Follow these instructions to access and complete an electronic copy of the Chapter 21 Framing Methods Test:

1. Go to cengagebrain.com
2. Enter the email address and password you used to register for the site (see Preface for full instructions).
3. Select the website from the **My Course & Materials** area of your home page. Select the chapter you want from the pull-down menu at the top of the page. Choose the resources for that chapter from the menu on the left.
4. Type your name, the chapter number, and the date at the top of the sheet.
5. Answer the following questions with short, complete statements using a word processor.

NOTE:

The answers to some questions may not be contained in this chapter and will require you to do additional research using the Internet. Use your favorite search engine to search for specific professional companies or general categories of information.

Questions

21.1. Explain two advantages of platform framing.

21.2. Sketch a section view showing platform construction methods for a one-level house.

21.3. Why is balloon framing not commonly used today?

21.4. List five methods that can be used to frame a residence.

21.5. Sketch and label a section showing a post-and-beam foundation system.

21.6. How is brick typically used in residential construction?

21.7. What factor dictates the reinforcing in masonry walls?

21.8. Why would a post-and-beam construction roof be used with platform construction walls?

21.9. What would be the R-value for a wood wall 4" wide?

21.10. What is the typical spacing of posts and beams in residential construction?

21.11. List three qualities that make steel framing a popular residential method.

21.12. List four classifications of CMUs.

21.13. Sketch two methods of framing a header with advanced framing technology. Label each major component.

21.14. What is a fire cut, and how is it used?

21.15. How is moisture removed from a masonry cavity wall?

21.16. What are two materials typically used to reinforce concrete block construction?

21.17. What is the maximum height of studs allowed by the IRC without special framing conditions?

21.18. What do the letters AFT mean in relationship to framing?

21.19. What makes steel framing such an earth-friendly material?

21.20. Explain the difference between traditional corner framing and a corner built using AFT.

21.21. Why are engineered lumber products considered earth-friendly?

21.22. List the various parts of a tree that can be used for engineered lumber products.

21.23. Explain the term *SIPS* as it relates to framing.

21.24. Explain the term *VOC* and how it relates to construction.

21.25. Contact the closest manufacturer of SIP in your area, and get a rough estimate of framing the home you started in Chapter 12 using SIPS.

21.26. Contact a steel framing company and get enough information to write a report about the benefits and problems in framing a home with steel framing members in your area.

21.27. Contact the closest supplier of insulated concrete form materials in your area and get enough information to write a report about the benefits and problems in framing a home with ICFs in your area. Get a rough estimate for building the home you started in Chapter 12 using their products.

21.28. Research and write a report on the use of an alternative building material such as strawbales, cob, or rammed earth. Incorporate the benefits and problems that your method presents, and provide a preliminary floor plan of the home you started in Chapter 12 using an alternative method. Provide a list of resources that were used.

21.29. Using the material presented in earlier chapters and information from the Internet, provide a preliminary floor plan showing the redesign of the home you started in Chapter 12 to include a greenhouse with solar storage mass. In addition to the preliminary floor plan, provide a list of specifications for the use of advanced framing techniques for all exterior walls, and insulation that exceeds the minimum standards for your area.

21.30. After making an appointment, contact a manager or project coordinator at an international construction company. Discuss how federal, state, and local agencies regulate the transportation and use of hazardous chemicals and products at the job site. Compare these practices with requirements in dealing with the same issues in other countries. Discuss how the company trains its employees in:
- Dealing with hazardous chemicals and materials.
- Recognizing, handling and dealing with the dangers of mixing incompatible construction materials.
- Applying chemical processes to the materials that will be on site and their effect on the environment.
- The procedures employees are required to implement when chemicals are being transported to and handled at the job site.

Chapter 22
Structural Components

As with every other phase of drafting, construction drawings have their own terminology. The terms used in this chapter describe the structural components of residential construction. These terms refer to floor, wall, and roof components.

Key Terms

Barge rafter

Bearing wall

Bird blocking

Bird's mouth

Blocking

Bolt

Bottom chord

Braced wall line

Camber

Cantilever

Carriage bolt

Ceiling joists

Collar tie

Column

Common rafters

Cornice

Decking

Diaphragm

Double-wall construction

Drift bolt

Eave

Engineered studs

Expansion bolt

Fascia

Field weld

Finished floor

Flange

Flashing

Flitch beam

Floor joists

Girder

Gypsum board

Hardboard

Header

Hip rafter

I-joists

Infiltration

Jack rafter

Jack stud

King stud

Lag bolt

Laminated-strand lumber

Laminated-veneer lumber

Lateral force

Let-in brace

Machine bolt

Mudsill

Nested joists

Nonbearing wall

Oriented strand board

Overhang

Parallel-strand lumber

Penny

Post

Power-driven stud

Purlin

Purlin brace

Rafter

Rafter/ceiling joists

Ridge

Ridge beam

Ridge block

Ridge board

Ridge braces

Rim joist

Rise	Skip sheathing	Toggle bolt	Underlayment
Roof sheathing	Sole plate	Tongue-and-groove	Uplift
Run	Solid sheathing	Top chord	Valley rafter
Sawn lumber	Span	Top plate	Vapor barrier
Shear panel	Stiffener plate	Trimmer	waferboard
Sheathing	Strong back	Truss	Web
Single-wall construction	Stud	Truss clip	Wide flange
	Subsill	Tubes	Yield point

FLOOR CONSTRUCTION

Two common methods of framing the floor system are conventional joist and post-and-beam. In some areas of the country, it is common to use post-and-beam framing for the lower floor when a basement is not used and conventional framing for the upper floor. The project designer chooses the floor system or systems to use. The size of the framing crew and the shape of the ground at the job site are the two main factors in the choice of framing methods. Floor joists are often used when the slope of the site or other design considerations dictate minimal pier placement for floor support. A post-and-beam system requires more concrete but eliminates the need for floor joist.

Conventional Floor Framing

Conventional or stick framing involves the use of 2" (50 mm) wide framing members placed one at a time in a repetitive manner. Basic terms in this system are mudsill, floor joist, girder, and rim joist. Each can be seen in Figure 22.1 and throughout this chapter.

Mudsill

The **mudsill**, or base plate, is the first of the structural lumber used in framing the home. The mudsill is the plate that rests on the masonry foundation and provides a base for all framing. Because of the moisture content of concrete and soil, the mudsill is required to be pressure-treated or made of foundation-grade redwood or cedar. A 2 × 6 (50 × 150) mudsill is usually set along the entire perimeter of the foundation and attached to the foundation with anchor bolts. The IRC requires anchor bolts to be a minimum of 1/2 × 10" (13 × 250 mm). Bolt spacing of 6'-0" (1800 mm) is the maximum allowed by code for 1/2" (13 mm) bolts and is common for most single-level residential homes. Bolts with a diameter of 5/8 and 3/4" (16 and 19 mm) are also common depending on the lateral loads to be resisted. Areas of a structure that are subject to lateral loads or uplifting, multilevel homes,

and retaining walls will require bolts at a much closer spacing based on the engineer's load calculations. Section 7 explores the use of anchor bolts further.

Girders

With the mudsills in place, the girders can be set to support the floor joists. A **girder** is used to support the floor joists

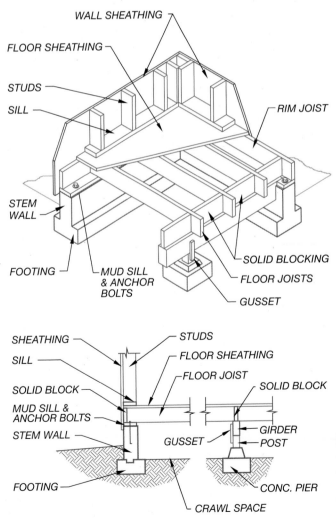

FIGURE 22.1 Conventional, or stick floor, framing at the concrete perimeter wall.

NOTE:

The IRC only requires a small portion of the framing lumber used in home construction to be pressure treated to protect against the effects of nature. Products such as Frameguard™, Bluwood™, and QuanTIM™ can protect all of the above-ground wood framing components of a residence against moisture, rot, fungi, and wood-ingesting insects. Each system features wood that is easily recognizable because of its blue color. A blue chemical film is placed on all six sides of the framing lumber forming a vapor barrier. The barrier functions in a similar manner to how a house wrap such as Tyvek protects the building envelope. The film placed on the individual framing products prevents moisture from seeping into the wood, but it allows moisture to escape from the wood. The chemicals are absorbed below the surface of the wood so eventually the inside of the wood is treated, allowing the member to be cut but still remain protected. In addition to providing moisture protection, the film also prevents termites and fungus from attacking the wood and destroying its structural properties.

FIGURE 22.2 Glu-lam beams span longer distances than sawn lumber and eliminate problems with twisting, shrinking, and splitting.

as they span across the foundation. Girders are usually *sawn lumber*, 4 or 6" (100 or 150 mm) wide, with the depth determined by the load to be supported and the span to be covered. Sawn members 2" (50 mm) wide can be joined together to form a girder. If only two members are required to support the load, they can be nailed, according to the nailing schedule provided in the IRC (see Figure 2.14). If more than three members must be joined to support a load, the IRC requires them to be bolted together. Another form of built-up beam is a *flitch beam*. Chapter 24 introduces formulas that designers use to determine beam sizes.

Laminated Girders. In areas such as basements, where a large open space is desirable, laminated (glu-lam) beams are often used. They are made of sawn lumber that is glued together under pressure to form a beam stronger than its sawn-lumber counterpart. Beam widths of 3 1/8, 5 1/8, and 6 3/4" (80, 130, and 170 mm) are typical in residential construction. Although much larger sizes are available, depths typically range from 9 through 16 1/2" (225 through 412 mm) at 1 1/2" (38 mm) intervals (see Figure 22.2). As the span of the beam increases, a *camber* is built in to help resist the tendency of the beam to sag when a load is applied. Glu-lams are often used where the beam will be left exposed because they do not drip sap and do not twist or crack as a sawn beam does as it dries.

Engineered Wood Girders. Engineered wood girders and beams are common throughout residential construction. Unlike glu-lam beams, which are laminated from sawn

lumber, *parallel-strand lumber* (PSL) is laminated from veneer strips of fir and southern pine, which are coated with resin and then compressed and heated. Typical widths are 3 1/2, 5 1/4, and 7" (90, 130, and 180 mm). Depths range from 9 1/4" through 18" (230 through 460 mm). PSL beams have no crown or camber. PSL columns and posts are available in a range of sizes, including 3 1/2 × 3 1/2", 5 1/4 × 5 1/4", and 7 × 7" (90 × 90 mm, 135 × 135 mm, and 175 × 175 mm) and combinations of these sizes such as 3 1/2 × 7" (90 × 175 mm).

Laminated-veneer lumber (LVL) is made from ultrasonically graded Douglas fir veneers, which are laminated with all grains parallel to each other with exterior-grade adhesives under heat and pressure (see Figure 22.3). LVL beams are 1 3/4" (45 mm) wide with depths ranging from 5 1/2 through 20" (140 through 500 mm). LVL beams provide performance and durability superior to that of other engineered products and often offer the smallest and lightest wood girder solution.

Laminated-strand lumber (LSL) is made from strands of lumber up to 12" (300 mm) long that are coated with resin and then laminated together. LSL beams range in thickness from 1 3/4 to 3 1/2" (44 to 90 mm) with depths ranging from 9 1/4 to 16" (230 to 400 mm).

Steel Girders. Steel girders such as those in Figure 22.4 are often used where foundation supports must be kept to a minimum; they offer a tremendous advantage over wood for total load that can be supported on long spans. Steel beams are often the only type of beam that can support a specified load and still be hidden within the depth of the floor framing. They also offer the advantage of no expansion or shrinkage due to moisture content. Steel beams are named for their shape, depth, and weight. Common steel shapes listed by the American Institute of Steel Construction include W, S, M, C, MC, L, WT, and MT.

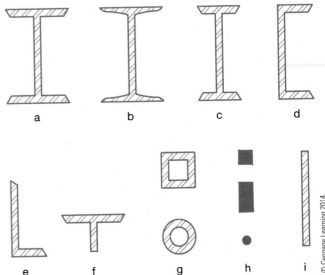

FIGURE 22.5 Common steel shapes found in construction include: (a) wide flange, (b) I-beam; (c) M shape; (d) channel; (e) angle; (f) tee; (g) tubes; (h) bars; and (i) plates.

FIGURE 22.3 Laminated-veneer lumber beams made from ultrasonically graded Douglas fir veneers are a popular alternative to glu-lam beams.

FIGURE 22.4 Steel girders allow greater spans with fewer supporting columns compared to a wood framed floor system.

These common shapes can be seen in Figure 22.5. A steel beam with the designation W16 × 19 would represent a *wide-flange* steel beam with an I shape. The beam is composed of two horizontal faces referred to as a *flange*

and a vertical surface called the web. The 16 represents the approximate depth of the beam in inches, and the 19 represents the approximate weight of the beam in pounds per linear foot. Floor joists are usually set on top of the girder, as shown in Figure 22.4, but they also may be hung from the girder with joist hangers if headroom space is limited.

Girder Supports

Posts are used to support the girders. As a general rule of thumb, a 4 × 4 (100 × 100) post is used below a 4" (100 mm) wide girder, and a post 6" (150 mm) wide is used below a 6" (150 mm) wide girder. Sizes can vary, depending on the load and the height of the post. LVL posts ranging in size from 3 1/2 through 7" (90 through 180 mm) are also used for their ability to support loads. A 1 1/2" (38 mm) minimum bearing surface is required to support a girder resting on a wood or steel support; a 3" (75 mm) bearing surface is required if the girder is resting on concrete or masonry. Because a wooden post will draw moisture out of the concrete foundation, it must rest on 55-lb felt or an asphalt roofing shingle. If the post is subject to *uplift* or lateral forces, a metal post base or strap may be specified by the engineer to attach the post firmly to the concrete. Figure 22.6 shows the steel connectors used to keep a post from lifting off the foundation. Forces causing uplift are discussed further in Chapter 23.

Steel Girder Supports. Steel columns and tubes may be used in place of a wooden post, depending on the load to be transferred to the foundation. Steel *columns* or pipes are hollow circular shapes of steel used to support loads (see Figure 22.5g). Steel *tubes* are hollow square shapes

Courtesy Benigno Molina

FIGURE 22.6 Steel connectors are often used to resist stress from lateral and uplift by providing a connection between the residential frame and the foundation.

© Cengage Learning 2014

FIGURE 22.7 Sawn lumber joists typically range in size from 2 × 6 (50 × 150) through 2 × 14 (50 × 350).

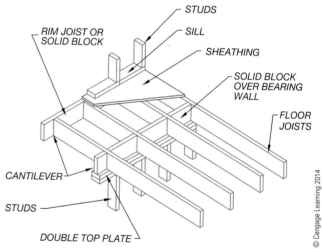

© Cengage Learning 2014

FIGURE 22.8 A floor joist or beam that extends past its supporting member is cantilevered.

of steel. Figure 22.6 shows both tubes and steel base and gusset plates, which provide support to steel beams, and bracing rods that were used to support the floor of a hill-side home. Square tubes are available in sizes ranging from 2 × 2" to 10 × 10" (50 × 50 mm to 250 × 250 mm) with the wall thickness ranging from 3/16 to 5/8" (5 to 16 mm) thick. Rectangular tubes range from 2 × 3" to 8 × 12" (50 × 75 mm to 200 × 300 mm) with a wall thickness of 3/16 to 1/2" (5 to 13 mm). Circular steel columns range from 1/2 to 12" (13 to 300 mm) with wall thickness ranging from 0.216 to 0.50" (5 to 13 mm) thick. Chapter 25 will include a further discussion of steel columns and tubes.

Floor Joists

Once the framing crew has set the support system, the floor joists can be set in place.

Floor joists are the repetitive structural members shown in Figure 22.7 used to support the subfloor. Floor joists usually span between the foundation walls and a girder, but, as shown in Figure 22.8, a joist may extend past its support. This extension is known as a ***cantilever***. Joists are typically made from sawn lumber, engineered lumber, steel, or open web trusses.

Sawn Floor Joists. Sawn floor joists range in size from 2 × 6 (50 × 150) through 2 × 14 (50 × 350) and may be spaced at 12, 16, or 24" (300, 400, or 600 mm) o.c., depending on the load, span, and size of joists to be used. A spacing of 16" (400 mm) is most common. See Chapter 24 for an explanation of sizing joists.

I-Joists. ***I-joists*** similar to those in Figure 22.9 are a high-strength, lightweight, cost-efficient alternative to sawn lumber. I-joists form a uniform size, have no crown, and do not shrink. They come in depths of 9 1/2, 11 7/8, 14, and 18" (240, 300, 350, and 450 mm). I-joists are able to span greater distances than comparable-sized sawn joists and are suitable for spans up to 40' (12 190 mm) for residential uses. Webs can be made from plywood or ***oriented strand board*** (OSB) or laminated-veneer lumber (LVL). OSB is made from wood fibers arranged in a precisely

FIGURE 22.9 Engineered lumber is a common material for residential floor joists. The web (the center of the joist) can be made from oriented strand board (OSB), laminated-veneer lumber (LVL), or plywood. These floor joists are made with LVL flanges and OSB webs.

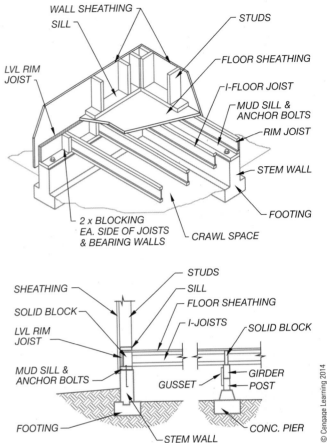

FIGURE 22.10 When engineered joists are used to frame the floor, a rim joist of made of engineered lumber such as the OSB rim joist is used.

controlled pattern; the fibers are coated with resin and then compressed and cured under heat. Holes can be placed in the web to allow for HVAC ducts and electrical requirements based on the manufacturer's specifications. Figure 22.10 shows joists made with OSB supported by a PSL girder. Joists made of laminated-veneer lumber (LVL) are made the same way as LVL beams. LVL joists are 1 3/4" (45 mm) wide and range in depths of 5 1/2 through 18" (140 through 460 mm).

FIGURE 22.11 Floor framing using the western platform system and engineered lumber. Depending on the loads to be supported, blocks may need to be placed beside each joist to provide additional support.

Figure 22.11 shows typical floor construction using engineered floor joists. Depending on the loads to be supported, blocks may need to be placed beside each joist to provide additional support. Figure 22.12 shows another common method of supporting engineered floor joists. The requirements of the manufacturer will need to be verified prior to completing any joist details. Most joist manufacturers supply standard construction details similar to Figure 22.13 that can be modified and inserted into the construction drawings.

Open-Web Floor Trusses. Open-web floor trusses are a common alternative to using 2× sawn lumber for floor joists. Open-web trusses are typically spaced at 24" (600 mm) o.c. for residential floors. Open-web trusses are typically available for spans up to 38' (11 590 mm) for residential floors. Figure 22.14 shows open-web floor trusses used to frame a floor system. The horizontal members of the truss are called top and bottom chords respectively and are typically made from 1.5 × 3" (40 × 75 mm) lumber laid flat. The diagonal members, called webs, are made of wood or

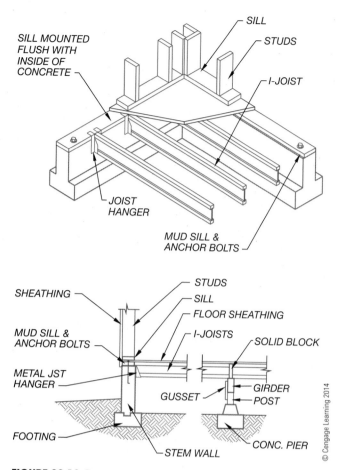

SILL MOUNTED
FLUSH WITH
INSIDE OF
CONCRETE

SILL

STUDS

I-JOIST

JOIST
HANGER

MUD SILL &
ANCHOR BOLTS

SHEATHING

STUDS
SILL
FLOOR SHEATHING
I-JOISTS

MUD SILL &
ANCHOR BOLTS

SOLID BLOCK

METAL JST
HANGER

GUSSET

GIRDER
POST

FOOTING

STEM WALL

CONC. PIER

© Cengage Learning 2014

FIGURE 22.12 Engineered and sawn floor joists can be supported using metal hangers, allowing the floor level to be closer to the finished grade.

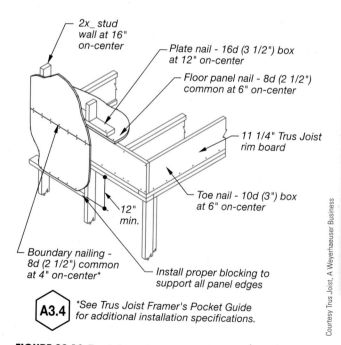

2x_ stud
wall at 16"
on-center

Plate nail - 16d (3 1/2") box
at 12" on-center

Floor panel nail - 8d (2 1/2")
common at 6" on-center

11 1/4" Trus Joist
rim board

Toe nail - 10d (3") box
at 6" on-center

12"
min.

Boundary nailing -
8d (2 1/2") common
at 4" on-center*

Install proper blocking to
support all panel edges

A3.4 *See Trus Joist Framer's Pocket Guide
for additional installation specifications.

Courtesy Trus Joist, A Weyerhaeuser Business

FIGURE 22.13 The intersection of the solid-web floor truss to the support members must be included in the construction documents. This manufacturer provided this detail for insertion. The text font can be altered to match other details in the project.

Courtesy Southern Pine Council

FIGURE 22.14 Open-web floor joists can be used to span large distances for residential designs.

tubular steel approximately 1" (25 mm) in diameter. When drawn in section or details, the webs can be represented with a bold centerline drawn at a 45° angle. The manufacturer determines the exact angle, which is unimportant to the detail. If sections are drawn showing floor trusses, work with the manufacturer's details to find exact sizes and truss depth. Most truss manufacturers supply copies of common truss connections.

Steel Floor Joists. Steel joists similar to those shown in Figure 22.5 offer greater dimensional stability and a level surface without problems such as attack by termites, rotting, shrinkage, splitting, or warping associated with wood construction. Steel joists are available in sizes ranging from 3 5/8 to 13 1/2" (90 to 340 mm) depths. Common steel joists found in residential construction include:

COMMON COLD-FORMED STEEL JOIST SIZES			
		MINIMUM	MAXIMUM
MEMBER DESIGNATION	WEB DEPTH	FLANGE WIDTH	FLANGE WIDTH
550S162-t	5.5	1.625"	2"
800S162-t	8	1.625"	2"
1000S162-t	10	1.625"	2"
1200S162-t	12	1.625"	2"

© Cengage Learning 2014

The first number of the member designation represents the joist depth in hundredths of an inch. The *S* represents that the member is a stud or joist, followed by a number that represents the flange width in hundredths of an inch. The letter *t* is a space holder that represents a number that corresponds to the minimum base thickness in mils. Common design thicknesses of steel joists include:

MINIMUM THICKNESS OF COLD-FORMED STEEL MEMBERS	
MINIMUM THICKNESS IN MILS	MINIMUM BASE STEEL THICKNESS
33	0.0329
43	0.0428
54	0.0538
68	0.0677
97	0.0966

© Cengage Learning 2014

FIGURE 22.16 Steel joists used to support the plywood decking for a lightweight concrete floor slab.

Courtesy Carol Ventura

Joists are typically made from steel ranging from 12- to 25-gauge, with a *yield point* of 40 ksi. Joists are available in lengths up to approximately 40' (12 200 mm) depending on the manufacturer.

Many joists are manufactured so that one joist may be placed around another, or nested. *Nested joists* allow the strength of a joist to be greatly increased without increasing the size of the framing members. A nested joist is often used to support a bearing wall above the floor. If a post is to be supported by a metal joist, a steel *stiffener plate* can be placed between the flanges of the joist at the bearing point to prevent the web from bending.

When steel joists are used to support the floor, a 6 × 6" × 54-mil L clip angle is bolted to the foundation to support the track, which will support the floor joist, as shown in Figure 22.15. The IRC requires a minimum of 1/2" bolts and clip angle at 6'-0" o.c. to be used to attach the angle to the concrete foundation wall. Eight #8 screws

are required to attach the angle to the floor joist track. Floor joists are then bolted to the track using two #8 screws at each joist. Additional fasteners should be used if winds exceed 90 mph. Figure 22.16 shows the use of steel joists to frame a residential floor.

Floor Blocking

Because of the height-to-depth proportions of a joist, it will tend to roll over onto its side as loads are applied. To resist this tendency, a *rim joist* or blocking is used to support the joist. A rim joist is aligned with the outer face of the foundation and mudsill. Some framing crews set a rim joist around the entire perimeter and then end-nail the floor joists that are perpendicular to the rim joist. An alternative to the rim joist is to use solid blocking placed between the between floor joists. Figure 22.17 shows the difference between a rim joist and solid blocking at an exterior wall.

Blocking is used in the floor system at the end of the floor joists and at their bearing points. Blocking is also used at the center of the joist span, as shown in Figure 22.18, if joist spans are longer than 10' (3000 mm). The block at the center span helps to transfer *lateral forces* from one joist to another and then to the foundation system. These blocks help keep the entire floor system rigid and are used in place of the rim joist. Blocking can be used to provide added support to the floor sheathing.

Often walls are reinforced to resist lateral loads. These loads are, in turn, transferred to the foundation through the floor system and are resisted by a *diaphragm*, a rigid plate that acts similarly to a beam and can be found in the roof level, walls, or floor system. In a floor diaphragm, 2 × 4 (50 × 100) blocking is typically laid flat between the floor joists to allow the edges of plywood panels to be supported. Nailing all edges of a plywood panel allows for approximately one-half to two times the design load

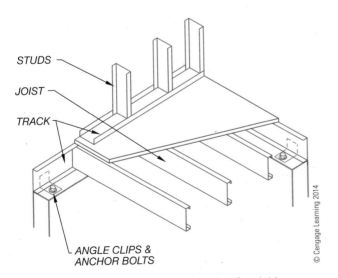

STUDS

JOIST

TRACK

ANGLE CLIPS & ANCHOR BOLTS

© Cengage Learning 2014

FIGURE 22.15 Floor construction using steel floor joists.

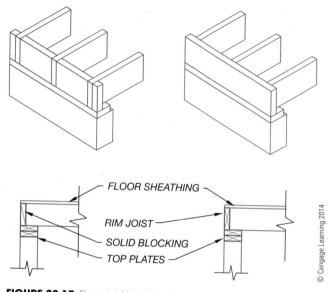

Courtesy APA—The Engineered Wood Association®

FIGURE 22.19 T&G floor sheathing is screwed and glued to the supporting floor joists to provide a quiet floor system.

© Cengage Learning 2014

FIGURE 22.17 Floor joist blocking is placed at the end of each span and at the center. At the mid span of each joist, solid or cross-blocking may be used. At the ends of the floor joists, solid blocking or a continuous rim joist may be used to provide stability.

© Cengage Learning 2014. Courtesy Jordan Jefferis

FIGURE 22.18 When the joists rest on a girder, solid blocking is placed between floor joists to help resist lateral loads and to transfer loads from the floor into the girder.

to be resisted over unblocked diaphragms. The architect or engineer determines the size and spacing of nails and blocking required. Blocking is also used to reduce the spread of fire and smoke through the floor system.

Floor Sheathing

Floor *sheathing* can be seen in Figure 22.19 and is installed over the floor joists to form the subfloor. The sheathing

provides a surface for the base plate of the wall to rest on. Plywood and OSB are the most common materials used for floor sheathing for structures built after the mid-twentieth century. When completing drawings for renovations of older structures, keep in mind that 1 × 4 or 1 × 6 (25 × 100 or 25 × 150) sawn lumber, laid perpendicularly or diagonally to the floor joists, was often used for floor sheathing.

Plywood Sheathing. Plywood is usually laid so that the face grain on each surface is perpendicular to the floor joists. This provides a rigid floor system that usually does not require blocking the edges of the plywood. Depending on the spacing of the joists, plywood with a thickness of 15/32, 19/32, or 23/32" (11.9, 15.1, or 18.3 mm) with an APA grade of STURD-I-FLOOR® EXP 1 or 2, EXT, STRUCT I-EXP-1, or STRUCT 1-EXT is used for sheathing. EXT represents exterior grade, STRUCT represents structural, and EXP represents exposure. Plywood also is printed with a number to represent the span rating, which represents the maximum spacing from center to center of supports. The span rating is listed as two numbers, such as 32/16, separated by a slash. These numbers, as well as the other common markers on plywood and OSB, will be explained shortly.

OSB Floor Sheathing. Oriented strand board (OSB) is a common alternative to traditional plywood subfloors. OSB is made from three layers of small strips of wood that have been saturated with a binder and then compressed under heat and pressure. The exterior layers of strips are parallel to the length of the panel, and the core layer is laid in a random pattern.

Common Stamp Markings for Engineered Sheathing

The IRC regulations for engineered products such as plywood and OSB are based on guidelines provided by the Engineered Wood Association (APA), which was formerly

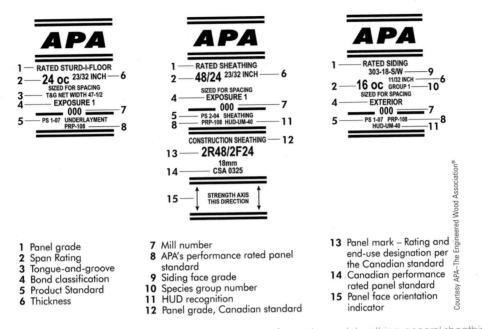

1 Panel grade
2 Span Rating
3 Tongue-and-groove
4 Bond classification
5 Product Standard
6 Thickness

7 Mill number
8 APA's performance rated panel standard
9 Siding face grade
10 Species group number
11 HUD recognition
12 Panel grade, Canadian standard

13 Panel mark – Rating and end-use designation per the Canadian standard
14 Canadian performance rated panel standard
15 Panel face orientation indicator

Courtesy APA–The Engineered Wood Association®

FIGURE 22.20 Common APA specifications found in the products stamps for engineered sheathing, general sheathing, and siding.

the American Plywood Association. The APA rates engineered materials by their structural grade designation, span rating, bond classification, exposure rating, and group number. These and other specifications are stamped on each piece of engineered material regulated by the APA. Figure 22.20 illustrates the stamp symbols. Major specifications that will affect referencing plywood in drawings include grade designations, span ratings, bond classifications, thickness, and group number.

Grade Designations. Structural panel grades (see Figure 22.20, callout #1) are identified by a name suggesting their intended use or by a letter that represents the veneer grade used to construct the panel. Veneer grades define the appearance of the product in terms of the exposed surface veneer and the amount and size of repairs that can be made to the veneer during the manufacturing process. Common letter grades can be seen in Table 22.1. A-grade veneer is the highest veneer grade. The minimum grade allowed for use in exterior-grade plywood is C-grade. D-grade veneers are allowed only where the veneer will be protected from long-term exposure to weather.

Span Rating. APA specifications for general sheathing often provide two numbers separated by a slash such as 32/16 (see Figure 22.20, callout #2). These numbers are the span rating and are used to specify (in inches) the maximum allowable center-to-center spacing of the supports for the product. The first number represents the maximum recommended spacing of supporters if the panel is used for roof sheathing and the long dimension of the sheathing is placed across three or more supports. The second number represents the maximum recommended

TABLE 22.1 Common APA Veneer Grades

SYMBOL	DESCRIPTION
A	Smooth, paintable, with not more than 18 neatly made repairs that are parallel to the grain permitted. Wood or synthetic repairs permitted. May be used for natural finish in less demanding applications.
B	Solid surface. Shims, sled or router repairs, and tight knots to 1" across grain permitted. Wood or synthetic repairs permitted. Some minor splits permitted.
C-Plugged	Improved C veneer with splits limited to 1/8" width and knotholes or other open defects limited to 1/4" × 1/2". Wood or synthetic repairs permitted. Admits some broken grain.
C	Tight knots to 1 1/2". Knotholes to 1" across grain and some to 1 1/2" if total width of knots and knotholes within specified limits. Synthetic or wood repairs. Discoloration and sanding permitted. Limited splits allowed. Stitching permitted.
D	Knots and knotholes to 2 1/2" width across grain and 1/2" larger within specified limits. Limited splits are permitted. Stitching permitted. Limited to Exposure 1.

© Cengage Learning 2014

spacing of supports if the panel is used for floor sheathing and the long dimension of the sheathing is placed across three or more supports. Floor sheathing that will support ceramic tile is typically 32/16 APA span rated and 15/32" (12 mm) thick or span rated 40/20 and 19/32" (15 mm) thick. For products made for a specific application such as Sturd-I-Floor and siding, the span rating will appear as a single number. Common span ratings for Sturd-I-Floor sheathing include 16, 20, 24, 32, and 48. Common span ratings for sheathing for siding are 16 and 24.

Bond Classifications. The APA bond classification of an engineered product describes the moisture resistance of the glue used to bond the fibers of the product together (see Figure 22.20, callout #4). Bond classifications can be either Exterior or Exposure 1.

- *Exterior* panels are suitable for long-term exposure to weather, repeated wetting and redrying, or other severe conditions. This classification is referenced by the letters EXT in the grade stamp.
- *Exposure 1* panels are sometimes referred to as CDX or EXP1 panels and are suitable for uses not involving long-term exposure to weather. Products in this bond group can resist moisture caused by construction delays but are not intended to be exposed to weather for the life of the product. Exposure 1 panels can be used in protected uses such as an eave where exposure to moisture is on the underside only.

Thickness. The thickness of engineered sheathing is expressed as a fraction beside the span rating. Available thicknesses for floor sheathing include 1/2, 19/32, 5/8, 23/32, 3/4, 7/8, 1 3/32, and 1 1/8". Available metric sizes listed by the Canadian Plywood Association© include 15.5 mm (5/8"), 18.5 mm (3/4"), 20.5 mm (13/16"), 22.5 mm (7/8"), 25.5 mm (1"), and 28.5 mm (1 1/8"). The spacing of the supports and the load the floor sheathing will support determine the thickness used. By general practice, 5/8 or 3/4" plywood is used for floor sheathing supported by joists or trusses. For floors that will support tile flooring, 19/32, 23/32, or 7/8" thick T&G decking is recommended by the Tile Council of America© (TCA©). APA recommendations for panel use can be seen in Table 22.2.

TABLE 22.2 APA-Rated Sturd-I-Floor

SPAN RATING	THICKNESS
16	19/32, 5/8"
20	19/32, 5/8"
24	23/32, 3/4, 7/8"
32	7/8"
48	1 3/32, 1 1/8"

© Cengage Learning 2014

Group Number. A group number is assigned to each product to define more than 70 species of wood that are used to create engineered materials (see Figure 22.20, callout #10). Species are divided into one of five groups based on the strength and stiffness of the species. Species in Group 1 are the strongest and those in Group 5 are the weakest.

Underlayment

Once the subfloor has been installed, an **underlayment** for the finish flooring is put down. The underlayment is not installed until the walls, windows, and roof are in place, making the house weather-tight. The underlayment provides a smooth impact-resistant surface on which to install the finished flooring. Underlayment is usually plywood, but hardboard and OSB are also used. Plywood underlayment is usually 1/4, 11/32, 19/32, and 23/32" thick ply, depending on the type of flooring to be supported. **Hardboard** is typically referred to as medium- or high-density fiberboard (MDF or HDF) and is made from wood particles of various sizes that are bonded together with a synthetic resin under heat and pressure. The underlayment may be omitted if the holes in the plywood subfloor are filled. APA Sturd-I-Floor rated plywood 19/32" through 1 3/32" (15 through 28 mm) thick can also be used to eliminate the underlayment.

Post-and-Beam Construction

Terms to be familiar with in working with post-and-beam floor systems include girder, post, decking, and **finished floor**. Each can be seen in Figure 22.21. Notice that there are no floor joists with this system. A mudsill is installed with post-and-beam construction, just as with platform construction. Once set, the girders are placed so that the top of the girder is flush with the top of the mudsill. With post-and-beam construction, the girder rather than floor joists supports the floor **decking**. Girders are usually 4 × 6 (100 × 150) beams spaced at 48" (1200 mm) o.c., but the size and distance will vary depending on the loads to be supported. As with conventional methods, posts are used to support the girders. Typically 4 × 4 (100 × 100) is the minimum size used for a post, with a 4 × 6 (100 × 150) post used to support joints in the girders. With the support system in place, the floor system can be installed. Figure 22.22 shows the components of a post-and-beam floor system.

Decking is the material laid over the girders to form the subfloor. Typically decking is 2 × 6 or 2 × 8 (50 × 150 or 50 × 200) **tongue-and-groove** (T&G) boards similar to those shown in Figure 22.23 or 1 3/32 (28 mm) APA rated 2-4-1 STURD-I-FLOOR EXP-1 plywood T&G floor sheathing. The decking is usually finished similarly to conventional decking with a hardboard overlay.

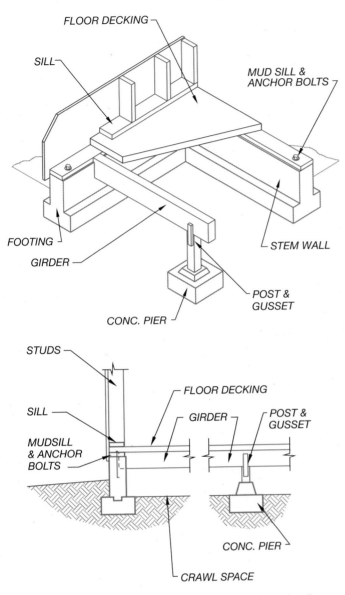

FIGURE 22.22 Floors built with a post-and-beam system require no floor joists to support the floor sheathing. Girders are placed at 4'-0" o.c. with support posts placed at 8'-0" o.c. The posts are attached to the girders with an OSB gusset. In some areas the posts must be attached to the concrete with steel rebar.

FIGURE 22.21 Components of post-and-beam construction.

FIGURE 22.23 Decking for a post-and-beam floor system is typically 2 × 6 tongue-and-groove material supported by the girders and mudsill. The rough plumbing has been completed prior to placing the decking, with holes provided in the decking for fresh- and wastewater lines.

FRAMED WALL CONSTRUCTION

Two types of walls, bearing and nonbearing, must be understood as you explore construction methods. A *bearing wall* supports not only itself but also the weight of the roof or other floors constructed above it. A bearing wall requires some type of support under it at the foundation or lower floor level in the form of a girder or another bearing wall. Nonbearing walls are sometimes called partitions. A *nonbearing wall* serves no structural purpose. It is a partition used to divide rooms and could be removed without causing damage to the building. Bearing and nonbearing walls are shown in Figure 22.24. As a general rule, if the roof system is framed with trusses, any interior walls placed between exterior walls are nonbearing walls. For very large spans or if the ceiling has an irregular

shape, an interior wall may be required to be a bearing wall. Major components of wall construction include the framing members and sheathing.

Sawn Framing Members

Bearing and nonbearing walls made of wood or engineered lumber are both constructed using studs, a sole plate, and a top plate. Each can be seen in Figure 22.25. Western platform construction allows wall components to be assembled on the platform provided by the floor. Once the wall members are assembled, exterior sheathing can be applied.

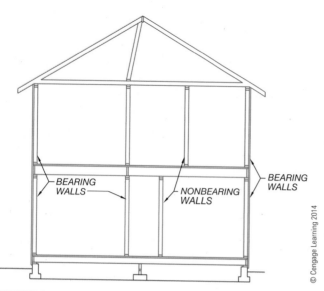

FIGURE 22.24 Bearing and nonbearing walls. A bearing wall supports its own weight and the weight of floor and roof members. A nonbearing wall supports only its own weight. The IRC allows ceiling weight to be supported on a wall and still be considered a nonbearing wall.

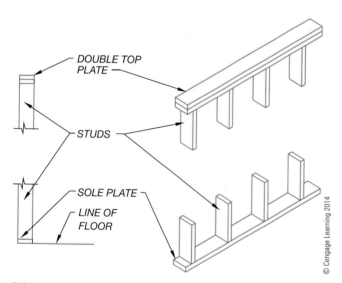

FIGURE 22.25 Standard wall construction uses a double top plate on the top of the wall, a sole plate at the bottom of the wall, and studs.

For small walls, windows can also be installed before the wall is lifted into place. Figures 22.26a and 22.26b show the construction and placement of an exterior wall.

Studs

Studs are the vertical framing members used to transfer loads from the top of the wall to the floor system. Typically 2×4 (50×100) studs are spaced at 16" (400 mm) o.c. and provide a nailing surface for the wall sheathing on the exterior side and the drywall on the interior side. Studs 2×6 (50×150) are often substituted for 2×4 (50×100) studs to provide added resistance for lateral

loads and a wider area to install insulation. Stud-length lumber can be cut in lengths of 88 5/8, 92 5/8, or 96" (2250, 2350, or 2440 mm) long material. Walls more than 10' (3400 mm) high must be blocked at mid-height.

Sole Plate

The **sole plate**, or bottom plate, supports the studs and is used to help disperse the loads from the wall studs to the floor system. The sole plate also holds the studs in position as the wall is tilted into its vertical position. A $2 \times$ ($50 \times$) member is typically used for a sole plate, although $3 \times$ ($75 \times$) members may be used to transfer lateral wall loads into the floor system. The loads to be supported dictate the size and the material used for the sole plate. The sole plate is end-nailed into the studs while the wall is horizontal,

FIGURE 22.26a Western platform construction allows wall components to be assembled on the platform provided by the floor.

FIGURE 22.26b Once assembled, walls can be lifted into place.

and then nailed to the floor system. The sole plate is nailed into the floor sheathing and the rim joist below the exterior walls and into solid blocking or double joists below interior partitions. Nailing is specified in details or by a nailing schedule. Special nailing required to transfer lateral loads through the sole plate to the floor system is specified by the engineer in the calculations and indicated on the framing plan.

Top Plates

Two *top plates*, as shown in Figures 22.27a and 22.27b, are the horizontal members used at the top of a wall to tie the studs together and to provide a bearing surface for the roof or upper floors. Two top plates are required for bearing walls. The lower plate is used to tie wall studs to each other. The upper top plate must lap the lower plate at splices by 48" (1200 mm). This lap distance provides a continuous member on top of the wall to keep the studs from separating. An alternative to the double top plate is to

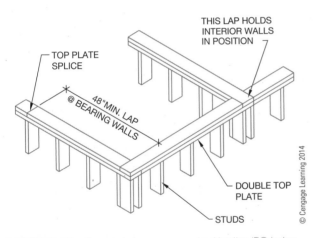

FIGURE 22.27a Top plate laps are required by the IRC to be 48" (1200 mm) minimum in bearing walls or held together with steel straps.

FIGURE 22.27b Top plates sit on top of the studs to keep them in position and provide a level surface for the next floor level or the roof. At this corner intersection, the upper plate overlaps the lower plate to provide rigidity.

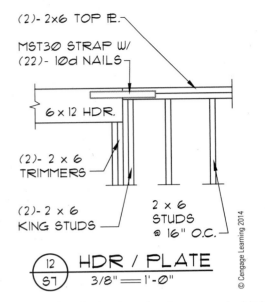

FIGURE 22.27c Standard wall construction uses a double top plate placed on top of the studs. A header can be set level with the top of the top plate if a metal strap is used to tie the header to the top plates.

use one plate with a steel strap at each joint in the plate. As seen in Figure 22.27c, both plates can be eliminated and substituted with a flush header if the header is connected to the top plate at each end by a steel strap. Although this situation is not typically used, it allows an opening to be set at its highest position in a wall. Top plates are usually shown on wall sections. A flush header is usually specified on the framing plan and in the framing details.

Engineered Studs

An alternative to sawn lumber, *engineered studs* are made from short sections of stud-grade lumber that have had the knots and splits removed. Quick-growing, small-diameter aspen and yellow poplar are often used instead of the materials traditionally used for sawn studs. Sections of wood are joined together with 5/8" (16 mm) finger joints. Engineered studs in 2 × 4 or 2 × 6 (50 × 100 or 50 × 150) are available in standard lengths of 8, 9, and 10' (2440, 2740, and 3400 mm), but lengths up to 48' (14 400 mm) can be ordered. LVL and PSL studs are also available. Walls framed with engineered studs require bottom and top plates that meet the same standards as sawn lumber walls. The top plate, located on top of the studs, holds the wall together and provides a bearing surface for the floor joists from an upper level or for the roof members.

Steel Studs

Steel studs, as shown in Figure 22.28, are used to frame homes because they offer lightweight, noncombustible, corrosion-resistant framing. Steel products also offer greater

Courtesy Lisa Echols

FIGURE 22.28 Steel studs and joists provide the support for the upper floor.

dimensional stability and a level surface and eliminate problems such as termites, rotting, shrinkage, splitting, or warping associated with wood construction.

Studs are designed for rapid assembly and are predrilled for electrical and plumbing conduits. The standard 24" (600 mm) spacing reduces the number of studs required by about one-third when compared with traditional wood framing. Stud widths range from 3 5/8" to 10" (90 to 250 mm) but can be manufactured in any width. Stock lengths include 8', 9', 10', 12', and 16' (2400, 2700, 3100, 3700, and 4900 mm), with custom lengths available up to 40' (12 200 mm). Studs are made of steel, ranging from 12 to 25-gauge, with a yield point of 40 ksi. The designer selects the gauge based on the loads to be supported and the usage.

When steel studs are used, a track is placed above and below the studs. This channel is similar to the top and bottom plates of a standard stud wall and is fastened with a minimum of two #8 screws to each stud. The size of the screws will vary depending on the gauge of the track and the thickness of the steel studs.

Stud Specifications

Section properties and steel specifications vary among manufacturers; therefore, the material to be specified on the plans will vary. Consult catalogs developed by the Steel Stud Manufacturers Association® to determine the structural properties of the desired stud. The architect or engineer determines the size of stud to use, but the CAD technician often needs to consult vendor materials to completely specify the studs. As a minimum, specify the gauge and usage on the framing plan, details, and sections. If a manufacturer is to be specified, the callout will include the size, style, gauge, and manufacturer of the stud. An example of a steel stud specification would read.

362SJ20 STEEL STUDS BY UNIMAST

Modular Wall Framing

Chapter 21 briefly examined modular framing methods of assembling modules of a home in a factory and then transferring the modules to the job site. Modular wall framing methods allow portions of homes, such as the wall assembly shown in Figure 22.29, to be assembled in a clean environment, packed into a cargo container, and shipped to the job site for assembly. Drafters involved with homes assembled in modules not only have to be concerned with the overall home design, but they also must consider how the home will be divided into modules. The home in Figure 22.30 shows a different type of modular construction. Trusses have been used for years to form the roof assembly. The upper floor of this home is constructed of trusses that not only form the roof, but also

Courtesy Cardinal Homes, Inc.

FIGURE 22.29 Homes can be assembled as modules in a clean, dry, and warm environment, and shipped to the job site for assembly.

© Cengage Learning 2014

FIGURE 22.30 This home is assembled from modules that contain the roof, walls, and floor system in one truss assembly. Components are lifted in place by crane, and placed at 24" o.c.

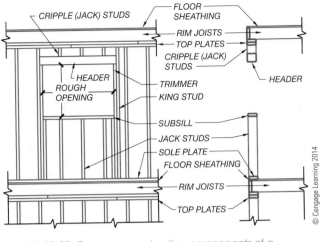

FIGURE 22.31 Common construction components of a wall opening.

FIGURE 22.32 Framing members for a wall opening include the header, king stud, trimmer, sill, and jack studs.

combine the wall and floor members into one unit. These units can be assembled quickly, allowing an entire home to be assembled in one day.

Door and Window Framing

In addition to the major wall components, several other terms are used to describe the members used to frame an opening in a wall. These members include headers, trimmers, king studs, subsills, and jack studs. Each can be seen in Figure 22.31.

A **header** is used over an opening such as a door or window when one or more studs must be omitted. A header supports the weight that the missing studs would have carried. A **trimmer** supports each end of the header. Depending on the weight the header is supporting, double trimmers may be required. The trimmers also provide a nailing surface for the window and the interior and exterior finishing materials. A **king stud** is placed beside each trimmer and extends from the sill to the top plates. It provides support for the trimmers so that the weight imposed from the header can go only downward, not sideways. Between the trimmers is a **subsill** located on the bottom side of a window opening. It provides a nailing surface for the window and the interior and exterior finishing materials. **Jack studs**, or cripples, are studs that are not full height. They are placed between the subsill and the sole plate and between a header and the top plates. Figure 22.32 shows each component of a window opening.

Exterior Wall Sheathing

OSB and plywood sheathing are used to insulate against the weather and to provide resistance to lateral stress. They also serve as backing for the exterior siding. Wall sheathing may be considered optional, depending on your area of the country. When sheathing is used on exterior

walls as shown in Figure 22.33, it provides what is called **double-wall construction**. In **single-wall construction**, wall sheathing is not used, and the siding is attached over a vapor barrier such as Tyvek, Pinkwrap®, Typar®, or the traditional 15-lb felt placed over the studs, as in Figure 22.34. Additional information on vapor barriers can be found later in this chapter.

The cost of the home and its location will have a great influence on whether wall sheathing is used. In areas where double-wall construction is required for weather or structural reasons, 1/2" (13 mm) OSB is used for wall sheathing below the finished siding. Exterior walls that will be used to resist seismic or wind loads may require plywood underlayment.

FIGURE 22.33 When the exterior siding is installed over OSB or plywood sheathing, it is referred to as double-wall construction.

FIGURE 22.34 The siding material can be placed directly over the vapor barrier and studs in what is referred to as single-wall construction. Wire mesh is being installed over the building paper in preparation for the base coat of exterior stucco.

Structural Sheathing

The design of the home may require the use of plywood sheathing for its ability to resist the tendency of a wall to twist or rack. Racking, which can be caused by wind or seismic forces, will try to turn a rectangular wall into a parallelogram (see Figure 22.35). The IRC refers to plywood used to resist these forces as a **braced wall line**. Panels designed by engineers to resist lateral loads are referred to as **shear panels**. Chapter 25 explores the use of braced wall lines and shear panels. For single-wall construction, an alternative to plywood shear panels is to use let-in braces. A notch is cut into the studs, and a 1 × 4

(25 × 100) is laid flat in this notch at a 45° angle to the studs. The **let-in brace** forms a triangle between the brace, the studs, and floor system. If plywood siding rated APA Sturd-I-Wall is used, no underlayment or let-in braces are required.

When plywood is to be used for the underlayment, 3/8 or 1/2" plywood is used on exterior walls as an underlayment. Other sizes that are available are 5/16, 7/16, 15/32, 19/32, 5/8, 23/32, and 3/4". Span ratings for underlayment include 24/0, 24/16, 32/16, and 40/20" depending on the thickness of the sheathing. Whatever the reason for using wall sheathing, plywood sheathing should be APA-rated SHEATHING, EXP 1 or 2, EXT, STRUCT 1, EXT 1, or STRUCT 1 EXT. In areas where single-wall construction is the norm, APA-rated SIDING is available with a variety of surface textures and patterns including T1-11, rough-sawn, reverse board and batten, channel groove, and brushed. Panels are available in 4 × 8', 4 × 9', and 4 × 10' in thicknesses of 11/32, 3/8, 7/16, 15/32, 1/2, 19/32, and 5/8". Engineered lap siding is available in lengths up to 16' (4800 mm) and widths of up to 12" (300 mm).

Wall Blocking

Blocking is common in walls framed with balloon construction methods. Blocking is generally not required when walls are framed using western platform methods. Blocking for structural or fire reasons may also be necessary. Blocking may be required as a backing for structural sheathing in some seismic zones. It is required if a wall exceeds 10' (3000 mm) in height to slow the spread of fire through the wall cavities formed between the studs. Blocking is often installed for a nailing surface for mounting cabinets and plumbing fixtures.

Exterior Wall Weather Protection

Prior to installing the siding material, a weather-resistant exterior wall envelope must be installed. This envelope can consist of a water vapor or air barrier and the use of caulking and weather stripping.

Water Barriers

A key goal of the building envelope is to keep water out of the structure. Leaking water rots wood, grows mold, corrodes steel, and lowers insulating R-values. The IRC requires that a water barrier be provided to help keep water from entering the living environment. Although many building programs focus on keeping water vapor out, most structural problems are caused by water intrusion. Water can enter the structure at any break in a wall or roof surface, such as a window or skylight, butt joints in sidings, knots, and siding overlaps. Water is driven through these leakage points by wind, gravity, and capillary forces.

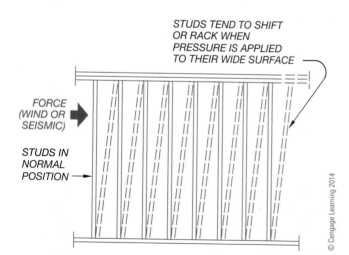

FIGURE 22.35 Wall racking occurs when wind or seismic forces push the studs out of their normal position. Plywood panels can be used to resist these forces and keep the studs perpendicular to the floor. These plywood panels are called shear panels when designed by an engineer or braced wall panels when constructed to meet the prescriptive path of the IRC (see Chapter 25).

During a storm, air pressure causes water to move up, down, and sideways, moving from areas of high pressure to areas of low pressure. The area directly behind a windblown wall surface is at a lower pressure than its exterior face. This pressure difference creates siphon points pulling water into the building. Once water is wicked into the wood sheathing or framing material, it can cause structural problems. Small strips of felt generally are provided along each edge of openings to create overlapping layers of protection (see Figure 22.36a). Metal *flashing* that directs water outward around the tops of openings provides added protection. Once wall openings are protected, walls are typically protected with building felt. The IRC requires the use of a minimum of 15-lb per sq ft (0.683 kg/m²) of asphalt-saturated felt to resist water intrusion (see Figure 22.36b). Also referred to as 15-lb building paper, the felt must be installed in horizontal rows, with the upper layer lapped 2" (50 mm) over the lower row. In addition to carefully covering the wall, care must be taken to ensure that water can't enter the envelope at the tops of doors or windows. Grade D Kraft paper instead of 15-lb felt can be used to protect the structural members behind stucco, brick, stone, and other porous veneers. Panel siding with shiplap joints, battens, and paper-backed stucco lath are not required to have building paper.

FIGURE 22.36b Once openings in the wall are protected, 15-1b felt can be installed to provide an underlayment for the siding.

Moisture and Air Barriers

The IRC allows other approved water-resistant materials to be used to seal the exterior envelope. In place of the building paper, many designers use plastic house wraps that comply with ASTM standards. Plastic house wraps are engineered materials designed to keep out water and prevent air *infiltration* while allowing water vapor to escape from inside of the home. Common wraps include Tyvek, Pinkwrap, and Typar, but many other brands are available. These materials have microscopic pores small enough to resist water and air molecules but large enough to let smaller moisture vapor molecules pass through. These house wraps are available in rolls up to 12' (3600 mm) wide, allowing for fewer seams than with building felt. Any seams required in the house wrap are taped, providing a seamless envelope around the home. Equally important to specifying the underlayment to be used is to specify that the underside of the siding material is to be primed. Because water will get behind the siding, the interior side of the siding must be protected from water intrusion.

FIGURE 22.36a Small strips of felt are generally provided along each edge of openings to provide overlapping layers of moisture protection.

Exterior Caulking

In addition to the siding and building felt or wrap, caulking provides a third line of defense against water and air intrusion. The construction documents generally specify the type and location of caulking and weather stripping. The IRC requires the following areas to be filled with caulking:

- All joints, seams, and penetrations in the exterior shell.
- Doors, window and skylight assemblies, and their respective frames.
- Any other source of air infiltration.

Because this final category is very general, most design professionals provide specific locations that must be caulked or weather-stripped. Common areas include:

- Joints between chimney and siding.
- Joints between eaves and gable molding.
- Joints between window sill and siding.
- Joints between window drip cap and siding.
- Joints between window sash and siding.
- Joints between windows and masonry.
- Joints between masonry or concrete parts (steps, porches, etc.) and main part of house.
- Inside corners formed by siding.

A list of common caulking notes can be found on the textbook's website in the BLOCKS folder.

Interior Moisture Protection

A **vapor barrier** is a membrane that is placed on the warm side of the walls and ceilings between the drywall and the insulation. This barrier prevents water vapor from inside the home from entering the insulated wall cavity, where it can condense and cause structural damage. The barrier can be provided by the insulation facing, paint, or primer applied to the drywall or a sheet of 4-mil polyethylene film applied to the wall (see Figure 22.37). If a film is used, the seams between sheets should be taped. Any penetrations for electrical fixtures should also be sealed.

In addition to the vapor barrier, interior caulking should be specified to reduce air infiltration. Common locations for interior caulking include:

- Where pipes enter the structure. Especially critical are any holes placed in the sole plate.
- Outlets and switch plates located in exterior walls. Gaskets for outlets and switch plates can help prevent air leakage through the walls as well as through caulking holes where wiring passes through the sill or top plates.

© Cengage Learning 2014

FIGURE 22.37 A 4-mil vapor barrier is placed over insulation to keep moisture from the interior from entering the wall cavity. Once the barrier is in place, 1/2" drywall is attached to the structural frame using screws.

- Where vents exit the structure. Provide caulking around the vent, but also provide self-sealing ducts that restrict airflow when exhaust fans are not in use.
- Between the fireplace and exterior walls.
- Between sheets of paneling.
- The interior side of door frames.
- The interior side of window frames.
- Baseboards (even if you have wall-to-wall carpeting).

Interior Finish

The final element of wall construction to consider is the interior finish. For most homes the interior finish consists of **gypsum board**. Gypsum board is the generic name for a family of sheet products such as Sheetrock, drywall, or wallboard that consist of a noncombustible core primarily of gypsum with paper surfacing. Gypsum wallboard is a type of gypsum board used for walls, ceilings, or partitions; it affords a surface suitable to receive decoration. Gypsum board is used to describe a manufactured panel that is typically 1/2" (13 mm) thick made of gypsum plaster and encased in a thin cardboard. Panels that are 5/8" (16 mm) thick are recommended for ceiling use with trusses spaced at 24" (600 mm) o.c. The panels are nailed or screwed onto the framing and the joints are taped and covered with a joint compound. Figure 22.38a shows the application of joint compound and taping of joints. Figure 22.38b shows the joints and nail holes prepared for the final texture to be applied. The other types of drywall often found in a residence include green board, type X, and sound-deadening board:

- Green board is a water-resistant material used in areas with high moisture content, such as those near a shower, tub, or spa.

FIGURE 22.38a Once the drywall has been installed, joint compound is placed over screw heads and in all joints. Tape is applied in the "mud" to resist cracking.

FIGURE 22.38b With all joints and screw heads filled and sanded, the finished texture can be applied.

- Type X gypsum board 5/8" (16 mm) thick is often used on the wall that separates the garage from the living areas. Municipalities vary on the need to use type X gypsum board. The IRC allows standard sheetrock to be used if it extends the full height of the separating wall or if the separating wall and ceiling are covered with sheetrock. Although the use of standard gypsum board is allowed to separate the garage from the home, type X offers superior protection. Type X gypsum board is also used at the bottom of stairs to protect any usable space below the stairs (see Chapter 31).

- Sound-deadening board is used in many custom homes to muffle mechanical and plumbing sounds near living and sleeping areas. Specially designed drywall composed of gypsum, elastic polymers, and sound-isolation layers (used to absorb sound) is often used in home theaters.

ROOF CONSTRUCTION

Roof framing includes both conventional and truss framing methods. Each has its own special terminology, but many terms apply to both systems. The common terms are described first, followed by the terms for conventional and truss framing methods.

Basic Roof Terms

Roof terms common to conventional and trussed roofs are eave, cornice, eave blocking, fascia, ridge, sheathing, finished roofing, flashing, and roof pitch dimensions.

The *eave* is the portion of the roof that extends beyond the walls. The *cornice* is the ornamental molding located at the top of an exterior wall just below a roof. Each term was introduced in Chapter 16. Common methods for constructing the eave are shown in Figure 22.39. Eave or *bird blocking* is a spacer block placed between the *rafters* or truss tails at the eave. This block keeps the spacing of the rafters or trusses uniform and keeps small animals from entering the attic. It also provides a cap to the exterior siding, as seen in Figure 22.40a and Figure 22.40b.

A *fascia* is a trim board placed at the end of the rafter or truss tails that are parallel to the building wall. It hides the truss or rafter tails and also provides a surface on which to mount the gutters. The fascia can be made from either 1 × or 2 × (25 × or 50 ×) material, depending on the need to resist warping (see Figure 22.40). The fascia is typically 2" (50 mm) deeper than the rafter or truss tails. On roofs with a gable end wall, the fascia is referred to as a *barge rafter*. A barge rafter is an inclined trim board that extends from the fascia to the *ridge*. Boards called outlookers or lookouts support the barge rafter. Figure 22.41 shows the use of outlookers to support the barge rafter. On some historic styles, decorative brackets are used to support the barge rafter. At the end of the barge rafter is the ridge. The ridge is the highest point of a roof and is formed by the intersection of the rafters or the *top chords* of a truss.

Roof sheathing is similar to wall and floor sheathing in that it is used to cover the structural members. Roof sheathing may be either solid or skip. The area of the country and the finished roofing to be used will determine which type of sheathing is used. For *solid sheathing*, 1/2" (13 mm) OSB or CDX plywood is generally used. CDX is the specification given by the Engineered Wood Association (APA) to designate standard grade plywood. It provides an economical, strong covering for the framing as well as an even base for installing the finished roofing. Common span ratings used for residential roofs are 24/16, 32/16, 40/20, and 48/24. Figure 22.42 shows plywood sheathing being applied to a conventionally framed roof.

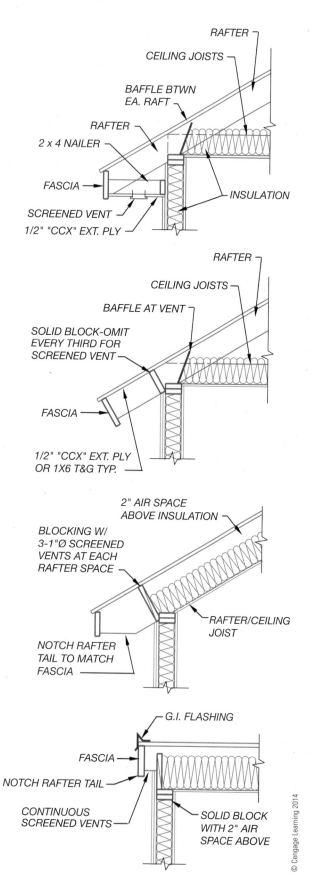

FIGURE 22.39 Typical methods for constructing eaves. Methods shown in each example are interchangeable. The rafter/ceiling joists could be enclosed similar to the top example, or the tails could be cut similar to the second example.

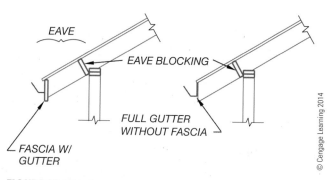

FIGURE 22.40a Key eave components include the bird blocking, fascia, gutter, and roof sheathing.

FIGURE 22.40b Screened bird blocks are usually provided by the truss manufacturer.

Skip sheathing is used with either tile or shakes. In colder climates, the skip sheathing is installed over OSB or plywood sheathing. Typically 1 × 4s (25 × 100s) are laid perpendicular to the rafters with a 4" (100 mm) space between pieces of sheathing (see Figure 22.43). Water-resistant sheathing must be used when the eaves are exposed to weather. This usually consists of plywood rated CCX or 1" (25 mm) T&G decking. CCX is the specification for exterior-grade plywood. It is designated for exterior use because of the glue and the types of veneers used to make the panel.

The finished roofing is the weather-protection system. Roofing might include built-up roofing, asphalt shingles, fiberglass shingles, cedar, tile, or metal panels (see Chapter 16). Flashing is generally 20- to 26-gauge metal used at wall and roof intersections to keep water out. Pitch, span, and overhang are dimensions needed to

FIGURE 22.41 A barge rafter is the outermost rafter, which extends from the fascia to the ridge. It can be supported by braces referred to as outlookers or a lookout. Some home styles use decorative brackets to support the barge rafter.

FIGURE 22.42 One-half inch thick CDX plywood is typically used at exposed eaves and 1/2" thick OSB is generally used to sheath the balance of the roof.

FIGURE 22.43 Skip or spaced sheathing is used under shakes and tile roofs. In colder climates, skip sheathing is placed over OSB sheathing.

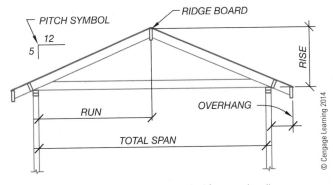

FIGURE 22.44 Roof dimensions needed for construction.

The **span** is the horizontal measurement between the inside edges of the supporting walls. Chapter 24 discusses spans further. The **overhang** is the horizontal measurement between the exterior face of the wall and the end of the rafter tail.

Conventionally Framed Roofs

Conventional, or stick, framing methods involve the use of wood members placed in repetitive fashion. Stick framing involves the use of members such as a ridge board, rafter, and ceiling joists. The **ridge board** is the horizontal member at the ridge that runs perpendicular to the rafters. It is centered between the exterior walls when the pitch on each side is equal. The ridge board resists the downward thrust resulting from the force of gravity, which tends to push the rafters into a "V" shape between the walls. The ridge board does not support the rafters but is used to align the rafters so that their forces are pushing against each other.

Types of Rafters

Rafters are the sloping members used to support the roof sheathing and finished roofing. Rafters are typically

define the angle, or steepness, of the roof. Each is shown in Figure 22.44. Pitch, used to describe the slope of the roof, is the ratio between the horizontal **run** and the vertical **rise** of the roof. The run is the horizontal measurement from the outside edge of the wall to the centerline of the ridge. The rise is the vertical distance from the top of the wall to the highest point of the rafter being measured. Review Chapter 16 for a complete discussion of roof pitch.

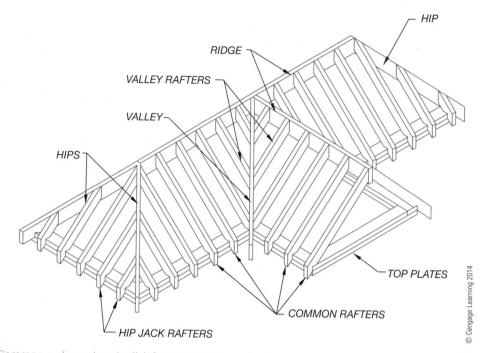

FIGURE 22.45 Common roof members in stick (conventional) construction.

spaced at 24" (600 mm) o.c., but rafters spaced at 12 and 16" (300 and 400 mm) centers are also used. Engineered rafters similar to those used for floor joists are also used for residential roof construction. Various kinds of rafters include: common, hip, valley, and jack. Each is illustrated in Figure 22.45.

Common rafters similar to those in Figure 22.46 are used to span and support the roof loads from the ridge to the top plate. Common rafters run perpendicular to both the ridge and the wall supporting them. The upper end rests squarely against the ridge board and the lower end receives a *bird's mouth* notch and rests on the top

plate of the wall. This notch increases the contact area of the rafter by placing more rafter surface against the top of the wall, as shown in Figure 22.47. *Hip rafters* are used when adjacent slopes of the roof meet to form an inclined edge. The hip rafter extends diagonally across the common rafters and provides support to the upper end of the rafters (see Figure 22.48). The hip is inclined at the same pitch as the rafters. A *valley rafter* is similar to a hip rafter. It is inclined at the same pitch as the common rafters that it supports. Valley rafters get their name because they are located where the adjacent roof slopes meet to form a valley. *Jack rafters* span from a wall to a hip or

FIGURE 22.46 Rafters are used to span and support the roof loads from the ridge to the top plate.

FIGURE 22.47 A bird's mouth is a notch cut into the rafter to increase the bearing surface.

FIGURE 22.48 A hip rafter is used when adjacent roof planes meet to form an inclined edge. Each rafter is longer than the previous rafter. The hip rafter extends diagonally across the common rafters and provides support to the upper end of the rafters. A valley rafter is located where adjacent roof slopes meet to form a valley.

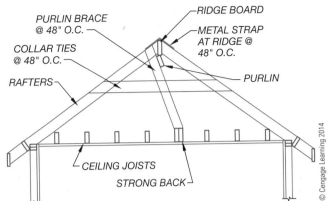

FIGURE 22.50 When ceiling joists are perpendicular to the rafters, the purlin brace may need to be supported on a strong back. A metal strap may also be required to resist the outward force of the rafters.

valley rafter. They are similar to common rafters but span a shorter distance. Typically, a section will show only common rafters, with hip, valley, and jack rafters reserved for a more complex section.

Roof Bracing

Rafters settle because of the weight of the roof. As the rafters settle, they push supporting walls outward. These two actions, downward and outward, require special members to resist them. These members are ceiling joists, ridge bracing, collar ties, purlins, and purlin blocks and braces. Each is shown in Figure 22.49. When the ceiling joists are laid perpendicular to the rafters, in addition to using a collar tie, a metal strap may be required over the ridge to keep the rafters from separating, as shown in Figure 22.50. Usually double joists are used to support the purlin brace.

Ceiling joists span between the top plates of bearing walls to resist the outward force placed on the walls from the rafters. The ceiling joists also support the finished ceiling. *Collar ties* are also used to help resist the outward thrust of the rafters. They are usually the same cross-section size as the rafter and are placed in the upper third of the roof. *Ridge braces* are used to support the downward

action of the ridge board. The brace is usually a 2 × 4 (50 × 100) spaced at 48" (1200 mm) o.c. maximum. The brace must be set at 45° maximum from vertical. A *purlin* is a brace used to provide support for the rafters as they span between the ridge and the wall. The purlin is usually the same cross-section size as the rafter and is placed below the rafter to reduce the span. As the rafter span is reduced, the size of the rafter can be reduced. See Chapter 23 for a further explanation of rafter sizes. *Purlin braces* are typically 2 × 4s (50 × 100s) spaced at 48" (1200 mm) o.c. along the purlin and transfer weight from the purlin to a supporting wall. The brace is supported by an interior wall, or a 2 × 4 (50 × 100) laid across the top of the ceiling joist. It can be installed at no more than 45° from vertical. A scrap block of wood is used to keep the purlin from sliding down the brace. When there is no wall to support the ridge brace, a strong back is added. A *strong back* is a beam placed between the ceiling joist to support the ceiling and roof loads. Figure 22.51 shows a strong back.

Framing Vaulted Ceilings

If a vaulted ceiling is to be represented, two additional terms must be understood: rafter/ceiling joist and ridge beam. Both are illustrated in Figure 22.52. A *rafter/ceiling joist* is a combination of rafter and ceiling joist. It is used to support both the roof loads and the finished ceiling. Typically 2 × 12 (50 × 300) rafter/ceiling joists are used to allow room for 10" (250 mm) of insulation and 2" (50 mm) of air space above the insulation. The size of the rafters/ceiling joists must be determined by the load and span. A *ridge beam* is used to support the upper end of the rafter/ceiling joist. Because there are no horizontal ceiling joists, metal joist hangers must be used to keep the rafters from separating from the ridge beam.

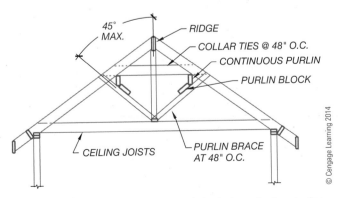

FIGURE 22.49 Common roof supports include collar ties, purlins, and purlin braces.

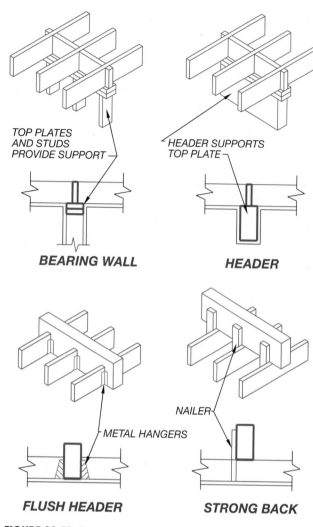

BEARING WALL   **HEADER**

FLUSH HEADER   **STRONG BACK**

FIGURE 22.51 Common methods of supporting loads include bearing walls, headers, flush headers, and the strong back. When a header is used, the loads rest on the header. With a flush header, the ceiling joists are supported by metal hangers. A piece of scrap wood can be used to hang the ceiling joist to the strong back.

Framing Members for Roof Openings

The final terms to be familiar with in order to draw a stick roof are header and trimmer. Both terms are used in wall construction, and they have a similar function when used as roof members (see Figure 22.53). A header at the roof level consists of two members nailed together and laid perpendicular to the rafters. It is used to support rafters around an opening such as a skylight or chimney. Trimmers are two rafters nailed together to support the roofing on the inclined edge of an opening (parallel to other rafters).

Truss Roof Construction

A *truss* is a component used to span large distances without intermediate supports. Residential trusses can be as short as 15' (4500 mm) or as long as 50' (15 000 mm).

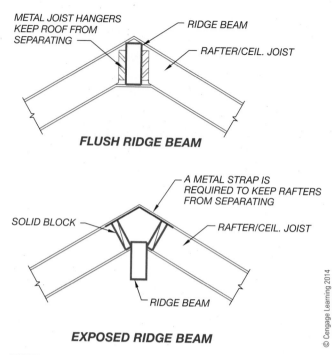

FLUSH RIDGE BEAM

EXPOSED RIDGE BEAM

FIGURE 22.52 Common connections between exposed and hidden ridge beams and rafters. The ridge may be exposed or hidden.

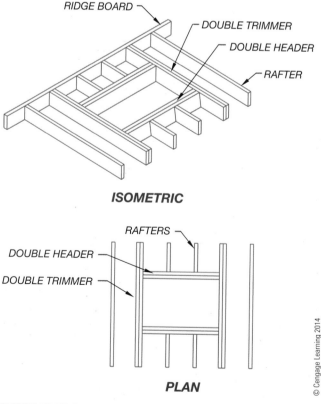

ISOMETRIC

PLAN

FIGURE 22.53 Typical construction at a roof opening includes the use of headers and trimmers.

FIGURE 22.54 Assembled at the truss company and shipped to the job site, trusses can quickly be set in place. Here a gable end wall with sheathing already in place is lifted into position.

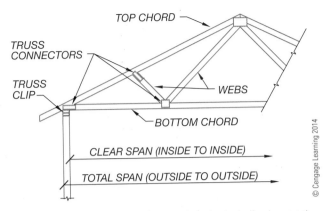

FIGURE 22.55 Common truss members include the top and bottom chords, webs, and truss clips.

Trusses can be either prefabricated or job-built. Prefabricated trusses are commonly used in residential construction. Assembled at the truss company and shipped to the job site, the truss roof can quickly be set in place, as seen in Figure 22.54. A roof that might take 2 or 3 days to frame using conventional framing can be set in place in 2 or 3 hours using trusses, which are set in place by crane. The size of material used to frame trusses is smaller than with conventional framing. Typically 2 × 4s (50 × 100s) are used to frame a truss, but an engineer working for the truss manufacturer will determine the exact size. When drawing a structure framed with trusses, the CAD technician's only responsibility is to represent the span of the trusses on the framing plan and show the general truss shape and bearing points in the section drawings. Chapter 25 introduces framing plans and Chapter 30 introduces sections. Knowledge of truss terms is helpful in making these drawings.

Truss Components

Terms common to construction using roof trusses are top chord, bottom chord, webs, ridge block, and truss clips. Each is illustrated in Figure 22.55. The ***top chord*** serves a function similar to a rafter. It is the upper member of the truss and supports the roof sheathing. The ***bottom chord*** serves a purpose similar to a ceiling joist. It resists the outward thrust of the top chord and supports the finished ceiling material. ***Webs*** are the interior members of the truss that span between the top and bottom chords. The manufacturer attaches the webs to the chords using

metal plate connectors. ***Ridge blocks*** are blocks of wood used at the peak of the roof to provide a nailing surface for the roof sheathing and as a spacer in setting the trusses into position. ***Truss clips***, also known as hurricane ties, are used to strengthen the connection between the truss and top plate or header, which is used to support the truss. The truss clips transfer wind forces applied to the roof, which causes uplift down through the wall framing into the foundation. A block is also used where the trusses intersect a support. Common truss intersections with blocking and hurricane ties are shown in Figure 22.56a and Figure 22.56b.

Truss Construction

A truss gains its strength from triangles formed throughout it. The shape of each triangle cannot be changed unless the length of one of the three sides is altered. The entire truss will tend to bend under the roof loads as it spans between its bearing points. Most residential trusses can be supported by a bearing point at or near each end of the truss. As spans exceed 40' (12 000 mm) or as the shape of the bottom chord is altered, it may be more economical to provide a third bearing point at or near the center. For a two-point bearing truss, the top chords are in compression from the roof loads and tend to push out at the heels and down at the center of the truss. The bottom chord is attached to the top chords and provides tension as it resists the outward thrust of the top chords. The webs closest to the center are usually stressed by tension, and the outer webs are usually stressed by compression. Figure 22.57 shows how the tendency of the truss to bend under the roof loads is resisted and the loads are transferred to the bearing points.

Common Types of Trusses

Computers and sophisticated design software have enabled trusses to be manufactured easily in nearly any shape.

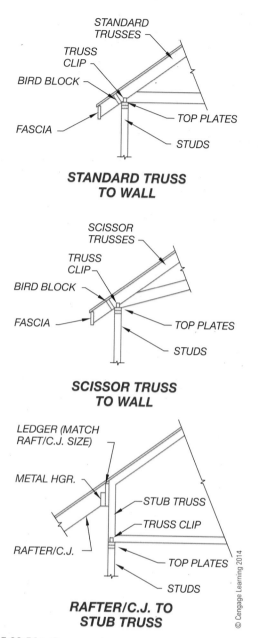

STANDARD TRUSS TO WALL

SCISSOR TRUSS TO WALL

RAFTER/C.J. TO STUB TRUSS

FIGURE 22.56a Common truss connections normally shown in the sections. Notice that the top chord aligns with the outer face of the top plate. When detailing a scissor truss, the bottom chord is typically drawn a minimum of two pitches less than the top chord.

FIGURE 22.56b The rectangular plate is used to bond truss components together and does not need to be specified in details. The truss tie or hurricane tie is used to connect each truss to the top plate. The connector must be specified on the construction documents.

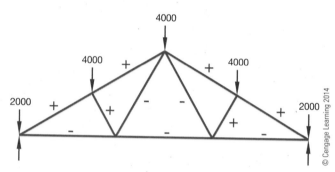

FIGURE 22.57 Trusses are designed so that the weight to be supported is spread to the outer walls. This is done by placing some members in tension and some in compression. A member in compression is indicated by a plus sign (+) and one in tension is represented by a minus sign (−).

Several of the common shapes and types of trusses available for residential roof construction are shown in Figure 22.58. Common trusses include:

- **Standard truss**—The truss most often used in residential construction is a standard truss, which is used to frame gable roofs.

- **Valley truss**—A valley truss is used where two roofs are perpendicular to each other. Valley trusses are standard trusses that decrease in height as they get closer to the ridge of the roof they are intersecting.

- **Gable end wall truss**—A gable end wall truss is used to form the exterior ends of the roof system and is aligned with the exterior side of the end walls of a structure. This truss is more like a wall than a truss, with the vertical supports typically spaced at 24" (600 mm) o.c. to support exterior finishing material.

- **Girder trusses**—A girder truss is used on houses with an L- or U-shaped roof where the roofs intersect. To form a girder truss, the manufacturer typically bolts two or three standard trusses together. The manufacturer determines the size and method of constructing the girder truss. Figure 22.59 shows how a girder truss would appear on a roof framing plan.

- **Cantilevered trusses**—The cantilevered truss is used where a truss must extend past its support to align with other roof members. Cantilevered trusses are

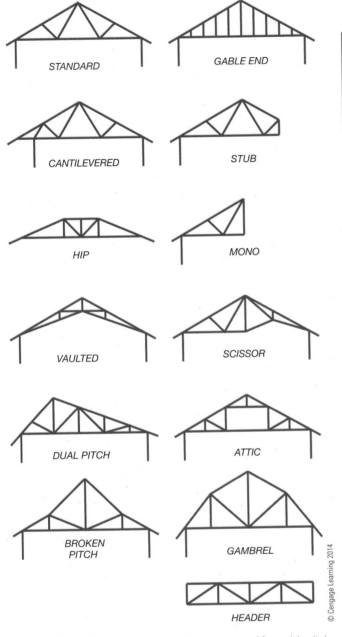

FIGURE 22.58 Common types of roof trusses used for residential construction.

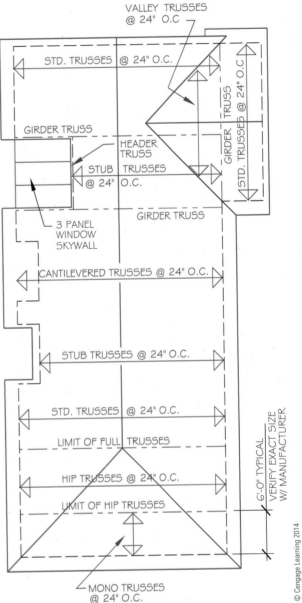

FIGURE 22.59 Standard, valley, girder, header, stub, cantilever, hip, and mono trusses can each be used to form different roof shapes.

typically used where walls jog to provide an interior courtyard or patio.

- **Stub trusses**—A stub truss can be used where an opening will be provided in the roof or the roof must be interrupted. Rooms with glass skywalls, as shown in Figure 22.59, can often be framed using stub trusses. The shortened end of the truss can be supported by a bearing wall, a beam, or a header truss.

- **Header trusses**—A header truss has a flat top and is used to support stub trusses. The header truss has a depth to match that of the stub truss and is similar

in function to a girder truss. The header truss spans between and is hung from two girder trusses. Stub trusses are hung from the header truss.

- **Hip trusses**—Hip trusses are used to form hip roofs. Each truss has a horizontal top chord, and each succeeding truss increases in height. As the height of the truss increases, the length of the top chord decreases until the full height of the roof is achieved and standard trusses can be used. The height of each hip truss decreases as they get closer to the exterior wall, which is perpendicular to the ridge. Typically hip trusses must be 6' (1500 mm) from the exterior wall to achieve enough height to

Courtesy Southern Pine Council

FIGURE 22.60 Hip trusses have a horizontal top chord and are used to form hip roofs. Each succeeding truss increases in height until the full height of the roof is achieved and standard trusses can be used.

Courtesy Southern Pine Council

FIGURE 22.61 The bottom chord of a standard truss can altered to provide a curved ceiling.

support the roof loads. Figure 22.59 shows where hip trusses can be used to frame a roof. Figure 22.60 shows a hip truss being lifted into position. The exact distance will be determined by the truss manufacturer and is further explained in Chapter 25.

- **Mono trusses**—A mono truss is a single pitched truss, which can often be used in conjunction with hip trusses to form the external 6' (1500 mm) of the hip. A mono truss is also useful in blending a one-level structure with a two-level structure.

If a vaulted roof is desired, vaulted or scissor trusses can be used. Vaulted and scissor trusses have inclined bottom chords. Typically there must be at least a two-pitch difference between the top and bottom chord. If the top chord is set at a 6/12 pitch, the bottom chord usually cannot exceed a 4/12 pitch. A section will need to be drawn to give the exact location for the vaulted portion of the truss. If a portion of the truss needs to have a flat ceiling, it may be more economical to frame the lowered portion with conventional framing materials, a process often referred to as "scabbing on." Although this process requires extra labor at the job site, it can eliminate a third bearing point near the center of the truss. An alternative to a scissor is to have a barrel vault. A barrel vault provides a curved ceiling (see Figure 22.61).

COMMON CONNECTION METHODS

Up to this point, the chapter has explored each of the construction materials common to residential construction. The remainder of this chapter will explore how these materials are attached to each other. The stress to be

resisted and the materials to be connected will determine the connection method to be used. Common connection methods include nails, staples, power-driven studs, screws, metal connectors, bolts, and welds.

Nails

Nails are the common connectors for wood-to-wood members with a thickness of less than 1 1/2" (40 mm). A nail is required by code to penetrate into the supporting member by half the depth of the supporting member. If two 2× (50×) members are being attached, a nail would be required to penetrate 3/4" (20 mm) into the lower member. Thicker wood assemblies are normally bolted. The types and sizes of nails to be used as well as the placement and nailing pattern will all affect the joint. The IRC provides a schedule for specifying the method, quantity, and size of nailing to be used. A nailing schedule is shown in Figure 22.62.

Types of Nails

The most common nails specified on construction drawings include common, deformed, box, and spike. The type of nail and other related information is usually found on the framing plan, in general and local notes and in details. Most nails are made of stainless steel, but copper and aluminum are also used. Figure 22.63 shows common types of nails used for construction. A common nail is typically used for most rough framing applications. Box nails are slightly thinner and have less holding power than common nails. Box nails are used because they generate less resistance in penetration and are less likely to split the lumber. Box nails come in sizes up to 16d. Spikes are nails larger than 20d.

Nail Sizes

Nail sizes are described by the term *penny*, which is represented by the symbol d. Standard nails range from 2d through 60d. Penny is a weight classification; it compares

FASTENER SCHEDULE

ALTERNATIVE ATTACHMENTS

NOMINAL THICKNESS	DESCRIPTION (1,2) OF FASTENERS & LENGTH	SPACING OF FASTENERS	
		EDGES	INTERMEDIATE SUPPORTS
5/16	.097-.009 NAIL 1\		
	STAPLE 15 GA. 1 3/8"	6"	12"
3/8"	STAPLE 15 GA. 1 3/8"	6	12
	.097-.099 NAIL 1 \	4	10
15/32 & 1/2"	STAPLE 15 GA. 1 1/2"	6	12"
	.097-.099 NAIL 1 5/8	3	6"
19/32 & 5/8"	.113 NAIL 1 1"	6	12"
	STAPLE 15 & 16 GA. 1)		
	.097-.099 NAIL 1 7/8"	3"	6"
23/32 & 3/4	STAPLE 15 GA. 1 3/4"	6	12
	.097-.099 NAIL 2 7/8"	5	10
		3	6
1"	STAPLE 14 GA. 2"	5	10"
	.113 NAIL 2 1/4"	4"	8"
	STAPLE 15 GA. 2"		
	.097-.099 NAIL 2 1/8"	3"	6"

FLOOR UNDERLAYMENT:
PLYWOOD, HARDBOARD, PARTICLEBOARD

1" & 5/16"	.097-.099 NAIL 1 1/2 STAPLE 15 & 16 GA. 1 1/4"	6"	12"
	.080 NAIL 1 1/4"	5"	10"
	STAPLE 18 GA. 3/16CROWN 7/8"	3"	6"
3/8"	.097-.099 NAIL 1 1/2" STAPLE 15 & 16 GA. 1 3/8"	6"	12"
	.080 NAIL 1 3/8"	5"	10"
1/2"	.113 NAIL 1 7/8" STAPLE 15 & 16 GA. 1 1/2"	6"	12"
	.097-.099 NAIL 1 3/4"	5"	6"

1. NAIL IS A GENERAL DESCRIPTION AND MAY BE T-HEAD, MODIFIED ROUND HEAD, OR ROUND HEAD.
2. STAPLES SHALL HAVE A MINIMUM CROWN WIDTH OF 7/16" O.D. EXCEPT AS NOTED.
3. NAILS OR STAPLES SHELL BE SPACED AT NOT MORE THAN 6" O.C. AT ALL SUPPORTS WHERE SPANS ARE 48" OR GREATER. NAILS OR STAPLES SHALL BE SPACED AT NOT MORE THAN 10" O.C. AT INTERMEDIATE SUPPORTS FOR FLOORS.

	DESCRIPTION OF BUILDING MATERIAL	NUMBER & TYPE OF FASTENERS (1,2,3,5,)
1	JOIST TO SILL OR GIRDER, TOE NAIL	3-8d
2	BRIDGING TO JOIST, TOENAIL EA. END	2-8d
3	1 x 6 (25 X 150) SUBFLOOR OR LESS TO EACH JOIST, FACE NAIL	2-8d
4	WIDER THAN 1 x 6 (25 x 150) SUBFLOOR TO EACH JOIST, FACE NAIL	3-8d
5	2" (50) SUBFLOOR TO JOIST OR GIRDER BLIND AND FACE NAIL	2-16d
6	SOLE PLATE TO JOIST OR BLOCKING FACE NAIL	16d @ 16" (406mm) O.C.
	SOLE PLATE TO JOIST OR BLOCKING AT BRACED WALL PANELS	3-16d PER 16" (406mm)
7	TOP OR SOLE PLATE TO STUD, END NAIL	2-16d
8	STUD TO SOLE PLATE, TOE NAIL	3-8d, TOENAIL OR 2-16d END NAIL
9	DOUBLE STUDS, FACE NAIL	10d @ 24" (610mm) O.C.
10	DOUBLE TOP PLATE, FACE NAIL DOUBLE TOP PLATE, LAP SPLICE	10d @ 24" (406mm) O.C. 8-16d
11	BLOCKING BTWN. JOIST OR RAFTERS TO TOP PLATE, TOENAIL	3-8d
12	RIM JOIST TO TOP PLATE, TOE NAIL	8d @ 6" (152mm) O.C.
13	TOP PLATES, LAPS & INTERSECTIONS, FACE NAIL	2-10d
14	CONTINUED HEADER, TWO PIECES	16d @ 16" (406mm) O.C. ALONG EACH EDGE
15	CEILING JOIST TO PLATE, TOE NAIL	3-8d
16	CONTINUOUS HEADER TO STUD, TOE NAIL	4-8d
17	CEILING JOIST, LAPS OVER PARTITIONS, FACE NAIL	3-10d
18	CEILING JOIST TO PARALLEL RAFTERS, FACE NAIL	3-16d
19	RAFTERS /TRUSSES TO PLATE, TOE NAIL	3-16d BOX OR 3-10d COMMON
20	1" (25mm) BRACE TO EA. STUD & PLATE FACE NAIL	2-8d
21	1 x 8 (25 x 203mm) SHEATHING OR LESS TO EACH BEARING, FACE NAIL	2-8d
22	WIDER THAN 1 x 8 (25 X 203mm) SHEATHING TO EACH BEARING, FACE NAIL	3-8d
23	BUILT-UP CORNER STUDS	16d @ 24" (610 mm) O.C.
24	BUILT-UP GIRDER AND BEAMS	20d @ 32" (813 mm) O.C. @ TOP/BOTTOM & STAGGER 2-20d @ ENDS & @ EACH SPLICE.

	DESCRIPTION	NUMBER & TYPE
25	2" PLANKS	2-16d AT EA. BEAR.
26	WOOD STRUCTURAL PANELS AND PARTICLEBOARD: SUBFLOOR, ROOF AND WALL SHEATHING (TO FRAMING) 1" = 25.4 mm)	2
	1/2" OR LESS	6d [3]
	19/32 - 3/4"	8d [4]OR 6d [5]
	7/8 - 1"	8d [3]
	1 1/8 - 1 1/4"	10d [4]OR 8d [5]
	COMBINATION SUBFLOOR-UNDERLAYMENT (TO FRAMING) 1" = 25.4 mm)	
	3/4 AND LESS	6d [5]
	7/8" - 1"	8d [5]
	1 1/8 - 1 1/4"	10d [4]OR 8d [5]
27	PANEL SIDING (TO FRAMING): 1/2" (13 mm)	6d [6]
	5/8" (16 mm)	8d [6]
28	FIBERBOARD SHEATHING: [7] 1/2" (13 mm)	No. 11 ga.[8] 6d [4] No. 16 ga.[9]
	25/32" (20 mm)	No. 11 ga.[8] 8d [4] No. 16 ga. [9]
29	INTERIOR PANELING 1/4" (6.4 mm)	4d [10]
	3/8" (9.5 mm)	6d [11]

1. - COMMON OR BOX NAILS MAY BE USED EXCEPT WHERE OTHERWISE STATED.
2. - NAILS SPACED @ 6" (152 mm) ON CENTER @ EDGES, 12" INTERMEDIATE SUPPORTS EXCEPT 6" (152 mm) AT ALL SUPPORTS WHERE SPANS ARE 48" (220 mm OR MORE. FOR NAILING OF WOOD STRUCTURAL PANEL AND PARTICLEBOARD DIAPHRAGMS AND SHEAR WALLS, REFER TO SECTION 2314.3. NAIL FOR WALL SHEATHING MAY BE COMMON, BOX OR CASING.
3. - COMMON OR DEFORMED SHANK.
4. - COMMON.
5. - DEFORMED SHANK..
6. - CORROSION-RESISTANT SIDING OR CASING NAILS
7. - FASTENERS SPACED @ 3" (76 mm) O.C. AT EXTERIOR EDGES AND 6" (152 mm) O.C. AT INTERMEDIATE SUPPORTS.
8. - CORROSION-RESISTANT ROOFING NAILS W/ 7/16" Ø (11 mm) HEAD & 1 1/2" (38 mm) LENGTH FOR 1/2" (13 mm) SHEATHING AND 1 3/4" (44 mm) LENGTH (FOR 25/32" (20 mm) SHEATHING CONFORMING TO THE REQUIREMENTS OF SECTION 2325.1.
9. - CORROSION-RESISTANT STAPLES WITH NOMINAL 7/16" (11 mm) CROWN AND 1 1/8" (29 mm) LENGTH FOR 1/2" (13 mm) SHEATHING AND 1 1/2" (38 mm) LENGTH FOR 25/32" (20 mm) SHEATHING CONFORMING TO THE REQUIREMENTS OF SECTION 2325.1.
10. - PANEL SUPPORTS @ 16" (406 mm) O.C. 20" (506 mm) IF STRENGTH AXIS IN LONG DIRECTION OF THE PANEL, UNLESS OTHERWISE MARKED. CASING OR FINISH NAILS SPACED 6" (152 mm) ON PANEL EDGES, 12" (305 mm) AT INTERMEDIATE SUPPORTS.
11. - PANEL SUPPORTS @ 24" (610 mm). CASING OR FINISH NAILS SPACED 6" (152 mm) ON PANEL EDGES, 12" (305 mm) AT INTERMEDIATE SUPPORTS.

FIGURE 22.62 The IRC provides specifications that regulate each connection specified on the construction documents. The provision of a nailing schedule with the working drawings will eliminate having to specify nailing for each detail.

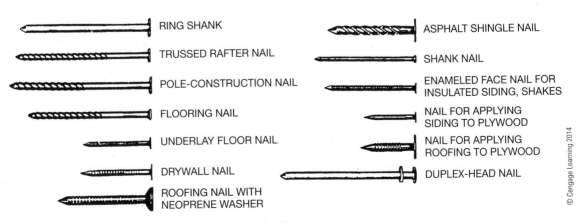

RING SHANK

TRUSSED RAFTER NAIL

POLE-CONSTRUCTION NAIL

FLOORING NAIL

UNDERLAY FLOOR NAIL

DRYWALL NAIL

ROOFING NAIL WITH NEOPRENE WASHER

ASPHALT SHINGLE NAIL

SHANK NAIL

ENAMELED FACE NAIL FOR INSULATED SIDING, SHAKES

NAIL FOR APPLYING SIDING TO PLYWOOD

NAIL FOR APPLYING ROOFING TO PLYWOOD

DUPLEX-HEAD NAIL

FIGURE 22.63 Common types of nails used in construction.

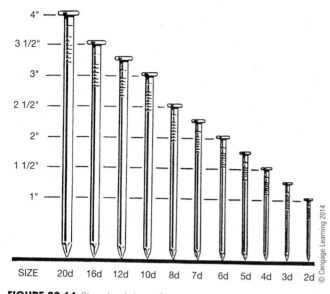

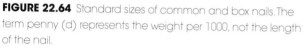

FIGURE 22.64 Standard sizes of common and box nails. The term penny (d) represents the weight per 1000, not the length of the nail.

pounds per 1000 nails. For instance, one thousand 8d nails weigh 8 lb. Figure 22.64 shows common sizes of nails. The size, spacing, and quantity of nails to be used are typically specified in structural details.

Nailing Specifications

Nails smaller than 20d are typically specified by penny size and by spacing for continuous joints, such as attaching a plate to a floor system. An example of a nailing note found on a framing plan or detail is:

2 × 6 DFL SILL W/ 20d's @ 4" O.C.

Specify nails by describing the quantity and penny size for repetitive joints such as a joist to a sill. The specification on a section or detail would simply read "3-8d's" and would point to the area in the detail where the nails will be placed. Depending on the scale of the drawing, the nails may or may not be shown. Give specifications for spikes in a manner similar to those for nails, but replace the penny size with spike diameter.

Nailing Placement

Nailing placements are described by the manner in which they are driven into the members being connected. Common methods of driving nails include face, end, toe, and blind nailing (see Figure 22.65). The type of nailing to use is determined by how accessible the head of the nail is during construction and by the type of stress to be resisted. The designer will specify if nailing other than that recommended by the nailing schedule of the prevailing code is to be used. Nails that are required to resist

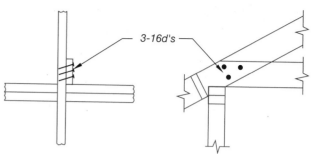

FACE NAILING

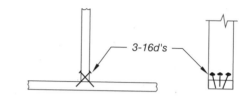

TOE NAILING

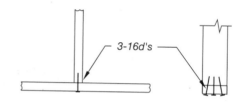

END NAILING

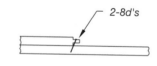

BLIND NAILING

FIGURE 22.65 Methods of placing nails affect the holding power of the nail.

shear are strongest when perpendicular to the grain. Nails placed parallel to the end grain, such as end nailing, are weakest and tend to pull out as stress is applied. Common nailing placements include:

- **Face nailing**—driving a nail through the face or surface of one board into the face of another. Face nailing is used to connect sheathing to rafters or studs, to nail a plate to the floor sheathing, or to nail a let-in brace to a stud.

- **End nailing**—driving a nail through the face of one member into the end of another member. A plate is end-nailed into the studs as a wall is assembled.

- **Toe nailing**—driving a nail through the face of one board into the face of another. With face and end nailing, nails are driven in approximately 90° to the face. With toe-nailing, the nail is driven in at approximately a 30° angle. Connections of rafters to top plates or a header to a trimmer are toe-nailed joints.

- **Blind nailing**—used where it is not desirable to see the nail head. Attaching wood flooring to the subfloor is done with blind nailing. Nails are driven at approximately a 45° angle through the tongue of tongue-and-groove flooring and hidden by the next piece of flooring.

Nailing Patterns

Nail specifications for sheathing and other large areas of nailing often refer to nail placement along an edge, boundary, or field. Common placements include:

- **Edge nailing**—nails placed at the edge of a sheet of plywood.
- **Field nailing**—nails placed in the supports for a sheet of plywood excluding the edges.
- **Boundary nailing**—nailing at the edge of a specific area of plywood.

Staples

Power-driven nails have greatly increased the speed and ease with which nails can be inserted. Staples have replaced nailing for some applications. Staples are most often used for connecting asphalt roofing and for attaching sheathing to roof, wall, and floor supports.

Power-Driven Studs

Power-driven studs can be used to anchor wood or metal to masonry. These studs range in diameter from 1/4 through 1/2" (6 to 13 mm) and in length from 3/4 to 6" (20 to 150 mm). Power-driven studs are made from heat-treated steel and inserted by a powder charge from a gun-like device. They are typically used where it would be difficult to insert the anchor bolts at the time the concrete is poured. Studs can also be used to join wood to steel construction.

Screws

Screws are specified for use in wood connections that must be resistant to withdrawal. Three common screws are used throughout the construction industry. Each is identified by its head shape (see Figure 22.66). Common screws include:

- **Flathead (countersunk) screws**—specified in the architectural drawings for finish work where a nail head is not desirable.

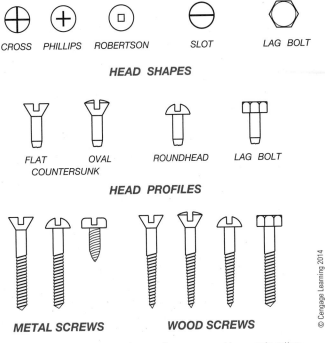

FIGURE 22.66 Common types of screws used in construction.

© Cengage Learning 2014

- **Roundhead screws**—used at lumber connections where a head is tolerable. Roundhead screws are also used to connect lightweight metal to wood.
- **Lag bolt**—Referred to as a bolt because of its head, it is also referred to as a screw because of its shape. Lag bolts (screws) have hexagonal or square heads designed to be tightened by a wrench rather than a screwdriver. Lag screws are used for lumber connections 1 1/2" (40 mm) and thicker. Lag bolts are available with diameters ranging from 1/4" to 1 1/4" (6 to 30 mm). A washer is typically used with a ***lag bolt*** to guard against crushing wood fibers near the bolt. A pilot hole that is approximately three-quarters of the shaft diameter is often specified to reduce wood damage and increase resistance to withdrawal.

Flathead and roundhead screws are designated by the gauge, which specifies a diameter, by length in inches, and by head shape. A typical specification might be:

#10 × 3" F.H.W.S. (flathead wood screw)

Lag screws are designated by their length and diameter. A typical specification might be:

5/8" Ø × 6" LAG SCREW THROUGH 1 1/2" Ø WASHER.

Metal Framing Connectors

Pre-manufactured metal connectors by companies such as Simpson Strong-Tie are used at many wood connections to strengthen nailed connections. Joist hangers, post caps, post bases, and straps are some of the most common light-weight metal hangers used with wood construction (see Figures 22.6, 22.7, and 22.56b). Each connector comes in a variety of gauges of metal with sizes to fit a wide variety of lumber. Metal connectors are typically specified on the framing plans, sections, and details by listing the model number and type of connector. A metal connector specification for connecting (2)-2 × 12 joists to a beam would resemble:

SIMPSON CO. HHUS212-2TF JST. HGR.

The supplier is typically specified in general notes and within the written specifications. Depending on the connection, the nails or bolts used with the metal fastener may or may not be specified. If no specification is given, it is assumed that all nail holes in the connector will be filled. If bolts are to be used, they will normally be specified with the connector based on the manufacturer's recommendations. Nails associated with metal connectors are typically labeled with the letter n instead of d. These nails are equal to their d counterpart, but the length has been modified by the manufacturer to fit the metal hanger.

Bolts and Washers

Bolts used in the construction industry include anchor bolts, carriage bolts, and machine bolts. Each is illustrated in Figure 22.67. A washer is used under the head and nut for most bolting applications. Washers keep the bolt head and nut from pulling through the lumber and reduce damage to the lumber by spreading the stress from the bolt across more wood fibers. Typically a circular washer, specified by its diameter, is used. Common bolts used

with construction include anchor, carriage, machine, and miscellaneous bolts.

Anchor Bolts

An anchor bolt is an L-shaped bolt used to attach lumber to the concrete (Figure 22.67a). The short leg of the L is inserted into the concrete to resist withdrawal. The upper end of the long leg is threaded to receive a nut. A 2" (50 mm) washer is typically used with anchor bolts. Anchor bolts are represented in structural drawings with the letters A.B., along with a specification including the size of the member to be connected, the bolt diameter, length, embedment into concrete, spacing, and washer size. A typical note might resemble:

2 × 6 DFPT SILL W/ 5/8" Ø × 12" A.B. @ 48" O.C. W/2" Ø WASHERS. PROVIDE 9" MIN. EMBEDMENT.

Carriage Bolts

A **carriage bolt** is used for connecting steel and other metal members as well as timber connections (Figure 22.67b). Carriage bolts have a rounded head with the lower portion of the shaft threaded. Directly below the head, at the upper end of the shaft, is a square shank. As the shank is pulled into the lumber, it will keep the bolt from spinning as the nut is tightened. Diameters range from 1/4 to 1" (6 to 25 mm), with lengths typically available to 12" (300 mm). The specification for a carriage bolt will be similar to that for an anchor bolt except for the designation of the bolt type.

Machine Bolts

A **machine bolt** is a bolt with a hexagonal head and a threaded shaft (Figure 22.63c). Machine bolts are used for attaching steel to steel, steel to wood, or wood to wood. Machine bolts are often used in steel joints to provide a temporary connection while field welds are completed. Bolts are referred with a note such as:

USE (3)-3/4" Ø 3 8" M.B. @ 3" O.C. W/ 1 1/2" Ø WASHERS.

The project manager or engineer will determine the bolt locations based on the stress to be resisted. Common spacing of bolts include:

- 1 1/2" (40 mm) in from an edge parallel to the grain.
- 3" (75 mm) minimum from the edge when perpendicular to the grain.
- 1 1/2" (40 mm) from the edge of steel members.
- 2" (50 mm) from the edge of concrete.

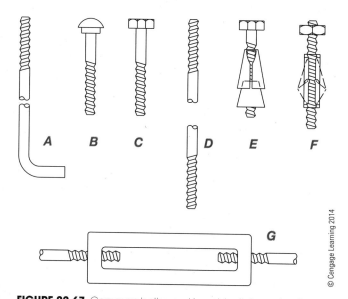

A   B   C   D   E   F

G

© Cengage Learning 2014

FIGURE 22.67 Common bolts used in residential construction.

Miscellaneous Bolts

Several other types of bolts are used in special circumstances. These include studs, drift bolts, expansion bolts, and toggle bolts:

- **Stud**—a bolt that has no head. A stud is welded to a steel beam so that a wood plate can be bolted to the beam.

- **Drift bolt**—a steel rod that has been threaded (Figure 22.67d). Threaded rods can be driven into one wood member with another member bolted to the threaded protrusion. Threaded rods may also be used to span between metal connectors on two separate beams.

- **Expansion bolts**—bolts with a special expanding sleeve (Figure 22.67e). These bolts are designed so that the sleeve, once inserted into a hole, will expand to increase holding power. Expansion bolts are typically used for connecting lumber to masonry.

- **Toggle bolt**—a bolt that has a nut designed to expand when it is inserted through a hole, so that it cannot be removed. Toggle bolts (Figure 22.67f) are used where one end of the bolt may not be accessible because of construction parameters.

Welds

Structural steel is increasingly being used in residential construction to meet the stress imposed by lateral loads. The use of steel members generally requires welded connections and an understanding of basic welding methods. Welding is the method of providing a rigid connection between two or more pieces of steel. In welding, metal is heated to a temperature high enough to cause melting. The parts that are welded become one, with the welded joint actually stronger than the original material. Welding offers better strength, better weight distribution of supported loads, and a greater resistance to shear or rotational forces than a bolted connection. The most common welds in residential construction are shielded metal-arc welding, gas tungsten-arc welding, and gas metal-arc welding. In each case, the components to be welded are placed in contact with each other and the edges are melted to form a bond. Additional metal is also used to form a sufficient bond.

Welds are specified in detail, as shown in Figure 22.68. A horizontal reference line is connected to the parts to be welded by an inclined line with an arrow. The arrow touches the area to be welded. It is not uncommon to see a welding line bend several times to point into difficult-to-reach places or to see more than one leader line extending from the reference line. Specify information about the type of weld, the location of the weld, the welding

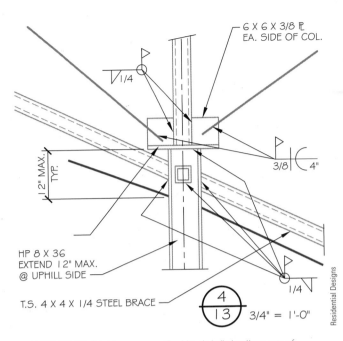

FIGURE 22.68 Welds are specified in details by the use of specialized symbols that are referenced to the area to receive the weld. Several fillet and two U-groove welds have been specified.

process, and the size and length of the weld on or near the reference line. Figure 22.69 shows a welding symbol and the proper location of information.

Welded Joints

The way that steel components intersect greatly influences the method used to weld the materials together and is often included in the specification. Common methods of arranging components to be welded are butt, lap, tee, outside corner, and edge joint (see Figure 22.70).

Types of Welds

The type of weld is associated with the weld shape or the type of groove in the metal components that will receive the weld or both. Welds typically specified on the construction drawings include fillet, groove, and plug welds. The methods of joining steel and the symbol for each method are shown in Figure 22.71.

- **Fillet weld**—The most common weld used in construction, a fillet weld (Figure 22.71a) is formed at the internal corner of two intersecting pieces of steel. The fillet can be applied to one or both sides and can be continuous or of a specified length and spacing.

- **Square-groove weld**—applied when two pieces with perpendicular edges are joined end to end. The spacing between the two pieces of metal is called the root opening. The root opening is shown to the left of the symbol in Figure 22.71b.

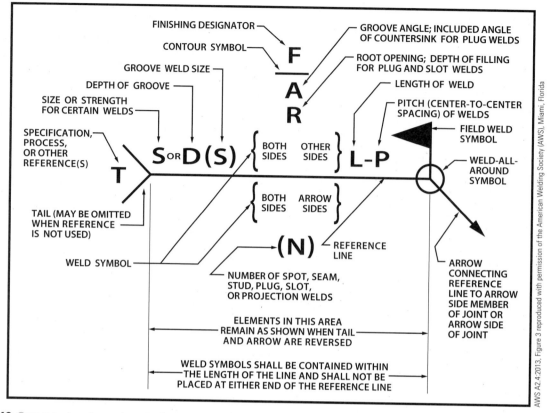

FINISHING DESIGNATOR

GROOVE ANGLE; INCLUDED ANGLE
OF COUNTERSINK FOR PLUG WELDS

CONTOUR SYMBOL

ROOT OPENING; DEPTH OF FILLING
FOR PLUG AND SLOT WELDS

GROOVE WELD SIZE

DEPTH OF GROOVE

LENGTH OF WELD

SIZE OR STRENGTH
FOR CERTAIN WELDS

PITCH (CENTER-TO-CENTER
SPACING) OF WELDS

FIELD WELD
SYMBOL

SPECIFICATION,
PROCESS,
OR OTHER
REFERENCE(S)

WELD-ALL-
AROUND
SYMBOL

TAIL (MAY BE OMITTED
WHEN REFERENCE
IS NOT USED)

ARROW
CONNECTING
REFERENCE
LINE TO ARROW
SIDE MEMBER
OF JOINT OR
ARROW SIDE
OF JOINT

WELD SYMBOL

REFERENCE
LINE

NUMBER OF SPOT, SEAM,
STUD, PLUG, SLOT,
OR PROJECTION WELDS

ELEMENTS IN THIS AREA
REMAIN AS SHOWN WHEN TAIL
AND ARROW ARE REVERSED

WELD SYMBOLS SHALL BE CONTAINED WITHIN
THE LENGTH OF THE LINE AND SHALL NOT BE
PLACED AT EITHER END OF THE REFERENCE LINE

BOTH SIDES / OTHER SIDES

BOTH SIDES / ARROW SIDES

AWS A2.4-2013, Figure 3 reproduced with permission of the American Welding Society (AWS), Miami, Florida

FIGURE 22.69 Common locations of each element of a welding symbol.

- **V-groove weld**—applied when each piece of steel to be joined has an inclined edge that forms a V. The included angle is often specified, as well as the root opening. See Figure 22.71c.

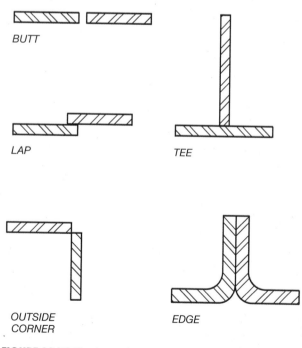

BUTT

LAP

TEE

OUTSIDE CORNER

EDGE

© Cengage Learning 2014

FIGURE 22.70 The type of welded joint to be used depends on how the members to be welded intersect.

- **Beveled weld**—created when only one piece of steel has a beveled edge. An angle for the bevel and the root opening is typically given.

- **U-groove weld**—created when the groove between the two mating parts forms a U. See Figure 22.71d.

- **J-groove weld**—results when one piece has a perpendicular edge and the other has a curved grooved edge. See Figure 22.71e. The included angle, the root opening, and the weld size are typically given for U- and J-groove welds.

Welding Locations and Placements

Welds specified on structural drawings may be done away from the job site and then shipped ready to be installed. Large components that must be assembled at the job site are called *field welds*. Two symbols used to refer to a field weld are shown in Figure 22.72.

The placement of the welding symbol in relationship to the reference line is critical in explaining where the actual weld will take place. Figure 22.73 shows three examples and the effects of placing a fillet weld symbol on the reference. The distinction of symbol placement can be quite helpful if adequate space for a symbol is not available on the proper side of the detail. The welding symbol can be placed on either side of the drawing, and the relationship

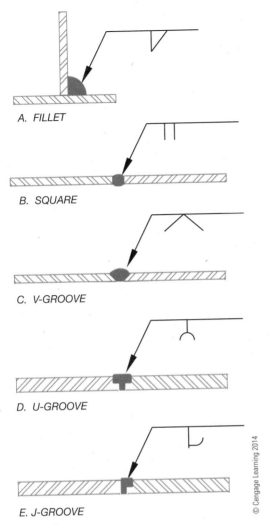

A. FILLET

B. SQUARE

C. V-GROOVE

D. U-GROOVE

E. J-GROOVE

FIGURE 22.71 The type of weld required is represented by the shape of the material to be welded.

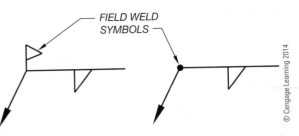

FIELD WELD SYMBOLS

FIGURE 22.72 The welding symbol can be used to represent on-site (field) or off-site welding.

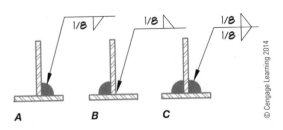

A B C

FIGURE 22.73 The welding symbol can be used to describe the placement of the weld. (A) Symbol below the reference line places the weld on this side. (B) Symbol above the reference line places the weld on the other side. (C) Symbols on each side of the reference line place the welds on each side of the material.

to the reference line can be used to clarify the exact location. Options include:

- **All-around**—used for circular and rectangular parts to indicate that a weld is to be placed around the entire intersection. A circle placed at the intersection of the leader and reference line indicates that a feature is to be welded all around.

- **Weld length and increment**—If a weld does not surround the entire part, the length and spacing of the weld should be placed beside the weld symbol. The number preceding the weld symbol indicates the size of the weld. The number following the weld symbol indicates the length each weld is to be. The final size indicates the spacing of the weld along a continuous intersection of two mating parts.

Going Green

Environmentally Friendly Materials

This chapter presents the many components that go into building a home. Most of us live and work in structures that are constructed of these components but we never even think about the building materials. The Environmental Protection

(Continued)

Agency (EPA) has a list of more than 48,000 chemicals, with no information on the toxic effects of 79 percent of them. Of the chemicals that have been tested, many are found in the residential construction industry and can cause severe medical problems to individuals who are chemically sensitive. Allergies and diseases such as chronic fatigue syndrome are being linked to construction materials. The indoor air of new homes often contains as much as six times the acceptable outdoor levels of pollutants. The greatest indoor health risks come from airborne pollutants from products containing formaldehyde-based resins and solvents containing volatile organic compounds (VOCs), which are used in the construction process.

Formaldehyde-Based Resins

Formaldehyde is a colorless gas compound composed of carbon, hydrogen, and oxygen and is found in most resin-based construction products. Resin is used in products such as plywood, HDF (high-density fiberboard), MDF (medium-density fiberboard), PSL (parallel-strand lumber), OSB (oriented strand board), LVL (laminated-strand lumber), linoleum, lacquer, gypsum board, paneling, wallpaper, caulking compounds, insulation, adhesives, upholstery, and carpet. The toxins contained in the products can be present in levels harmful to healthy adults for up to 20 years after installation. Many household cleaning products also contain small amounts of formaldehyde. Exposure to low-level concentrations can cause irritation of the nose, throat, and eyes, as well as headaches, coughing, and fatigue. Higher levels of exposure can cause severe allergic reactions, skin rash, and possibly some types of cancer.

Alternatives to formaldehyde-based products are often expensive and difficult to find. The AIA is becoming a leader in providing education in environmentally friendly construction methods. Many groups are now expressing concern for the need to examine the effects of manufacturing, using, and disposing of specific products in relation to the environment.

Alternative Construction Products

Pressure-treated lumber can be removed from a residence by substituting products with a natural ability to repel moisture, such as cedar or redwood. Products with low toxicity such as Aqua Mix® Penetrating Sealer, Protek©, and Bora-Care® Tim-Bor Impel can be used to protect lumber from moisture.

Sheets of grass-based boards such as MeadowBoard™ or Medite® can be used in place of plywood sheathing. These boards resemble OSB in appearance but contain no dangerous resins. If plywood must be used, exterior grades contain lower levels of formaldehyde than most interior grades. The sides, edges, and interior side of plywood can be sealed with sealers such as Aqua Mix Safe Seal or Crystal Aire© to prevent fumes from leaking into the home. Fiberglass insulation materials are also harmful to chemically sensitive people. Products such as AirKrete® can be sprayed into the stud space to provide a toxin-free insulation. Foil-based insulation materials such as K-Shield™ or Denny Foil, with taped joints, also can be used to shield the interior of a structure from toxins contained in wall-cavity material.

(Continued)

Adhesives, joint compound, strippers, paints, and sealants all contain volatile organic chemicals, which can be harmful for years. Such products as Aqua Mix, Murco®, Crystal Aire, and Auro are nontoxic or have low toxicity.

Interior Product Alternatives

Carpeting is one of the worst causes of indoor pollution. Typically, carpeting contains more than 50 chemicals that are used as bonding and protective agents. In addition to its chemical content, carpet harbors pollutants such as dust, mold, and pet dander, which affect many people with allergies. All-natural carpets of untreated wool, cotton, or other natural blends such as coir or sea grass are the best choices for allergy-sensitive people. Nylon is the most inert of the synthetic materials used for carpets. Stain treatments, foam pads, and the adhesives used for attaching the pad must be carefully considered because of their chemical content. AFM Safecoat® seals noxious fumes into most carpets.

For a chemically sensitive person, hard-surface floors are a better alternative than carpet. Tile, hardwood, linoleum, and slate are safe choices. Hardwood floors made of natural wood are safe, but the protective coating should be carefully considered. Wood parquet flooring should not be used because of the resins in the products and the adhesives used to bond them to the subfloor. Vinyl flooring is typically chemically saturated. Natural linoleum made from linseed oil and wood floors with jute backing provide a nontoxic durable flooring.

Equipment and Appliance Alternatives

In addition to the material used for construction, heating equipment, appliances, and furnishings also must be considered to reduce toxins in the home. Although gas and oil furnaces are cost effective, the fumes created by the burning of fossil fuels cause allergies for many people. Electric forced air and radiant heating are nontoxic.

Many appliances within a residence also should be carefully considered. Gas appliances should be avoided; they create the same problems associated with gas heaters. Ovens should not be self-cleaning and should be heated initially outside the residence to burn off oils, paints, and plastic fumes. Dishwashers and clothes dryers also typically contain materials that affect chemically sensitive users.

Additional Resources

The following websites can be used as a resource to help you keep current with changes in building materials.

Address	Company or Organization
www.airkrete.com	Air Krete® Green Insulation
www.hardboard.org	American Hardboard Association
www.alsc.org	American Lumber Standards Commission, Inc.

www.amfsafecoat.com	AMF Safecoat Sealer©
www.apawood.org	APA—The Engineered Wood Association
www.bc.com	Boise Cascade
www.canply.ca	Canadian Plywood
www.csa.ca	Canadian Standards Association
www.cwc.ca	Canadian Wood Council
www.celotex.co.uk	Celotex© Corporation (insulating sheathing)
www.conradfp.com	Conrad Forest Products
www.crystalaire.net	Crystal Aire
www.gp.com	Georgia-Pacific Corporation
www.greenbuilderadvisor.com	Green Builder Advisor
www.greensage.com	Green Sage Directory
www.gypsum.org	Gypsum Association
www.hpva.org	Hardwood Plywood & Veneer Association
www.iilp.org	International Institute for Lath, Plaster, & Drywall
www.internationalpaper.com	International Paper (high-performance building products)
www.paintwithceramic.com	Key Solutions
www.simplex-products.com	Ludlow Coated Products (thermo-ply sheathing and house wraps)
www.masonrysociety.org	The Masonry Society
www.naad.org	National Association of Aluminum Distributors
www.nahb.com	National Association of Home Builders
www.owenscorning.com	Owens Corning (house wrap and insulation)
www.typarhousewrap.com	Reemay (Typar house wrap)
www.strongtie.com	Simpson Strong-Tie Company, Inc.
www.sfpa.org	Southern Forest Products Association
www.woodtruss.com	Structural Building Components Portal
www.sips.org	Structural Insulated Panel Association
www.trimjoist.com	TrimJoist Engineered Wood Products
www.treatedwood.com	Viance Treated Wood Solutions
www.weyerhaeuser.com	Weyerhaeuser

Structural Components Test

Follow these instructions to access and complete an electronic copy of the Chapter 22 Structural Components Test:

1. Go to cengagebrain.com

2. Enter the email address and password you used to register for the site (see Preface for full instructions).

3. Select the website from the **My Course & Materials** area of your home page. Select the chapter you want from the pull-down menu at the top of the page. Choose the resources for that chapter from the menu on the left.

4. Type your name, the chapter number, and the date at the top of the sheet.

5. Answer the following questions with short, complete statements using a word processor.

> **NOTE:**
>
> *The answers to some questions may not be contained in this chapter and will require you to do additional research using the Internet. Use your favorite search engine to search for specific professional companies or general categories of information.*

Questions

22.1. List two different above-ground floor framing methods and explain the differences. Provide sketches to illustrate your answer.

22.2. How do a girder, a header, and a beam differ?

22.3. List the differences between a rim joist and solid blocking at the sill.

22.4. How wide are girders typically for a residence framed with a conventional floor system?

22.5. What are let-in braces and wall sheathing used for?

22.6. A let-in brace must be at what maximum angle?

22.7. Define the following abbreviations:

PSL	MDF	APA
OSB	EXP	EXT
LVL	HDF	STRUCT

22.8. How is a foundation post protected from the moisture in the concrete support?

22.9. Blocking is required in walls over how many feet high?

22.10. List common materials suitable for residential beams and girders.

22.11. What purpose does the bird's mouth of a rafter serve?

22.12. What do the numbers 4/12 mean when placed on a roof pitch symbol?

22.13. How do ridge, ridge blocking, and ridge board differ?

22.14. List three types of truss web materials.

22.15. Sketch, list, and define four types of rafters.

22.16. List two functions of a ceiling joist.

22.17. Define the four typical parts of a truss.

22.18. What two elements are typically applied to wood to make an engineered wood product?

22.19. What purpose does a mudsill serve?

22.20. What function does a purlin serve?

22.21. Explain the difference between a bearing and a nonbearing wall.

22.22. What is the minimum lap for top plates in a bearing wall?

22.23. Sketch, label, and define the members supporting the loads around a window.

22.24. What is the most common spacing for rafters?

22.25. What is the function of the top plate of a wall?

22.26. What is the advantage of providing blocking at the edge of a floor diaphragm?

22.27. List the common sizes of engineered wood studs.

22.28. What are the common span ratings for plywood suitable for roof sheathing?

22.29. What grades of plywood are typically used for floor sheathing?

22.30. List eight different qualities typically given in an APA wood rating.

22.31. Sketch the proper symbol for a 3/16" fillet weld, opposite side, and field weld.

22.32. List five pieces of information that might be included in a bolt specification.

22.33. What type of nail is most typically used for wood framing?

22.34. List the names of the following bolts: A.B. C.B. H.S. M.B.

22.35. How long is an 8-penny nail?

22.36. Use the nailing schedule in this chapter to determine (1) how a rafter will be connected to a top plate and (2) how to secure 3/4" plywood to the floor joist.

22.37. List the three possible locations for placing a weld and give the symbol that represents each location.

22.38. Why is a washer used in placing a bolt?

22.39. List five types of joints where welds can be applied.

22.40. Sketch the symbol used for a 3/16" × 3" long V groove weld applied to this side.

22.41. Visit the job site of a home under construction, and with the permission of the job supervisor, take photos of a minimum of ten structural components listed in the Key Terms section at the beginning of the chapter. Use the photos to document the construction of either a floor, wall, or roof system. Create a slide show or mount the photos in a neat display.

22.42. Visit a lumberyard (not a big box store) in your area and get the price of 2 × 6 through 2 × 14 lumber per foot based on standard framing lumber species for your area.

22.43. Visit the website of a local truss supplier and research limitations of shape, length, and delivery problems that may be encountered if you ordered roof trusses for the home you started in Chapter 12.

22.44. Visit the website of your local building department and research special fastening requirements for the roofing material underlayment that was specified for the home you drew in Chapters 12, 17, and 19.

22.45. Visit the website of your local building department and obtain a copy of the required nailing schedule for common roof, wall, and floor connections.

Chapter 23

Design Criteria for Structural Loading

To advance in the field of architecture requires a thorough understanding of how to support the weight of the materials used for construction, including knowledge of loads and determining how they are dispersed throughout a structure. Several types of forces or loads affect structures. The most common are gravity, lateral loads, uplift, temporary loads, and moving loads.

Gravity is a uniform force that affects all structures. **Gravity loads** cause a downward motion on each building component. Lateral loads produce a sideways motion on a structure. Wind and seismic activity cause **lateral loads** that vary in intensity according to the location of the structure and seismic zone. In addition to producing lateral force, wind can also produce uplift. **Temporary loads** are loads that must be supported for only a limited time. Storing 30 sheets of OSB roof sheathing on a few trusses is an example of a temporary load. Moving loads are loads that are not stationary. Automobiles and construction equipment produce the most common **moving loads** in residential construction.

This chapter explores gravity loads, how they are transferred throughout a structure, and how to achieve equilibrium with the forces acting on the structure.

Key Terms

Braced wall line	Gravity load	Seismic load	Temporary load
Complex beam	Lateral load	Shear wall	Uplift
Dead load	Live load	Simple beam	
Dynamic load	Moving load		

TYPES OF LOADS

As you start to evaluate the loads on a structure, you must be concerned with several types of loads acting on a building: dead, live, and dynamic loads. Because of the complexity of determining these loads exactly, building codes have tables of conventional safe loads, which can help to determine the amount of weight or stress acting on any given member.

Dead Loads

Dead loads consist of the weight of the structure including walls, floors, and roofs, plus any permanently fixed loads such as fixed service equipment. Building codes typically require design values to be based on a minimum dead load of 10 lb per square foot (psf) (0.48 kN/m²) for floors and ceilings. A design value between 7 and 15 psf (0.48 and 0.72 kN/m²) for rafters is used, depending on the weight of the finished roofing materials. Verify the design load for dead loads in the design criteria section of each joist and rafter table (see Chapter 24). The letters DL represent the values for dead loads.

Live Loads

Live loads are superimposed on the building through its use. These loads include people, furniture, and weather-related items such as wind, ice, snow, and water (rain). The most common live loads are moving, roof, and snow loads. The letters LL represent live loads.

Floor Live Loads

Buildings are designed for a specific use or occupancy. The floor live load varies based on occupancy. The IRC requires that floor members be designed to support a minimum live load of 30 psf (1.44 kN/m²) for sleeping rooms and 40 psf for all other rooms. Exterior balconies must be able to support a minimum live load of 60 psf (2.88 kN/m²), and decks must be designed to support a minimum live load of 40 psf (1.92 kN/m²).

Moving Live Loads

In residential construction, moving loads typically occur only in garage areas due to the weight of a car or truck. When a slab is supporting the weight over soil, these loads do not usually cause concern. When moving weights are supported by wood framing members, the designer must take special care in the design. The IRC requires a minimum load of 50 psf (2.40 kN/m²) to be used in the design of residential garage floors. You should also consult with the local building department to determine if additional design weight should be used.

Roof Live Loads

Roof live loads vary from 20 to 40 psf (0.96 to 1.92 kN/m²) depending on the pitch and the use of the roof. Some roofs also are used for sundecks and are designed in a manner similar to floors. Other roofs are so steep that they may be designed like a wall. Many building departments use 30 psf (1.44 kN/m²) as a safe live load for roofs. Consult the building department in your area for roof live load values.

Snow Loads

Snow loads may or may not be a problem in the area for which you are designing. You may be designing in an area where snow is something you dream about, not design for. If you are designing in an area where snow is something you shovel, it is also something you must allow for in your design. Because snow loads vary so greatly, the designer should consult the local building department to determine the design snow load to be used. In addition to climatic variables, the elevation, wind frequency, duration of snowfall, and the exposure of the roof all influence the amount of live load design.

Dynamic Loads

Dynamic loads are imposed on a structure from a sudden gust of wind or from an earthquake.

Wind Loads

Although only an architect or engineer should conduct wind design, understanding the areas of a structure that are subject to failure will help you advance in the office. The IRC and many municipalities include maps detailing the basic wind speeds that should be used in the design of a structure. Wind pressure creates wind loads on a structure. These loads vary greatly, depending on the location and the height of the structure above the ground. The IRC defines four basic wind exposure categories based on ground surface irregularities of the job site. These include:

- **Exposure A:** A construction site in large city centers where 50 percent of the surrounding structures have a height of 70' (21 300 mm) or greater for a distance of 0.5 mi (0.8 km) or 10 times the building height.

- **Exposure B:** This wind exposure is the assumed design standard for the IRC. It includes urban, suburban, wooded areas, or other terrain with multiple closely spaced structures that are the size of a single-family residence or larger.

- **Exposure C:** Open terrain with scattered obstructions with a height of less than 30' (9100 mm) that extend more than 1500' (457 200 mm) in any direction from the building site.

- **Exposure D:** Structures built on flat unobstructed sites within 1500' (457 200 mm) of shorelines exposed to wind flowing over open bodies of water 1 mi (1.6 km) wide or larger. Sites built near shorelines in hurricane-prone regions are excluded from this category. Because of the potential for wide variations in wind speed, the designer must rely on the local building department to provide information.

Figure 23.1 shows a simplified explanation of how winds can affect a house. Wind affects a wall just as it would the sail of a boat. With a boat, the desired effect is to move the boat. With a structure, this tendency to move must be resisted. The walls resisting the wind tend to bow under the force of the wind pressure. The tendency can be resisted by roof and foundation and perpendicular support walls. The expected winds can be partially resisted by increasing the bolts that attach the wall and floor systems to the foundation. The supporting walls that are parallel to

the wind will tend to become parallelograms and collapse. The designer determines the anticipated wind speed and designs walls, typically referred to as **braced wall lines** or **shear walls**, which are strong enough to resist this pressure.

In planning for loads from wind, prevailing wind direction cannot be assumed. Winds act in *any* horizontal direction and will create a positive pressure on the windward side of a structure. A negative pressure on the leeward (downwind) side of the structure creates a partial vacuum. Design pressures for a structure are based on the total possible pressure a structure might encounter which is equal to the sum of the positive and negative pressure. A design value of 30 psf (1.44 kN/m²) is common for residential projects, but this value should be verified with local building departments. Thirty psf (1.44 kN/m²) equals a wind speed of 108 miles per hour (mph). Other common values include those shown in the table below.

Areas subject to high winds from hurricanes or tornados must withstand minimum winds of 125 mph (201 km/h), with 3-second gusts as high as 160 mph (257 km/h). Consult local building department standards in areas prone to severe wind damage. Using the specified design values, the designer can determine existing wall areas and the resulting wind pressure that must be resisted. This information is then used to determine the size and spacing of anchor bolts and any necessary metal straps or ties needed to reinforce the structure.

Wind pressure is also critical to the design and placement of doors and windows. The design wind pressure affects the size of the glazing area and the method of framing the rough openings for doors and windows. Openings in shear walls reduce the effectiveness of the wall. Framing around openings must be connected to the frame and foundation to resist forces of uplift from wind pressure. *Uplift* is the tendency of members to move upward in response to wind or seismic pressure. Steel straps or connectors that join the trimmer and king studs beside the wall openings to the foundation or to framing members in the floor level below are used to resist uplift. Wall areas

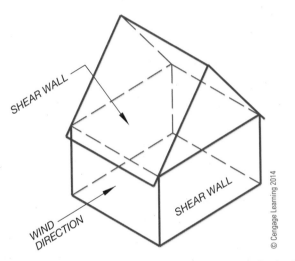

© Cengage Learning 2014

FIGURE 23.1 Wind pressure on a wall will be resisted by the bolts connecting the wall sill to the foundation and by the roof structure. The wind is also resisted by shear walls, which are perpendicular to the wall under pressure.

PSF	N/M²	MPH	KM/H	PSF	KN/M²	MPH	KM/H
15	0.72	76	122	50	2.40	140	225
20	0.96	88	142	55	2.64	147	237
25	1.20	99	159	60	2.88	153	246
30	1.44	108	174	70	3.36	165	266
35	1.68	117	188	80	3.84	177	285
40	1.92	125	201	90	4.32	188	303
45	2.16	133	214	100	4.80	198	319

© Cengage Learning 2014

with large areas of openings also require design studies to determine the amount of wall area necessary to resist the lateral pressure created by wind pressure. As a general rule of thumb, a wall 4'-0" (1200 mm) long is required for each 25 lineal feet (7500 mm) of wall. The amount of wall to be reinforced is based on the wall height, the seismic zone, the size of openings by the shear panel, and the method of construction used to reinforce the wall. Chapter 25 explores methods of resisting the forces of shear using the prescriptive methods of the building codes.

Wind pressure also creates the tendency of a structure to overturn. Structures built on pilings or other posted foundations allow wind pressure under the structure to exceed the pressure on the leeward side of the structure. Codes require that the resistance of the dead loads of a building be 1 1/2 times the overturning effect of the wind. Metal ties are used to connect the walls to the floor, the floor joist to support beams, the support beams to supporting columns, and columns to the foundation. These ties are determined by an architect or engineer for each structure and are based on the area exposed to the wind and the wind pressure.

Seismic Loads

Seismic loads result from earthquakes. The IRC contains seismic maps of the United States and the risk in each area of damage from earthquakes. The IRC bases its specific requirements for seismic design on the location and soil type of the building site and the building shape. Chapter 25 explores building shape as it relates to construction materials. Chapter 26 discusses soil types and their effects on structures.

The IRC defines six seismic zones ranging from A through E. Zone A is the least prone to seismic damage, and structures in Zone E are most likely to be damaged by earthquakes. Zones A, B, and C do not require special construction methods. The IRC provides special provisions for structures built in Zones D1 and D2. The **IBC (International Building Code)** governs structures built in Zone E.

Seismic load refers to stress that results from an earthquake. It is usually treated as a lateral load that involves the entire structure. While lateral loads created by wind affect only certain parts of a structure, lateral forces created by seismic forces affect the entire structure. As the ground moves in varying directions at varying speeds, the entire structure is set in motion. Even after the ground comes to rest, the structure tends to wobble like Jell-O®.

Typically, structures fall to seismic forces in much the same way as they do to wind pressure. Intersections of roofs-to-wall, wall-to-floor, and floor-to-foundation are critical for a structure to resist seismic forces. An architect or engineer should design these connections. Typically, a structure

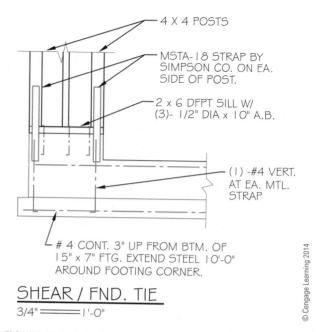

4 X 4 POSTS

MSTA-18 STRAP BY SIMPSON CO. ON EA. SIDE OF POST.

2 x 6 DFPT SILL W/ (3)- 1/2" DIA x 10" A.B.

(1) -#4 VERT. AT EA. MTL. STRAP

4 CONT. 3" UP FROM BTM. OF 15" x 7" FTG. EXTEND STEEL 10'-0" AROUND FOOTING CORNER.

SHEAR / FND. TIE
3/4" = 1'-0"

© Cengage Learning 2014

FIGURE 23.2 Hold-down anchors are used to resist seismic forces and to help form a stable intersection between the floor and foundation.

must be fluid enough to move with the shock wave but so connected that individual components move as a unit and all units of a structure move as one. Figure 23.2 shows a detail of an engineer's design for a connection of a garage-door king stud designed to resist seismic forces. The straps that are attached to the wall cause the wall and foundation to move as one unit.

LOAD DESIGN

Once the floor plan and elevations have been designed, the designer can start the process of determining how the structure will resist the loads that will be imposed on it. The goal of load design is to achieve equilibrium between the structure and the forces that will act upon it. For the gravity loads pushing down on the structure, an opposite and equal force or reaction must resist them. The structural members of the home form a load path to transfer gravity loads into the foundation and then into the soil. The load path is the route for transferring the roof loads into the walls, then into the floor, and then to the foundation. The structural members must be of sufficient size to resist the loads above them.

To determine the sizes of material required, it is always best to start at the roof and work down to the foundation. When you calculate from the top down, the loads will be accumulating and when you work down to the foundation, you will have the total loads needed to size the footings.

As a new employee, you are not expected to design the structural components. In most offices, a designer or an engineer completes the structural design of even the simplest buildings. The information in this chapter is a brief introduction to the size of structural members.

LOAD DISTRIBUTION

A beam may be simple or complex. A ***simple beam*** has a uniform load evenly distributed over the entire length of the beam and is supported at each end. With a simple beam, its load is equally dispersed to each support. Individual floor joists, rafters, trusses, or walls may be thought of as simple beams. For instance, the wall resisting the wind load in Figure 23.1 can be thought of as a simple beam because it spans between two supporting walls and has a uniform load. If a beam is supporting a uniformly distributed load of 10,000 lb (4536 kg), each supporting post is resisting 5000 lb (2268 kg). A ***complex beam*** has a non-uniform load at any point of the beam, or has supports that are not located at the end of the beam. Chapter 24 introduces methods of determining beam sizes when the loads are not evenly distributed. Because of the complexity of the process, most architectural programs offer an entire class on determining structural loads and sizing complex beams.

Figure 23.3 shows a summary of typical building weights based on minimum design values from the IRC. Figure 23.4 shows the bearing walls for a one-story structure framed with a truss roof system and a post-and-beam floor system. Remember that with a typical truss roof system, all interior walls are nonbearing. The left exterior

MEMBER	MINIMUM DESIGN LOADS		
	DL	LL	TOTAL
Floors (nonsleeping)	10	40	50
Floors (sleeping rooms)	10	30	40
Exterior balconies	10	60	70
Decks	10	40	50
Walls	10	—	—
Attics (without storage)	5	10	15
Attics (with storage)	10	20	30
Roofs (light coverings)	10	30	40
Roofs (tile)	25	30	55

FIGURE 23.3 Typical live, dead, and total loads for residential construction based on the IRC.

wall supports half of the roof weight, and the right exterior wall supports half of the roof weight. For a structure 32' wide with 2' overhangs × 1' wide, the roof weighs 1440 lb (36' × 1' × 40#) per linear foot (plf). Each linear foot of wall (a section of wall 12" long) holds 720 lb plf (18 × 40# psf), which is half the total roof weight.

If the walls are 8' tall, each wall weighs 80 lb (8' × 10#) per linear feet of wall. The foundation holds 100 lb of floor load (2' × 50#) per linear foot. Only 2' of floor is supported, because beams are typically placed at 48" o.c. Half of the floor weight (2' × 50#) is on the stem wall, and half of the weight (2' × 50#) is supported by the girder

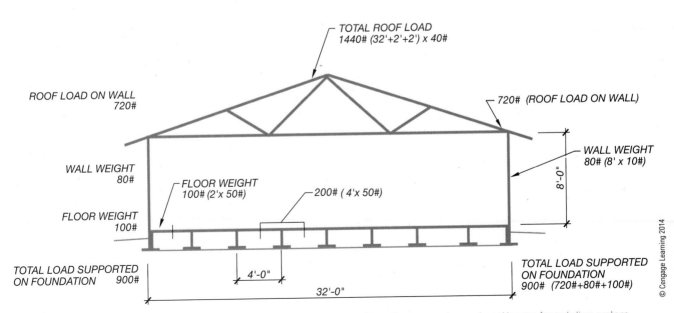

FIGURE 23.4 Loads for a one-level structure framed with a truss roof with 2' overhangs and a post-and-beam foundation system.

parallel to the stem wall. Each interior girder supports 200 lb (4' × 50#) per linear foot of floor weight. The total weight on the stem wall per foot is the sum of the roof, wall, and floor loads, which equals 900 lb. This was determined by adding:

Roof load	720#
Wall load	80#
Floor load	100#
Total load plf	900#

When using a software program to determine loads, most programs require that you enter the LL and DL separately. This produces the following results:

Roof DL	180#
Wall load	80#
Floor DL	80#
Total DL plf	340#
Roof LL	540#
Wall load	0#
Floor LL	20#
Total LL plf	560#

Figure 23.5 shows the bearing walls of a two-level structure framed using western platform construction methods. This building has a bearing wall located approximately halfway between the exterior walls. For this type of building, one-half of the total building loads is on the central bearing wall, and one-quarter of the total building loads is on each exterior wall. Examine the building one floor at a time to see why.

NOTE:

Hopefully it goes without saying that the total DL and total LL should add up to the total load. Because architecture students are often trained in higher math classes, and we're all human, we're prone to making stupid human errors. Please check your work!

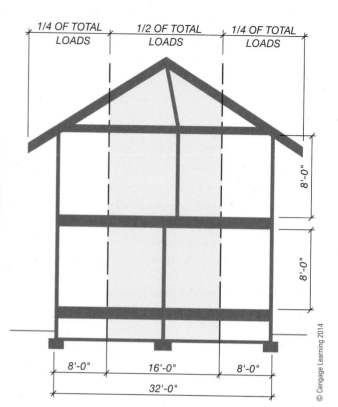

FIGURE 23.5 Bearing walls and load distribution of a two level home framed using western platform construction methods.

Upper Floor

At the upper floor level, the roof and ceiling loads are being supported. In a building 32 × 15', as shown in Figure 23.6, each rafter spans 16' (the horizontal measurement). If the loads are distributed uniformly throughout the roof, half of the weight of the roof is supported at each end of the rafter. At the ridge, half of the total roof weight is supported. At each exterior wall, one-quarter of the total roof load is supported. At the ceiling and the other floor levels, the loading is the same. One-half of each joist is supported at the center wall and half at the outer wall. Use the loads from Figure 23.3 to calculate the weights being supported. To figure the total weight that a wall supports is a matter of multiplying the area being supported by the weight.

Roof

The area being supported at an exterior wall is 15' long by 10' wide (8' of rafter plus 2' overhang), which is 150 sq ft. The roof load equals the sum of the live and dead loads. Assume a live load of 30 psf. For the dead load, assume the roof is built with asphalt shingles, 1/2" ply, and 2 × 8 rafters—for a dead load of approximately 8 psf. For simplicity, round 8 up to 10 psf for the dead load. By adding the dead and live loads, you get a total roof load of 40 psf.

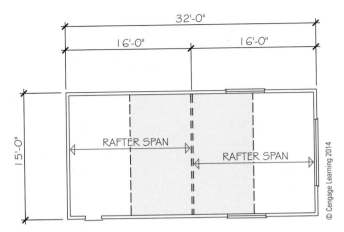

FIGURE 23.6 Load distribution on a simple beam.

The weight for one linear foot of roof is 400 lb plf ($10' \times 40\# \times 1'$). Multiply the linear load by 15' and it can be determined that the total roof weight on each exterior wall is 6000 lb ($15' \times 400$ lb = 6000 lb).

Because the center area in the example is twice as big, the weight is twice as big. But just to be sure, check the total weight on the center wall. The linear load is 640 lb ($16' \times 40\# \times 1'$). The wall holds 8' of rafters on each side for a total of 16'. Using a LL of 40 lb, the wall is supporting 640 plf. To determine the total load, use $15' \times 640$ lb for your calculations. Because the wall is 15' long, the total load on the wall is 9600 lb.

Ceiling

The procedure for calculating a ceiling is the same as for a roof, but the loads are different. A typical loading pattern for a ceiling with storage is 30 lb. At the outer walls, the formula to determine the linear load is $8' \times 30$ lb $\times 1'$, or 240 lb. The total load is $15' \times 240$ lb or 3600 lb. The center wall is holding $16' \times 30\# \times 1'$, or 480 plf, and the total load is $15' \times 480\#$, or 7200 lb.

Lower Floor

Finding the weight of a floor is the same as finding the weight of a ceiling, but the loads are much greater. The LL for residential floors is 40 lb and the DL is 10 lb, for a total of 50 lb/sq ft. One linear foot of wall supports $8' \times 50$ lb or 400 plf. The floor load at the center wall is $16' \times 50$ lb or 800 plf.

Walls

Finally, determine the weight of the walls. Generally, walls are 8'-0" high and average about 10 lb psf. To find area of a wall, multiply its height by its length. Then, multiply the area by the weight per square foot to get the total wall weight for one linear foot of wall. Figure 23.7 shows the total weight that will be supported by the footings.

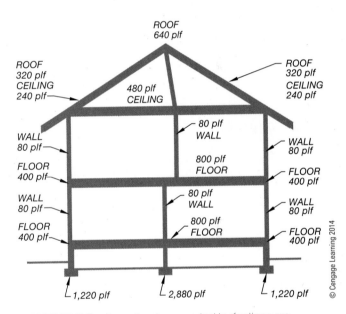

FIGURE 23.7 The linear loads supported by footings are determined by adding all of the linear loads for each level above the footing. Values are expressed as pounds per linear foot (plf).

Design Criteria for Structural Loading Test

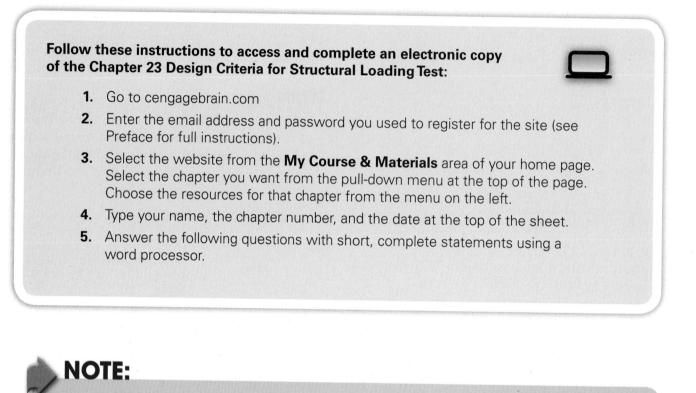

Follow these instructions to access and complete an electronic copy of the Chapter 23 Design Criteria for Structural Loading Test:

1. Go to cengagebrain.com
2. Enter the email address and password you used to register for the site (see Preface for full instructions).
3. Select the website from the **My Course & Materials** area of your home page. Select the chapter you want from the pull-down menu at the top of the page. Choose the resources for that chapter from the menu on the left.
4. Type your name, the chapter number, and the date at the top of the sheet.
5. Answer the following questions with short, complete statements using a word processor.

NOTE:

The answers to some questions may not be contained in this chapter and will require you to do additional research.

Questions

23.1. What are the two major categories of loads that affect buildings?
23.2. What is the safe design live load for a residential floor?
23.3. What is the safe design total load for a residential floor?
23.4. What factors cause snow loads to vary so widely within the same area?
23.5. How is weight distributed on a uniformly loaded joist?
23.6. What load will a floor 15' wide × 25' long generate per linear foot on the stem wall if floor joists are parallel to the long wall? What is the load if the joists are parallel to the short wall?
23.7. If the floor in question 23.6 has a girder to support the floor joists 12'–6" in from the edge of the short wall (centered), how much weight does each foot of the girder support?

23.8. A building is 20' wide with 24" overhangs and a tile roof supported by trusses. The roof shape is a gable, and the building is 30' long. How much roof weight do the walls support? How much weight does a footing at the bottom of the 8'-0" high wall support? Express all answers in pounds per linear foot.
23.9. A foundation for a one-story home with a post-and-beam floor must be designed. Girders will be placed at 4' o.c. with support every 8'. What weight will the girders support in non-sleeping areas? What weight will the stem wall at the end of the girder support in sleeping areas?
23.10. A two-story home is 26' wide with 24" overhangs and a 300-lb composition shingle roof supported by trusses. The roof shape is a

gable and the upper floor is supported on a wall that is 12' from the left, exterior 30' long wall. The walls for the upper floor are 8' tall, and the lower walls are 9' tall. The lower floor is a concrete slab. Create a sketch of the plan view and a section of this structure, and submit the sketch with your answers. Unless different instructions are given, express each answer in plf:

a. How much total load does the top plate of the upper exterior walls support?
b. How much total load will each of the two long exterior walls support?
c. How much total load does the upper interior wall support?

d. How much total load does the lower interior wall support?
e. How much total load does a footing below the left exterior bearing wall support? The right exterior wall?
f. How much dead load is transferred to the slab under the interior bearing wall?

23.11. Use the Internet to search the websites of lumberyards in your area to determine the availability of sawn, and engineered lumber and beams. Submit a verbal or written report on availability and price fluctuations over a 30-day period.

Problems

Show all work and provide a sketch of the plan view and a simple section showing how loads will be supported. Assume standard spacing.

23.1   If a joist with a total uniform load of 500 lb is supported at each end, how much weight will each end support?

23.2   If a joist with a total uniform load of 700 lb is supported at the midpoint and at each end, how much weight will each point support?

23.3   A 16' rafter ceiling joist at a 6/12 pitch supports a cedar shake roof. What is the total weight supported if the rafters are at 12" spacings? 16"? 24"?

23.4   A stub truss with 24" overhangs spans 28' over a residence and supports 300 lb. composition shingles. It is supported by a wall at one end and a girder truss with a metal hanger at the other end. How much weight does the hanger support?

23.5   Steel columns will be used at each end to support a girder 16' long with a weight of 1260 plf. How much weight will the columns support?

23.6   A residence will be built with a truss roof spanning 24', with built-up roofing and 30" overhangs. How much weight would a header

over a window 8' wide in a bearing wall support? How much weight is supported on an 8' header if it is in the wall perpendicular to the ridge. Provide the answers in plf and for the total load.

Use the following information to complete problems 23.7 through 23.11. Answer the questions by providing the weight per linear foot. A one-level residence will be built using trusses with 36" overhangs. The residence will be 24' wide. The roof is 235 lb composition shingles. Floor joists will be placed at 16" o.c. with girders spaced at 12'-0" o.c. All walls will be 8'-0" high.

23.7   How much weight will a header over a window 6' wide in an exterior bearing wall support?

23.8   A wall is to be built 11'-9" from the right bearing wall. If a 2'-6" pocket door is to be installed in the wall, how long will the header need to be and how much total weight will it support?

23.9   Determine the load to be supported and specify the width of footing required if a wall is placed 14' from the left bearing wall.

23.10   What is the total dead load per linear foot that the exterior bearing wall on the right side will support?

23.11   What is the total roof load that the bearing wall on the left side will support?

Chapter 24
Sizing Joists, Rafters, and Beams

This chapter introduces loads, defines structural lumber, and explores how to determine the sizes of wood framing members. The complexity of the structure and the experience of the CAD technician will determine who will size the framing members. Even if an engineer will determine each framing member, your knowledge of the methods used will help you advance. The following are among several skills you will need to determine the sizes of structural members:

- Understand span tables found in the IRC and in vendor catalogs.
- Distinguish loading patterns on beams.
- Recognize standard engineering symbols used in beam formulas.
- Recognize common causes of beam failure.
- Understand how to select beams.

Key Terms

Bending moment	Fiber bending stress	Nominal size	Tributary width
Cantilevered	Horizontal shear	Reaction	Vertical shear
Compression	Modulus of elasticity	Sawn lumber	
Deflection	Moment	Tension	
Dimension lumber	Net size	Timber	

the placement of loads on a beam and helps identify loads that must be resisted to achieve equilibrium.

I: Moment of inertia is the sum of the products of each of the elementary areas of a beam multiplied by the square of their distance from the neutral axis of the cross section. This sounds technical, but a value for *I* is listed in the tables later in this chapter for use in deflection calculations.

S: Section modulus is the moment of inertia divided by the distance from the neutral axis to the extreme fiber of the cross section. Once again, this sounds technical, but a value for *S* appears in the tables later in this chapter for use in determining bending strength calculations.

Grain: Wood grain is composed of fibers that can be visualized as grains of rice aligned in the same direction. The wood fibers are strongest in their long direction. Common relationships of loads to grain include loads placed parallel and perpendicular to the grain. How a beam reacts depends on the relationship of the load to the grain of the wood.

- When a load is applied in the same direction as the fibers of a structural member, the force is parallel to the grain. The symbol // represents loads that are parallel to the grain.
- When a load is applied across the direction of the fibers of a structural member, the force is perpendicular to the grain and is represented by the symbol ⊥. Figure 24.2 shows a force applied to a beam in each direction.

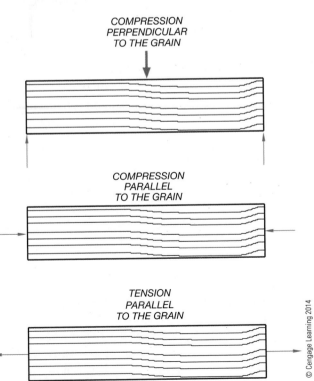

FIGURE 24.2 Forces acting on horizontal members.

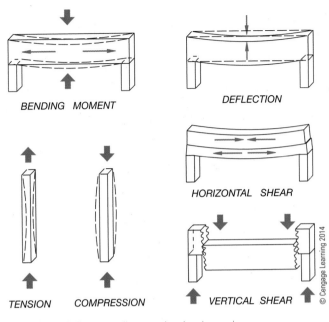

FIGURE 24.3 Forces acting on structural members.

Loads typically affect structural members in five different ways: *bending strength, deflection, horizontal shear, vertical shear,* and *bearing area.* These forces create stress that affects the fibers inside the beam. The forces of tension and compression from outside of a beam are also considered. Each force is shown in Figure 24.3.

LOADING AND SUPPORT PATTERNS OF STRUCTURAL MEMBERS

There are two common ways to load and support a joist or beam. Loads are uniformly distributed over the entire span of a structural member (see Chapter 23) or are concentrated in one small area of a beam. A support post from an upper floor resting on a beam in a lower floor or the weight of a car being transferred through a wheel into the floor system are examples of concentrated loads. Occasionally you must deal with increasing loads that result from triangular loading patterns. A beam used to frame a hip or valley supports a triangular load (see Figure 24.4). The load starts at zero at the low end of the hip. The maximum load is near the upper end of the hip beam, where it intersects the ridge.

There is usually support for a beam at each end. Common alternatives are to support a beam at the center of the span in addition to the ends or to support it at one end and near the other end. The type of beam that extends past the support is a **cantilevered** beam. Figure 24.5 includes examples of each type of load and their support systems.

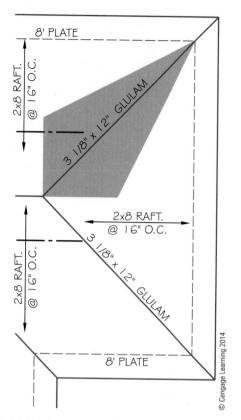

FIGURE 24.4 The beam used to support a hip or valley supports a triangular load. The triangle is formed because half of the weight of each rafter is supported on the beam.

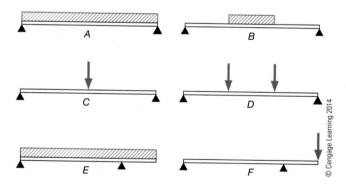

FIGURE 24.5 Common loading patterns on a beam include the following: (A) simple beam with a uniformly distributed load; (B) beam with a partially distributed load at the center; (C) beam with a concentrated load at the center; (D) beam with two equal concentrated loads placed symmetrically; (E) cantilevered beam with a uniform load; (F) cantilevered beam with a concentrated load at the free end.

Loading Reactions of Wood Members

For every action there is an equal and opposite reaction. This law of physics affects every structure. There are several actions or stresses that must be understood before considering beam reactions. These stresses include *fiber bending stress, deflection, horizontal shear, vertical shear,* and *compression.*

It is not necessary to know how these stresses are generated, only that they exist, to determine the size of a framing member using standard loading tables. Previous chapters in this book discuss design loads. Review Figure 23.3 for a partial list of design live (LL) and dead (DL) loads. These design loads will be useful in determining the load on a beam. Table 24.2 shows a partial listing of base design values for the design of beams. This table includes a column of values for fiber bending stress (F_b), modulus of elasticity (E), and horizontal shear (F_v).

Fiber Bending Stress

The bending strength of a wood beam is measured in units of *fiber bending stress.* Earlier you read about extreme fiber stress (compression) that occurs on the beam surface supporting the load. Extreme fiber stress (tension) also occurs on the surface opposite the surface in compression. The relationship of allowable fiber bending stress to the maximum bending stress is used to determine the required strength of a framing member. The symbol F_b represents fiber bending stress. The values in beam tables indicate the safe, allowable fiber bending.

Bending Strength

Bending strength is the determination of the beam strength required to resist the force applied to a beam measured in moments. The *bending moment* at any point of the beam is the measure of the tendency of the beam to bend due to the force acting on it. The magnitude of the bending moment varies throughout the length of the beam. The maximum bending stress occurs at the midpoint of a simple beam with a uniform load. The location for maximum bending moment in complex beams is discussed later in this chapter.

The letter *M* represents bending moment in engineering formulas. The relationship of the allowable extreme fiber bending stress (F_b) to the maximum bending moment (M) equals the required section modulus (S) of a beam. The design equation is $S = M/F_b$. Use Table 24.2 to find the F_b base design value listed in psi for various lumber species. The base F_b value for 4× members varies depending on the depth of the beam. The base design value for 6× material remains fixed up to and including 6 × 12. Determining the required section modulus of a beam provides one of the pieces of information necessary for determining the size of beam that will support a specific load over a given span.

Deflection

Deflection deals with the stiffness of a beam. Deflection measures the tendency of a structural member to bend under a load and as a result of gravity. As a load is placed on a beam, the beam will sag between its supports. As the span increases, the tendency to deflect increases.

TABLE 24.2 Partial Listing of Safe Design Values of Common Types of Lumber Used for Beams

SIZE, SPECIES, AND COMMERCIAL GRADE	DESIGN VALUES FOR BEAMS			HORIZONTAL SHEAR F_v	MODULUS OF ELASTICITY (E)
	EXTREME FIBER BENDING F_b				
DFL #2	Base Value	Modifier	Increased Value		
4 × 8	875	(1.3)	1138	85	1.6
4 × 10	875	(1.2)	1050	85	1.6
4 × 12	875	(1.1)	963	85	1.6
DFL #1					
6 × 8	1350			85	1.6
6 × 10	1350			85	1.6
6 × 12	1350			85	1.6
Reduce the base value of all members larger than 6 × 12 by (12/d)1/9_Cf.					
Hem-Fir					
6 × _	1050			70	1.3

All values are based on National Design Specifications for Wood Construction (NDS®), published by the American Forest and Paper Association®.

Deflection rarely causes a beam to break, but greatly affects the materials that the beam supports. When floor joists sag too much, sheetrock cracks or doors and windows stick.

Two formulas are used to determine deflection. The first is the legal limit of deflection that establishes how much the building code will allow a specific beam to bend. The IRC sets limits expressed as a ratio of the length of the beam in inches over a deflection value. The ratio L/360 represents the allowable deflection for a floor beam. A 10' long floor beam may deflect 0.33" (10' × 12" = 120" = 120/360). The allowable deflection value defines the maximum amount of deflection (the "can sag" value). The IRC's allowable deflections include:

L/360 (floors)
L/240 (roofs supporting ceilings)
L/180 (roofs with a slope of 3/12 or greater with no ceiling loads)

Modulus of Elasticity

Modulus of elasticity also deals with the stiffness of a structural member. *Modulus of elasticity* is a ratio of the amount a member will deflect in proportion to the applied load. Beam tables and design formulas use the letter E to represent the value for the modulus of elasticity. The E value represents how much the member will deflect (the "will sag" value). For a beam to be safe, the E value (will sag) must not exceed the deflection value (can sag). Different formulas for varied loading conditions are introduced throughout the balance of this chapter. These formulas consider the load and span of the beam, the modulus of elasticity, and the moment of inertia of the beam. The symbol D represents deflection. The value for the modulus of elasticity is expressed as E for the species and grade of the beam, and I represents the moment of inertia.

Horizontal Shear

Horizontal shear is the tendency for the wood fibers to slide past each other at the neutral axis and fail along the length of the beam. Horizontal shear is a result of forces that affect the beam fibers parallel to the wood grain. Under severe bending pressure, adjacent wood fibers are pushed and pulled in opposite directions. The top portion of the beam nearest the load is in compression. The edge of the beam away from the load is under stress from tension. The line where the compression and tension forces meet is the point at which the beam will fail. Horizontal shearing stresses are greatest at the neutral surface. The maximum horizontal shear stress for a rectangular beam is one and one half times the average unit shear stress. The design formula is $v = (1.5)(V)/A$, where:

v = maximum unit horizontal shear stress in psi.
V = total vertical shear in pounds.
A = area of the structural member in square inches.

Table 24.2 lists the maximum allowable horizontal shear values in psi for major species of framing lumber. The value for V must be less than the maximum safe F_v value.

Horizontal shear has the greatest effect on beams with a relatively heavy load spread over a short span. Visualize a yardstick with supports at each end supporting a 2-lb load at the center. While the yardstick will bow, it probably will not break. Move the supports toward the center of the beam so they are 1' apart. While the beam will not bend as much, it will be more prone to failure from breaking from the stress of horizontal shear.

Vertical Shear

Vertical shear is the tendency of a beam to fail perpendicular to the fibers of the beam from two opposing forces. Vertical shear causes a beam to break and fall between its supporting posts. Vertical shear is rarely a design concern in residential construction, since a beam will first fail by horizontal shear.

Tension

In addition to the forces of tension that act within a beam, *tension* stresses attempt to lengthen a structural member. Tension is rarely a problem in residential beam design. It is more likely to affect the intersection of beams than the beam itself. Beam details typically reflect a metal strap to join beams laid end to end, or a metal seat may be used to join beams to a column.

Compression

Compression is the tendency to compress a structural member. The fibers of a beam resting on a column tend to compress, but residential loads are usually not sufficient to cause structural problems. Posts are another area where compression can be seen. Wood is strongest along the grain. The loads in residential design typically are not large enough to cause problems in columns. However, the length of the post is important in relation to the load to be supported. As the length of the post increases, the post tends to bend rather than compress. Building departments often require the approval from a structural engineer or architect for structures with posts longer than 10'. This book does not analyze the forces of tension and compression.

USING SPAN TABLES TO SIZE DIMENSIONAL LUMBER

Standard framing practice is to place structural members such as *joists* and *rafters* at 12, 16, or 24" (300, 400, or 600 mm) o.c. As a result, standard tables exist for the sizing of repetitive members. Joists and rafters are considered simple beams with uniform loads, allowing sizes to be determined from the IRC's span tables. Span tables for dimensional lumber are also available from major lumber manufacturers such as the **Western Wood Products Association** or the **Southern Forest Products Association**. To use these tables you must understand a few basic facts, including typical loading reactions of framing members and the structural capabilities of various species and grades of wood.

The most common types of framing lumber are Douglas fir-larch (DFL #2), southern pine (SP #2), spruce-pine-fir (SPF #2), and hemlock-fir (Hem-Fir #2). Notice that each species is followed by #2. This number refers to the grade value of the species. Usually only #1 or #2 grade lumber is used as structural lumber. The wood listed as #3 has too many checks and cracks to provide the needed strength for structural lumber. SS represents select structural lumber, a high-quality wood that is generally too expensive to use for anything except exposed beams for the rich and famous.

Determining Size and Span

Once the species of the framing lumber is known, the size and span can be determined. The IRC, as well as each major lumber producer, provides allowable span tables for floor joists, ceiling joists, and rafters. Determine how the wood is to be used, then proceed to the proper table. Before identifying any spans, locate a few simple headings and subheadings at the top of the table. See Figure 24.6 to become familiar with the basics of the span table. Some of the key information available from this part of the table includes:

- **Title:** Most codes include several different span charts, making it easy to use the wrong table. Double-check the title to ensure you use the right one.

- **Loads:** Within some categories of tables, the values are determined by the loads that need to be supported. In Figure 24.6, the table is based on an assumed LL value of 40 lb per sq ft and dead loads of 10 or 20 lb. The values in this table will work well for a residence.

- **Deflection:** A symbol such as $L/\Delta = 360$ represents the code allowable deflection, where L equals the length of the joist in feet and Δ represents the deflection value. Other allowable options include $L/\Delta = 240$ and $L/\Delta = 180$. The IRC lists the allowable deflection in the design criteria of each span table. The allowable deflection listed in the design criteria defines how much a member is allowed to sag (can sag).

- **Size and spacing of lumber:** The left side of the span table is the size and spacing of the framing lumber. In Figure 24.7 each size of structural member has a value for the spacing of 12, 16, 19.2, or 24" o.c.

TITLE — | LUMBER SIZE | DEAD LOAD VALUE | DEFLECTION VALUE

FLOOR JOIST SPANS FOR COMMON LUMBER SPECIES (Residential living areas, live load=40 psf, L/Δ=360)

JOIST SPACING (inches)	SPECIE AND GRADE	DEAD LOAD = 10 psf				DEAD LOAD = 20 psf			
		2x6	2x8	2x10	2x12	2x6	2x8	2x10	2x12
		Maximum floor joist spans							
		(ft.- in.)	(ft.- in.)	(ft.- in.)	(ft.- in.)	(ft.- in.)	(ft.- in.)	(ft.- in.)	(ft.- in.)
12	Douglas fir-larch SS	11- 4	15- 0	19- 1	23- 3	11- 4	15- 0	19- 1	23- 3
	Douglas fir-larch #1	10-11	14- 5	18- 5	22- 0	10-11	14- 2	17- 4	20- 1
	Douglas fir-larch #2	10- 9	14- 2	17- 9	20- 7	10- 6	13- 3	16- 3	18-10
	Douglas fir-larch #3	8- 8	11- 0	13- 5	15- 7	7-11	10- 0	12- 3	14- 3
	Hem-fir SS	10- 9	14- 2	18- 0	21-11	10- 9	14- 2	18- 0	21-11

SPECIES — | SPAN.

FIGURE 24.6 Because of a wide variety of span tables with a similar appearance, it is critical that a few basic facts be studied before using each table. Before determining a span, verify the table title, the live and dead loads, the deflection limits, the lumber size, and spacing.

Sizing Floor Joists

The IRC provides tables that are divided by living areas and sleeping areas to determine floor joists size and spans. The table shown in Figure 24.7 is for residential living areas. Although joists from this table can be used in sleeping areas, do not use joist spans from Figure 24.8 in general living areas.

Sizing Floor Joists for Living Joists. To use Figure 24.7, find the column that represents proper species and grade for the lumber used in your area. This example uses Douglas fir #2. The first listing in the column is 11-4 representing a maximum allowable span of 11'-4". Because the most common spacing for floor joists is 16" o.c., drop down to the 16" spacing box. Using the Douglas fir-larch #2 option of the 16" row and the Dead load =10 psf column, you will find spans listed for 2 × 6 = 9-9, 2 × 8 = 12-7, 2 × 10 = 15-5, and 2 × 12 = 17-10. If you are looking for floor joists to support a living room floor that is 14'-6" wide, the 2 × 10 floor joists are suitable. Using 2 × 12 floor joists at 24" o.c. is also suitable with a maximum span of 14'-7".

Using Figure 24.7, determine the distance that 2 × 8 hem-fir #2 floor joists will span at 16" o.c. Work to the right until you come to 2 × 8, then work down to the 16" spacing row. The span for a 2 × 8 at 16" o.c. with a 10-lb DL is 12'-0". Use the same procedure to determine the span for a 2 × 10 SP #2 floor joist at 16" o.c. The listed span is 16'-1".

While the span is typically known, the size of the member will need to be determined. For instance, determine the size of floor joists needed for a living area 15' wide. Assume southern pine with a dead load of 10 lb will be used. Using joists spaced at 24" or 19.2" o.c., 2 × 12 could be used. With a spacing of 16" o.c., either 2 × 10 or 2 × 12 joists could be used. Even if using select structural lumber, 2 × 8 joists cannot be used to span 15'-0". If a

girder is used at the midpoint to reduce the span, 2 × 6 SP #2 joists placed at 24" o.c. could be used safely

Finally, determine if it is more cost effective to use 2 × 6 joists at 24" o.c. and a girder or 2 × 10 joists at 16" o.c. with no girder. For most markets, the cost of labor is the deciding factor and not the cost of the lumber. To reduce labor cost, use the 2 × 10 SP #2 at 16" o.c.

Sizing Floor Joists for Sleeping Joists. The IRC allows the floor live load of sleeping areas to be reduced from 40 to 30 lb. Use the table in Figure 24.8 to determine floor joists with a live load of 30 lb and a dead load of either 10 or 20 psf. Values from this table are determined using the same methods that were used with Figure 24.7. Notice when determining the size of the DFL#2 floor joists needed to support a bedroom with a 14'-6" span, that either a 2 × 8 at 12" o.c. or 2 × 10 at 16" o.c. can be used.

Sizing Ceiling Joists

To determine the size of a ceiling joist, use the proper table and the same procedure that was used to size a floor joist. Because they are both horizontal members, they will have similar loading patterns. A table for sizing ceiling joists is shown in Figure 24.9. For ceiling joists, the live load is only 10 psf. Span tables are available for ceiling joists with and without storage. Using Figure 24.9, determine the smallest size DFL #2 ceiling joists that will span 16' at 16" o.c. You will find that 2 × 6 joists at 16" o.c. will span 17'-8". Figure 24.10 shows a table for ceiling joists with limited attic storage. This table is more realistic for most residential uses. Notice the dead load has been increased from 5 to 10 psf. Using DFL #2 joists at 16" o.c. to span 16' will require 2 × 8 joists. These joists are suitable for spanning distances of up to 16'-3".

FLOOR JOIST SPANS FOR COMMON LUMBER SPECIES (Residential living areas, live load=40 psf, L/Δ=360)

JOIST SPACING (inches)	SPECIE AND GRADE		DEAD LOAD = 10 psf				DEAD LOAD = 20 psf			
			2x6	2x8	2x10	2x12	2x6	2x8	2x10	2x12
			Maximum floor joist spans							
			(ft.- in.)	(ft.- in.)	(ft.- in.)	(ft.- in.)	(ft.- in.)	(ft.- in.)	(ft.- in.)	(ft.- in.)
12	Douglas fir-larch	SS	11-4	15-0	19-1	23-3	11-4	15-0	19-1	23-3
	Douglas fir-larch	#1	10-11	14-5	18-5	22-0	10-11	14-2	17-4	20-1
	Douglas fir-larch	#2	10-9	14-2	17-9	20-7	10-6	13-3	16-3	18-10
	Douglas fir-larch	#3	8-8	11-0	13-5	15-7	7-11	10-0	12-3	14-3
	Hem-fir	SS	10-9	14-2	18-0	21-11	10-9	14-2	18-0	21-11
	Hem-fir	#1	10-6	13-10	17-8	21-6	10-6	13-10	16-11	19-7
	Hem-fir	#2	10-0	13-2	16-10	20-4	10-0	13-1	16-0	18-6
	Hem-fir	#3	8-8	11-0	13-5	15-7	7-11	10-0	12-3	14-3
	Southern pine	SS	11-2	14-8	18-9	22-10	11-2	14-8	18-9	22-10
	Southern pine	#1	10-11	14-5	18-5	22-5	10-11	14-5	18-5	22-5
	Southern pine	#2	10-9	14-2	18-0	21-9	10-9	14-2	16-11	19-10
	Southern pine	#3	9-4	11-11	14-0	16-8	8-6	10-10	12-10	15-3
	Spruce-pine-fir	SS	10-6	13-10	17-8	21-6	10-6	13-10	17-8	21-6
	Spruce-pine-fir	#1	10-3	13-6	17-3	20-7	10-3	13-3	16-3	18-10
	Spruce-pine-fir	#2	10-3	13-6	17-3	20-7	10-3	13-3	16-3	18-10
	Spruce-pine-fir	#3	8-8	11-0	13-5	15-7	7-11	10-0	12-3	14-3
16	Douglas fir-larch	SS	10-4	13-7	17-4	21-1	10-4	13-7	17-4	21-0
	Douglas fir-larch	#1	9-11	13-1	16-5	19-1	9-8	12-4	15-0	17-5
	Douglas fir-larch	#2	9-9	12-7	15-5	17-10	9-1	11-6	14-1	16-3
	Douglas fir-larch	#3	7-6	9-6	11-8	13-6	6-10	8-8	10-7	12-4
	Hem-fir	SS	9-9	12-10	16-5	19-11	9-9	12-10	16-5	19-11
	Hem-fir	#1	9-6	12-7	16-0	18-7	9-6	12-0	14-8	17-0
	Hem-fir	#2	9-1	12-0	15-2	17-7	8-11	11-4	13-10	16-1
	Hem-fir	#3	7-6	9-6	11-8	13-6	6-10	8-8	10-7	12-4
	Southern pine	SS	10-2	13-4	17-0	20-9	10-2	13-4	17-0	20-9
	Southern pine	#1	9-11	13-1	16-9	20-4	9-11	13-1	16-4	19-6
	Southern pine	#2	9-9	12-10	16-1	18-10	9-6	12-4	14-8	17-2
	Southern pine	#3	8-1	10-3	12-2	14-6	7-4	9-5	11-1	13-2
	Spruce-pine-fir	SS	9-6	12-7	16-0	19-6	9-6	12-7	11-1	13-2
	Spruce-pine-fir	#1	9-4	12-3	15-5	17-10	9-6	12-7	16-0	19-6
	Spruce-pine-fir	#2	9-4	12-3	15-5	17-10	9-1	11-6	14-1	16-3
	Spruce-pine-fir	#3	7-6	9-6	11-8	13-6	6-10	8-8	10-7	12-4
19.2	Douglas fir-larch	SS	9-8	12-10	16-4	19-10	9-8	12-10	16-4	19-2
	Douglas fir-larch	#1	9-4	12-4	15-0	17-5	8-10	11-3	13-8	15-11
	Douglas fir-larch	#2	9-1	11-6	14-1	16-3	8-3	10-6	12-10	14-10
	Douglas fir-larch	#3	6-10	8-8	10-7	12-4	6-3	7-11	9-8	11-3
	Hem-fir	SS	9-2	12-1	15-5	18-9	9-2	12-1	15-5	18-9
	Hem-fir	#1	9-0	11-10	14-8	17-0	8-8	11-3	13-4	15-6
	Hem-fir	#2	8-7	11-3	13-10	16-1	8-2	10-4	12-8	14-8
	Hem-fir	#3	6-10	8-8	10-7	12-4	6-3	7-11	9-8	11-3
	Southern pine	SS	9-6	12-7	16-0	19-6	9-6	12-7	16-0	19-6
	Southern pine	#1	9-4	12-4	15-9	19-2	9-4	12-4	16-0	19-6
	Southern pine	#2	9-2	12-1	14-8	17-2	8-8	11-3	14-11	17-9
	Southern pine	#3	7-4	9-5	11-1	13-2	6-9	8-7	13-5	15-8
	Spruce-pine-fir	SS	9-0	11-10	15-1	18-4	9-0	11-10	10-1	12-1
	Spruce-pine-fir	#1	8-9	11-6	14-1	16-3	8-3	10-6	15-1	17-9
	Spruce-pine-fir	#2	8-9	11-6	14-1	16-3	8-3	10-6	12-10	14-10
	Spruce-pine-fir	#3	6-10	8-8	10-7	12-4	6-3	7-11	9-8	11-3
24	Douglas fir-larch	SS	9-0	11-11	15-2	18-5	9-0	11-11	14-9	17-1
	Douglas fir-larch	#1	8-8	11-0	13-5	15-7	7-11	10-0	12-3	14-3
	Douglas fir-larch	#2	8-1	10-3	12-7	14-7	7-5	9-5	11-6	13-4
	Douglas fir-larch	#3	6-2	7-9	9-6	11-0	5-7	7-1	8-8	10-1
	Hem-fir	SS	8-6	11-3	14-4	17-5	8-6	11-3	14-4	16-10[a]
	Hem-fir	#1	8-4	10-9	13-1	15-2	7-9	9-9	11-11	13-10
	Hem-fir	#2	7-11	10-2	12-5	14-4	7-4	9-3	11-4	13-1
	Hem-fir	#3	6-2	7-9	9-6	11-0	5-7	7-1	8-8	10-1
	Southern pine	SS	8-10	11-8	14-11	18-1	8-10	11-8	14-11	18-1
	Southern pine	#1	8-8	11-5	14-7	17-5	8-8	11-3	13-4	15-11
	Southern pine	#2	8-6	11-0	13-1	15-5	7-9	10-0	12-0	14-0
	Southern pine	#3	6-7	8-5	9-11	11-10	6-0	7-8	9-1	10-9
	Spruce-pine-fir	SS	8-4	11-0	14-0	17-0	8-4	11-0	13-8	15-11
	Spruce-pine-fir	#1	8-1	10-3	12-7	14-7	7-5	9-5	11-6	13-4
	Spruce-pine-fir	#2	8-1	10-3	12-7	14-7	7-5	9-5	11-6	13-4
	Spruce-pine-fir	#3	6-2	7-9	9-6	11-0	5-7	7-1	8-8	10-1

For SI: 1 inch = 25.4 mm, 1 foot = 308.4 mm.

NOTES:
a. Check sources for availability of lumber in lengths greater than 20 feet.
b. End bearing length shall be increased to 2 inches.

FIGURE 24.7 This span table is suitable for determining floor joists for living areas with a live load of 40 psf and dead load of either 10 or 20 psf.

FLOOR JOIST SPANS FOR COMMON LUMBER SPECIES
(Residential sleeping areas, live load=30 psf, L/Δ=360)

JOIST SPACING (inches)	SPECIE AND GRADE		DEAD LOAD = 10 psf				DEAD LOAD = 20 psf			
			2x6	2x8	2x10	2x12	2x6	2x8	2x10	2x12
			Maximum floor joist spans							
			(ft.- in.)	(ft.- in.)	(ft.- in.)	(ft.- in.)	(ft.- in.)	(ft.- in.)	(ft.- in.)	(ft.- in.)
12	Douglas fir-larch	SS	12-6	16-6	21-0	25-7	12-6	16-6	21-0	25-7
	Douglas fir-larch	#1	12-0	15-10	20-3	24-8	12-0	15-7	19-0	22-0
	Douglas fir-larch	#2	11-10	15-7	19-10	23-0	11-6	14-7	17-9	20-7
	Douglas fir-larch	#3	9-8	12-4	15-0	17-5	8-8	11-0	13-5	15-7
	Hem-fir	SS	11-10	15-7	19-10	24-2	11-10	15-7	19-10	24-2
	Hem-fir	#1	11-7	15-3	19-5	23-7	11-7	15-2	18-6	21-6
	Hem-fir	#2	11-0	14-6	18-6	22-6	11-0	14-4	17-6	20-4
	Hem-fir	#3	9-8	12-4	15-0	17-5	8-8	11-0	13-5	15-7
	Southern pine	SS	12-3	16-2	20-8	25-1	12-3	16-2	20-8	25-1
	Southern pine	#1	12-0	15-10	20-3	24-8	12-0	15-10	20-3	24-8
	Southern pine	#2	11-10	15-7	19-10	18-8	11-10	15-7	18-7	21-9
	Southern pine	#3	10-5	13-3	15-8	18-8	9-4	11-11	14-0	16-8
	Spruce-pine-fir	SS	11-7	15-3	19-5	23-7	11-7	15-3	19-5	23-7
	Spruce-pine-fir	#1	11-3	14-11	19-0	23-0	11-3	14-7	17-9	20-7
	Spruce-pine-fir	#2	11-3	14-11	19-0	23-0	11-3	14-7	17-9	20-7
	Spruce-pine-fir	#3	9-8	12-4	15-0	17-5	8-8	11-0	13-5	15-7
16	Douglas fir-larch	SS	11-4	15-0	19-1	23-3	11-4	15-0	19-1	23-0
	Douglas fir-larch	#1	10-11	14-5	18-5	21-4	10-8	13-6	16-5	19-1
	Douglas fir-larch	#2	10-9	14-1	17-2	19-11	9-11	12-7	15-5	17-10
	Douglas fir-larch	#3	8-5	10-8	13-0	15-1	7-6	9-6	11-8	13-6
	Hem-fir	SS	10-9	14-2	18-0	21-11	10-9	14-2	18-0	21-11
	Hem-fir	#1	10-6	13-10	17-8	20-9	10-4	13-1	16-0	18-7
	Hem-fir	#2	10-0	13-2	16-10	19-8	9-10	12-5	15-2	17-7
	Hem-fir	#3	8-5	10-8	13-0	15-1	7-6	9-6	11-8	13-6
	Southern pine	SS	11-2	14-8	18-9	22-10	11-2	14-8	18-9	22-10
	Southern pine	#1	10-11	14-5	18-5	22-5	10-11	14-5	17-11	21-4
	Southern pine	#2	10-9	14-2	18-0	21-1	10-5	13-6	16-1	18-10
	Southern pine	#3	9-0	11-6	13-7	16-2	8-1	10-3	12-2	14-6
	Spruce-pine-fir	SS	10-6	13-10	17-8	21-6	10-6	13-10	17-8	21-4
	Spruce-pine-fir	#1	10-3	13-6	17-2	19-11	9-11	12-7	15-5	17-10
	Spruce-pine-fir	#2	10-3	13-6	17-2	19-11	9-11	12-7	15-5	17-10
	Spruce-pine-fir	#3	8-5	10-8	13-0	15-1	7-6	9-6	11-8	13-6
19.2	Douglas fir-larch	SS	10-8	14-1	18-0	21-10	10-8	14-1	18-0	21-0
	Douglas fir-larch	#1	10-4	13-7	16-9	19-6	9-8	12-4	15-0	17-5
	Douglas fir-larch	#2	10-1	12-10	15-8	18-3	9-1	11-6	14-1	16-3
	Douglas fir-larch	#3	7-8	9-9	11-10	13-9	6-10	8-8	10-7	12-4
	Hem-fir	SS	10-1	13-4	17-0	20-8	10-1	13-4	17-0	20-7
	Hem-fir	#1	9-10	13-0	16-4	19-0	9-6	12-0	14-8	17-0
	Hem-fir	#2	9-5	12-5	15-6	17-1	8-11	11-4	13-10	16-1
	Hem-fir	#3	7-8	9-9	11-10	13-9	6-10	8-8	10-7	12-4
	Southern pine	SS	10-6	13-10	17-8	21-6	10-6	13-10	17-8	21-6
	Southern pine	#1	10-4	13-7	17-4	21-1	10-4	13-7	16-4	19-6
	Southern pine	#2	10-1	13-4	16-5	19-3	9-6	12-4	14-8	17-2
	Southern pine	#3	8-3	10-6	12-5	14-9	7-4	9-5	11-1	13-2
	Spruce-pine-fir	SS	9-10	13-0	16-7	20-2	9-10	13-0	16-7	19-6
	Spruce-pine-fir	#1	9-8	12-9	15-8	18-3	9-1	11-6	14-1	16-3
	Spruce-pine-fir	#2	9-8	12-9	15-8	18-3	9-1	11-6	14-1	16-3
	Spruce-pine-fir	#3	7-8	9-9	11-10	13-9	6-10	8-8	10-7	12-4
24	Douglas fir-larch	SS	9-11	13-1	16-8	20-3	9-11	13-1	16-2	18-9
	Douglas fir-larch	#1	9-7	12-4	15-0	17-5	8-8	11-0	13-5	15-7
	Douglas fir-larch	#2	9-1	11-6	14-1	16-3	8-1	10-3	12-7	14-7
	Douglas fir-larch	#3	6-10	8-8	10-7	12-4	6-2	7-9	9-6	11-0
	Hem-fir	SS	9-4	12-4	15-9	19-2	9-4	12-4	15-9	18-5
	Hem-fir	#1	9-2	12-0	14-8	17-0	8-6	10-9	13-1	15-2
	Hem-fir	#2	8-9	11-4	13-10	16-1	8-0	10-2	12-5	14-4
	Hem-fir	#3	6-10	8-8	10-7	12-4	6-2	7-9	9-6	11-0
	Southern pine	SS	9-9	12-10	16-5	19-11	9-9	12-10	16-5	19-11
	Southern pine	#1	9-7	12-7	16-1	19-6	9-7	12-4	14-7	17-5
	Southern pine	#2	9-4	12-4	14-8	17-2	8-6	11-0	13-1	15-5
	Southern pine	#3	7-4	9-5	11-1	13-2	6-7	8-5	9-11	11-10
	Spruce-pine-fir	SS	9-2	12-1	15-5	18-9	9-2	12-1	15-0	17-5
	Spruce-pine-fir	#1	8-11	11-6	14-1	16-3	8-1	10-3	12-7	14-7
	Spruce-pine-fir	#2	8-11	11-6	14-1	16-3	8-1	10-3	12-7	14-7
	Spruce-pine-fir	#3	6-10	8-8	10-7	12-4	6-2	7-9	9-6	11-0

For SI: 1 inch = 25.4 mm, 1 foot = 304.8 mm.

NOTE: Check sources for availability of lumber in lengths greater than 20 feet.

FIGURE 24.8 This span table is suitable for determining floor joists for sleeping areas with a live load of 30 psf and a dead load of either 10 psf or 20 psf.

CEILING JOIST SPANS FOR COMMON LUMBER SPECIES
(Uninhabitable attics without storage, live load = 10 psf, L/Δ = 240)

CEILING JOIST SPACING (inches)	SPECIE AND GRADE		DEAD LOAD = 5 psf			
			2x4	2x6	2x8	2x10
			Maximum ceiling joist spans			
			(ft. - in.)	(ft. - in.)	(ft. - in.)	(ft. - in.)
12	Douglas fir-larch	SS	13-2	20-8	(a)	(a)
	Douglas fir-larch	#1	12-8	19-11	(a)	(a)
	Douglas fir-larch	#2	12-5	19-6	25-8	(a)
	Douglas fir-larch	#3	10-10	15-10	20-1	24-6
	Hem-fir	SS	12-5	19-6	25-8	(a)
	Hem-fir	#1	12-2	19-1	25-2	(a)
	Hem-fir	#2	11-7	18-2	24-0	(a)
	Hem-fir	#3	10-10	15-10	20-1	24-6
	Southern pine	SS	12-11	20-3	(a)	(a)
	Southern pine	#1	12-8	19-11	(a)	(a)
	Southern pine	#2	12-5	19-6	25-8	(a)
	Southern pine	#3	11-6	17-0	21-8	25-7
	Spruce-pine-fir	SS	12-2	19-1	25-2	(a)
	Spruce-pine-fir	#1	11-10	18-8	24-7	(a)
	Spruce-pine-fir	#2	11-10	18-8	24-7	(a)
	Spruce-pine-fir	#3	10-10	15-10	20-1	24-6
16	Douglas fir-larch	SS	11-11	18-9	24-8	(a)
	Douglas fir-larch	#1	11-6	18-1	23-10	(a)
	Douglas fir-larch	#2	11-3	17-8	23-0	(a)
	Douglas fir-larch	#3	9-5	13-9	17-5	21-3
	Hem-fir	SS	11-3	17-8	23-4	(a)
	Hem-fir	#1	11-0	17-4	22-10	(a)
	Hem-fir	#2	10-6	16-6	21-9	(a)
	Hem-fir	#3	9-5	13-9	17-5	21-3
	Southern pine	SS	11-9	18-5	24-3	(a)
	Southern pine	#1	11-6	18-1	23-1	(a)
	Southern pine	#2	11-3	17-8	23-4	(a)
	Southern pine	#3	10-0	14-9	18-9	22-2
	Spruce-pine-fir	SS	11-0	17-4	22-10	(a)
	Spruce-pine-fir	#1	10-9	16-11	22-4	(a)
	Spruce-pine-fir	#2	10-9	16-11	22-4	(a)
	Spruce-pine-fir	#3	9-5	13-9	17-5	21-3
19.2	Douglas fir-larch	SS	11-3	17-8	23-3	(a)
	Douglas fir-larch	#1	10-10	17-0	22-5	(a)
	Douglas fir-larch	#2	10-7	16-7	21-0	25-8
	Douglas fir-larch	#3	8-7	12-6	15-10	19-5
	Hem-fir	SS	10-7	16-8	21-11	(a)
	Hem-fir	#1	10-4	16-4	21-6	(a)
	Hem-fir	#2	9-11	15-7	20-6	25-3
	Hem-fir	#3	8-7	12-6	15-10	19-5
	Southern -pine	SS	11-0	17-4	22-10	(a)
	Southern pine	#1	10-10	17-0	22-5	(a)
	Southern pine	#2	10-7	16-8	21-11	(a)
	Southern pine	#3	9-1	13-6	17-2	20-3
	Spruce-pine-fir	SS	10-4	16-4	21-6	(a)
	Spruce-pine-fir	#1	10-2	15-11	21-0	25-8
	Spruce-pine-fir	#2	10-2	15-11	21-0	25-8
	Spruce-pine-fir	#3	8-7	12-6	15-10	19-5
24	Douglas fir-larch	SS	10-5	16-4	21-7	(a)
	Douglas fir-larch	#1	10-0	15-9	20-1	24-6
	Douglas fir-larch	#2	9-10	14-10	18-9	22-11
	Douglas fir-larch	#3	7-8	11-2	14-2	17-4
	Hem-fir	SS	9-10	15-6	20-5	(a)
	Hem-fir	#1	9-8	15-2	19-7	23-11
	Hem-fir	#2	9-2	14-5	18-6	22-7
	Hem-fir	#3	7-8	11-2	14-2	17-4
	Southern pine	SS	10-3	16-1	21-2	(a)
	Southern pine	#1	10-0	15-9	20-10	(a)
	Southern pine	#2	9-10	15-6	20-1	23-11
	Southern pine	#3	8-2	12-0	15-4	18-1
	Spruce-pine-fir	SS	9-8	15-2	19-11	25-5
	Spruce-pine-fir	#1	9-5	14-9	18-9	22-11
	Spruce-pine-fir	#2	9-5	14-9	18-9	22-11
	Spruce-pine-fir	#3	7-8	11-2	14-2	17-4

For SI: 1 inch = 25.4 mm, 1 foot = 304.8 m, 1 psf = 0.0479 kN/m².

a. Span exceeds 26 feet in length. Check sources for availability of lumber in lengths greater than 20 feet.

FIGURE 24.9 This span table is suitable for determining ceiling joists without storage areas with a live load of 10 psf and a dead load of 5 psf.

CEILING JOIST SPANS FOR COMMON LUMBER SPECIES
(Uninhabitable attics with limited storage, live load = 10 psf, L/Δ = 240)

CEILING JOIST SPACING (inches)	SPECIE AND GRADE		DEAD LOAD = 10 psf			
			2x4	2x6	2x8	2x10
			Maximum ceiling joist spans			
			(ft. - in.)	(ft. - in.)	(ft. - in.)	(ft. - in.)
12	Douglas fir-larch	SS	10-5	16-4	21-7	(a)
	Douglas fir-larch	#1	10-0	15-9	20-1	24-6
	Douglas fir-larch	#2	9-10	14-10	18-9	22-11
	Douglas fir-larch	#3	7-8	11-2	14-2	17-4
	Hem-fir	SS	9-10	15-6	20-5	(a)
	Hem-fir	#1	9-8	15-2	19-7	23-11
	Hem-fir	#2	9-2	14-5	18-6	22-7
	Hem-fir	#3	7-8	11-2	14-2	17-4
	Southern pine	SS	10-3	16-1	21-2	(a)
	Southern pine	#1	10-0	15-9	20-10	(a)
	Southern pine	#2	9-10	15-6	20-1	23-11
	Southern pine	#3	8-2	12-0	15-4	18-1
	Spruce-pine-fir	SS	9-8	15-2	19-11	25-5
	Spruce-pine-fir	#1	9-5	14-9	18-9	22-11
	Spruce-pine-fir	#2	9-5	14-9	18-9	22-11
	Spruce-pine-fir	#3	7-8	11-2	14-2	17-4
16	Douglas fir-larch	SS	9-6	14-11	19-7	25-0
	Douglas fir-larch	#1	9-1	13-9	17-5	21-3
	Douglas fir-larch	#2	8-9	12-10	16-3	19-10
	Douglas fir-larch	#3	6-8	9-8	12-4	15-0
	Hem-fir	SS	8-11	14-1	18-6	23-8
	Hem-fir	#1	8-9	13-5	16-10	20-8
	Hem-fir	#2	8-4	12-8	16-0	19-7
	Hem-fir	#3	6-8	9-8	12-4	15-0
	Southern pine	SS	9-4	14-7	19-3	24-7
	Southern pine	#1	9-1	14-4	18-11	23-1
	Southern pine	#2	8-11	13-6	17-5	20-9
	Southern pine	#3	7-1	10-5	13-3	15-8
	Spruce-pine-fir	SS	8-9	13-9	18-1	23-1
	Spruce-pine-fir	#1	8-7	12-10	16-3	19-10
	Spruce-pine-fir	#2	8-7	12-10	16-3	19-10
	Spruce-pine-fir	#3	6-8	9-8	12-4	15-0
19.2	Douglas fir-larch	SS	8-11	14-0	18-5	23-4
	Douglas fir-larch	#1	8-7	12-6	15-10	19-5
	Douglas fir-larch	#2	8-0	11-9	14-10	18-2
	Douglas fir-larch	#3	6-1	8-10	11-3	13-8
	Hem-fir	SS	8-5	13-3	17-5	22-3
	Hem-fir	#1	8-3	12-3	15-6	18-11
	Hem-fir	#2	7-10	11-7	14-8	17-10
	Hem-fir	#3	6-1	8-10	11-3	13-8
	Southern pine	SS	8-9	13-9	18-1	23-1
	Southern pine	#1	8-7	13-6	17-9	21-1
	Southern pine	#2	8-5	12-3	15-10	18-11
	Southern pine	#3	6-5	9-6	12-1	14-4
	Spruce-pine-fir	SS	8-3	12-11	17-1	21-8
	Spruce-pine-fir	#1	8-0	11-9	14-10	18-2
	Spruce-pine-fir	#2	8-0	11-9	14-10	18-2
	Spruce-pine-fir	#3	6-1	8-10	11-3	13-8
24	Douglas fir-larch	SS	8-3	13-0	17-1	20-11
	Douglas fir-larch	#1	7-8	11-2	14-2	17-4
	Douglas fir-larch	#2	7-2	10-6	13-3	16-3
	Douglas fir-larch	#3	5-5	7-11	10-0	12-3
	Hem-fir	SS	7-10	12-3	16-2	20-6
	Hem-fir	#1	7-6	10-11	13-10	16-11
	Hem-fir	#2	7-1	10-4	13-1	16-0
	Hem-fir	#3	5-5	7-11	10-0	12-3
	Southern pine	SS	8-1	12-9	16-10	21-6
	Southern pine	#1	8-0	12-6	15-10	18-10
	Southern pine	#2	7-8	11-0	14-2	16-11
	Southern pine	#3	5-9	8-6	10-10	12-10
	Spruce-pine-fir	SS	7-8	12-0	15-10	19-5
	Spruce-pine-fir	#1	7-2	10-6	13-3	16-3
	Spruce-pine-fir	#2	7-2	10-6	13-3	16-3
	Spruce-pine-fir	#3	5-5	7-11	10-0	12-3

For SI: 1 inch = 25.4 mm, 1 foot = 304.8 mm, 1 psf = 0.0479 kN/m².

a. Span exceeds 26 feet in length. Check sources for availability of lumber in lengths greater than 20 feet.

FIGURE 24.10 This span table is suitable for determining ceiling joists with limited storage and a live load of 10 psf and a dead load of 10 psf.

Sizing Rafters

Although the selection of rafters is similar to the selection of joists, there are two major differences. Tables are available for rafters with and without the ceiling attached to the rafters and based on the ground snow load. Load tables with ground snow loads of 30, 50, and 70 psf are available in the IRC. Remember to verify the required load to be supported with the building department that will govern the job site. They will determine which live load value to use.

The dead load is determined by the construction materials. The table in Figure 24.11 with a dead load of 10 psf is suitable for rafters supporting most materials except tile or slate with no interior finish. The column in Figure 24.12 with a load of 20 psf is suitable for supporting most tiles. Consult vendor catalogs to determine the required dead loads.

Once you determine the live and dead loads, choose the appropriate table. Determine what size hem-fir rafter will be needed to support a roof over a room 18' wide framed with a gable roof. Assume the roof is supporting 235-lb composition shingles with a live load of 20 psf, a dead load of 10 psf, and 24" spacing. Because of the gable roof, the actual horizontal span is only 9'-0". Figure 24.11 shows that 2 × 6 HF #2 rafters spaced at 24" o.c. are suitable for spans up to 11'-7". If the same room is framed with DFL #2 lumber, 2 × 6 members are suitable for spans up to 11'-9". If the spacing is reduced to 16" o.c., 2 × 4 DFL #2 rafters can span up to 9'-10". Even though they are legal, many framers will not use 2 × 4 members because they tend to split as they are attached to the wall top plates.

WORKING WITH ENGINEERED LUMBER

Determining the span of engineered lumber is similar to sizing sawn lumber, although span tables vary slightly for each manufacturer. Most suppliers of engineered joists provide materials for determining floor joists and rafters. The balance of this section explores materials supplied by Weyerhaeuser.

Sizing Engineered Floor Joists

Figure 24.13 shows a floor span table for engineered floor joists. Notice that the lower portion of this table describes spans based on code-allowed deflections and the upper portion describes spans based on the manufacturer's suggested deflection limits of L/480. The increased deflection limits produce an excellent floor system with little

or no vibration or squeaking. To determine the joist size required to span 16'-0" requires the following steps:

- Determine the deflection limit. For this example, use *L/360*.
- Identify the loading condition. For this example, use a 40 psf LL and a 10 psf DL.
- Select the spacing. For this example, use 24" o.c.
- Scan down the spacing column until a distance that exceeds the span is located. For this example, the first joist that meets the design criteria is the 11 7/8" TJI®/210 joist with a span of 16'-10".

Compare the same joist with the top half of the table. Using the stricter deflection limits, the 11 7/8" TJI/210 joist will span 16'-5". If the spacing is changed to 12" o.c., a 9 1/2" TJI/110 can be used with a maximum span of 16'-5".

Selecting Engineered Rafters

Figure 24.14 shows an example of a table for determining the sizes of engineered rafters. Before using the table, notice the deflections and the divisions in the table. Deflection is limited to L/180, and the table is divided into non-snow and snow load areas and low- and high-sloped roofs. Use the low listing for roofs with a slope of less than 6/12, and the high listing for slopes greater than 6/12. Use the following steps to determine the required rafter size to span 16'-0" on a 5/12 pitch supporting composition shingles:

- Determine the roof loading. For this example, use a LL of 20 lb and a DL of 15 lb with no snow.
- Identify the appropriate slope column. For this example, use the low column.
- Move down the 20LL + 15DL low column into a row that reflects the desired spacing until a value is found that equals or exceeds the required span. All of the values for 16" and 19.2 rafters exceed the required 16'-0" span. A 9 1/2" TJI150 @ 24" o.c. can be used for the required span.

As with other types of engineered materials, consult all of the manufacturer's instructions.

DETERMINING SIMPLE BEAM SIZES

Throughout this chapter you've explored methods of identifying the size of structural members using tables. The balance of this chapter explores methods of solving

TABLE R802.5.1(1)[a]
RAFTER SPANS FOR COMMON LUMBER SPECIES
(Roof live load=20 psf, ceiling not attached to rafters, L/Δ=180)

RAFTER SPACING (inches)	SPECIE AND GRADE		DEAD LOAD = 10 psf					DEAD LOAD = 20 psf				
			2 X 4	2 X 6	2 X 8	2X10	2 X 12	2 X 4	2 X 6	2 X 8	2 X 10	2 X 12
			Maximum rafter spans[b]									
			(ft. - in.)	(ft. - in.)	(ft. - in.)	(ft. - in.)	(ft. - in.)	(ft. - in.)	(ft. - in.)	(ft. - in.)	(ft. - in.)	(ft. - in.)
12	Douglas fir-larch	SS	11-6	18-0	23-9	(b)	(b)	11-6	18-0	23-5	(b)	(b)
	Douglas fir-larch	#1	11-1	17-4	22-5	(b)	(b)	10-6	15-4	19-5	23-9	(b)
	Douglas fir-larch	#2	10-10	16-7	21-0	25-8	(b)	9-10	14-4	18-2	22-3	25-9
	Douglas fir-larch	#3	8-7	12-6	15-10	19-5	22-6	7-5	10-10	13-9	16-9	19-6
	Hem-fir	SS	10-10	17-0	22-5	(b)	(b)	10-10	17-0	22-5	(b)	(b)
	Hem-fir	#1	10-7	16-8	21-10	(b)	(b)	10-3	14-11	18-11	23-2	(b)
	Hem-fir	#2	10-1	15-11	20-8	25-3	(b)	9-8	14-2	17-11	21-11	25-5
	Hem-fir	#3	8-7	12-6	15-10	19-5	22-6	7-5	10-10	13-9	16-9	19-6
	Southern pine	SS	11-3	17-8	23-4	(b)	(b)	11-3	17-8	23-4	(b)	(b)
	Southern pine	#1	11-1	17-4	22-11	(b)	(b)	11-1	17-3	21-9	25-10	(b)
	Southern pine	#2	10-10	17-0	22-5	(b)	(b)	10-6	15-1	19-5	23-2	(b)
	Southern pine	#3	9-1	13-6	17-2	20-3	24-1	7-11	11-8	14-10	17-6	20-11
	Spruce-pine-fir	SS	10-7	16-8	21-11	(b)	(b)	10-7	16-8	21-9	(b)	(b)
	Spruce-pine-fir	#1	10-4	16-3	21-0	25-8	(b)	9-10	14-4	18-2	22-3	25-9
	Spruce-pine-fir	#2	10-4	16-3	21-0	25-8	(b)	9-10	14-4	18-2	22-3	25-9
	Spruce-pine-fir	#3	8-7	12-6	15-10	19-5	22-6	7-5	10-10	13-9	16-9	19-6
16	Douglas fir-larch	SS	10-5	16-4	21-7	(b)	(b)	10-5	16-0	20-3	24-9	(b)
	Douglas fir-larch	#1	10-0	15-4	19-5	23-9	(b)	9-1	13-3	16-10	20-7	23-10
	Douglas fir-larch	#2	9-10	14-4	18-2	22-3	25-9	8-6	12-5	15-9	19-3	22-4
	Douglas fir-larch	#3	7-5	10-10	13-9	16-9	19-6	6-5	9-5	11-11	14-6	16-10
	Hem-fir	SS	9-10	15-6	20-5	(b)	(b)	9-10	15-6	19-11	24-4	(b)
	Hem-fir	#1	9-8	14-11	18-11	23-2	(b)	8-10	12-11	16-5	20-0	23-3
	Hem-fir	#2	9-2	14-2	17-11	21-11	25-5	8-5	12-3	15-6	18-11	22-0
	Hem-fir	#3	7-5	10-10	13-9	16-9	19-6	6-5	9-5	11-11	14-6	16-10
	Southern pine	SS	10-3	16-1	21-2	(b)	(b)	10-3	16-1	21-2	(b)	(b)
	Southern pine	#1	10-0	15-9	20-10	25-10	(b)	10-0	15-0	18-10	22-4	(b)
	Southern pine	#2	9-10	15-1	19-5	23-2	(b)	9-1	13-0	16-10	20-1	23-7
	Southern pine	#3	7-11	11-8	14-10	17-6	20-11	6-10	10-1	12-10	15-2	18-1
	Spruce-pine-fir	SS	9-8	15-2	19-11	25-5	(b)	9-8	14-10	18-10	23-0	(b)
	Spruce-pine-fir	#1	9-5	14-4	18-2	22-3	25-9	8-6	12-5	15-9	19-3	22-4
	Spruce-pine-fir	#2	9-5	14-4	18-2	22-3	25-9	8-6	12-5	15-9	19-3	22-4
	Spruce-pine-fir	#3	7-5	10-10	13-9	16-9	19-6	6-5	9-5	11-11	14-6	16-10
19.2	Douglas fir-larch	SS	9-10	15-5	20-4	25-11	(b)	9-10	14-7	18-6	22-7	(b)
	Douglas fir-larch	#1	9-5	14-0	17-9	21-8	25-2	8-4	12-2	15-4	18-9	21- 9
	Douglas fir-larch	#2	8-11	13-1	16-7	20-3	23-6	7-9	11-4	14-4	17-7	20- 4
	Douglas fir-larch	#3	6-9	9-11	12-7	15-4	17-9	5-10	8-7	10-10	13-3	15- 5
	Hem-fir	SS	9-3	14-7	19-2	24-6	(b)	9-3	14-4	18-2	22-3	25- 9
	Hem-fir	#1	9-1	13-8	17-4	21-1	24-6	8-1	11-10	15-0	18-4	21- 3
	Hem-fir	#2	8-8	12-11	16-4	20-0	23-2	7-8	11-2	14-2	17-4	20- 1
	Hem-fir	#3	6-9	9-11	12-7	15-4	17-9	5-10	8-7	10-10	13-3	15- 5
	Southern pine	SS	9-8	15-2	19-11	25-5	(b)	9-8	15-2	19-11	25-5	(b)
	Southern pine	#1	9-5	14-10	19-7	23-7	(b)	9-3	13-8	17-2	20-5	24- 4
	Southern pine	#2	9-3	13-9	17-9	21-2	24-10	8-4	11-11	15-4	21- 6	
	Southern pine	#3	7-3	10-8	13-7	16-0	19-1	6-3	9-3	11-9	13-10	16- 6
	Spruce-pine-fir	SS	9-1	14-3	18-9	23-11	(b)	9-1	13-7	17-2	21-0	24- 4
	Spruce-pine-fir	#1	8-10	13-1	16-7	20-3	23-6	7-9	11-4	14-4	17-7	20- 4
	Spruce-pine-fir	#2	8-10	13-1	16-7	20-3	23-6	7-9	11-4	14-4	17-7	20- 4
	Spruce-pine-fir	#3	6-9	9-11	12-7	15-4	17-9	5-10	8-7	10-10	13-3	15- 5
24	Douglas fir-larch	SS	9-1	14-4	18-10	23-4	(b)	8-11	13-1	16-7	20-3	23-5
	Douglas fir-larch	#1	8-7	12-6	15-10	19-5	22-6	7-5	10-10	13-9	16-9	19-6
	Douglas fir-larch	#2	8-0	11-9	14-10	18-2	21-0	6-11	10-2	12-10	15-8	18-3
	Douglas fir-larch	#3	6-1	8-10	11-3	13-8	15-11	5-3	7-8	9-9	11-10	13-9
	Hem-fir	SS	8-7	13-6	17-10	22-9	(b)	8-7	12-10	16-3	19-10	23-0
	Hem-fir	#1	8-4	12-3	15-6	18-11	21-11	7-3	10-7	13-5	16-4	19-0
	Hem-fir	#2	7-11	11-7	14-8	17-10	20-9	6-10	10-0	12-8	15-6	17-11
	Hem-fir	#3	6-1	8-10	11-3	13-8	15-11	5-3	7-8	9-9	11-10	13-9
	Southern pine	SS	8-11	14-1	18-6	23-8	(b)	8-11	14-1	18-6	22-11	(b)
	Southern pine	#1	8-9	13-9	17-9	21-1	25-2	8-3	12-3	15-4	18-3	21-9
	Southern pine	#2	8-7	12-3	15-10	18-11	22-2	7-5	10-8	13-9	16-5	19-3
	Southern pine	#3	6-5	9-6	12-1	14-4	17-1	5-7	8-3	10-6	12-5	14-9
	Spruce-pine-fir	SS	8-5	13-3	17-5	21-8	25-2	8-4	12-2	15-4	18-9	21-9
	Spruce-pine-fir	#1	8-0	11-9	14-10	18-2	21-0	6-11	10-2	12-10	15-8	18-3
	Spruce-pine-fir	#2	8-0	11-9	14-10	18-2	21-0	6-11	10-2	12-10	15-8	18-3
	Spruce-pine-fir	#3	6-1	8-10	11-3	13-8	15-11	5-3	7-8	9-9	11-10	13-9

For SI: 1 inch = 25.4 mm, 1 foot = 304.8 mm, 1 psf = 0.0479 kN/m².

a. The tabulated rafter spans assume that ceiling joists are located at the bottom of the attic space or that some other method of resisting the outward push of the rafters on the bearing walls, such as rafter ties, is provided at that location. When ceiling joists or rafter ties are located higher in the attic space, the rafter spans shall be multiplied by the factors given below:

FIGURE 24.11 (Continued)

H_C/H_R	Rafter Span Adjustment Factor
2/3 or greater	0.50
1/2	0.58
1/3	0.67
1/4	0.76
1/5	0.83
1/6	0.90
1/7.5 and less	1.00

where: H_C = Height of ceiling joists or rafter ties measured vertically above the top of the rafter support walls.

H_R = Height of roof ridge measured vertically above the top of the rafter support walls.

b. Span exceeds 26 feet in length. Check sources for availability of lumber in lengths greater than 20 feet.

FIGURE 24.11 This span table is suitable for determining rafters that do not support ceiling loads. Design loads include a live load of 20 psf and a dead load of either 10 psf or 20 psf.

RAFTER SPANS FOR COMMON LUMBER SPECIES
(Ground snow load=30 psf, ceiling not attached to rafters, L/Δ=180)

RAFTER SPACING (inches)	SPECIES AND GRADE		DEAD LOAD = 10 psf					DEAD LOAD = 20 psf				
			2 X 4	2 X 6	2 X 8	2 X 10	2 X 12	2 X 4	2 X 6	2 X 8	2 X 10	2 X 12
			Maximum rafter spansª									
			(feet - inches)	(feet - inches)	(feet - inches)	(feet - inches)	(feet - inches)	(feet - inches)	(feet - inches)	(feet - inches)	(feet - inches)	(feet - inches)
12	Douglas fir-larch	SS	10-0	15-9	20-9	Note b	Note b	10-0	15-9	20-1	24-6	Note b
	Douglas fir-larch	#1	9-8	14-9	18-8	22-9	Note b	9-0	13-2	16-8	20-4	23-7
	Douglas fir-larch	#2	9-5	13-9	17-5	21-4	24-8	8-5	12-4	15-7	19-1	22-1
	Douglas fir-larch	#3	7-1	10-5	13-2	16-1	18-8	6-4	9-4	11-9	14-5	16-8
	Hem-fir	SS	9-6	14-10	19-7	25-0	Note b	9-6	14-10	19-7	24-1	Note b
	Hem-fir	#1	9-3	14-4	18-2	22-2	25-9	8-9	12-10	16-3	19-10	23-0
	Hem-fir	#2	8-10	13-7	17-2	21-0	24-4	8-4	12-2	15-4	18-9	21-9
	Hem-fir	#3	7-1	10-5	13-2	16-1	18-8	6-4	9-4	11-9	14-5	16-8
	Southern pine	SS	9-10	15-6	20-5	Note b	Note b	9-10	15-6	20-5	Note b	Note b
	Southern pine	#1	9-8	15-2	20-0	24-9	Note b	9-8	14-10	18-8	22-2	Note b
	Southern pine	#2	9-6	14-5	18-8	22-3	Note b	9-0	12-11	16-8	19-11	23-4
	Southern pine	#3	7-7	11-2	14-3	16-10	20-0	6-9	10-0	12-9	15-1	17-11
	Spruce-pine-fir	SS	9-3	14-7	19-2	24-6	Note b	9-3	14-7	18-8	22-9	Note b
	Spruce-pine-fir	#1	9-1	13-9	17-5	21-4	24-8	8-5	12-4	15-7	19-1	22-1
	Spruce-pine-fir	#2	9-1	13-9	17-5	21-4	24-8	8-5	12-4	15-7	19-1	22-1
	Spruce-pine-fir	#3	7-1	10-5	13-2	16-1	18-8	6-4	9-4	11-9	14-5	16-8
16	Douglas fir-larch	SS	9-1	14-4	18-10	23-9	Note b	9-1	13-9	17-5	21-3	24-8
	Douglas fir-larch	#1	8-9	12-9	16-2	19-9	22-10	7-10	11-5	14-5	17-8	20-5
	Douglas fir-larch	#2	8-2	11-11	15-1	18-5	21-5	7-3	10-8	13-6	16-6	19-2
	Douglas fir-larch	#3	6-2	9-0	11-5	13-11	16-2	5-6	8-1	10-3	12-6	14-6
	Hem-fir	SS	8-7	13-6	17-10	22-9	Note b	8-7	13-6	17-1	20-10	24-2
	Hem-fir	#1	8-5	12-5	15-9	19-3	22-3	7-7	11-1	14-1	17-2	19-11
	Hem-fir	#2	8-0	11-9	14-11	18-2	21-1	7-2	10-6	13-4	16-3	18-10
	Hem-fir	#3	6-2	9-0	11-5	13-11	16-2	5-6	8-1	10-3	12-6	14-6
	Southern pine	SS	8-11	14-1	18-6	23-8	Note b	8-11	14-1	18-6	23-8	Note b
	Southern pine	#1	8-9	13-9	18-1	21-5	25-7	8-8	12-10	16-2	19-2	22-10
	Southern pine	#2	8-7	12-6	16-2	19-3	22-7	7-10	11-2	14-5	17-3	20-2
	Southern pine	#3	6-7	9-8	12-4	14-7	17-4	5-10	8-8	11-0	13-0	15-6
	Spruce-pine-fir	SS	8-5	13-3	17-5	22-1	25-7	8-5	12-9	16-2	19-9	22-10
	Spruce-pine-fir	#1	8-2	11-11	15-1	18-5	21-5	7-3	10-8	13-6	16-6	19-2
	Spruce-pine-fir	#2	8-2	11-11	15-1	18-5	21-5	7-3	10-8	13-6	16-6	19-2
	Spruce-pine-fir	#3	6-2	9-0	11-5	13-11	16-2	5-6	8-1	10-3	12-6	14-6
19.2	Douglas fir-larch	SS	8-7	13-6	17-9	21-8	25-2	8-7	12-6	15-10	19-5	22-6
	Douglas fir-larch	#1	7-11	11-8	14-9	18-0	20-11	7-1	10-5	13-2	16-1	18-8
	Douglas fir-larch	#2	7-5	10-11	13-9	16-10	19-6	6-8	9-9	12-4	15-1	17-6
	Douglas fir-larch	#3	5-7	8-3	10-5	12-9	14-9	5-0	7-4	9-4	11-5	13-2
	Hem-fir	SS	8-1	12-9	16-9	21-4	24-8	8-1	12-4	15-7	19-1	22-1
	Hem-fir	#1	7-9	11-4	14-4	17-7	20-4	6-11	10-2	12-10	15-8	18-2
	Hem-fir	#2	7-4	10-9	13-7	16-7	19-3	6-7	9-7	12-2	14-10	17-3
	Hem-fir	#3	5-7	8-3	10-5	12-9	14-9	5-0	7-4	9-4	11-5	13-2
	Southern pine	SS	8-5	13-3	17-5	22-3	Note b	8-5	13-3	17-5	22-0	25-9
	Southern pine	#1	8-3	13-0	16-6	19-7	23-4	7-11	11-9	14-9	17-6	20-11
	Southern pine	#2	7-11	11-5	14-9	17-7	20-7	7-1	10-2	13-2	15-9	18-5
	Southern pine	#3	6-0	8-10	11-3	13-4	15-10	5-4	7-11	10-1	11-11	14-2
	Spruce-pine-fir	SS	7-11	12-5	16-5	20-2	23-4	7-11	11-8	14-9	18-0	20-11
	Spruce-pine-fir	#1	7-5	10-11	13-9	16-10	19-6	6-8	9-9	12-4	15-1	17-6
	Spruce-pine-fir	#2	7-5	10-11	13-9	16-10	19-6	6-8	9-9	12-4	15-1	17-6
	Spruce-pine-fir	#3	5-7	8-3	10-5	12-9	14-9	5-0	7-4	9-4	11-5	13-2

FIGURE 24.12 (Continued)

RAFTER SPACING (Inches)	SPECIES AND GRADE		DEAD LOAD = 10 psf					DEAD LOAD = 20 psf				
			2 X 4	2 X 6	2 X 8	2 X 10	2 X 12	2 X 4	2 X 6	2 X 8	2 X 10	2 X 12
			Maximum rafter spans[a]									
			(feet - inches)	(feet - inches)	(feet - inches)	(feet - inches)	(feet - inches)	(feet - inches)	(feet - inches)	(feet - inches)	(feet - inches)	(feet - inches)
24	Douglas fir-larch	SS	7-11	12-6	15-10	19-5	22-6	7-8	11-3	14-2	17-4	20-1
	Douglas fir-larch	#1	7-1	10-5	13-2	16-1	18-8	6-4	9-4	11-9	14-5	16-8
	Douglas fir-larch	#2	6-8	9-9	12-4	15-1	17-6	5-11	8-8	11-0	13-6	15-7
	Douglas fir-larch	#3	5-0	7-4	9-4	11-5	13-2	4-6	6-7	8-4	10-2	11-10
	Hem-fir	SS	7-6	11-10	15-7	19-1	22-1	7-6	11-0	13-11	17-0	19-9
	Hem-fir	#1	6-11	10-2	12-10	15-8	18-2	6-2	9-1	11-6	14-0	16-3
	Hem-fir	#2	6-7	9-7	12-2	14-10	17-3	5-10	8-7	10-10	13-3	15-5
	Hem-fir	#3	5-0	7-4	9-4	11-5	13-2	4-6	6-7	8-4	10-2	11-10
	Southern pine	SS	7-10	12-3	16-2	20-8	25-1	7-10	12-3	16-2	19-8	23-0
	Southern pine	#1	7-8	11-9	14-9	17-6	20-11	7-1	10-6	13-2	15-8	18-8
	Southern pine	#2	7-1	10-2	13-2	15-9	18-5	6-4	9-2	11-9	14-1	16-6
	Southern pine	#3	5-4	7-11	10-1	11-11	14-2	4-9	7-1	9-0	10-8	12-8
	Spruce-pine-fir	SS	7-4	11-7	14-9	18-0	20-11	7-1	10-5	13-2	16-1	18-8
	Spruce-pine-fir	#1	6-8	9-9	12-4	15-1	17-6	5-11	8-8	11-0	13-6	15-7
	Spruce-pine-fir	#2	6-8	9-9	12-4	15-1	17-6	5-11	8-8	11-0	13-6	15-7
	Spruce-pine-fir	#3	5-0	7-4	9-4	11-5	13-2	4-6	6-7	8-4	10-2	11-10

Check sources for availability of lumber in lengths greater than 20 feet.

For SI: 1 inch = 25.4 mm, 1 foot = 304.8 mm, 1 pound per square foot = 0.0479 kN/m².

a. The tabulated rafter spans assume that ceiling joists are located at the bottom of the attic space or that some other method of resisting the outward push of the rafters on the bearing walls, such as rafter ties, is provided at that location. When ceiling joists or rafter ties are located higher in the attic space, the rafter spans shall be multiplied by the factors given below:

H_C/H_R	Rafter Span Adjustment Factor
2/3 or greater	0.50
1/2	0.58
1/3	0.67
1/4	0.76
1/5	0.83
1/6	0.90
1/7.5 and less	1.00

where: H_C = Height of ceiling joists or rafter ties measured vertically above the top of the rafter support walls.

H_R = Height of roof ridge measured vertically above the top of the rafter support walls.

b. Span exceeds 26 feet in length.

FIGURE 24.12 This span table is suitable for determining rafters that do not support ceiling loads with a ground snow load of 30 psf.

beam sizes without the use of tables. It examines methods used to solve beams, common notations in beam formulas, and the process for solving wood beams.

Methods of Beam Design

Professionals use four methods of beam design, including computer programs, a span computer, wood design books, and, of course, the old-fashioned way of pencil, paper, and a few formulas.

Computer Programs

Computer programs that size beams are available for many personal and business computers. Each national wood distributor supplies a program that can determine spans and needed materials and then prints out all appropriate stresses. Software that sizes beams made of wood, engi-

developers. Two popular programs include StruCalc™ by Cascade Consulting Associates and BeamChek™ by AC Software, Inc. Figure 24.15 shows the prompts for solving a hip using BeamChek. Websites for each firm appear in the list at the end of this chapter. These programs typically ask for loading information and then identify the span size within seconds. Using a computer program to solve beam spans is easy, but you must be able to answer questions that require an understanding of the basics of beam design and loading.

Span Computers

Western Wood Products offers DesignEasy-Joists, a span calculator for sizing uniformly loaded western lumber joist, rafters, headers and DesignEasy-Beams for sizing headers and beams. The Western Wood Products website or the iTunes App Store provides ordering information for each product.

FLOOR SPAN TABLES

Not all products are available in all markets.

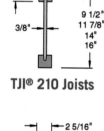

TJI® 110 Joists

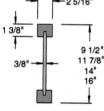

TJI® 210 Joists

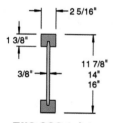

TJI® 230 Joists

TJI® 360 Joists

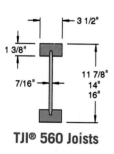

TJI® 560 Joists

L/480 Live Load Deflection

Depth	TJI®	40 PSF Live Load / 10 PSF Dead Load				40 PSF Live Load / 20 PSF Dead Load			
		12" o.c.	16" o.c.	19.2" o.c.	24" o.c.	12" o.c.	16" o.c.	19.2" o.c.	24" o.c.
9½"	110	16'-5"	15'-0"	14'-2"	13'-2"	16'-5"	15'-0"	13'-11"	12'-5"
	210	17'-3"	15'-9"	14'-10"	13'-10"	17'-3"	15'-9"	14'-10"	13'-8"
	230	17'-8"	16'-2"	15'-3"	14'-2"	17'-8"	16'-2"	15'-3"	14'-2"
11⅞"	110	19'-6"	17'-10"	16'-10"	15'-5"(1)	19'-6"	17'-3"	15'-8"	14'-0"(1)
	210	20'-6"	18'-8"	17'-8"	16'-5"	20'-6"	18'-8"	17'-3"	15'-5"(1)
	230	21'-0"	19'-2"	18'-1"	16'-10"	21'-0"	19'-2"	18'-1"	16'-3"(1)
	360	22'-11"	20'-11"	19'-8"	18'-4"	22'-11"	20'-11"	19'-8"	17'-10"(1)
	560	26'-1"	23'-8"	22'-4"	20'-9"	26'-1"	23'-8"	22'-4"	20'-9"(1)
14"	110	22'-2"	20'-3"	18'-9"	16'-9"(1)	21'-8"	18'-9"	17'-1"(1)	14'-7"(1)
	210	23'-3"	21'-3"	20'-0"	18'-4"(1)	23'-3"	20'-7"	18'-9"(1)	16'-2"(1)
	230	23'-10"	21'-9"	20'-6"	19'-1"	23'-10"	21'-8"	19'-9"	17'-1"(1)
	360	26'-0"	23'-8"	22'-4"	20'-9"(1)	26'-0"	23'-8"	22'-4"(1)	17'-10"(1)
	560	29'-6"	26'-10"	25'-4"	23'-6"	**29'-6"**	**26'-10"**	25'-4"(1)	20'-11"(1)
16"	210	25'-9"	23'-6"	22'-0"(1)	19'-5"(1)	25'-5"	22'-0"(1)	20'-1"(1)	16'-2"(1)
	230	26'-5"	24'-1"	22'-9"	20'-7"(1)	**26'-5"**	23'-2"	21'-2"(1)	17'-1"(1)
	360	28'-9"	26'-3"	24'-8"(1)	21'-5"(1)	**28'-9"**	26'-3"(1)	22'-4"(1)	17'-10"(1)
	560	32'-8"	29'-8"	28'-0"	25'-2"(1)	**32'-8"**	**29'-8"**	26'-3"(1)	20'-11"(1)

L/360 Live Load Deflection (Minimum Criteria per Code)

Depth	TJI®	40 PSF Live Load / 10 PSF Dead Load				40 PSF Live Load / 20 PSF Dead Load			
		12" o.c.	16" o.c.	19.2" o.c.	24" o.c.	12" o.c.	16" o.c.	19.2" o.c.	24" o.c.
9½"	110	18'-2"	16'-7"	15'-3"	13'-8"	17'-8"	15'-3"	13'-11"	12'-5"
	210	19'-1"	17'-5"	16'-6"	15'-0"	19'-1"	16'-9"	15'-4"	13'-8"
	230	19'-7"	17'-11"	16'-11"	15'-9"	19'-7"	17'-8"	16'-1"	14'-5"
11⅞"	110	21'-7"	18'-11"	17'-3"	15'-5"(1)	19'-11"	17'-3"	15'-8"	14'-0"(1)
	210	22'-8"	20'-8"	18'-11"	16'-10"	21'-10"	18'-11"	17'-3"	15'-5"(1)
	230	23'-3"	21'-3"	19'-11"	17'-9"	**23'-0"**	19'-11"	18'-2"	16'-3"(1)
	360	25'-4"	23'-2"	21'-10"	20'-4"(1)	**25'-4"**	**23'-2"**	**21'-10"(1)**	17'-10"(1)
	560	28'-10"	26'-3"	24'-9"	23'-0"	**28'-10"**	**26'-3"**	**24'-9"**	20'-11"(1)
14"	110	23'-9"	20'-6"	18'-9"	16'-9"(1)	21'-8"	18'-9"	17'-1"(1)	14'-7"(1)
	210	25'-8"	22'-6"	20'-7"	18'-4"(1)	23'-9"	20'-7"	18'-9"(1)	16'-2"(1)
	230	26'-4"	23'-9"	21'-8"	19'-4"(1)	**25'-0"**	21'-8"	19'-9"	17'-1"(1)
	360	28'-9"	26'-3"	24'-9"(1)	21'-5"(1)	**28'-9"**	**26'-3"(1)**	22'-4"(1)	17'-10"(1)
	560	32'-8"	29'-9"	28'-0"	25'-2"(1)	**32'-8"**	**29'-9"**	**26'-3"(1)**	20'-11"(1)
16"	210	27'-10"	24'-1"	22'-0"(1)	19'-5"(1)	25'-5"	22'-0"(1)	20'-1"(1)	16'-2"(1)
	230	29'-2"	25'-5"	23'-2"	20'-7"(1)	**26'-9"**	23'-2"	21'-2"(1)	17'-1"(1)
	360	31'-10"	29'-0"	26'-10"(1)	21'-5"(1)	**31'-10"**	**26'-10"(1)**	22'-4"(1)	17'-10"(1)
	560	36'-1"	32'-11"	31'-0"(1)	25'-2"(1)	**36'-1"**	**31'-6"(1)**	26'-3"(1)	20'-11"(1)

Long term deflection under dead load, which includes the effect of creep, has not been considered. **Bold italic** spans reflect initial dead load deflection exceeding 0.33".

(1) Web stiffeners are required at intermediate supports of continuous-span joists when the intermediate bearing length is *less* than 5¼" and the span on either side of the intermediate bearing is greater than the following spans:

TJI®	40 PSF Live Load / 10 PSF Dead Load				40 PSF Live Load / 20 PSF Dead Load			
	12" o.c.	16" o.c.	19.2" o.c.	24" o.c.	12" o.c.	16" o.c.	19.2" o.c.	24" o.c.
110	N.A.	N.A.	N.A.	15'-4"	N.A.	N.A.	16'-0"	12'-9"
210	N.A.	N.A.	21'-4"	17'-0"	N.A.	21'-4"	17'-9"	14'-2"
230	N.A.	N.A.	N.A.	19'-2"	N.A.	N.A.	19'-11"	15'-11"
360	N.A.	N.A.	24'-5"	19'-6"	N.A.	24'-5"	20'-4"	16'-3"
560	N.A.	N.A.	29'-10"	23'-10"	N.A.	29'-10"	24'-10"	19'-10"

FIGURE 24.13 Weyerhaeuser engineered TJI floor joist span tables.

ROOF SPAN TABLE

Maximum Horizontal Clear Spans—Roof

O.C. Spacing	Depth	TJI®	Non-Snow (125%) 20LL + 15DL Low	High	20LL + 20DL Low	High	Snow Load Area (115%) 25LL + 15DL Low	High	30LL + 15DL Low	High	40LL + 15DL Low	High	50LL + 15DL Low	High
16"	9 1/2"	110	19'-3"	17'-2"	18'-4"	16'-3"	18'-5"	16'-6"	17'-9"	15'-11"	16'-7"	15'-0"	15'-6"	14'-3"
		210	20'-5"	18'-2"	19'-5"	17'-3"	19'-6"	17'-6"	18'-9"	16'-11"	17'-7"	15'-11"	16'-7"	15'-1"
		230	21'-0"	18'-9"	20'-0"	17'-9"	20'-2"	18'-0"	19'-4"	17'-5"	18'-1"	16'-4"	17'-1"	15'-6"
	11 7/8"	110	23'-0"	20'-6"	21'-11"	19'-5"	22'-0"	19'-9"	20'-11"	19'-1"	19'-0"	17'-11"	17'-6"	16'-11"
		210	24'-4"	21'-9"	23'-3"	20'-7"	23'-4"	20'-11"	22'-5"	20'-2"	20'-10"	19'-0"	19'-2"	18'-0"
		230	25'-1"	22'-5"	23'-11"	21'-3"	24'-1"	21'-7"	23'-1"	20'-10"	21'-7"	19'-7"	20'-3"	18'-7"
		360	27'-9"	24'-9"	26'-5"	23'-5"	26'-7"	23'-10"	25'-6"	23'-0"	23'-11"	21'-7"	22'-7"	20'-6"
		560	31'-11"	28'-6"	30'-5"	27'-0"	30'-7"	27'-5"	29'-5"	26'-5"	27'-6"	24'-10"	26'-0"	23'-7"
	14"	110	26'-3"	23'-5"	25'-0"	22'-2"	24'-1"	22'-6"	22'-9"	21'-9"	20'-8"	19'-11"	19'-1"	18'-5"
		210	27'-9"	24'-9"	26'-5"	23'-5"	26'-5"	23'-9"	25'-0"	22'-11"	22'-8"	21'-7"	20'-11"	20'-3"
		230	28'-7"	25'-6"	27'-2"	24'-2"	27'-4"	24'-6"	26'-4"	23'-8"	23'-11"	22'-3"	22'-0"	21'-1"
		360	31'-6"	28'-2"	30'-0"	26'-8"	30'-2"	27'-1"	29'-0"	26'-1"	27'-2"	24'-7"	25'-8"	23'-4"
		560	36'-3"	32'-4"	34'-6"	30'-7"	34'-8"	31'-1"	33'-4"	30'-0"	31'-2"	28'-3"	29'-6"	26'-9"
	16"	210	30'-9"	27'-5"	29'-4"	26'-0"	28'-3"	26'-5"	26'-9"	25'-6"	24'-3"	23'-4"	22'-4"	21'-8"
		230	31'-8"	28'-3"	30'-2"	26'-9"	29'-10"	27'-2"	28'-2"	26'-3"	25'-7"	24'-7"	23'-7"	22'-10"
		360	34'-11"	31'-2"	33'-3"	29'-6"	33'-5"	30'-0"	32'-2"	28'-11"	30'-1"	27'-2"	26'-0"	25'-10"
		560	40'-1"	35'-9"	38'-2"	33'-11"	38'-4"	34'-5"	36'-11"	33'-2"	34'-6"	31'-3"	31'-8"	29'-8"
19.2"	9 1/2"	110	18'-1"	16'-1"	17'-3"	15'-3"	17'-4"	15'-6"	16'-8"	15'-0"	15'-5"	14'-1"	14'-2"	13'-4"
		210	19'-2"	17'-1"	18'-3"	16'-2"	18'-4"	16'-5"	17'-8"	15'-10"	16'-6"	14'-11"	15'-7"	14'-2"
		230	19'-9"	17'-7"	18'-10"	16'-8"	18'-11"	16'-11"	18'-2"	16'-4"	17'-0"	15'-4"	16'-1"	14'-7"
	11⅞"	110	21'-7"	19'-3"	20'-7"	18'-3"	20'-3"	18'-6"	19'-1"	17'-11"	19'-0"	17'-10"	17'-6"	16'-11"
		210	22'-11"	20'-5"	21'-10"	19'-4"	21'-11"	19'-8"	20'-11"	18'-11"	20'-0"	18'-4"	18'-5"	17'-5"
		230	23'-7"	21'-1"	22'-6"	19'-11"	22'-7"	20'-3"	21'-8"	19'-6"	20'-3"	18'-5"	18'-8"	17'-10"
		360	26'-1"	23'-3"	24'-10"	22'-0"	24'-11"	22'-4"	24'-0"	21'-7"	22'-5"	20'-3"	21'-2"	19'-3"
		560	30'-0"	26'-9"	28'-7"	25'-4"	28'-8"	25'-9"	27'-7"	24'-10"	25'-9"	23'-4"	24'-4"	22'-2"
	14"	110	24'-6"	22'-0"	22'-9"	20'-10"	22'-0"	20'-11"	20'-9"	19'-10"	18'-10"	18'-2"	17'-0"	16'-10"
		210	26'-0"	23'-3"	24'-10"	22'-0"	24'-2"	22'-4"	22'-10"	21'-7"	21'-10"	20'-11"	20'-1"	19'-5"
		230	26'-10"	23'-11"	25'-7"	22'-8"	25'-5"	23'-0"	24'-0"	22'-3"	22'-3"	20'-8"	20'-6"	19'-7"
		360	29'-7"	26'-5"	28'-2"	25'-0"	28'-4"	25'-5"	27'-3"	24'-6"	25'-6"	23'-1"	23'-8"	21'-5"
		560	34'-0"	30'-4"	32'-5"	28'-9"	32'-7"	29'-2"	31'-4"	28'-2"	29'-3"	26'-6"	26'-5"	25'-2"
	16"	210	28'-8"	25'-9"	26'-9"	24'-5"	25'-10"	24'-6"	24'-5"	23'-4"	22'-1"	21'-4"	20'-9"	19'-8"
		230	29'-9"	26'-7"	28'-2"	25'-2"	27'-3"	25'-6"	25'-9"	24'-7"	23'-4"	22'-6"	21'-7"	20'-9"
		360	32'-10"	29'-3"	31'-3"	27'-9"	31'-5"	28'-2"	30'-2"	27'-2"	25'-7"	25'-3"	21'-7"	21'-8"
		560	37'-8"	33'-7"	35'-10"	31'-10"	36'-0"	32'-4"	34'-8"	31'-2"	31'-3"	29'-4"	26'-5"	25'-5"
24"	9 1/2"	110	16'-9"	14'-11"	15'-11"	14'-2"	16'-0"	14'-4"	15'-2"	13'-10"	13'-11"	13'-1"	12'-8"	12'-3"
		210	17'-9"	15'-10"	16'-11"	15'-0"	17'-0"	15'-3"	16'-4"	14'-8"	14'-8"	13'-10"	13'-11"	13'-1"
		230	18'-3"	16'-4"	17'-5"	15'-5"	17'-6"	15'-8"	16'-10"	15'-2"	15'-8"	14'-3"	14'-8"	13'-6"
	11 7/8"	110	20'-0"	17'-10"	18'-9"	16'-11"	18'-1"	17'-2"	17'-1"	16'-4"	17'-0"	16'-6"	15'-0"	15'-2"
		210	21'-2"	18'-11"	20'-2"	17'-11"	19'-10"	18'-2"	18'-9"	17'-7"	17'-0"	17'-0"	16'-6"	16'-0"
		230	21'-10"	19'-6"	20'-10"	18'-5"	20'-11"	18'-9"	19'-9"	18'-1"	17'-11"	17'-0"	17'-3"	17'-4"
		360	24'-1"	21'-6"	23'-0"	20'-5"	23'-1"	20'-8"	22'-2"	20'-0"	20'-5"	18'-9"	17'-3"	17'-4"
		560	27'-9"	24'-9"	26'-5"	23'-6"	26'-7"	23'-10"	25'-6"	23'-0"	23'-10"	21'-7"	21'-1"	20'-3"
	14"	110	21'-10"	20'-4"	20'-4"	19'-1"	19'-8"	18'-8"	18'-7"	17'-9"	16'-0"	16'-3"	13'-7"	14'-2"
		210	24'-0"	21'-6"	22'-4"	20'-5"	21'-7"	20'-6"	20'-4"	19'-6"	17'-10"	17'-9"	15'-0"	16'-7"
		230	24'-10"	22'-2"	23'-7"	21'-0"	22'-9"	21'-4"	21'-6"	20'-6"	19'-6"	18'-9"	16'-11"	17'-4"
		360	27'-5"	24'-6"	26'-1"	23'-2"	26'-3"	23'-6"	25'-0"	22'-8"	20'-5"	20'-2"	17'-3"	17'-4"
		560	31'-6"	28'-1"	30'-0"	26'-8"	30'-2"	27'-0"	29'-0"	26'-1"	24'-11"	23'-7"	21'-1"	20'-3"
	16"	210	25'-8"	23'-11"	23'-11"	22'-4"	23'-1"	21'-11"	21'-9"	20'-1"	20'-0"	19'-4"	16'-11"	16'-7"
		230	27'-1"	24'-7"	25'-2"	23'-3"	24'-4"	23'-1"	23'-0"	22'-0"	20'-5"	20'-2"	17'-3"	17'-4"
		360	30'-4"	27'-1"	28'-11"	25'-8"	28'-2"	26'-1"	25'-0"	24'-1"	24'-11"	23'-7"	21'-1"	20'-3"
		560	34'-10"	31'-2"	33'-2"	29'-6"	33'-4"	29'-11"	30'-6"	28'-3"	24'-11"	23'-7"	21'-1"	20'-3"

FIGURE 24.14 Weyerhaeuser engineered TJI rafter span tables.

Span Tables for Beams

Other practical methods of sizing beams are found in books published by various wood associations. Two of the most common span books used in architectural offices are *Wood Structural Design Data* from the **National Forest Products Association** and *Western Woods Use Book* from the Western Wood Products Association. These books contain design information of wood members, standard formulas, and design tables that provide beam loads for a specific span. Table 24.3 shows a partial listing for the 8' span table. By following the instructions provided with the table, information on size, span, and loading patterns can be determined.

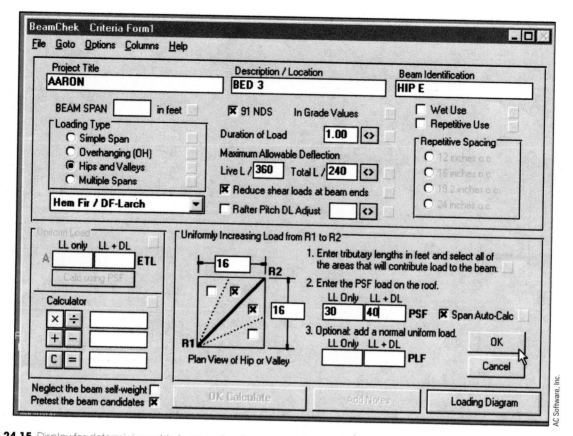

FIGURE 24.15 Display for determining a hip beam using the program BeamChek developed by AC Software, Inc.

Beam Formulas

The final method of beam design is to use standard formulas to determine how the beam will be stressed. Figure 24.16 shows the formulas and the loading, shear, and moment diagrams for a simple beam. These are diagrams that can be drawn by the designer to determine where the maximum stress will occur. With a simple beam and a uniformly distributed load, the diagrams typically are not drawn because the results remain constant.

Notations for Formulas

Engineering and architectural communities have adopted standard symbols to simplify the design of beams. Many symbols have been introduced throughout this chapter. Table 24.4 gives a list of the notations needed to design residential beams. Notice that some are written in upper-case letters and some in lowercase letters. Uppercase letters, such as W and L, represent measurements expressed in feet. W is the total load in pounds per square foot; L is the beam span in feet. Lowercase letters represent measurements expressed in inches. The letters b and d represent the beam size in inches, and l represents the beam span in inches. As a beginning technician, you need not understand why the formulas work, but it is important to know the notations used in the formulas.

Sizing Wood Beams Using Standard Formulas

Wood beams can be determined using the following steps:

1. Determine the area to be supported by the beam.
2. Determine the weight supported by 1 linear foot of beam.
3. Determine the reactions.
4. Determine the pier sizes.
5. Determine the horizontal shear.
6. Determine the bending moment.
7. Determine the deflection.

Step 1: Determining the Area to Be Supported

To determine the size of a beam, determine the weight the beam must support. To find the weight, find the area the beam is to support and multiply it by the total loads. Figure 24.17 shows a sample floor plan with a beam of undetermined size. The beam is supporting an area 10'-0" long (the span). Floor joists are being supported on each side of the beam. Chapter 23 covers methods of load dispersal.

In this example, each joist on each side of the beam can be thought of as a simple beam. Half of the weight of

TABLE 24.3 Partial Listing of a Typical Span Table

Once W, w, F_b, E, and F_v are known, spans can be determined for a simple beam. See Appendix G on the Student website.

WOOD BEAMS—SAFE LOAD TABLES

Symbols used in the tables are as follows:

F_b = Allowable unit stress in extreme fiber in bending, psi.

W = Total uniformly distributed load, pounds

w = Load per linear foot of beam, pounds

F_v = Horizontal shear stress, psi, induced by load W

E = Modulus of elasticity, 100 psi, induced by load W for l/360 limit

Beam sizes are expressed as nominal sizes, inches, but calculations are based on net dimensions of S4S sizes.

SIZE OF BEAM		F_b									
		900	1000	1100	1200	1300	1400	1500	1600	1800	2000
		8'–0" SPAN									
2 × 14	W	3291	3657	4023	4389	4754	5120	5486	5852	6583	7315
	w	411	457	502	548	594	640	685	731	822	914
	F_v	124	138	151	165	179	193	207	220	248	276
	E	489	543	597	652	706	760	815	869	978	1086
6 × 8	W	3867	4296	4726	5156	5585	6015	6445	6875	734	8593
	w	483	537	590	644	698	751	805	859	966	1074
	F_v	70	78	85	93	101	109	117	125	140	156
	E	864	960	1055	1152	1247	1343	1439	1535	1727	1919
4 × 10	W	3743	4159	4575	4991	5407	5823	6238	6654	7486	8318
	w	467	519	571	623	675	727	779	831	935	1039
	F_v	86	96	105	115	125	134	144	154	173	192
	E	700	778	856	934	1011	1089	1167	1245	1401	1556
3 × 12	W	3955	4394	4833	5273	5712	6152	6591	7031	7910	8789
	w	494	549	604	659	714	769	823	878	988	1098
	F_v	105	117	128	140	152	164	175	187	210	234
	E	576	640	704	768	832	896	959	1024	1151	1279

Courtesy American Wood Council, Leesburg, VA

each joist on side A will be supported by a wall and half of the weight of joist A will be supported by the beam. Because the total length of the joist on side A is 10', the beam will support 5' (half the length of each joist) of floor on side A. This 5'-wide area is referred to as a tributary area. In this case, it is tributary load A. On the right side of the beam, tributary load B is 5' wide (half of the total span of 10').

A *tributary width* is defined as the accumulation of loads that are directed to a structural member. The tributary width will always be half of the distance between the beam and the next bearing point. A second point to remember about tributary loads is that the total tributary width will always be half of the total distance between the bearing points on each side of the beam, no matter where the beam is located. Figure 24.18 shows why this is true.

Once the tributary width is known, determine the total area that the beam is supporting. Adding the width of tributary $A + B$ and then multiplying this sum by the beam length measured in feet, represented by L, determines the area that the beam will support. For the beam in Figure 24.17, the area is (5' + 5') (10') = 100 sq ft. Using the loads from Figure 23.3, determine the loads for floors. The live load for a floor is 40 lb, the dead load is 10 lb, and the total load is 50 lb. By multiplying the area by the load per square foot, the total load (W) can be determined. For this example, with an area of 100 sq ft and a total load of 50 psf, the total load is 5000 lb. The letter W in beam formulas represents the total load.

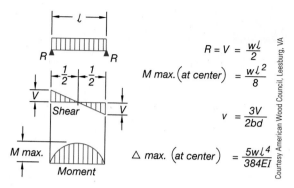

Courtesy American Wood Council, Leesburg, VA

$$R = V = \frac{wl}{2}$$

$$M \text{ max.} (\text{at center}) = \frac{wl^2}{8}$$

$$v = \frac{3V}{2bd}$$

$$\triangle \text{ max.} (\text{at center}) = \frac{5wl^4}{384EI}$$

FIGURE 24.16 Loading, shear, and moment diagrams for simple beam with uniform loads, showing where stress will affect a beam and the formulas for computing these stresses.

TABLE 24.4 Common Notations Used in Beam Formulas

BEAM FORMULA NOTATIONS

b	=	breadth of beam in inches
d	=	depth of beam in inches
D	=	deflection due to load
E	=	modulus of elasticity
F_b	=	allowable unit stress in extreme fiber bending
F_v	=	unit stress in horizontal shear
I	=	moment of inertia of the section
l	=	span of beam in inches
L	=	span of beam in feet
M	=	bending or resisting moment
P	=	total concentrated load in pounds
S	=	section modulus
$V = R$	=	end reaction of beam
W	=	total uniformly distributed load in pounds
w	=	load per linear foot of beam in pounds

© Cengage Learning 2014

> ## NOTE:
>
> If you're using a computer program to solve beam sizes, it may prompt you to provide the total load or the total live load and the total dead load. For this example, the total dead load is 10 lb × 100 sq ft, or 1000 lb. The total live load is 40 lb × 100 sq ft, or 4000 lb. Although this may seem obvious, the sum of the total live load and the total dead load should equal the total load supported. Taking the time to check the obvious can help to eliminate stupid human errors.

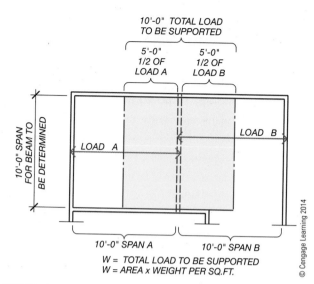

W = TOTAL LOAD TO BE SUPPORTED
W = AREA x WEIGHT PER SQ.FT.

© Cengage Learning 2014

FIGURE 24.17 A floor plan with a beam to be determined. This beam is supporting an area of 100 sq ft, with an assumed weight of 40 psf LL, 10 psf DL, and 50 psf total load. When solving problems manually, the total load of W = 5000 lb can be used. Computers programs often require loads to be divided by the dead and live load for each side of the beam. The tributary loads A and B are each 2,2000-lb LL and 500-lb DL.

> ## NOTE:
>
> Last reminder! If you're using a computer program to solve beam sizes, some programs ask for the combined loads and some ask for the live and dead loads separately. Take time to verify what the prompt is asking for.

Step 2: Determining Linear Weight

In some formulas, only the weight per linear foot of beam is desired rather than the total load. The letter w represents the weight per linear foot on the beam. In Figure 24.19, it can be seen that w is the product of the area to be supported (the total tributary width), multiplied by the weight per square foot. This can also be calculated by dividing the total weight (W) by the length of the beam. In this example, if the span (L) is 10', w = 5000/10 or 500 lb.

Step 3: Determining Reactions

Even before the size of a beam is known, the supports for the beam can be determined. The letter R, for reactions, represents these supports. The letter V is also sometimes used in place of the letter R. On a simple beam, half of the weight the beam is supporting (W) is dispersed to each end. In the example, W = 5000 lb and R = 2500 lb. At this point W, w, and R have been determined (W = 5000 lb, w = 500 lb, and R = 2500 lb).

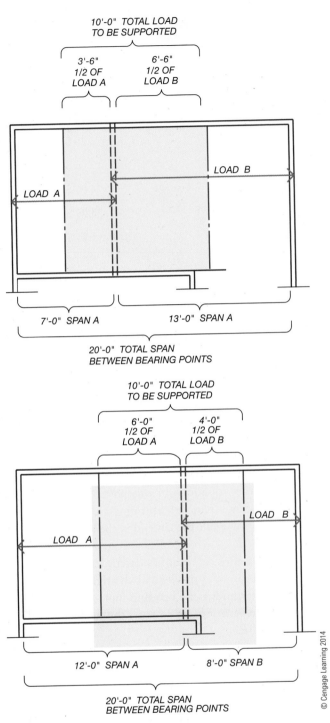

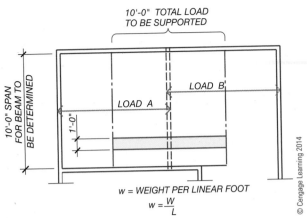

FIGURE 24.19 Determining linear weights. For an area of 10 sq ft, with an assumed weight of 50 psf, w = 500 lb.

FIGURE 24.18 The sum of the tributary widths is equal to half the total distance between the bearing point on each side of the beam being determined. With a total width of 20', the tributary width supported by the beam will be 10' no matter where the beam is placed.

Step 4: Determining Pier Sizes

The *reaction* is the load from the beam that must be transferred to the soil. The reaction from the beam will be transferred by a post to the floor and foundation system. A concrete pier supports the loads at the foundation level. To determine the size of the pier, the working stress of the concrete and the bearing value of the soil must be considered.

In residential construction, concrete with a working stress between 2000 to 3500 psi is typically used. The working stress of concrete specifies the amount of weight in pounds that each square inch (psi) of concrete surface can support. It would seem that if each square inch of concrete can support 2500 lb, only 1 sq in. of concrete would be required to support a load of 2500 lb. The bearing value of the soil must also be considered. The pier size is determined by dividing the load to be supported (R) by the soil pressure.

See Table 24.5 for safe soil-loading values. Many building departments use either 1500 or 2000 psf for the assumed safe working value of soil. Don't skim over these numbers. The concrete is listed in pounds per square inch. Soil is listed in pounds per square foot. A pier supporting 2500 lb must be divided by the assumed soil-bearing value to find the area of the pier needed. Using a bearing value of 2000 lb will result in an area of 1.25 sq ft of concrete needed to support the load. See Table 24.6 to determine the size of pier needed to obtain the proper soil support area.

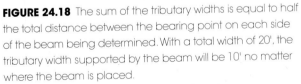

NOTE:

Piers located under the stem wall are typically square because they are dug with a shovel or a backhoe. Piers located in what will be the crawl space or below a slab are typically round because they are formed with pre-manufactured forms.

Step 5: Determining Horizontal Shear

To compute the size of the beam required to resist the forces of horizontal shear, use this formula:

$$F_v = \frac{(3)\,(v)}{(2)\,(b)\,(d)} = \# < 85 \quad \text{(the safe design value for DFL lumber).}$$

This formula determines the minimum *2bd* value needed to resist the load of 5000 lb. For a simple beam $V = R$, and R has been determined to be 2500 lb. To determine the *b* and *d* values, use the actual size of the beam. Since you don't know the size of beam to use, the *b* and *d* values remain unknown. Divide the *3V* value, by the safe limits for the wood (85) to solve this problem, and determine the needed *2bd* value to resist the 5000-lb load as follows:

$$F_v = \frac{(3)\,(v)}{85} = \# < 2bd$$ (The required *2bd* value to resist the load).

$$F_v = \frac{(3)\,(2500)}{85} = 88.23$$ (The minimum *2bd* value needed. The *2bd* value of the selected beam must exceed this value).

Use Table 24.7 to find a *2bd* value that exceeds 88.23. A 4 × 14 or 6 × 10 will meet the requirements of horizontal shear. Now solve for the required bending moment.

TABLE 24.5 Safe Soil-Bearing Values

PRESUMPTIVE LOAD-BEARING VALUES OF FOUNDATION MATERIALS[a]

Class Of Material	Load-Bearing Pressure (Pounds Per Square Foot)
Crystalline bedrock	12,000
Sedimentary and foliated rock	4,000
Sandy gravel and/or gravel (GW and GP)	3,000
Sand, silty sand, clayey sand, silty gravel and clayey gravel (SW, SP, SM, SC, GM and GC)	2,000
Clay, sandy clay, silty clay, clayey silt, silt and sandy silt (CI, ML, MH and CH)	1,500[b]

For SI: 1 psf = 0.0479 kN/m² .

a. When soil tests are required by Section R401.4, the allowable bearing capacities of the soil shall be part of the recommendations.

b. Where the building official determines that in-place soils with an allowable bearing capacity of less than 1,500 psf are likely to be present at the site, the allowable bearing capacity shall be determined by a soils investigation.

Reproduced from 2012 International Residential Building Code®.

TABLE 24.6 Common Pier Areas and Sizes

PIER AREAS AND SIZES

ROUND PIERS (interior)	SQUARE PIERS (exterior)
15" DIA. = 1.23 SQ FT	15" SQ = 1.56 SQ FT
18" DIA. = 1.77 SQ FT	18" SQ = 2.25 SQ FT
21" DIA. = 2.40 SQ FT	21" SQ = 3.06 SQ FT
24" DIA. = 3.14 SQ FT	24" SQ = 4.00 SQ FT
27" DIA. = 3.97 SQ FT	27" SQ = 5.06 SQ FT
30" DIA. = 4.90 SQ FT	30" SQ = 6.25 SQ FT
36" DIA. = 7.07 SQ FT	36" SQ = 9.00 SQ FT
42" DIA. = 9.60 SQ FT	42" SQ = 12.25 SQ FT

The area of the concrete pier can be determined by dividing the load to be supported by the soil-bearing pressure. Areas are shown for common pier sizes. Round piers are typically used for interiors, and square piers are generally used when piers are added to support the exterior foundation.

© Cengage Learning 2014

Step 6: Determining the Bending Moment

A *moment* is the tendency of a force to cause rotation about a certain point. In figuring a simple beam, W is the force and R is the point around which the force rotates. Think of a simple beam supported by two posts. If the post at the right end of beam is removed, the right end of the beam will rotate downward, while the left end of the beam and the left post remained fixed. The tendency to rotate (the moment) of the right end of the beam is determined based on the load on the beam and distance of the right post from the left post. Determining the bending moment will calculate the size of the beam needed to resist the tendency for W to rotate around R.

To determine the size of the beam required to resist the force (W), use the following formula:

$$M = \frac{(w)\,(l^2)}{8}$$

Once the moment is known, divide it by the F_b value of the wood to determine the size of the beam required to resist the load ($S = M/F_b$). Simplify this whole process using the following formula:

$$S = \frac{(3)\,(w)\,(L^2)}{(2)\,(F_b)}$$

Because F_b values for 4× members are size-dependent, it is important to solve for horizontal shear before solving

TABLE 24.7 Structural Properties of Wood Beams

Columns (2) (b) (d) and (384) (E) (I) can be used in the horizontal shear and deflection formulas. These two columns are set up for Douglas fir no. 2. For different types of wood, use NDS values for these columns.

PROPERTIES OF STRUCTURAL LUMBER

NOMINAL SIZE	(b) (d)	(2) (b) (d)	S	A	I	(384) (E) (I)*
2 × 6	1.5 × 5.5	16.5	7.6	8.25	20.8	12,780
2 × 8	1.5 × 7.25	21.75	13.1	10.875	47.6	29,245
2 × 10	1.5 × 9.25	27.75	21.4	13.875	98.9	60,764
2 × 12	1.5 × 11.25	33.75	31.6	16.875	177.9	109,302
2 × 14	1.5 × 13.25	39.75	43.9	19.875	290.8	178,668
4 × 6	3.5 × 5.5	38.5	17.6	19.25	48.5	29,798
4 × 8	3.5 × 7.25	50.75	30.7	25.375	111.0	68,198
4 × 10	3.5 × 9.25	64.75	49.9	32.375	230.8	141,804
4 × 12	3.5 × 11.25	78.75	73.8	39.375	415.3	255,160
4 × 14	3.5 × 13.5	94.5	106.3	47.250	717.6	440,893
6 × 8	5.5 × 7.5	82.5	51.6	41.25	193.4	118,825
6 × 10	5.5 × 9.5	104.5	82.7	32.25	393.0	241,459
6 × 12	5.5 × 11.5	126.5	121.2	63.25	697.1	428,298
6 × 14	5.5 × 13.5	148.5	167.1	74.25	1127.7	692,859

*384 × E × I values are listed in units per million, with E value assumed to be 1.6 for DFL.

© Cengage Learning 2014

the bending moment. If you solve for S first, you'll need to guess a beam size for a starting point. To determine if a 4 × 10 DFL #2 is suitable, use the values for Douglas fir from Table 24.2. According to Table 24.2 the base value for a 4 × 10 DFL#2 is 875, with a modifier of 1.2, and with the increased value of 1050. Apply the 1050 value to the formula to solve the beam shown in Figure 24.17:

$$S = \frac{(3)\,(500)\,(100)}{(2)\,(1050)} = \frac{150,000}{2100} = 71.4 = S$$

This formula determines the section modulus required to support a load of 5000 lb. Look at Table 24.7 to determine if a 4 × 10 is adequate. Select a beam with an S value larger than the S value found. By examining the S column of the table, you will find that a 4 × 10 has an S value of only 49.9, so the beam is not adequate. Because it was determined that a 6 × 10 is safe for horizontal shear, check to see if it will provide the needed section modulus. Determine the F_b value for a 6 × 10 of 1350 by using Table 24.2. The formula 150,000/2700 requires a minimum S value of 55.6. Table 24.7 shows that a 6 × 8 has an S value of only 55.6, which makes it unsuitable. A 6 × 10

has an S value of 82.7, which is suitable to resist the forces of bending moment.

Step 7: Determining Deflection

Deflection is the amount of sag in a beam. Deflection limits are determined by building codes and are expressed as a fraction of an inch in relation to the span of the beam in inches. Limits set by the IRC are:

l/360 Floors and ceilings
l/240 Roofs under 3/12 pitch, tile roofs, and vaulted ceilings
l/180 Roofs over 3/12 pitch

To determine deflection limits, the maximum allowable limit must be known. Use the formula:

$$D_{max} = \frac{L \times 12}{360} = \text{maximum allowable deflection.}$$

This formula requires the span in feet (L) to be multiplied by 12 (12" per ft) and then divided by 360 (the safe limit for floors and ceiling).

In the example used in this chapter, L equals 10'. The maximum safe limit is:

$$D_{max} = \frac{L \times 12}{360} = \frac{10 \times 12}{360} = D = \frac{120}{360} = 0.33"$$

= maximum allowable deflection.

The maximum amount the beam is allowed to sag is 0.33". Now determine how much the beam will actually sag under the load it is supporting.

The values for E and I must be known before determining the deflection. These values are shown in Table 24.7. You must also know l^3 and W, but these values are not available in tables. W has been determined to be 5000 lb. For our example:

$$l = 10 \times 12 = 120$$

$$l^3 = (l)(l)(l) = (120)(120)(120) = 1{,}728{,}000 \text{ or } 1.728$$

Because the E value was reduced from 1,600,000 to 1.6, change the l^3 value from 1,728,000 to 1.728 or 1.73. These numbers are easier to use for calculating. To determine how much a beam will sag, use the following formula:

$$D = \frac{5(w)(l^3)}{(384)(E)(I)} \text{ or } D = 22.5\frac{(w)(l^3)}{(E)(I)}$$

The values determined thus far are $W = 5000$, $w = 500$, $R = V = 2500$, $L = 10$, $l = 120$, $l^3 = 1.73$, and $I = 393$ (see Table 24.7, column I). Find the value of $(384)(E)(I)$ for a 6×10 beam from Table 24.7 (241,459). Now insert the values into the formula:

$$D = \frac{5(w)(l^3)}{(384)(E)(I)} = \frac{5 \times 5000 \times 1.73}{241{,}459} = \frac{43{,}200}{241{,}459} = 0.178"$$

Because 0.178" is less than the maximum allowable deflection of 0.33", a 6×10 beam can be used to safely support the load.

Review

In what may seem like an endless string of formulas, tables, and values, you have determined the loads and stresses on a 10' beam. The following seven basic steps were required:

1. Determine the values for W, w, L, l, l^3, and R.
   W = area to be supported × weight (LL + DL)
   $w = W/L$

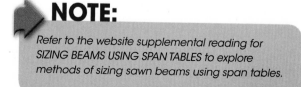

NOTE:
Refer to the website supplemental reading for SIZING BEAMS USING SPAN TABLES to explore methods of sizing sawn beams using span tables.

L = span in feet
l = span in inches
$l^3 = (l)(l)(l)$ (express this value in parts per million)
$R = V = W/2$

2. Determine post supports: $R = W/2$
3. Determine piers size: R / assumed soil bearing pressure
4. Determine F_v:

$$F_v = \frac{(3)(V)}{(2)(b)(d)} = \# < 85 \text{ or } \frac{(3)(V)}{85} = \# > (2)(b)(d)$$

5. Determine S:

$$S = \frac{(3)(w)(L^2)}{(2)(F_b)}$$

6. Determine the value for D_{max} based on what the beam will support:

$$D = l/360 \text{ or } l/240 \text{ or } l/180$$

7. Determine D:

$$D = \frac{(5)(w)(l^3)}{(384)(E)(I)}$$

Practice. Figure 24.20 shows a floor plan with a ridge beam that needs to be determined. The beam will be DFL with no snow loads. Use the following seven steps to determine the size of the beam.

Step 1. Determine the values.
   $W = 10 \times 12 \times 40 \times 4800$ lb
   $w = W/L = 4800/12 = 400$ lb
   $R = V = 2400$
   $L = 12'$
   $L^2 = 144$
   $l = 12' \times 12" = 144$
   $l^3 = 2.986$

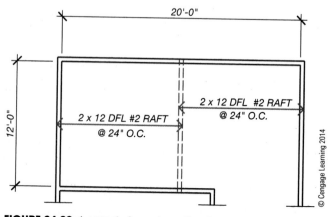

20'-0"

12'-0"

2 x 12 DFL #2 RAFT @ 24" O.C.

2 x 12 DFL #2 RAFT @ 24" O.C.

© Cengage Learning 2014

FIGURE 24.20 A sample floor plan with a beam of undetermined size.

F_b = (see Table 24.2 or 24.28)
F_v = 85 max (Table 24.2 or 24.28)
E = 1.6 max (Table 24.2 or 24.28)

Step 2. Determine reactions:

$$R = W/2 = 2400$$

Step 3. Determine piers. R/soil value (assume 2000 lb):

$$\frac{2400}{2000} = 1.2 \text{ sq ft}$$

According to Table 24.6, use either a 15" diameter or 15" square pier.

Step 4. Determine the section modulus:

$$S = \frac{(3)\,(w)\,(L^2)}{(2)\,(F_b)} = \frac{3 \times 400 \times 144}{2 \times 1350} = \frac{172,800}{2700}$$

= required section modulus = 64.

Because a 6 × 10 beam has a section modulus of 82.7 units of stress, it will be safe.

Step 5. Determine horizontal shear. The value from Table 24.7 or 24.28 is 85:

$$\frac{(3)\,(V)}{85} = \frac{3 \times 2400}{85} = \frac{7200}{85} = 84.70$$

According to Table 24.7, a 4 × 14 and a 6 × 10 each have a 2bd value larger than the required value of 84.70. Each of these beams, and any larger beam will meet the stress from horizontal shear:

Step 6. Determine D_{max}:

$$D_{max} = \frac{l}{180} = \frac{144}{180} = 0.8"$$

Step 7. Determine D:

$$D = \frac{(5)\,(W)\,(l^3)}{(384)\,(E)\,(I)} = \frac{5 \times 4800 \times 2.986}{384 \times 1.6 \times 393}$$

$$D = \frac{71,664}{241,459} = D = 0.296$$

Wood Adjustment Factors

To this point you've been introduced to the basics of solving simple beams using the NDF base design values for the particular species based on the size of the member. These values provide an accurate but conservative description of how a specific member can be used. Building codes and the NDS guidelines allow the beam values to be adjusted based on conditions that will reflect the true use of the structural member. These reductions include repetitive use, load duration, moisture and temperature content, size, and shear stress.

Repetitive Use Factor

When a load is spread over several members, a reduction in the F_b value is allowed. The fiber bending value of lumber 2" and 4" thick placed repetitively can be applied if all of the following conditions are met:

- The structural members receiving the reductions must be placed at 24" maximum spacing.
- A minimum of three members are used in the pattern.
- Each of the structural members are joined by sheathing or decking.

When all three conditions are met, an increase in the F_b value can be used. The increase is $F_b \times 1.15$. If you're using a computer program to solve beams, this adjustment will usually be made automatically if you specify repetitive use.

Load Duration Factor

Tests have shown that a piece of lumber can carry greater maximum loads over a short period of time than over a long period of time. When a wood member supports a load for a short duration, the member returns to its original shape when the load is reduced. When the load is supported for a long period of time, the member becomes permanently deformed. Design standards generally recognize several common duration periods that affect the maximum live load. These load factors include permanent, normal, two months, seven days, wind or earthquake, and impact. When supporting two or more loads of different duration, the factors are not cumulative. Use the load duration factor that best represents the lifetime of the load. Because wind, earthquake, and impact loads can vary so widely, base them on local codes and consult with a licensed professional. If you're using a computer program to determine beam sizes, this adjustment will usually be made automatically.

Laminated Beams

Two beam problems have now been solved using the tables in this chapter. Both beams were chosen from standard sawn lumber. Often, glu-lams are used because of their superior strength. Using a glu-lam can greatly reduce the depth of a beam as compared with conventional lumber. Glu-lam beams are determined in the same manner as standard lumber, but different values are used based on values provided by the **American Institute of Timber Construction** (see Table 24.8). Table 24.9 gives values for glu-lams made of Douglas fir. You will also need to consult the safe values for glu-lam beams. For beams constructed of Douglas fir, the values are:

$$F_b = 2200,\ F_v = 165,\ \text{and } E = 1.7.$$

TABLE 24.8 Comparative Values of Common Framing Lumber with Laminated Beams of Equal Materials

BASE DESIGN VALUES FOR BEAMS & STRINGERS

Species and Commercial Grade	Extreme Fiber Bending F_b	Horizontal Shear F_v	Modulus of Elasticity E
DFL #1	1350	85	1,600,000
24F_b V4 DF/DF	2400	165	1,700,000
Hem Fir #1	1050	70	1,300,000
24F_b E-2 HF/HF	2400	155	1,700,000
SPF #1	900	65	1,200,000
22F_b E-2 SP/SP	2200	200	1,700,000

BASE DESIGN VALUES FOR POSTS & TIMBERS

Species and Commercial Grade	Extreme Fiber Bending F_b	Horizontal Shear F_v	Modulus of Elasticity E
DLF #1	1200	85	1,600,000
Hem Fir #1	950	70	1,300,000
SPF #1	800	65	1,200,000

Values based on the Western Wood Products Association®.

TABLE 24.9 Structural Properties of Glu-Lam Beams

Columns (2)(b)(d) and (384)(E)(I) are set up for Douglas fir. If a different type of wood is to be used, you must use different values for these columns. Values based on the Western Wood Products Association.

PROPERTIES OF GLU-LAM BEAMS

SIZE (b) (d)	S	A	(2) (b) (d)	I	(384) (E) (I)*
3⅛ × 9.0	42.2	28.1	56.3	189.8	123,901
3⅛ × 10.5	57.4	32.8	65.6	301.5	196,819
3⅛ × 12.0	75.0	37.5	75.0	450.0	293,760
3⅛ × 13.5	94.9	42.2	84.4	640.7	418,249
3⅛ × 15.0	117.2	46.9	93.8	878.9	573,746
5⅛ × 9.0	69.2	46.1	92.0	311.3	203,217
5⅛ × 10.5	94.2	53.8	107.6	494.4	322,744
5⅛ × 12.0	123.0	61.5	123.0	738.0	481,766
5⅛ × 13.5	155.7	69.2	138.4	1,050.8	685,962
5⅛ × 15.0	192.2	76.9	153.8	1,441.4	940,946
5⅛ × 16.5	232.5	84.6	169.0	1,918.5	1,252,397
6¾ × 10.5	124.0	70.9	141.8	651.2	425,103
6¾ × 12.0	162.0	81.0	162.0	972.0	634.522
6¾ × 13.5	205.0	91.1	182.6	1,384.0	903,475
6¾ × 15.0	253.1	101.3	202.0	1,898.4	1,239,276
6¾ × 16.5	306.3	111.4	222.8	2,526.8	1,649,495

*All values for 384 × E × I are written in units per million. All E values are figured for Doug fir @ E = 1.7. Verify local conditions.

Working with Engineered Beams

Most manufacturers of engineered joists and rafters also supply beams made of LVL, PSL, and LSL. Figure 24.21 shows an example of a table for sizing Parallam® beams made of PSL. To use this table, follow these steps:

- Determine the roof loading (snow duration and live and dead loads) and find the appropriate section of the table that represents the design loads.

- Find the house width from the appropriate loading section that meets or exceeds the span of the trusses.

- Locate the opening size in the "Rough Opening" column that meets or exceeds the required window or door rough opening.

- Use the header size for the beam listed at the intersection of the rough opening and the house width/roof load.

Because sizes vary with each manufacturer, obtain specific standards and tables from the beam supplier.

DETERMINING BEAMS WITH COMPLEX LOADS

Up to this point, you've been introduced to sizing structural members by using span tables and mathematical formulas. These procedures work because the loading patterns and support methods are constant. The final portion of this chapter introduces formulas that are needed when the loading patterns are altered. Don't skip over the word *introduce*. This chapter will not make you an engineer but it will acquaint you with some of the basic formulas for determining light framing members sizes with irregular loading patterns. Consult information provided by Western Wood Products Association for the formulas for additional loading patterns.

Sizing a Simple Beam with a Concentrated Load at the Center

Often in light construction, load-bearing walls of an upper floor may not line up with the bearing walls of the floor below, as shown in Figure 24.22. This type of loading occurs when the function of the lower room dictates that no post be placed in the center. As a result, a beam will be required to span between the bearing walls and be centered below the upper-level post. This beam will have no loads to support other than weight from the post.

> **NOTE:**
>
> Figure 24.23 provides a new formula that was not used to determine deflection for a simple beam in 24.19. Notice the formula for Δ_x (deflection at any point) has been provided. Other loading patterns that follow throughout the balance of this chapter will also offer formulas for solving additional moment values and deflection values at multiple points. Don't get distracted by all of the options. Remember this is an introduction to what an engineer does, not what the CAD technician does. You'll make most employers happy if you can identify structural members that carry or transfer loads and if you can follow the load path from the roof to the ground. It sounds simple, but as your projects get more complicated, so does the load path. That's why many architects hire engineers to provide structural calculations.

To size the beam needed to support the upper area, use the formulas in Figure 24.23. Notice that a new symbol P has been added to represent a point or a concentrated load in the formula for determining the maximum bending moment (M). The point load is the sum of the reactions from each end of the beam.

Figure 24.24 shows a sample worksheet for this beam. Notice that the procedure used to solve for this beam is similar to the one used to determine a simple beam with uniform loads. With this procedure, you must determine the amount of point loads for the upper beams. The sketch shows the upper floor plan with each point load.

Once the point loads are known, determine M. Once the value for M is known, use it to find the required section modulus (S). Use the formula $M/F_b = S$. This provides the S value for the beam. Try to use a beam that has a depth equal to the depth of the floor joists.

> **NOTE:**
>
> Notice in Figure 24.23 that there is no formula for determining the value for F_v. This will also be true of the formulas for solving other complex beams. F_v is determined using one of the following formulas:
>
> $$3V/(2)\,(b)\,(d) = required\ F_v\ value$$
>
> or
>
> $$3V/max\ F_v\ value = the\ required\ minimum\ 2bd\ value.$$
>
> In Figure 24.24, two different beams have been selected that have the minimum required section modulus. Once the section modulus is known, check the beam for horizontal shear and deflection.

HEADERS SUPPORTING ROOF

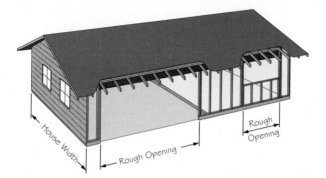

ROOF LOAD (psf)		HOUSE WIDTH	ROUGH OPENING						
			8'–0"	9'–3"	10'–0"	12'–0"	14'–0"	16'–3"	18'–3"
NON-SNOW AREA 125%	20LL + 15DL	24'–0"	$3^1/2$" x $9^1/4$"	$3^1/2$" x $9^1/4$"	$3^1/2$" x $9^1/4$"	$3^1/2$" x $9^1/4$"	$3^1/2$" x $11^1/4$" $5^1/4$" x $9^1/4$"	$3^1/2$" x $11^1/4$" 7" x $9^1/4$"	$3^1/2$" x 14" $5^1/4$" x $11^1/4$"
		30'–0"	$3^1/2$" x $9^1/4$"	$3^1/2$" x $9^1/4$"	$3^1/2$" x $9^1/4$"	$3^1/2$" x $9^1/4$"	$3^1/2$" x $11^1/4$" $5^1/4$" x $9^1/4$"	$3^1/2$" x $11^7/8$" $5^1/4$" x $11^1/4$"	$3^1/2$" x 14" $5^1/4$" x $11^7/8$"
		36'–0"	$3^1/2$" x $9^1/4$"	$3^1/2$" x $9^1/4$"	$3^1/2$" x $9^1/4$"	$3^1/2$" x $9^1/4$"	$3^1/2$" x $11^1/4$" $5^1/4$" x $9^1/2$"	$3^1/2$" x 14" $5^1/4$" x $11^1/4$"	$3^1/2$" x 14" 7" x $11^1/4$"
	20LL + 20DL	24'–0"	$3^1/2$" x $9^1/4$"	$3^1/2$" x $9^1/4$"	$3^1/2$" x $9^1/4$"	$3^1/2$" x $9^1/4$"	$3^1/2$" x $11^1/4$" $5^1/4$" x $9^1/4$"	$3^1/2$" x $11^7/8$" $5^1/4$" x 14"	$3^1/2$" x 14" $5^1/4$" x $11^1/4$"
		30'–0"	$3^1/2$" x $9^1/4$"	$3^1/2$" x $9^1/4$"	$3^1/2$" x $9^1/4$"	$3^1/2$" x $9^1/4$"	$3^1/2$" x $11^1/4$" $5^1/4$" x $9^1/4$"	$3^1/2$" x 14" $5^1/4$" x $11^1/4$"	$3^1/2$" x 14" 7" x $11^1/4$"
		36'–0"	$3^1/2$" x $9^1/4$"	$3^1/2$" x $9^1/4$"	$3^1/2$" x $9^1/4$"	$3^1/2$" x $11^1/4$" $5^1/4$" x $9^1/4$"	$3^1/2$" x $11^1/4$" 7" x $9^1/4$"	$3^1/2$" x 14" $5^1/4$" x $11^1/4$"	$3^1/2$" x 16" $5^1/4$" x 14"
SNOW AREA 115%	25LL + 15DL	24'–0"	$3^1/2$" x $9^1/4$"	$3^1/2$" x $9^1/4$"	$3^1/2$" x $9^1/4$"	$3^1/2$" x $9^1/4$"	$3^1/2$" x $11^1/4$" $5^1/4$" x $9^1/4$"	$3^1/2$" x $11^7/8$" $5^1/4$" x $11^1/4$"	$3^1/2$" x 14" $5^1/4$" x $11^7/8$"
		30'–0"	$3^1/2$" x $9^1/4$"	$3^1/2$" x $9^1/4$"	$3^1/2$" x $9^1/4$"	$3^1/2$" x $9^1/4$"	$3^1/2$" x $11^1/4$" $5^1/4$" x $9^1/2$"	$3^1/2$" x 14" $5^1/4$" x $11^1/4$"	$3^1/2$" x 14" 7" x $11^1/4$"
		36'–0"	$3^1/2$" x $9^1/4$"	$3^1/2$" x $9^1/4$"	$3^1/2$" x $9^1/4$"	$3^1/2$" x $11^1/4$" $5^1/4$" x $9^1/4$"	$3^1/2$" x $11^7/8$" $5^1/4$" x $11^1/4$"	$3^1/2$" x 14" $5^1/4$" x $11^7/8$"	$3^1/2$" x 16" $5^1/4$" x 14"
	30LL + 15DL	24'–0"	$3^1/2$" x $9^1/4$"	$3^1/2$" x $9^1/4$"	$3^1/2$" x $9^1/4$"	$3^1/2$" x $9^1/4$"	$3^1/2$" x $11^1/4$" $5^1/4$" x $9^1/4$"	$3^1/2$" x 14" $5^1/4$" x $11^1/4$"	$3^1/2$" x 14" $5^1/4$" x $11^7/8$"
		30'–0"	$3^1/2$" x $9^1/4$"	$3^1/2$" x $9^1/4$"	$3^1/2$" x $9^1/4$"	$3^1/2$" x $11^1/4$" $5^1/4$" x $9^1/4$"	$3^1/2$" x $11^1/4$" 7" x $9^1/4$"	$3^1/2$" x 14" $5^1/4$" x $11^7/8$"	$3^1/2$" x 16" $5^1/4$" x 14"
		36'–0"	$3^1/2$" x $9^1/4$"	$3^1/2$" x $9^1/4$"	$3^1/2$" x $9^1/4$"	$3^1/2$" x $11^1/4$" $5^1/4$" x $9^1/4$"	$3^1/2$" x 14" $5^1/4$" x $11^1/4$"	$3^1/2$" x 16" $5^1/4$" x 14"	$3^1/2$" x 16" $5^1/4$" x 14"
	40LL + 15DL	24'–0"	$3^1/2$" x $9^1/4$"	$3^1/2$" x $9^1/4$"	$3^1/2$" x $9^1/4$"	$3^1/2$" x $11^1/4$" $5^1/2$" x $9^1/4$"	$3^1/2$" x $11^1/4$" 7" x $9^1/4$"	$3^1/2$" x 14" $5^1/4$" x $11^7/8$"	$3^1/2$" x 16" $5^1/4$" x 14"
		30'–0"	$3^1/2$" x $9^1/4$"	$3^1/2$" x $9^1/4$"	$3^1/2$" x $9^1/4$"	$3^1/2$" x $11^1/4$" $5^1/4$" x $9^1/4$"	$3^1/2$" x 14" $5^1/4$" x $11^1/4$"	$3^1/2$" x 16" $5^1/4$" x 14"	$3^1/2$" x 18" $5^1/4$" x 14"
		36'–0"	$3^1/2$" x $9^1/4$"	$3^1/2$" x $9^1/4$"	$3^1/2$" x $9^1/2$" $5^1/4$" x $9^1/4$"	$3^1/2$" x $11^7/8$" $5^1/4$" x $9^1/2$"	$3^1/2$" x 14" $5^1/4$" x $11^1/4$"	$3^1/2$" x 16" $5^1/4$" x 14"	$5^1/4$" x 16" 7" x 14"

GENERAL NOTES

Table is based on:

- Uniform loads
- Worst case of simple or continuous span. When sizing a continuous span application, use the longest span. Where ratio of short span to long span is less than 0.4, use the TJ-Beam™ software program.
- Roof truss framing with 24" soffits
- Deflection criteria of L/240 live load and L/180 total load. All members 7 1/4" and less in depth are restricted to a maximum deflection of 5/16".

BEARING REQUIREMENTS

Minimum header support to be double trimmers (3" bearing).

In shaded areas, support headers with triple trimmers (4 1/2" bearing).

FIGURE 24.21 Design tables for solving exterior headers for a single-level residence using non-treated Parallam PSL beams.

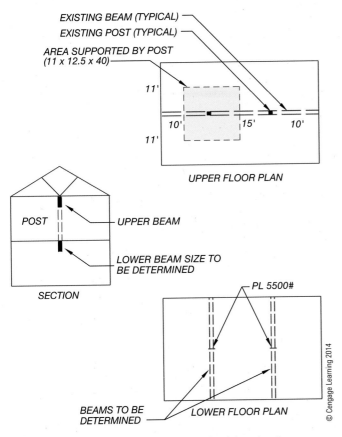

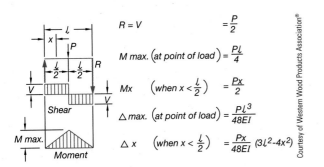

FIGURE 24.22 The sketch created to help determine the loads on a beam with a concentrated load at the center. Sketching a simple floor plan helps to determine the area to be supported. Sketching a simple section helps determine the load path so that all loads can be safely transferred to the soil.

FIGURE 24.23 Shear and moment diagrams for a simple beam with a load concentrated at the center.

Sizing a Simple Beam with a Concentrated Load at Any Point

Figure 24.25 shows a sample floor plan that will result in concentrated off-center loads at the lower floor level. Figure 24.26 shows the diagrams and formulas for determining the beams of the lower floor plan. Figure 24.27 shows the worksheet for this beam. Just as with the previous

22' BEAM @ LIVING RM.

$P = W = 5500\# \quad V = 2750 \quad L = 22' \quad \ell = 264 \quad \ell^3 = 18.399744$

$R_1 = 2750 \qquad R_2 = 2750$

$$M = \frac{(P)(\ell)}{4} = \frac{(5500)(264)}{4} = \frac{1,452,000}{4} = 363,000 = M$$

$$S = \frac{M}{fb} = \frac{363,000}{2400} = S = 151.25 \quad \begin{array}{l}\text{USE } 5\frac{1}{8} \times 13\frac{1}{2} \ (S = 155.7) \\ \text{OR } 6\frac{3}{4} \times 12 \ (S = 162)\end{array}$$

$$fv = \frac{(3)(V)}{165} = 2bd = \frac{(3)(2750)}{165} = \frac{8250}{165} = 50 \text{ BOTH BM. OK}$$

$$D_{max.} = \frac{\ell}{360} = \frac{264}{360} = .73 \qquad D = \frac{(P)(\ell^3)}{(48)(E)(I)} =$$

$$D = \frac{(5500)(18.4)}{(48 \times 1.7)(972)} = \frac{101,200}{79,315} = 1.2 > .73 = \text{FAIL}$$

$$? \ 6\frac{3}{4} \times 13\frac{1}{2} = I = 1384 = \frac{101,200}{85,745} = 1.1 > .73 = \text{FAIL}$$

$$? \ 6\frac{3}{4} \times 15 = I = 1898.4 = \frac{101,200}{154,909} = .65 < .73 =$$

> USE $6\frac{3}{4} \times 15$ fb 2200 GLU-LAM BEAM

FIGURE 24.24 The worksheet for a beam with a load concentrated at the center. Always include the location of the beam, a sketch of the loading, needed formulas, and the selected beam as part of your calculations.

example, once the point loads are known, determine M. Once the value for M has been determined, it can be used to find the required section modulus (S) from Table 24.7 or Table 24.9. Use the formula $M/F_b = S$. This will provide the S value for the beam.

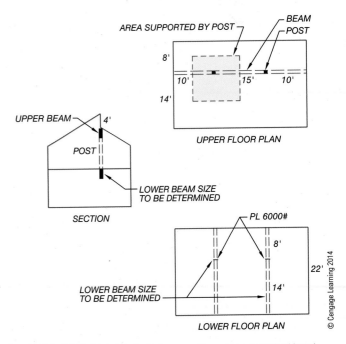

FIGURE 24.25 A sketch for a beam with a concentrated load placed at any point on the beam.

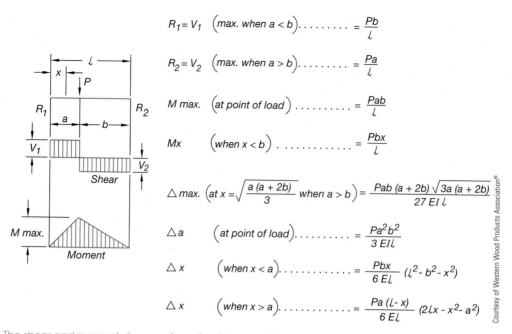

$$R_1 = V_1 \quad \left(max.\ when\ a < b\right)\ldots\ldots\ = \frac{Pb}{l}$$

$$R_2 = V_2 \quad \left(max.\ when\ a > b\right)\ldots\ldots\ = \frac{Pa}{l}$$

$$M\ max.\quad \left(at\ point\ of\ load\right)\ldots\ldots\ = \frac{Pab}{l}$$

$$Mx \quad \left(when\ x < b\right)\ldots\ldots\ldots = \frac{Pbx}{l}$$

$$\triangle max.\ \left(at\ x = \sqrt{\frac{a\,(a+2b)}{3}}\ when\ a > b\right) = \frac{Pab\,(a+2b)\,\sqrt{3a\,(a+2b)}}{27\,EI\,l}$$

$$\triangle a \quad \left(at\ point\ of\ load\right)\ldots\ldots = \frac{Pa^2 b^2}{3\,EIl}$$

$$\triangle x \quad \left(when\ x < a\right)\ldots\ldots\ldots = \frac{Pbx}{6\,El}\,(l^2 - b^2 - x^2)$$

$$\triangle x \quad \left(when\ x > a\right)\ldots\ldots\ldots = \frac{Pa\,(l-x)}{6\,El}\,(2lx - x^2 - a^2)$$

Courtesy of Western Wood Products Association®

FIGURE 24.26 The shear and moment diagrams for a simple beam with a load concentrated at any point on the beam.

22' SPAN @ LOWER FLOOR

5500#

$a = 96"$ $b = 168"$ $W = (4 + 7)\,(5 + 7.5)\,(40\#) = W = 5500\#$
                              $l = 264"$

$l = 264$

R_1 R_2

$R_1 = \dfrac{(P)(b)}{l} = \dfrac{(5500)(168)}{264} = \dfrac{924,000}{264} = 3500\# = R_1$

$R_2 = P - R_1 = 5500 - 3500 = 2000 = R_2$

$M = \dfrac{(P)(a)(b)}{l} = \dfrac{(5500)(96)(168)}{264} = \dfrac{88,704,000}{264} = 336,000 = M$

$S = \dfrac{M}{fb} = \dfrac{336,000}{2200} = 152.7$ USE $5\frac{1}{8} \times 13\frac{1}{2}$
                                              OR $6\frac{3}{4} \times 12$

$fv = \dfrac{(3)(V)}{165} = \dfrac{(3)(3500)}{165} = \dfrac{10,500}{165} = 63.6$ BOTH BM. OK

$D = \dfrac{l}{360} = \dfrac{264}{360} = .73\ max.$ $E = \dfrac{(P)(a)(b)(a+2b)\,\sqrt{3a(a+2b)}}{27(E)(l)(I)} =$

$D = \dfrac{(5500)(96)(168)(432)\,\sqrt{(288)(432)}}{(27)(1.7)(264)(I) = (12118)(I)} = \dfrac{13,516,525}{12,117.6\,(I)} =$

$?\ 5\frac{1}{8} \times 13\frac{1}{2} = \dfrac{13,516,525}{12,733,174} = 106 > .73 = $ FAIL

$?\ 5\frac{1}{8} \times 15 = \dfrac{13,516,525}{17,466,308} = .77 > .73 = $ FAIL

$?\ 6\frac{3}{4} \times 15 = \dfrac{13,516,525}{23,004,051} = .58 < .73 = $ ok   ┌ USE $6\frac{3}{4} \times 15$ fb 2200 ┐
                                                            └ GLU-LAM BEAM ┘

FIGURE 24.27 A sample worksheet for a beam with an off center concentrated load.

Cantilevered Beam with a Uniform Load

This loading pattern typically occurs where floor joists of a deck cantilever past the supporting wall. One major difference of this type of loading is that the live loads of

exterior balconies are almost double the normal floor live loads. A second consideration is that the IRC requires that cantilevered joists have a backspan ratio into the structure of 3:1. Determine the size of cantilevered floor joists from tables in the IRC. Figure 24.28 shows the diagrams and formulas for determining the size for a cantilevered beam or joist. Figure 24.29 shows the worksheet to determine the required size of floor beams placed at 24" o.c. with a 3' balcony cantilever. Once the value for M has been determined, use the formula $M/F_b = S$ to provide the S value for the beam from Tables 24.7 or 24.9. Engineered joists that cantilever often require additional support at the cantilever. Be sure to follow the manufacturer's instructions and span tables when using engineered lumber in cantilevered situations.

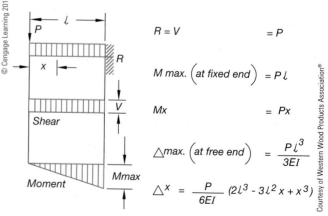

© Cengage Learning 2014

$$R = V \qquad\qquad\qquad = P$$

$$M\ max.\ \left(at\ fixed\ end\right) = Pl$$

$$Mx \qquad\qquad\qquad = Px$$

$$\triangle max.\ \left(at\ free\ end\right) = \frac{Pl^3}{3EI}$$

$$\triangle x = \frac{P}{6EI}\,(2l^3 - 3l^2 x + x^3)$$

Courtesy of Western Wood Products Association®

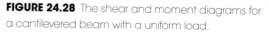

FIGURE 24.28 The shear and moment diagrams for a cantilevered beam with a uniform load.

FLOOR JOIST, 36" CANTILEVER

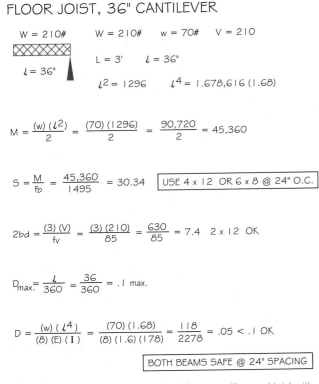

W = 210#   W = 210#   w = 70#   V = 210

L = 3' l = 36"

l = 36"

l^2 = 1296 l^4 = 1.678,616 (1.68)

$$M = \frac{(w)(l^2)}{2} = \frac{(70)(1296)}{2} = \frac{90,720}{2} = 45,360$$

$$S = \frac{M}{fb} = \frac{45,360}{1495} = 30.34 \quad \boxed{\text{USE 4 x 12 OR 6 x 8 @ 24" O.C.}}$$

$$2bd = \frac{(3)(V)}{fv} = \frac{(3)(210)}{85} = \frac{630}{85} = 7.4 \quad 2 \times 12 \quad OK$$

$$D_{max.} = \frac{l}{360} = \frac{36}{360} = .1 \text{ max.}$$

$$D = \frac{(w)(l^4)}{(8)(E)(I)} = \frac{(70)(1.68)}{(8)(1.6)(178)} = \frac{118}{2278} = .05 < .1 \text{ OK}$$

$$\boxed{\text{BOTH BEAMS SAFE @ 24" SPACING}}$$

FIGURE 24.29 A sample worksheet for a cantilevered joist with a uniform load.

Cantilevered Beam with a Point Load at the Free End

This type of beam results when a beam or joist is cantilevered and is supporting a point load. Floor joists that are cantilevered and support a wall and roof can be sized using tables in the IRC or the formulas in Figure 24.30. Figure 24.31 shows the worksheet for determining the size and spacing of floor joists to cantilever 2' and support a bearing wall.

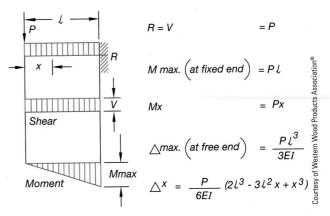

$R = V$ $= P$

$M\ max.\ \left(at\ fixed\ end\right) = Pl$

Mx $= Px$

$\triangle max.\ \left(at\ free\ end\right) = \dfrac{Pl^3}{3EI}$

$\triangle x = \dfrac{P}{6EI}(2l^3 - 3l^2x + x^3)$

FIGURE 24.30 The shear and moment diagrams for a cantilevered beam with a concentrated load at the free end.

24" CANTILEVER @ WALL

P = V = R = 780#

l = 24"

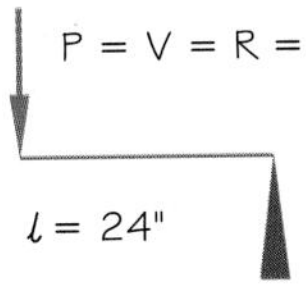

$$M = (P)(l) = (780)(24) = 18,720$$

$$S = \frac{M}{fb} = \frac{18,720}{1140} = 16.4 \quad \boxed{\text{USE 2 x 10 F.J. @ 12" O.C.}}$$

$$fv = \frac{(3)(V)}{85} = \frac{(3)(780)}{85} = \frac{2380}{85} = 28 = 2bd$$

$$\boxed{\begin{array}{l}\text{USE 2 x 10 FAIL}\\\text{USE 2 x12 F.J. OK}\end{array}}$$

$$D_{max.} = \frac{l}{360} = \frac{24}{360} = .06 \text{ max.}$$

$$D = \frac{(P)(l^3)}{(3)(E)(I)} = \frac{(780)(.013824)}{(3)(1.6)(177.9)} = \frac{10.78}{853.92} = .013 < .06$$

$$\boxed{\text{USE 2 x 10 F.J. @ 12" O.C.}}$$

FIGURE 24.31 A sample worksheet for a cantilevered beam with a concentrated load at the free end.

Additional Resources

The following websites can be used as a resource to help you keep current on lumber manufacturers.

Address	Company or Organization
www.apawood.org	APA—The Engineered Wood Association
www.afandpa.org	American Forest and Paper Association
www.aitc-glulam.org	American Institute of Timber Construction
www.awc.org	American Wood Council (NDS standards)
www.beamchek.com	BeamChek (AC Software, Inc.)
www.bc.com	Boise Cascade
www.bcewp.com	Boise Cascade (engineered wood products)
www.cwc.ca	Canadian Wood Council
www.strucalc.com	Strucalc (Cascade Consulting Engineers)
www.forestdirectory.com	Directory of forest products
www.gp.com	Georgia-Pacific
www.inpawood.org	International Wood Products Association
www.lpcorp.com	LP Building Products
www.sfpa.org	Southern Forest Products Association
www.trimjoist.com	Trim Joist (engineered wood products)
www.wwpa.org	Western Wood Products Association
www.weyerhaeuser.com	Weyerhaeuser
www.woodbywy.com	Weyerhaeuser (engineered products)
www.woodcom.com	Wood Industries Information Center
www.woodtruss.com	Structural Building Components Association

Sizing Joists, Rafters, and Beams Test

Follow these instructions to access and complete an electronic copy of the Chapter 24 Sizing Joists, Rafters, and Beams Test:

1. Go to cengagebrain.com
2. Enter the email address and password you used to register for the site (see Preface for full instructions).
3. Select the website from the **My Course & Materials** area of your home page. Select the chapter you want from the pull-down menu at the top of the page. Choose the resources for that chapter from the menu on the left.
4. Type your name, the chapter number, and the date at the top of the sheet.
5. Answer the following questions with short, complete statements using a word processor.

(Continued)

6. Unless something else is noted, answer all questions using the type of lumber common to your area, using a #2 material and typical spacing.

7. Provide the table number that is used for all appropriate questions.

8. Provide sketches for all questions that require the use of formulas to provide an answer. Write each formula necessary to find your solution and show all work.

> **NOTE:**
>
> The answers to some questions are not contained in this chapter and will require you to visit sites that provide engineered lumber in your area.

Questions

24.1. List four common types of lumber for framing throughout the country.

24.2. How is modulus of elasticity represented in engineering formulas?

24.3. What is deflection, and how do building codes express its limits?

24.4. What are two features that define a simple beam?

24.5. Explain the difference between a uniform and a concentrated load.

24.6. Determine the size of floor joist that will be required to span 15'-0" if spaced at 16" o.c.

24.7. You are considering the use of 2 × 8 floor joists to span 14'-0". Will they work?

24.8. Using 2 × 6 at 16" o.c., for ceiling joists, determine their maximum safe span for a ceiling with no storage and for a ceiling with limited storage.

24.9. Determine the size of lumber required to span 16'-6" with 16" and 24" spacings used for rafter/ceiling joists.

24.10. Determine the floor joist size needed to span 13'-0" to support a kitchen floor.

24.11. Determine the smallest size of floor joist needed to span 13'-0" to support a living room floor.

24.12. What is the smallest size floor joist that can be used to span 15'-9" beneath a dining area?

24.13. What size floor joist would be needed to support a den 12'-2" wide? A bedroom of the same size?

24.14. Determine the smallest floor joist that could be used to span a living area that is 12'-8" wide.

24.15. A bedroom is 17'-9" wide. What is the smallest ceiling joist that could be used for providing limited storage?

24.16. A contractor bought a truckload of 2 × 6s that are 18' long. Can they be used for ceiling joists with no attic storage if they are spaced at 16" o.c.?

24.17. What size rafter is needed for a home 28' wide with a gable roof, 4/12 pitch with 235-lb composition shingles if a 10-lb dead load and a 30-lb snow load is assumed?

24.18. What is the maximum span allowed using 2 × 10 rafters supporting built-up roofing if a 10-lb dead load and an assumed 20-lb live load?

24.19. Determine the rafter size for spanning 14' and support a 30-lb live load and a 10-lb dead load at a 6/12 pitch.

24.20. Determine the required sizes for engineered floor joists to span 17'-0" using L/360 and L/480 using a spacing of 16" o.c.; a 10-lb dead load and a 40-lb live load are assumed.

24.21. What is the advantage of using a deflection value of L/480 if the building codes allow a greater deflection?

24.22. List the smallest TJI size and spacing that can be used to span 17-0" if L/480 is to be used and a 10-lb dead load and a 40-lb live load is assumed?

24.23. A 9 1/2" TJI-110 at 19.2" o.c. will be used to cantilever 24". The joist will support a floor load of 45 psf and a wall that supports a truss 26' wide with 1' overhangs. How should the cantilevered joist be reinforced?

24.24. If the joists in question 24.24 were placed at 16" o.c., how should they be reinforced?

24.25. Engineered rafters are required to span 19' using 20LL + 15DL for a high-slope roof in an area where no snow is expected. What size TJI should be used if 24" spacing is desired?

24.26. Engineered rafters are required to span 17'-6" and support a DL of 20 lb on a 5/12 pitch in an area where no snow is expected. What is the smallest size TJI that can be used? What is the smallest size rafter that can be used if 24" spacing is desired?

24.27. Use the Internet, Sweets catalogs, or local vendor resources to locate five or more different manufacturers of engineered floor joists.

24.28. List three common categories of stress that must be known before determining a beam size.

24.29. Define the following notations: W, w, R, L, l, E, I, S, F_v, and F_b.

24.30. List two methods of determining beams other than using formulas.

24.31. List the values for W, w, and R for a floor beam that supports living areas, has an L of 10', and is centered under a room that is 20' wide. Provide a sketch to show the loading.

24.32. A 4 × 6 DFL beam with an L of 6' and a W of 2800 lb spans an opening for a window. Will the beam fail in F_v?

24.33. A 4 × 14 is being used as a ridge beam. L = 12', W = 4650 lb. Will this beam have a safe deflection value? Assume D_{max} = 1/360.

24.34. If the soil bearing pressure is 1500 psf and the concrete has a strength of 2500 psi, what size pier is needed to support a load of 4600 lb?

24.35. What size #2 girder is required if w = 600 and L = 6'? Determine all necessary values to find the needed S, F_v and deflection stresses.

24.36. What size glu-lam beam is required for a ridge beam with L = 14.5', W = 5500 lb, and l = 240 if an F_b value of 2400 is used?

24.37. A 16' long laminated ridge beam will support 800 lb per linear foot. Determine what depth 5 1/8" wide laminated beam should be used assuming an F_b value of 2400.

24.38. The ridge beam in question 24.38 will be supported at one end by a post and at the other end by a beam 4' long over a door. The point load from the ridge beam will be 12" from one end of the 4' header. What size door header should be used?

24.39. Determine the minimum size floor beam needed to span 14' with a concentrated load of 3200 lb at the center. What size piers will be needed to resist the reactions if the assumed safe soil loads are 2000 psf?

24.40. A two-level residence is 28' wide with a gable roof and 24" wide overhangs. The roof is cedar shakes at a 5/12 pitch, and local codes require a 30-lb live load. Wall heights are 9' at the upper floor. There are several windows in the upper exterior walls that are 60" wide. A wall is placed 13' from the left exterior bearing wall on the upper floor. The floor joists supporting the upper floor will be TJI and cantilever 18" past the lower wall on the right side of the residence so that the lower floor is only 26'-6" wide. A bearing wall on the main floor will be 16' from the left exterior wall. Part of the wall will be an opening. The walls of the lower floor will be 8' high. This home also has windows on the left side of the house on the lower floor that are directly below the windows on the upper floor. The lower floor joists will be sawn lumber supported by a girder directly below the bearing wall, with supports at 5'-0" maximum spacing. The owners of the house have two kids and a dog named Spot.

Determine the size of all framing members, assuming that the roof is framed with trusses. Provide the size of the following materials:

Upper headers =
Upper floor joists (left) =
Lower window header =
Upper floor joists (right) =
Lower floor joist =
Girder =

24.41. Use the Internet to determine the required live and dead loads used by your local building department.

24.42. Use the Internet to determine the deflection value of one of the major suppliers of engineered floor joists in your area. List the deflection value and the manufacturer.

24.43. Set up an appointment with a local builder to determine factors in choosing to use sawn lumber or engineered lumber. Get information on comparison pricing, availability, and installation advantages of one material over another. Include a business card with your information.

24.44. Visit the web pages for two major lumber suppliers and report on what they are doing to improve their environmental impact of their forest and their milling methods.

24.45. Visit the web pages of the Western Wood Products Association, American Forest and Paper Association, and the American Wood Council and report on any new developments in wood standards that will affect the design and selection of wood beams.

Section 7
Foundation Plans

Chapter 26
Foundation Systems

All structures are required to have a foundation that provides a base to distribute the weight of the structure onto the soil. The weight, or load, must be distributed evenly over enough soil to prevent the soil from becoming compressed. In addition to resisting gravity loads, the foundation must resist floods, winds, and earthquakes. Where flooding is a problem, the foundation system must be designed for the possibility that much of the supporting soil may be washed away. The foundation must also resist any debris carried by floodwaters.

The forces of wind on a structure may also cause severe problems for a foundation. The walls of a structure act as a large sail. If the structure is not anchored properly to the foundation, the wind can rip the walls away. Wind tries to push a structure not only sideways but upward as well. If the structure is fastened securely at each intersection, wind pressure is transferred into the foundation. Proper foundation design will resist this upward movement. Figure 26.1 shows an example of anchor bolts and straps used to resist uplift.

Depending on the risk of seismic damage, special design may be required for a foundation. Although earthquakes may cause both vertical and horizontal movement, the horizontal movement causes the most damage to structures. The foundation system must be designed so that it can move with the ground yet keep its basic shape. Steel reinforcing and welded wire mesh are often required to help resist or minimize damage due to the movement of the earth.

Key Terms

Cripple stud	Jack stud	Rebar	Unified Soils Classification System
Damp proof	Key	Retaining wall	
Fill	Keyway	Slab-on-grade	Waterproof
Footing	Monolithic	Spread foundation	Window well
Grade beam	Piling	Stem wall	
Hydrostatic vent	Plenum	Turned-down footing	

FIGURE 26.1 In addition to resisting the forces of gravity, a foundation must be able to resist the forces of uplift created by wind pressure acting on the structure. Anchor bolts and metal framing straps embedded in the concrete are two common methods of resisting the forces of nature.

TABLE 26.1 Presumptive Load-Bearing Values of Foundation Materials[a]

CLASS OF MATERIAL	LOAD-BEARING PRESSURE (POUNDS PER SQUARE FOOT)
Crystalline bedrock	12,000 psf (574.8 kPa)
Sedimentary and foliated rock	4000 psf (191.6 kPa)
Sandy gravel and/or gravel (GW and GP)	3000 psf (143.7 kPa)
Sand, silty sand, clayey sand, silty gravel, and clayey gravel (SW, SP, SM, SC, GM, and GC)	2000 psf (95.8 kPa)
Clay, sandy clay, silty clay, clayey silt, silt, and sandy silt (CL, ML, MH, and CH)	1500 psf (47.9 kPa)[b]

[a] When soil tests are required, the allowable bearing capacities of the soil shall be part of the recommendations.
[b] Where the building official determines that in-place soils with an allowable bearing capacity of less than 1,500 psf (47.9 kPa) are likely to be present at the site, the allowable bearing capacity shall be determined by a soils investigation. See Table R401.4.1 of the 2012 International Residential Code for complete listings.

Portions of this publication reproduce excerpts from the 2012 International Residential Code® for One- and Two-Family Dwellings®, International Code Council®, Inc., Washington, D.C. Reproduced with permission. All rights reserved. www.iccsafe.org

SOIL CONSIDERATIONS

In addition to the forces of nature, the type of the soil supporting the foundation also must be considered. The texture of the soil and the tendency of the soil to freeze will influence the design of the foundation system.

Soil Texture

The texture of the soil will affect its ability to resist the load of the foundation. Before a foundation can be designed for a structure, the bearing capacity of the soil must be known. This is a design value specifying the amount of weight a square foot of soil can support. The bearing capacity of soil depends on its composition and the moisture content. Each of the five basic classifications for soil listed by the IRC can be seen in Table 26.1.

The soil types in Table 26.1 are based on studies done in the mid-twentieth century for the U.S. Army Corps of Engineers. Now known as the *Unified Soils Classification System* (USCS), the system is used in engineering and geology disciplines to describe the texture and grain size of soil. Common letters used in the USCS and their definition can be seen in Table 26.2.

Common groupings of letters and soils represented can be seen in Table 26.3. Building departments use the values in these tables to classify the general soil strength for each building site. A soils engineer may need to determine the specific allowable bearing capacity if the building department believes the soil is likely to have an allowable bearing of less than 1500 psf. Most stock home designs use a soil-bearing pressure of 2000 psf (1895.8 kPa) when the site conditions are not known.

Designing Foundations on Poor Soil

Structures built on soils with low bearing capacity require a *footing* that extends into stable soil or is spread over a wide area. Both options typically require an engineer to approve the design. In residential construction, the building department

TABLE 26.2 USCS Abbreviations

FIRST AND/OR SECOND LETTER	
LETTER	**DEFINITION**
C	Clay
G	Gravel
M	Silt
O	Organic
S	Sand
SECOND LETTER	
LETTER	**DEFINITION**
H	High plasticity
L	Low plasticity
P	Poorly graded (uniform particle sizes)
W	Well graded (diversified particle sizes)

Portions of this publication reproduce excerpts from the 2012 International Residential Code® for One- and Two-Family Dwellings®, International Code Council®, Inc., Washington, D.C. Reproduced with permission. All rights reserved. www.iccsafe.org

TABLE 26.3 Soils Symbols Chart

MAJOR DIVISIONS	GROUP SYMBOL		GROUP NAME	
Coarse-grained soil more than 50% retained on #200 (0.075 mm) sieve	Gravel > 50% of coarse fraction retained on #4 (4.75 mm) sieve	Clean gravel < 5% smaller than #200 sieve	GW GP	Well-graded gravel, fine to coarse gravel Poorly graded gravel
		Gravel with > 12% fines	GM GC	Silty gravel Clayey gravel
	Sand > 50% of coarse fraction passes #4 sieve	Clean sand	SW SP	Well-graded sand, fine to coarse sand Poorly graded sand
		Sand with > 12% fines	SM SC	Silty sand Clayey sand
Fine-grained soils more than 50% passes #200 sieve	Silt and clay liquid limit < 50	Inorganic	ML CL	Silt Clay
		Organic	OL	Organic silt, organic clay
	Silt and clay liquid limit > 50	Inorganic	MH CH	Silt of high plasticity, elastic silt Clay of high plasticity, fat clay
		Organic	OH	Organic clay, organic silt
Highly organic soils			Pt	Peat

may be able to provide information about the type of soil. For large custom homes, a soils engineer is often required to study the various types of soil at the job site and make recommendations for foundation design. The soil-bearing values must be determined before a suitable foundation material can be selected. In addition to the texture, the tendency of freezing must also be considered.

Cut and Fill Materials. Construction sites often include soil that has been brought to the site or moved on the site. Soil placed over the natural grade is called *fill* material (review Chapter 8). Fill material is often moved to a lot when an access road is placed in a sloping site, as in Figure 26.2. After a few years, vegetation covers the soil and gives it the appearance of natural grade. Footings resting on fill material will eventually settle under the weight of a structure. All discussion of foundation depths in this text refers to the footing depth into the natural grade.

Compaction

Fill material can be compacted to increase its bearing capacity. Vibrating, tamping, rolling, or adding a temporary weight are the common methods for compacting soil. There are three major ways to compact soil.

1. Static force: A heavy roller presses soil particles together.
2. Impact forces: A ramming shoe strikes the ground repeatedly at high speed.
3. Vibration: High-frequency vibration is applied to soil through a steel plate.

The soils engineer often specifies the type of compaction to be performed, and the CAD technician must place this information on the foundation drawing. Large job sites are usually compacted by mobile equipment. Small areas in the construction site are generally compacted by handheld mobile equipment. Granular soils are compacted by vibration, and soils containing large amounts of clay are best compacted by force. Each of these methods will reduce the air voids between grains of soil. Proper compaction lessens the effect of settling and increases the stability of the soil, which increases the load-bearing capacity. The effects of frost damage are minimized in

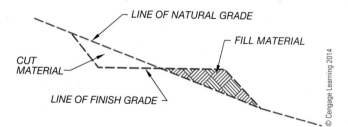

FIGURE 26.2 As access roads are created, soil is often cut away and pushed to the side of the roadway, creating areas of fill. Unless the foundation extends into the natural grade, the structure will settle.

© Cengage Learning 2014

compacted soil because penetration of water into voids in the soil is minimized.

Moisture content is the most important factor in efficient soil compaction because moisture acts as a lubricant to help soil particles move closer together. Compaction should be completed under the supervision of a geotechnical engineer or another qualified expert who understands the measurements of soil moisture. Compaction is typically accomplished in lifts of from 6 through 12" (150 through 300 mm). The soils or geotechnical engineer will specify the requirements for soils excavation and compaction. The CAD technician's job is to place the engineer's specifications clearly on the plans.

Freezing

Don't confuse ground freezing with blizzards. Even in the warmer southern states, ground freezing can be a problem. Frost penetration depths can range from 12 to 80" (300 to 2000 mm) for the United States (review Chapter 5). Exact design parameters must be determined with the local building department as the plans are being drawn. A foundation must be built to a depth where the ground is not subject to freezing. Water in the soil expands as it freezes and then contracts as it thaws. Expansion and shrinking of the soil will cause heaving in the foundation. As the soil expands, the foundation can crack. As the soil thaws, water that cannot be absorbed by the soil can cause the soil to lose much of its bearing capacity, causing further cracking of the foundation. In addition to geographic location, the type of soil also affects freezing. Fine-grained soil is more susceptible to freezing because it tends to hold moisture.

A foundation must rest on stable soil so that it does not crack. The designer will have to verify the required depth of foundations with the local building department. Once the soil's bearing capacity and the depth of freezing are known, the type of foundation system to be used can be determined.

Water Content

The amount of water the foundation will be exposed to, as well as the permeability of the soil, must also be considered in the design of the foundation. The soil expands as it absorbs water, causing the foundation to heave. In areas of the country with extended periods of rainfall, there is little variation in the soil's moisture content; this minimizes the risk of heaving that soil expansion causes. Greater danger results in areas of the country that receive only minimal rainfall followed by extended periods without moisture. Soil shrinkage from these conditions can cause severe foundation problems because of the moisture differential. To aid in the design of the foundation, the local building department website will often have information such as the Thornthwaite Moisture Index, which lists the amount of

water that would be returned to the atmosphere by evaporation from the ground surface and transpiration if there were an unlimited supply of water to the plants and soil.

On-grade concrete slabs are used primarily in dry areas from southern California to Florida, where the contrast between the dry soil under the slab and the damp soil beside the foundation creates a risk of heaving at the edge of the slab. If the soil beneath the slab experiences a change of moisture content after the slab is poured, the center of the slab can heave. Heaving can be resisted by proper drainage and reinforcement placed in the foundation and throughout the floor slab. The effects of soil moisture are investigated in Chapter 28, which considers concrete slab construction.

Surface water and groundwater must be properly diverted from the foundation so that the soil can support the building load. Proper drainage also minimizes water leaks into the crawl space or basement, thus reducing mildew and rotting. The IRC requires the finish grade to slope away from the foundation at a minimum slope of 6" (150 mm) within the first 10' (3000 mm). A 3 percent minimum slope is preferable for planted or grassy areas; a 1 percent slope is acceptable for paved areas.

Gravel or coarse-grained soils can be placed beside the foundation to increase percolation. In damp climates, a drain is often required beside the foundation at the base of a gravel bed to facilitate drainage (see Figure 26.3). When drains are required, gravel must extend 12" (305 mm) past the outside edge of the footing and 6" (152 mm) above the top of the footing. The gravel and drain must also be covered with an approved filter membrane. As the amount of water in the soil surrounding the foundation is reduced, the lateral loads imposed on the foundation are also reduced. The pressure of the soil becomes increasingly important as the height of the foundation wall is increased. Foundation walls enclosing basements should be waterproofed, as in Figure 26.4. Asphaltic emulsion often is used to prevent water penetration into the basement. Floor slabs below grade must be placed over a vapor barrier.

Radon

Structures built in areas of the country with high radon levels need to provide protection from this cancer-causing gas. The IRC and the Environmental Protection Agency (EPA) have identified by county areas in the continental United States with a high risk of exposure to radon. Minor modifications to the gravel placed below basement slabs can reduce the buildup of radon. A 4" (100 mm) PVC vent can be placed in a minimum layer of 4" (100 mm) of gravel covered with 6-mil polyethylene. The plastic barrier should have a minimum lap of 12" (300 mm) at intersections. Any joints, cracks, or penetrations in the floor slab

FIGURE 26.3 A gravel bed and a drain divert water away from the foundation.

FIGURE 26.4 A waterproof emulsion will reduce the risk of water penetrating the concrete wall.

must be caulked. The vent must run under the slab until it can be routed up through the framing system to an exhaust point, which is a minimum of 10' (3000 mm) from other openings in the structure and 12" (300 mm) above the roof. The system should include rough-in electrical wiring for future installation of a fan located in the vent stack and a system-failure warning device. This can usually be accomplished by placing an electrical junction box in an attic space for future installation of a fan.

TYPES OF FOUNDATIONS

The foundation is usually constructed of pilings or continuous footings.

Pilings

A *piling* foundation system uses beams placed between vertical supports, called pilings, to support structural loads. The columns extend into the natural grade or other

material that extends into stable soil may support them. Piling foundations are typically used:

- On steep hillside sites where it may not be feasible to use traditional excavating equipment.
- Where the load imposed by the structure exceeds the bearing capacity of the soil.
- On sites subject to flooding or other natural forces that might cause large amounts of soil to be removed.
- On sites subject to coastal high-hazards. These homes must be supported on pilings or columns, and a design professional must certify that their design and method of construction comply with IRC standards.

Coastal property and sites near inland bodies of water subject to flooding caused by storm tidal surges use a piling foundation to keep the habitable space of the structure above the flood plain level. Typically, a support beam is placed under or near each bearing wall. Beams are supported on a grid of vertical supports, which extend down to a more stable stratum of rock or dense soil. Beams can be steel, sawn, or laminated wood, or prestressed concrete. Vertical supports may be concrete columns, steel tubes or beams, wood columns, or a combination of these materials. Areas below the main floor can be left open or can be enclosed with walls as long as the walls are not required for structural reasons.

Piling Construction

On shallow pilings, a hole can be bored, and poured concrete with steel reinforcing can be used. Figure 26.5 shows a detail of a shallow poured-concrete piling. If the vertical support is required to extend deeper than 10' (3000 mm), a pressure-treated wood timber or steel column can be driven into the soil. Figure 26.6 shows a steel girder

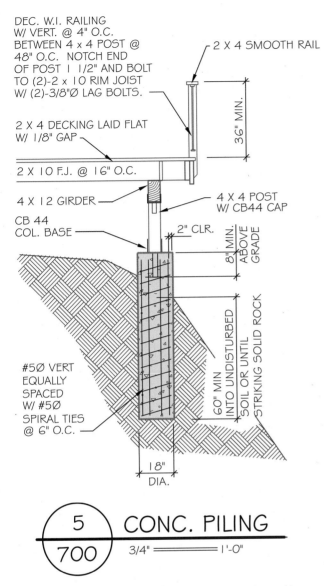

DEC. W.I. RAILING
W/ VERT. @ 4" O.C.
BETWEEN 4 x 4 POST @
48" O.C. NOTCH END
OF POST 1 1/2" AND BOLT
TO (2)-2 x 10 RIM JOIST
W/ (2)-3/8"Ø LAG BOLTS.

2 X 4 SMOOTH RAIL

36" MIN.

2 X 4 DECKING LAID FLAT
W/ 1/8" GAP

2 X 10 F.J. @ 16" O.C.

4 X 12 GIRDER

4 X 4 POST
W/ CB44 CAP

CB 44
COL. BASE

2" CLR.

8" MIN. ABOVE GRADE

60" MIN INTO UNDISTURBED
SOIL OR UNTIL STRIKING SOLID ROCK

#5Ø VERT
EQUALLY
SPACED
W/ #5Ø
SPIRAL TIES
@ 6" O.C.

18"
DIA.

5 / 700   CONC. PILING

3/4" = 1'-0"

FIGURE 26.5 A shallow piling made of concrete is used to transfer loads into stable soil. A detail will be required to explain building and steel reinforcement methods.

Residential Designs

FIGURE 26.6 If a site is too steep for shallow pilings to be dug or drilled, a steel piling can be driven until it reaches stable ground. For this hillside home, pilings averaged a depth of 30' (9000 mm) before striking solid rock.

resting on a steel piling that will be used to support the floor system of a hillside home. Figure 26.7 shows the components of a piling plan for the residence. In addition to the vertical columns supported by the pilings, diagonal steel cables or rods are placed between the columns to resist lateral and rotational forces. An engineer must design the piling foundation and the connection of the pilings to the superstructure. In addition to resisting gravity loads, a piling foundation must be able to resist forces from uplift, lateral force, and rotation. Figure 26.8 shows a detail of a concrete piling used to support steel columns, which in turn supports the floor system of the residence; it also shows a detail of a steel piling used to support steel columns above grade. Notice that the engineer has specified a system that uses braces approximately parallel to the ground (see Figure 26.6) to stabilize the tops of the pilings

against lateral loads. Show these braces on the foundation plan, and on the elevations, sections, and details.

Continuous or Spread Foundations

The most typical type of foundation used in residential construction is a continuous or **spread foundation**. The two major components of a spread foundation are the footing and stem wall. Other components of the foundation include anchor bolts, termite protection, beam supports, crawl space ventilation and access, foundation insulation, interior supports, reinforcement, and metal connectors.

Footings

The footing is the base of the foundation system and is used to displace the building loads over the soil. Figure 26.9 shows typical footings and how they are usually drawn on foundation plans. Footings are made of poured concrete and placed so that they extend below the freezing level.

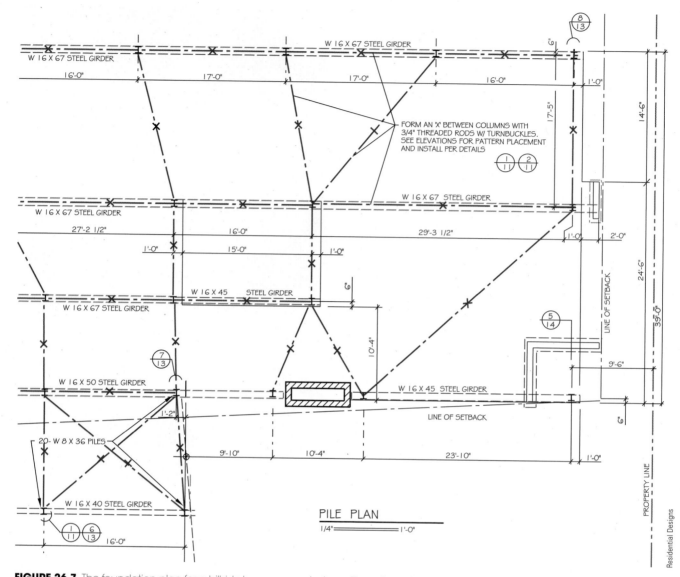

FIGURE 26.7 The foundation plan for a hillside home supported on pilings shows the location of all pilings, the beams that span between the pilings, and any diagonal bracing required to resist lateral loads.

Fully grouted masonry and wood foundations are also allowed by the IRC. The size of the footing is based on the soil's bearing value and the load to be supported. Tables 26.4a and 26.4b show common footing sizes and depths required by the IRC. The strength of the concrete must also be specified; this is based on the location of the

NOTE:

Braced wall panels located in exterior walls in structures built in seismic zones D_0, D_1, and D_2 must be supported by continuous footings. If exterior braced lines are located at more than 50' (15 000 mm) apart, an interior footing must be provided to support the interior braced wall panel. Review Chapter 25 for panel spacing requirements.

concrete in the structure and its chance of freezing. Table 26.5 lists IRC minimum comprehensive strength values.

For areas of soft soil or fill material, reinforcement steel is placed in the footing. Concrete is extremely durable when it supports a load and is compressed, but it is very weak under tension. If the footing is resting on fill material, the bottom of the concrete footing will bend. As the footing bends, the concrete will be under tension. Steel is placed near the bottom of the footing to resist the forces of tension in concrete. Reinforcing, or **rebar**, was introduced in Chapter 22. When required, it is typically placed 3" (75 mm) up from the bottom of the footing to resist the forces of tension in the footing. Figure 26.10 shows the forms set for a reinforced footing. This reinforcing steel is not shown on the foundation plan but it is specified in a note giving the size, quantity, grade, and spacing of the steel. The IRC allows only rebar that is a #4 diameter or larger to be considered as reinforcing; the use of smaller steel is considered

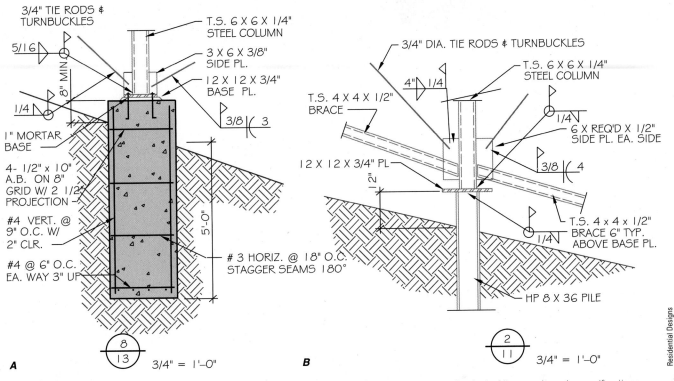

FIGURE 26.8 Details of the pilings are required to supplement the foundation plan to ensure that all of the engineer's specifications can be clearly understood. (A) The concrete piling on the left supports a steel column and (B) the piling on the right supports a steel column that extends up to the superstructure of the residence. Because of the loads to be supported, the depth of the pilings, and a severe risk of seismic damage, the engineer has specified horizontal steel-tube bracing to the top of the pilings. See Figure 26.6.

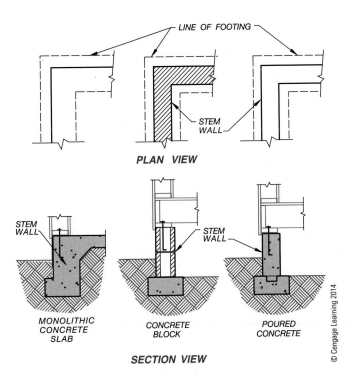

FIGURE 26.9 A footing, used to spread building loads evenly into the soil, is represented on the foundation plan by hidden lines.

© Cengage Learning 2014

non-reinforced concrete. Additional foundation reinforcement will be discussed later in this chapter as methods of binding together the stem wall and the footing are examined.

Grade Beams. To provide added support for a foundation in unstable soil, a *grade beam* may be used in place of the footing, as shown in Figure 26.11. The grade beam is similar to a wood beam that supports loads over a window. The grade beam is placed under the soil below the stem wall and spans between stable supports. The support may be stable soil or pilings. The depth and reinforcing required for a grade beam are determined by the load to be supported and are sized by an architect or engineer. A grade beam resembles a footing when drawn on a foundation plan. Steel reinforcing may be specified by notes and referenced to details rather than on the foundation plan.

Veneer Footings. If masonry or stone veneer is used, the footing must be wide enough to provide adequate support for the veneer. The footing is usually 4" (100 mm) wider than a standard footing, but the exact size will depend on the type of veneer to be supported. Figure 26.12 shows common methods of providing footing support for veneer. The footing size does not need to be altered if cultured stone is to be applied to the exterior wall.

TABLE 26.4a IRC Footing Requirements

MINIMUM WIDTH OF CONCRETE OR MASONRY FOOTINGS (INCHES) (A)

LOAD-BEARING VALUE OF SOIL (PSF)

	1,500	2,000	3,000	≥ 4,000
Conventional wood-frame construction				
1-story	12	12	12	12
2-story	15	12	12	12
3-story	23	17	12	12
4-inch brick veneer over wood frame or 8-inch hollow concrete masonry				
1-story	12	12	12	12
2-story	21	16	12	12
3-story	32	24	16	12
8-inch solid or fully grouted masonry				
1-story	16	12	12	12
2-story	29	21	14	12
3-story	42	32	21	16

For SI: 1 inch = 25.4 mm, 1 pound per square foot = 47.88 Pa.

MINIMUM WIDTH OF STEM WALL (B)

Plain Concrete	Minimum Width
Walls less than 4'-6" (1372 mm)	6" (152 mm)
Walls greater than 4'-6" (1372 mm)	7.5" (191 mm)
Plain Masonry	
Solid grout or solid units	6" (152 mm)
Non grouted units	8" (203 mm)

MINIMUM FOOTING DEPTH (C)*

Minimum 1-story	6" (152 mm)
Minimum 2-story	7" (178 mm)
Minimum 3-story	8" (203 mm)

*Values vary based on the type of soil. Verify local requirements with your building department.

MINIMUM FOOTING DEPTH INTO NATURAL GRADE (D)*

Minimum code value	12" (305 mm)
Recommended 2-story	8" (457 mm)
Recommended 3-story	24" (610 mm)

*Values vary based on the frost depth and the type of soil. Verify local requirements with your building department.

TABLE 26.4b IRC Footing Requirements Vary Based on Strength of Soil

Footing projections (P) must be a minimum of 2" (50 mm) but cannot exceed the depth of the footing. Although the IRC requires the stem wall to extend 6" (150 mm) above the finished grade, many municipalities require an 8" (200 mm) minimum projection.

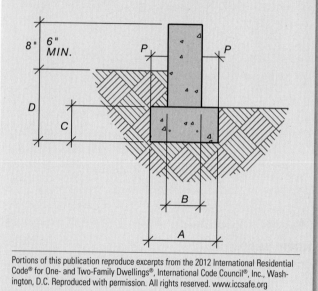

Fireplace Footings. Additional support must be provided if the footing is to support a masonry fireplace. The IRC requires the footing to be a minimum of 12" (300 mm) deep and to extend 6" (150 mm) past the face of the fireplace on each side. The footing is not required to extend under the hearth; it is used only to provide support for the chimney. Figure 26.13 shows how to represent fireplace footings on the foundation plan.

Stem Walls

The **stem wall** is the vertical wall extending from the top of the footing up to the first-floor level of the structure, as shown in Figure 26.9 and Table 26.4b. The wall is usually centered on the footing to help spread the loads being supported. The height of the wall must extend 6" (150 mm) above the ground to provide separation between wood supported by the concrete and the soil. Many municipalities require an 8" (200 mm) minimum distance between wood and the finished grade. The height can be reduced to 4" (100 mm) if masonry veneer is used. A stem wall width of 6" (150 mm) is standard for plain concrete and 8" (200 mm) for plain masonry walls. The required width of the wall varies depending on the wall height and the type of soil. Table 26.4 shows common wall dimensions.

TABLE 26.5 Compressive Strength of Concrete

TYPE OR LOCATION OF CONCRETE	MINIMUM COMPREHENSIVE STRENGTH WEATHER POTENTIAL		
	NEGLIGIBLE	MODERATE	SEVERE
Basement walls and foundations not exposed to weather	2500	2500	2500
Basement slabs and interior slabs on grade, except garage floor slabs	2500	2500	2500
Basement walls, foundation walls, exterior walls, and other vertical concrete work exposed to weather	2500	3000	3000
Porches, concrete slabs and steps exposed to the weather, and garage floor slabs	2500	3000	3500

Portions of this publication reproduce excerpts from the 2012 International Residential Code® for One- and Two-Family Dwellings®, International Code Council®, Inc., Washington, D.C. Reproduced with permission. All rights reserved. www.iccsafe.org

Common alternatives to the minimum code requirements based on local standards include:

- 8" (200 mm) wide stem walls supporting two-story construction.
- 10" (250 mm) wide stem walls supporting three-story construction.

Verify the minimum required stem wall sizes for your area prior to drawing a foundation plan.

Common methods of forming the footing and stem wall are shown in Figure 26.14. Figure 26.15a shows the forms for a poured concrete footing. Figure 26.15b shows the forms set for the stem wall, and Figure 26.15c shows

FIGURE 26.10 When concrete will be subjected to stress from tension, steel reinforcing is added to it. This footing has three continuous horizontal bars that will be held in place with circular ties placed at 24" (600 mm) along the footing.

© Cengage Learning 2014. Courtesy Aaron Jefferis

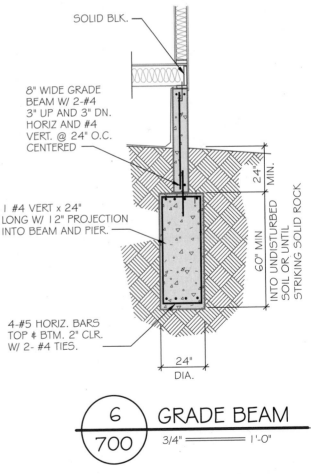

SOLID BLK.

8" WIDE GRADE BEAM W/ 2-#4 3" UP AND 3" DN. HORIZ AND #4 VERT. @ 24" O.C. CENTERED

I #4 VERT x 24" LONG W/ 12" PROJECTION INTO BEAM AND PIER.

4-#5 HORIZ. BARS TOP & BTM. 2" CLR. W/ 2- #4 TIES.

24" MIN.

60" MIN INTO UNDISTURBED SOIL OR UNTIL STRIKING SOLID ROCK

24" DIA.

6 / 700   GRADE BEAM   3/4" = I'-O"

© Cengage Learning 2014

FIGURE 26.11 A grade beam may be used in place of the foundation to provide added support for the stem wall in unstable soil. The grade beam is placed below the stem wall and spans between stable supports such as pilings.

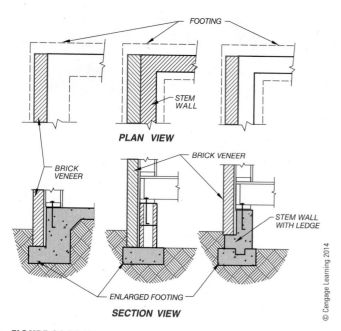

FIGURE 26.12 When a masonry veneer is added to a wall, additional footing width is needed to provide support.

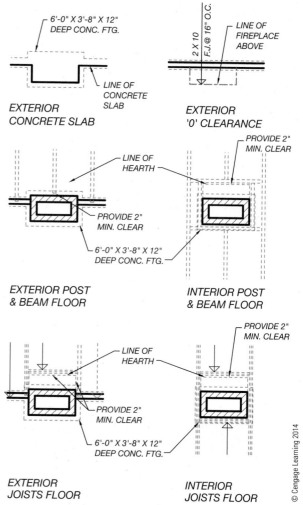

FIGURE 26.13 A masonry fireplace is required to have a 12" (300 mm) deep footing that extends 6" (150 mm) past the face of the chimney. The footing does not need to extend under the hearth projection. A wood stove, a zero-clearance fireplace, or a gas fireplace is not required to have a footing, but the outline of the unit should be represented on the foundation plan if it extends beyond the foundation.

the concrete being placed in the forms (see Figure 26.15c). Figure 26.15d shows the resulting stepped stem wall prepared for placing of the mudsill. In colder climates, a strip of foam insulation is often inserted to help control air infiltration. Figure 26.16 shows the insulation in place prior to the installation of the mudsill. Figures 26.17a, b, and c show the process of forming a wall with concrete blocks.

In addition to concrete block and poured concrete foundation walls, blocks made of expanded polystyrene foam (EPS) or other lightweight materials can be stacked into the desired position and fitted together with interlocking teeth. EPS block forms can be assembled in a much shorter time than traditional form work and remain in place to become part of the finished wall. Reinforcing steel can be set inside the block forms in patterns similar to traditional block walls. Once the forms are assembled, concrete can be pumped into the forms using any of the common methods of pouring. The finished wall has an R-value between R-22 and R-35, depending on the manufacturer. Figures 26.18a, 26.18b, and 26.18c show a foundation being built using EPS forms blocks.

Stem Wall Construction. Notice in Figure 26.9 that the footing, stem wall, and floor system are all constructed at one time. This construction practice is referred to as a *slab-on-grade* with a *turned-down footing*. Chapter 27 will examine this type of foundation and floor system. The other two foundation systems in Figure 26.9 use the footing and stem wall to support a wood floor system. To support a wood floor, the top of the stem wall

must be level. When the building site is not level, the foundation is often stepped. This helps reduce the material needed to build the foundation wall. As the ground slopes downward, the height of the wall is increased, as shown in Figure 26.19. Guidelines for stepped wall construction include:

- The foundation walls may not step more than 24" (600 mm) in one step.

- Each step must be a minimum of 32" (800 mm) long.

Wood framing used to frame between the stem wall and the floor system are referred to as *jack studs* or *cripple studs* and can be seen in Figure 26.19. These studs may not be less than 14" (350 mm) in height. Cripple walls

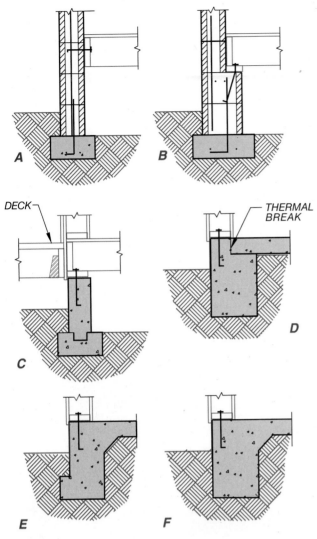

FIGURE 26.14 Common methods of forming stem walls. (A) Concrete masonry units with a pressure-treated ledger to support wood floor joists. (B) Floor joists supported on a pressure-treated sill with concrete masonry units. (C) Floor joists supported by pressure-treated sill with joists supporting a wood deck hung from a ledger. (D) Concrete floor slab supported on foundation with an isolation joint between the stem wall and slab to help the slab maintain heat. (E) Stem wall with projected footing. (F) Stem wall and foundation of equal width. Although more concrete is used, it can be formed quickly, saving time and material.

must be reinforced using the materials specified for any shear walls they support. Braced walls located above a cripple wall must be reinforced with the same type of reinforcement that they support.

Lines representing steps in the wall should be drawn for custom homes if a topography plan is available. Steps in the foundation wall are not represented for stock plans because grade contours are generally not known. Wall steps will be placed by the concrete crew as the foundation

forms are set. The foundation wall will also change heights for a sunken floor. Steps required in the foundation wall based on floor level changes must be represented on the foundation plan. Figure 26.20 shows how a sunken floor can be represented on a foundation plan.

Foundation Reinforcement

In addition to supporting the loads of the structure, the stem walls must be able to resist the lateral pressure of the soil against the wall. The material used to construct the stem wall and the area in which the building is to be located will affect how the wall and footing are tied together. If the wall and footing are made at different

FIGURE 26.15a Forms set in preparation for the concrete footing to be poured.

FIGURE 26.15b Once the footings have been poured, forms for the stem wall can be placed.

© Cengage Learning 2014

FIGURE 26.15c Concrete for the stem walls being poured. Before the concrete hardens, anchor bolts and any required metal straps or hold-downs will be placed.

Courtesy Lisa Echols

FIGURE 26.16 A strip of insulating foam has been placed in preparation for placing the mudsill. The foam helps fill seams in the building and reduce airflow into the crawl space.

© Cengage Learning 2014

FIGURE 26.15d With the forms removed and the concrete cured, the foundation is now ready to support wood framing. Notice that four of the bolts extend out of the concrete farther than the other bolts. These bolts will be used to secure hold-down anchors to the concrete to support braced wall panels.

Courtesy Carol Ventura

FIGURE 26.17a Forms are set and leveled in preparation for pouring the footings.

Courtesy Carol Ventura

NOTE:

In seismic zones D_0, D_1, and D_2, if the stem wall and footing are poured separately, the IRC requires a #4 vertical bar to be installed at 48" o.c., and hook around the top and bottom steel.

FIGURE 26.17b The concrete footing with reinforcing steel set to extend into the stem wall. Steel for the wall will be attached to the exposed steel to securely tie the wall to the footing.

FIGURE 26.17c The walls of a residence made of concrete blocks. The upper floor can either be supported directly on top of the wall or hung from the side of the wall using a ledger and metal hangers, as in Figure 26.14a.

Courtesy Reward Wall Systems

FIGURE 26.18c EPF block walls are reinforced using the same methods used with CMU block.

Courtesy PolySteel® Insulating Concrete Forms

FIGURE 26.18a Once the footing has been poured, blocks made of expanded polystyrene foam (EPS) can be stacked using similar methods to those used with CMU.

times, the IRC requires that a #4 bar be placed within 12" (305 mm) of the top of the stem wall and a #4 bar placed within 3" (76 mm) of the bottom of the footing. A *monolithic* concrete slab with a turned-down footing can be reinforced with either (1) #5 rebar or (2) #4 bars placed in the middle third of the footing. An alternative method of reinforcing monolithic slabs allows having a #4 bar 3" (76 mm) down from the top of the slab and 3" (76 mm) up from the bottom of the footing.

Courtesy Reward Wall Systems

FIGURE 26.18b Blocks made of EPS provide both a permanent form for pouring the stem wall and insulation to prevent heat loss.

© Cengage Learning 2014

FIGURE 26.19 A wood cripple wall built on the stepped footing poured in Figure 26.15d. As the stem wall steps to match the grade, short studs called cripple or jack studs are used to span between the stem wall and the floor system. Jack studs must be a minimum of 14" (350 mm) in length or the wall must be formed of solid wood.

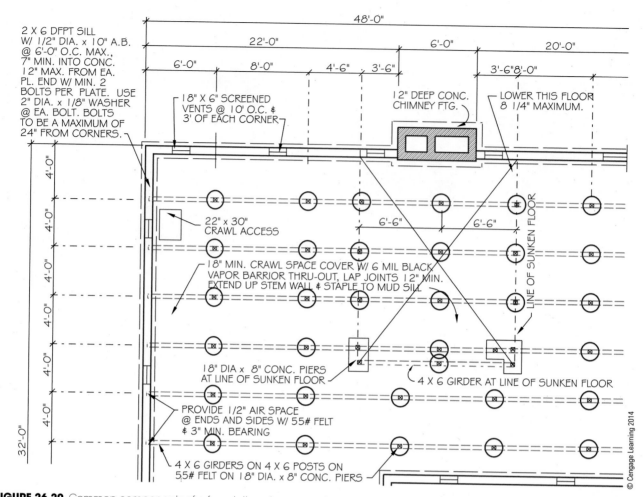

2 X 6 DFPT SILL W/ 1/2" DIA. x 10" A.B. @ 6'-0" O.C. MAX., 7" MIN. INTO CONC. 12" MAX. FROM EA. PL. END W/ MIN. 2 BOLTS PER PLATE. USE 2" DIA. x 1/8" WASHER @ EA. BOLT. BOLTS TO BE A MAXIMUM OF 24" FROM CORNERS.

18" X 6" SCREENED VENTS @ 10' O.C. & 3' OF EACH CORNER

12" DEEP CONC. CHIMNEY FTG.

LOWER THIS FLOOR 8 1/4" MAXIMUM.

22" x 30" CRAWL ACCESS

18" MIN. CRAWL SPACE COVER W/ 6 MIL BLACK VAPOR BARRIOR THRU-OUT, LAP JOINTS 12" MIN. EXTEND UP STEM WALL & STAPLE TO MUD SILL

LINE OF SUNKEN FLOOR

18" DIA x 8" CONC. PIERS AT LINE OF SUNKEN FLOOR

4 X 6 GIRDER AT LINE OF SUNKEN FLOOR

PROVIDE 1/2" AIR SPACE @ ENDS AND SIDES W/ 55# FELT & 3" MIN. BEARING

4 X 6 GIRDERS ON 4 X 6 POSTS ON 55# FELT ON 18" DIA. x 8" CONC. PIERS

48'-0" 22'-0" 6'-0" 20'-0" 6'-0" 8'-0" 4'-6" 3'-6" 3'-6" 8'-0" 6'-6" 6'-6"

32'-0" 4'-0" 4'-0" 4'-0" 4'-0" 4'-0"

© Cengage Learning 2014

FIGURE 26.20 Common components of a foundation plan are vents, crawl access, fireplace footings, sunken floors, beam pockets, stem walls, footings, and piers.

In seismic zones A, B, and C, placing a **keyway** in the footing can be used to strengthen the tie between the stem wall and footing if they are poured at different times. The keyway is formed by placing a 2 × 4 (50 × 100) in the top of the concrete footing while the concrete is still wet. Once the concrete has set, the 2 × 4 (50 × 100) is removed, leaving a keyway in the concrete. When the concrete for the stem wall is poured, it will form a **key** by filling in the keyway in the footing. If a stronger bond is desired, both steel and a keyway can be used to tie the footing to the foundation wall. Both methods of attaching the foundation wall to the footing can be seen in Figure 26.21a. Figure 26.21b shows footing forms with a 2× placed to form the keyway. Footing steel is not drawn on the foundation plan but is specified in a general note and shown in a footing detail similar to Figure 26.22.

Anchor Bolts

Steel anchor bolts are placed in the top of the stem wall to secure the wood mudsill to the concrete. The mudsill is required to be a 2 × 4 (50 × 100) and to be made from pressure-treated or some other water-resistant wood so that it will not absorb moisture from the concrete. Anchor bolts from the concrete extend through the mudsill. If concrete blocks are used, the cell containing the bolt must be filled with grout. An anchor bolt is required to be within 12" (300 mm) but not less than seven bolt diameters from each end of each plate section. A 2" (50 mm) round washer is placed over the bolt before the nut is installed to increase the holding power of the bolts. A 0.229" × 3" × 3" (5.8 × 76 × 76 mm) plate washer is required for each braced wall line for SDC D_0, D_1, and D_2. Review Chapter 26 for the use of plate washers for anchor bolts used to attach braced wall panels to the

NOTE:

The IRC requires steel to be placed in all footings in seismic zones D_0, D_1, and D_2 and for townhouses in SDC C. Requirements include:

- *One #4 horizontal bar, 3" (75 mm) down from the top of the stem wall.*
- *One #4 horizontal bar 3" (75 mm) up from the bottom of the foundation.*
- *One #4 vertical bar placed @ 48" (1200 mm) o.c., with a standard hook at its low end. The bar must extend to within 3" (75 mm) of the bottom of the footing.*
- *Slabs on grade with turned-down footings are required to have one #4 horizontal bar located 3" (75 mm) up from the bottom of the footing, and one #4 bar located 3" (75 mm) down from the top of the slab. On-grade slabs poured monolithically with the footing can have one #5 or two #4 bars located in the middle third of the footing.*

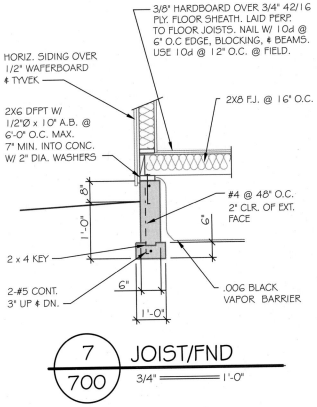

FIGURE 26.22 When steel is required in the foundation, it is usually specified in a general note on the foundation plan and in a detail.

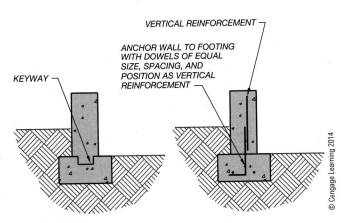

FIGURE 26.21a The footing can be bonded to the foundation wall with a key or steel reinforcing.

foundation. Other requirements for anchor bolts can be seen in Table 26.6.

The exact spacing will vary based on the height of the wall and the soil-bearing capacity. The mudsill and anchor bolts are not drawn on the foundation plan but are specified with a note, as in Figure 26.20. Figures 26.15d and 26.23 show the use of anchor bolts and the pressure-treated sill. Additional requirements for anchor bolts will be introduced as the construction of retaining walls is explored.

FIGURE 26.21b Footing forms with rebar placed and a 2× placed to form a keyway.

TABLE 26.6 Placement of Anchor Bolts

Min. diameter	1/2" Ø (13 mm)
Min. depth into concrete or masonry	7" (175 mm)
Max. spacing (1 story)	6'-0" (1800 mm)[a]
Max. spacing (2 stories) Zone D_1 and D_2	4'-0" (1200 mm)

[a] Walls 24" (610 mm) or shorter anchoring a braced wall panel can be anchored to the foundation with one anchor bolt placed in the center third of the plate. Walls 12" (305 mm) or shorter supporting a braced wall panel can be attached to the foundation without anchor bolts. See the braced wall details in Chapter 25 for additional information.

Portions of this publication reproduce excerpts from the 2012 International Residential Code® for One- and Two-Family Dwellings®, International Code Council®, Inc., Washington, D.C. Reproduced with permission. All rights reserved. www.iccsafe.org

FIGURE 26.23 Anchor bolts are used to attach the mudsill to the top of the stem wall. The tall bolt on the left end of the sill will be used to attach a metal connector to the floor system to provide additional resistance to uplift.

FIGURE 26.24b The beam seat must provide a minimum of 3" (75 mm) of bearing surface for the girder and must allow a minimum space of 1/2" (13 mm) for airflow. The girder must be wrapped with 55-lb felt to resist rotting. Notice that the girder is set flush with the top of the mudsill.

Wood Floor Support

If the house is to have a wood floor system, some method of securing the girders to the foundation must be provided. Typically a cavity or beam pocket is built into the foundation wall. The cavity provides a method of supporting the beam and helps tie the floor and foundation system together. A 3" (76 mm) minimum bearing surface must be provided for the beam where it rests on concrete. A 1/2" (13 mm) airspace must be provided around the beam in the pocket for air circulation. A second common method of beam support is to use a metal beam hanger. The top of the beam hanger extends over the mudsill and supports a U-shaped bracket that supports the girder. Figures 26.24a and 26.24b show common methods of beam support at the foundation wall.

Interior Supports. Foundation walls and footings support the exterior walls of the structure. Interior loads are supported on spot footings or piers, as seen in Figure 26.25. Poured concrete piers are formed by using either preformed or framed forms, or by excavation. The IRC allows masonry piers with a minimum thickness of 12" (305 mm) to support floor girders as long as the top of

FIGURE 26.25 Foundation walls and footings support the exterior walls of the structure. Interior loads are supported on piers formed by using either preformed or framed forms or by excavation. Pier depth is generally required to match that of the footings. Notice the continuous footing extending across the crawl space that will be used to support loads from multilevel floor systems.

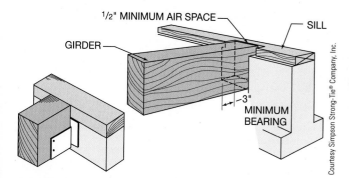

1/2" MINIMUM AIR SPACE — SILL
GIRDER
3"
MINIMUM BEARING

FIGURE 26.24a A beam seat, or pocket, can be recessed into the foundation wall, or the beam may be supported by metal connectors.

the footing to the girder does not exceed a maximum height of 10' (3048 mm). Pier depth of concrete piers is generally required to match that of the footings. Although Figure 26.25 shows the piers above the finished grade, many municipalities require the mass of the footing to be placed below grade to prevent problems with freezing and shifting from seismic activity. The type of floor system determines the placement of piers; this will be further explored in Chapter 27. The size of the pier depends on the load being supported and the soil's bearing pressure. Piers are usually drawn on the foundation plan with dashed lines, as shown in Figures 26.20 and 26.26.

Support for Lateral Loads

In addition to the exterior footings and interior piers, continuous footings are required under braced walls. Chapter 25 introduced braced walls and braced wall lines. When the distance between braced wall lines exceeds 35'-0" (10 500 mm), an interior braced wall line must be provided. A beam or double joist is required to support the interior braced wall line. At the foundation level, for single-level homes located in SDC D_2, braced wall panels must be supported on continuous foundations at intervals that exceed 50'-0" (15 000 mm). A continuous foundation must be provided below all braced wall panels for multilevel homes in seismic zone D_2.

Resisting Lateral Loads at a Garage Opening. Another consideration of foundation walls and footings is the placement of each by a garage door. For small openings such as a 36" (900 mm) door, the footing is continued under the door opening. The stem wall is omitted at the door to allow access to the garage without having to step over the wall each time the garage is entered. In areas of the country with low seismic risk, for large openings such as the main garage door, the footing is not continuous across the door opening. In areas at risk of seismic activity, the footing must extend across the entire width of the door. The continuous footing helps the walls on each side of the door to act as one wall unit. The stem wall is cut to allow the concrete floor to cover the stem wall, providing a smooth entry into the garage. If a braced wall panel is located adjacent to a garage door, the footing must be continuous and reinforced per the drawings in Chapter 25.

Metal Connectors. Metal connectors are often used at the foundation level to resist stress from wind and seismic forces. Three of the most commonly used metal connectors are shown in Figure 26.27. The senior drafter or designer will determine the proper connector and specify it on the foundation plan. How the connector is used will determine how to specify it. Figure 26.28 shows how these connectors might be specified on the foundation plan.

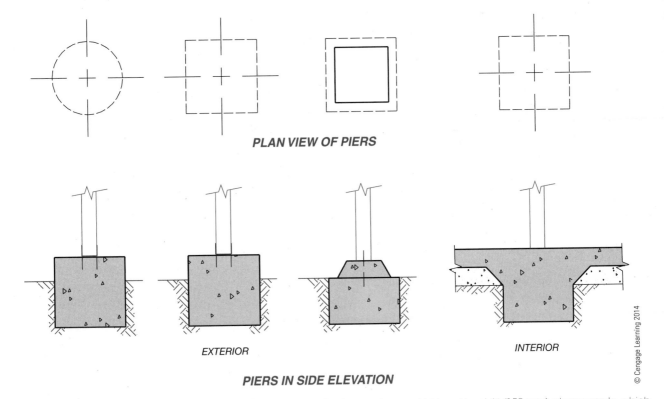

PLAN VIEW OF PIERS

EXTERIOR

INTERIOR

© Cengage Learning 2014

PIERS IN SIDE ELEVATION

FIGURE 26.26 Concrete piers are used to support interior loads. Codes require wood to be at least 6" (150 mm) above grade, which means that piers must also extend 6" (150 mm) above grade.

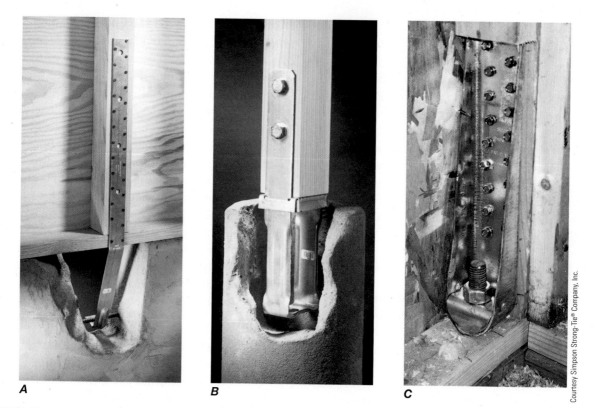

A   B   C

Courtesy Simpson Strong-Tie® Company, Inc.

FIGURE 26.27 Three common types of metal connectors used on the foundation systems to resist (A) uplift, (B) gravity loads, and (C) lateral loads. Vendor catalogs or the Internet are common sources of information that must be consulted to complete the foundation plan or details.

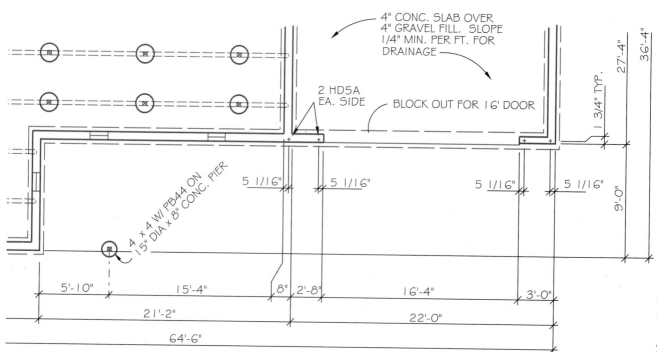

4" CONC. SLAB OVER
4" GRAVEL FILL. SLOPE
1/4" MIN. PER FT. FOR
DRAINAGE

2 HD5A
EA. SIDE   BLOCK OUT FOR 16' DOOR

4 x 4 W/ PB44 ON
15" DIA x 8" CONC. PIER

1 3/4" TYP.   27'-4"   36'-4"

5 1/16"   5 1/16"   5 1/16"   5 1/16"

9'-0"

5'-10"   15'-4"   8"   2'-8"   16'-4"   3'-0"

21'-2"   22'-0"

64'-6"

© Cengage Learning 2014

FIGURE 26.28 Metal connectors used at the foundation level must be clearly specified on the foundation plan.

> ## NOTE:
> *The requirement for placing corner vents often conflicts with the requirements for placing lateral bracing. Place the corner vents as close as possible, but so that they do not interfere with lateral bracing panels.*

Crawl Space Ventilation

If the foundation will support a wood floor system, air must be provided to circulate under the floor system. The air circulation is usually provided by cross-ventilation from screened, closable vents installed in the stem wall or between the floor framing members (see Figure 26.24b). The IRC requires that vents be provided to supply 1 sq ft of ventilation for each 150 sq ft (0.0929 m²/14 m²) of crawl space. To supply ventilation under the floor, vents must be set into the foundation wall, as shown in Figure 26.20. In addition to minimum size requirements, one vent must be provided within 3'-0" (900 mm) of each corner to provide air current throughout the crawl space.

Unvented Crawl Spaces. The IRC does allow the crawl space to be unvented under special circumstances. Usually vents are omitted from the crawl space to allow this space to be used as a *plenum*. To have an unvented crawl space, the soil in the crawl space must be covered with a Class I vapor retarder that is installed to meet the following guidelines.

- The edges of the vapor retarder must be overlapped by 6" (152 mm) and must be sealed or taped. The barrier must also extend up the stem wall 6" (150 mm) minimum and be attached and sealed to the stem wall.
- One of the following is provided:
  a. A continuously operated mechanical exhaust system that provides 1 cfm (0.47 L/s) for each 50 sq ft (4.7 m²) of crawl space floor area including an air pathway to the common area. Perimeter insulation that is permanently fastened to the stem wall that extends from the floor down the wall to the finished grade level, and then horizontally for 24" (150 mm), must also be supplied.
  b. Conditioned air supply sized to deliver at a rate equal to 1 cfm (0.47 L/s) for each 50 ft² (4.7 m²) of crawl space floor area including a return-air pathway to the common area. Perimeter insulation that is permanently fastened to the stem wall as per Option A must also be supplied.

Hydrostatic Venting. In addition to providing ventilation to the crawl space to provide cross ventilation, structures built in coastal high-hazard zones must be provided with hydrostatic venting. *Hydrostatic vents* are designed to allow floodwater to flow through the crawl space and resist the tendency of floodwater to push a structure off its foundation. During a flood event, water will enter the crawl space through foundation cracks, vents, or other openings in the stem wall. An equally dangerous problem arises from the pressure from floodwaters on the outside of the stem wall will tend to sweep a home from its foundation. Although the screened vents used for ventilation will allow water into the crawl space, they can't reduce the pressure fast enough to avoid severe damage. Screened vents intended for airflow can become clogged with flood debris, or may be sealed shut during cold weather.

Hydrostatic vents are designed to open fully to allow water pressure to equalize and reduce the risk of uneven pressure on the stem wall. Required vents must meet the following IRC requirements:

- A minimum of two hydrostatic openings on different sides of the foundation in high-hazard areas including zones A and V.
- A total net area of 1 sq inch (645 mm²) of venting for each square foot (0.093 m²) of enclosed area is required unless proof is provided by a design professional that the venting method will meet ASCE design standards.
- Vents are required to be within 12" (305 mm) of the adjacent ground level and the opening of the vent is required to be 3" (76 mm) in each direction.
- Any covers such as louvers or screens that are provided with the vent must allow for automatic opening of the vent to its full, required size.
- Vents can be placed in doors or windows, but a door or window itself can't be counted as a vent.

Crawl Space Access

Access must be provided to all underfloor spaces. If the access is provided in the floor of the residence, it must be a minimum of 18 × 24" (457 × 610 mm). Place the access in a closet or in an area where it will not be in a traffic path. If it is provided in an exterior foundation wall, the access opening is required to be 16 × 24" (400 × 600 mm). Figure 26.20 shows how a crawl access, vents, and girder pockets are typically represented on a foundation plan.

Foundation Insulation

When required by the IRC or if the foundation is for an energy-efficient structure, insulation is added to the wall. Two-inch (50 mm) rigid insulation is used to protect the wall from cold weather, as with the wall shown in Figure 26.4. This can be placed on either side of the wall. If the insulation is placed on the exterior side of the wall, the wall will retain heat from the building, but the insulation must be protected from damage. Figures 26.4 and 26.29a and b show exterior insulation placement.

Termite Protection

In many parts of the country, the local building department will require the mudsill to be protected from termites. Among the most common methods of protection are metal caps placed between the mudsill and the stem wall, chemical treatment of the soil around the foundation, and chemically treated wood near the ground. Treated wood products such as BluWood can be used to frame an entire structure in areas with severe termite problems. The metal shield is not drawn on the foundation plan but is specified in a note near the foundation plan or in a foundation detail.

RETAINING WALLS

Retaining walls can either be part of the structure or freestanding walls. Freestanding walls are used to control the height of the soil away from the structure and will not be covered in this text. Because they are only anchored at

FIGURE 26.29b Two-inch rigid insulation in place prior to backfilling the basement wall. The IRC requires any exposed insulation to be protected.

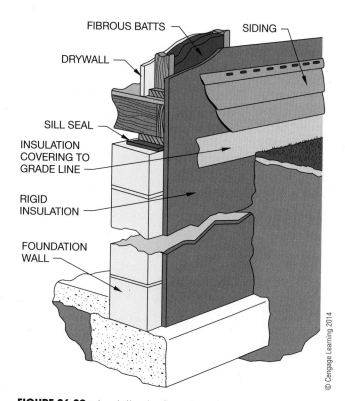

FIBROUS BATTS — SIDING

DRYWALL

SILL SEAL

INSULATION COVERING TO GRADE LINE

RIGID INSULATION

FOUNDATION WALL

FIGURE 26.29a Insulation is often placed on the foundation wall to help cut heat loss.

their base, they generally require wider footings and more reinforcing steel than a full-height retaining wall that is part of a structure. An engineer is usually required to certify the design of freestanding retaining walls, although many municipalities have stock details that can be used to build these walls. Common types of retaining walls that are part of the structure include full-height masonry walls, full-height wood walls, and partial-height walls.

Full-Height Masonry and Concrete Walls

Retaining or basement walls are walls that extend for the full height between the basement floor and the main floor level of the structure. This type of wall is anchored at the top by the main floor and at the bottom by the basement slab. They are primarily made of concrete blocks, poured concrete, or concrete-filled insulated concrete foam blocks. The IRC also allows the use of pressure-treated wood walls. The material used will depend on labor trends in your area and will affect the height of the wall. If concrete blocks are used, the wall is approximately 12 blocks high from the top of the footing. If poured concrete is used, the wall will normally be 8' (2400 mm) high from the top of the footing.

This will allow 4 × 8' (1200 × 2400 mm) sheets of plywood to be used as forms for the sides of the wall. Like a foundation wall, the basement wall needs to be protected from termites and reinforced. Neither type of information will be drawn on the foundation plan but both must be specified in notes.

Wall Reinforcement

Regardless of the material used, basement walls serve the same function as the shorter foundation walls. Because of the added height of these walls, the lateral forces acting on their sides are magnified. As seen in Figure 26.30, lateral soil pressure bends the wall inward, thus placing the soil side of the wall in compression and the interior face of the wall in tension. To resist this tensile stress, the building department may require steel reinforcing. The seismic zone will affect the size and placement of the steel. Figures 26.31 and 26.32 show common patterns of steel placement. Figure 26.33 shows a typical foundation detail used to represent the steel placement of a retaining wall. Figure 26.34 shows an example of steel placement for a poured concrete retaining wall.

Wall-to-Floor Connections

The footing for a retaining wall is usually 16" (400 mm) wide and either 8 or 12" (200 or 300 mm) deep. The depth depends on the weight to be supported and the soil bearing capacity. Steel is extended from the footing into the wall. At the top of the wall, anchor bolts are placed in the wall, using the same method as for a foundation wall. Anchor bolts are placed much closer together for retaining walls than for shorter walls. Common bolt spacing for retaining walls includes:

- 24" (600 mm) o.c. when floor joists are perpendicular to the wall
- 32" (800 mm) o.c. where joists are parallel to the retaining wall

It is very important that the wall and the floor system be tied together securely. The floor system is used to help strengthen the wall and resist soil pressure. Where seismic risk is great, metal angles are added to the anchor bolts to make the tie between the wall and the floor joist extremely rigid. These connections are shown on the foundation plan, as seen in Figure 26.35.

Soil Drainage

To reduce soil pressure next to the footing, a drain is installed. The drain is set at the base of the footing to collect and divert water from the face of the wall. Figure 26.3 shows how the drain is placed and Figure 26.35 shows how a drain can be represented on a foundation plan. The area above the drain is filled with gravel so that subsurface water will percolate to the drain and away from the wall. Reducing the water content of the soil reduces the lateral pressure on the wall. The drain is not drawn on the foundation plan but must be specified in a note on the foundation plan, sections, and foundation details.

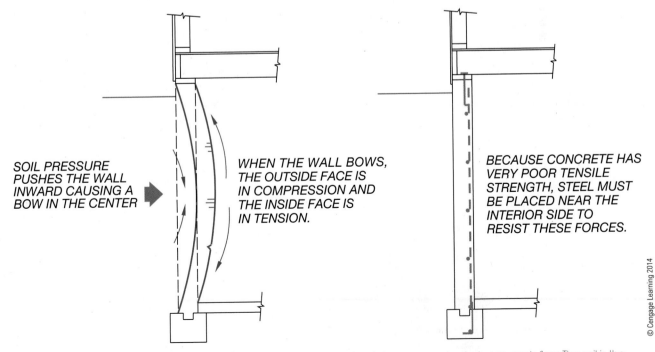

SOIL PRESSURE PUSHES THE WALL INWARD CAUSING A BOW IN THE CENTER

WHEN THE WALL BOWS, THE OUTSIDE FACE IS IN COMPRESSION AND THE INSIDE FACE IS IN TENSION.

BECAUSE CONCRETE HAS VERY POOR TENSILE STRENGTH, STEEL MUST BE PLACED NEAR THE INTERIOR SIDE TO RESIST THESE FORCES.

FIGURE 26.30 Stresses acting on a retaining wall cause it to act as a simple beam spanning between each floor. The soil is the supported load causing the wall to bow. The side of the wall closest to the soil will be in compression, and the opposite side of the wall will be in tension. Steel is added to the tension side of the wall to resist the tendency to stretch.

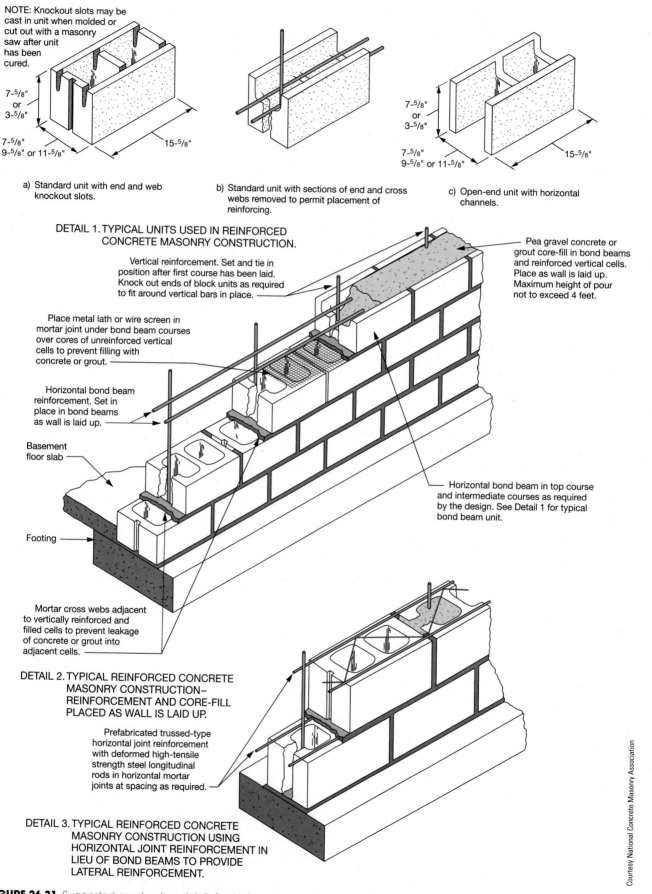

NOTE: Knockout slots may be cast in unit when molded or cut out with a masonry saw after unit has been cured.

7-5/8" or 3-5/8"

7-5/8" 9-5/8" or 11-5/8"

15-5/8"

a) Standard unit with end and web knockout slots.

b) Standard unit with sections of end and cross webs removed to permit placement of reinforcing.

c) Open-end unit with horizontal channels.

7-5/8" or 3-5/8"

7-5/8" 9-5/8" or 11-5/8"

15-5/8"

DETAIL 1. TYPICAL UNITS USED IN REINFORCED CONCRETE MASONRY CONSTRUCTION.

Vertical reinforcement. Set and tie in position after first course has been laid. Knock out ends of block units as required to fit around vertical bars in place.

Pea gravel concrete or grout core-fill in bond beams and reinforced vertical cells. Place as wall is laid up. Maximum height of pour not to exceed 4 feet.

Place metal lath or wire screen in mortar joint under bond beam courses over cores of unreinforced vertical cells to prevent filling with concrete or grout.

Horizontal bond beam reinforcement. Set in place in bond beams as wall is laid up.

Basement floor slab

Footing

Horizontal bond beam in top course and intermediate courses as required by the design. See Detail 1 for typical bond beam unit.

Mortar cross webs adjacent to vertically reinforced and filled cells to prevent leakage of concrete or grout into adjacent cells.

DETAIL 2. TYPICAL REINFORCED CONCRETE MASONRY CONSTRUCTION– REINFORCEMENT AND CORE-FILL PLACED AS WALL IS LAID UP.

Prefabricated trussed-type horizontal joint reinforcement with deformed high-tensile strength steel longitudinal rods in horizontal mortar joints at spacing as required.

DETAIL 3. TYPICAL REINFORCED CONCRETE MASONRY CONSTRUCTION USING HORIZONTAL JOINT REINFORCEMENT IN LIEU OF BOND BEAMS TO PROVIDE LATERAL REINFORCEMENT.

Courtesy National Concrete Masonry Association

FIGURE 26.31 Suggested construction details for reinforced concrete masonry foundation walls.

TABLE R404.1.2(3)
MINIMUM VERTICAL REINFORCEMENT FOR 8-INCH (203 mm) NOMINAL FLAT CONCRETE BASEMENT WALLS[b, c, d, e, f, h, i]

MAXIMUM UNSUPPORTED WALL HEIGHT (feet)	MAXIMUM UNBALANCED BACKFILL HEIGHT[g] (feet)	MINIMUM VERTICAL REINFORCEMENT-BAR SIZE AND SPACING (inches)		
		Soil classes[a] and design lateral soil (psf per foot of depth)		
		GW, GP, SW, SP 30	GM, GC, SM, SM-SC and ML 45	SC, ML-CL and inorganic CL 60
8	4	NR	NR	NR
	5	NR	NR	NR
	6	NR	NR	6 @ 37
	7	NR	6 @ 36	6 @ 35
	8	6 @ 41	6 @ 35	6 @ 26
9	4	NR	NR	NR
	5	NR	NR	NR
	6	NR	NR	6 @ 35
	7	NR	6 @ 35	6 @ 32
	8	6 @ 36	6 @ 32	6 @ 23
	9	6 @ 35	6 @ 25	6 @ 18
10	4	NR	NR	NR
	5	NR	NR	NR
	6	NR	NR	6 @ 35
	7	NR	6 @ 35	6 @ 29
	8	6 @ 35	6 @ 29	6 @ 21
	9	6 @ 34	6 @ 22	6 @ 16
	10	6 @ 27	6 @ 17	6 @ 13

For SI: 1 foot = 304.8 mm; 1 inch = 25.4 mm; 1 pound per square foot per foot = 0.1571 kPa²/m, 1 pound per square inch = 6.895 kPa.

NR = Not required.

a. Soil classes are in accordance with the Unified Soil Classification System. Refer to Table R405.1.
b. Table values are based on reinforcing bars with a minimum yield strength of 60,000 psi, concrete with a minimum specified compressive strength of 2,500 psi and vertical reinforcement being located at the centerline of the wall. See Section R404.1.2.3.7.2.
c. Vertical reinforcement with a yield strength of less than 60,000 psi and/or bars of a different size than specified in the table are permitted in accordance with Section R404.1.2.3.7.6 and Table R404.1.2(9).
d. NR indicates no vertical reinforcement is required.
e. Deflection criterion is $L/240$, where L is the height of the basement wall in inches.
f. Interpolation is not permitted.
g. Where walls will retain 4 feet or more of unbalanced backfill, they shall be laterally supported at the top and bottom before backfilling.
h. See Section R404.1.2.2 for minimum reinforcement required for basement walls supporting above-grade concrete walls.
i. See Table R611.3 for tolerance from nominal thickness permitted for flat walls.

FIGURE 26.32 Required sizes of plain and reinforced concrete foundation walls.

Water and Moisture Protection

No matter what the soil's condition, the basement wall must be protected to minimize moisture passing through the wall into the living area. The IRC specifies damp proofing and waterproofing as the two levels of basement wall protection. Each method must be applied to the exterior face of a foundation wall surrounding a habitable space. The protection must be installed from the top of the footing to the grade level. *Damp proof* a masonry or concrete wall by adding 3/8" (9.5 mm) of Portland cement parging to the exterior side of the wall. A bituminous coating, acrylic modified cement, or a coat of surface-bonding mortar must then protect the parging.

In areas with a high water table or other severe soil/water conditions, basement walls surrounding habitable space must be waterproofed. *Waterproof* concrete and mortar walls are constructed by using one of the following materials:

- 2-ply hot-mopped felts.
- 55-lb (25 kg) roll roofing.
- 6-mil (0.15 mm) polyethylene.
- 6-mil (0.15 mm) polyvinyl chloride.
- 40-mil (1 mm) polymer-modified asphalt.
- 60-mil (1.5 mm) flexible polymer cement.
- 1/8" (3 mm) cement-based, fiber-reinforced waterproof coating.
- 60-mil (1.5 mm) solvent-free liquid applied synthetic rubber.

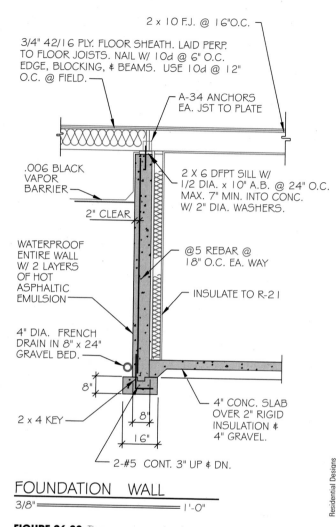

2 x 10 F.J. @ 16"O.C.

3/4" 42/16 PLY. FLOOR SHEATH. LAID PERP.
TO FLOOR JOISTS. NAIL W/ 10d @ 6" O.C.
EDGE, BLOCKING, & BEAMS. USE 10d @ 12"
O.C. @ FIELD.

A-34 ANCHORS
EA. JST TO PLATE

.006 BLACK
VAPOR
BARRIER

2" CLEAR

2 X 6 DFPT SILL W/
1/2 DIA. x 10" A.B. @ 24" O.C.
MAX. 7" MIN. INTO CONC.
W/ 2" DIA. WASHERS.

WATERPROOF
ENTIRE WALL
W/ 2 LAYERS
OF HOT
ASPHALTIC
EMULSION

@5 REBAR @
18" O.C. EA. WAY

INSULATE TO R-21

4" DIA. FRENCH
DRAIN IN 8" x 24"
GRAVEL BED.

8"

2 x 4 KEY

8"

16"

2-#5 CONT. 3" UP & DN.

4" CONC. SLAB
OVER 2" RIGID
INSULATION &
4" GRAVEL.

FOUNDATION   WALL
3/8" ═══════════ = 1'-0"

FIGURE 26.33 The components of a concrete retaining wall
are specified in a section or detail. Key components are the
building material of the wall, reinforcing material, floor attachment,
waterproofing, and drainage method.

Residential Designs

© Cengage Learning 2014

FIGURE 26.34 Reinforcing steel extends from the footing and ties
to the wall steel to provide strength for the retaining wall. Once
all of the wall steel has been placed, the balance of the wood
forms can be placed and then the concrete can be poured.

Adding Basement Windows

Adding windows to the basement can help cut down the
moisture content of the basement. Figure 26.36 shows the
framing for a window in an EPS foundation wall. This will
sometimes require adding a window well to prevent the
ground from being pushed in front of the window. Figure
26.35 shows how a ***window well***—or areaway, as it is sometimes called—can be represented on the foundation plan.

Treated-Wood Basement Walls

Pressure-treated lumber can be used to frame both crawl
space and basement walls. Treated-wood basement walls
allow for easy installation of electrical wiring, insulation, and finishing materials. Instead of a concrete foundation, a gravel bed supports the wall loads. Gravel is
required to extend 4" (100 mm) on each side of the wall
and be approximately 8" (200 mm) deep. A 2× (50×)

pressure-treated plate is laid on the gravel and the wall is
built using pressure-treated wood. Pressure-treated 1/2"
(13 mm) C–D grade plywood with exterior glue is laid
perpendicular to the studs, covered with 6-mil polyethylene, and sealed with an adhesive. Figure 26.37 shows a
detail for a wood retaining wall.

Partial-Height Retaining Walls

As seen in Figure 26.38, when a structure is built on a
sloping site, the masonry wall may not need to be full
height. Although less soil is retained than with a full-
height wall, more problems are encountered. Figure
26.39 shows the tendency of this type of wall to bend.
Because the wall is not supported at the top by the floor,
the soil pressure must be resisted through the footing.
This requires a larger footing than for a full-height wall.
If the wall and footing connection is rigid enough to keep

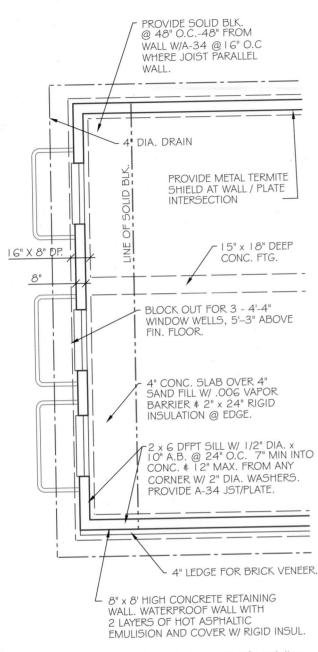

PROVIDE SOLID BLK.
@ 48" O.C.-48" FROM
WALL W/A-34 @ 16" O.C
WHERE JOIST PARALLEL
WALL.

4" DIA. DRAIN

LINE OF SOLID BLK.

PROVIDE METAL TERMITE
SHIELD AT WALL / PLATE
INTERSECTION

16" X 8" DP.

8"

15" x 18" DEEP
CONC. FTG.

BLOCK OUT FOR 3 - 4'-4"
WINDOW WELLS, 5'-3" ABOVE
FIN. FLOOR.

4" CONC. SLAB OVER 4"
SAND FILL W/ .006 VAPOR
BARRIER & 2" x 24" RIGID
INSULATION @ EDGE.

2 x 6 DFPT SILL W/ 1/2" DIA. x
10" A.B. @ 24" O.C. 7" MIN INTO
CONC. & 12" MAX. FROM ANY
CORNER W/ 2" DIA. WASHERS.
PROVIDE A-34 JST/PLATE.

4" LEDGE FOR BRICK VENEER.

8" x 8' HIGH CONCRETE RETAINING
WALL. WATERPROOF WALL WITH
2 LAYERS OF HOT ASPHALTIC
EMULISION AND COVER W/ RIGID INSUL.

© Cengage Learning 2014

FIGURE 26.35 Common elements shown on a foundation with a basement. If a window is to be placed in a full-height basement wall, a window well to restrain the soil around the window is required. On the interior side of the wall, blocking is placed between floor joists that are parallel to the retaining wall. The blocking provides rigidity to the floor system, allowing lateral pressure from the wall to be transferred into the floor system.

Courtesy Reward Wall Systems

FIGURE 26.36 Windows framed into an EPS foundation wall. Once the wall has been reinforced and the concrete has cured, window wells can be placed around the windows and backfill can be placed around the foundation.

footing has been discussed earlier as a means of tying the stem wall to the footing. A *key* is added to the bottom of the footing to help keep it from sliding as a result of soil pressure against the wall. The key is not shown on the foundation plan but is shown in a detail of the wall.

DIMENSIONING FOUNDATION COMPONENTS

This chapter presents components of a foundation system and explains how to draw them on the foundation plan. The manner in which they are dimensioned is equally important to the construction crew. Use the same line quality for the dimension and leader lines as on the framing plan. Dimension jogs in the foundation wall using the same methods used on the floor or framing plan. Most of the dimensions for major shapes will be the same as the corresponding dimensions on the framing plan. Place the foundation plan in the same drawing file as the floor and framing plans. This will allow the overall dimensions for the framing plan to be displayed on the foundation plan if different layers are used to place the dimensions. Layers such as *DIM BASE*, *DIM FRAM*, and *DIM FND* help differentiate between dimensions for the floor and foundation.

A different method is used to dimension the interior walls of a foundation than those used on a floor plan. Foundation walls are dimensioned from face to face rather than face to center, as on a floor plan. Footing widths are usually dimensioned to their center. Each type of dimension is shown in Figure 26.43 as well as in Figures 26.20, 26.28, and 26.41.

the wall in position, the soil pressure will try to overturn the whole foundation. The extra footing width is required to resist the tendency to overturn. Figure 26.40 shows a detail required to explain the construction of the wall. Figure 26.41 shows how a partial-height retaining wall will be represented on a foundation plan. Depending on the slope of the ground being supported, a key may be required, as in Figure 26.42. A keyway on the top of the

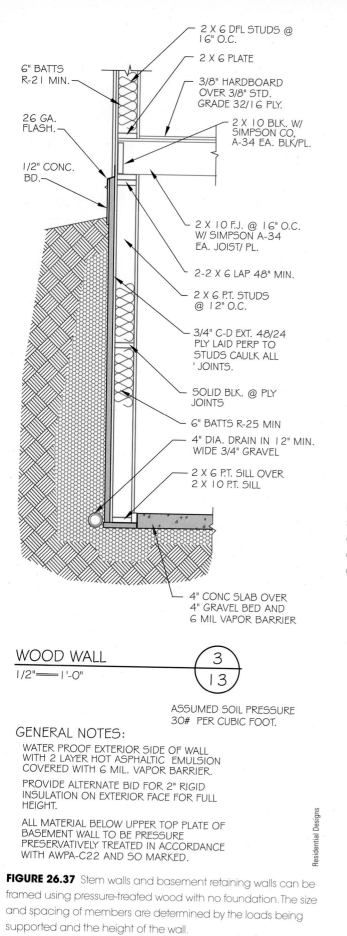

6" BATTS R-21 MIN.

26 GA. FLASH.

1/2" CONC. BD.

2 X 6 DFL STUDS @ 16" O.C.

2 X 6 PLATE

3/8" HARDBOARD OVER 3/8" STD. GRADE 32/16 PLY.

2 X 10 BLK. W/ SIMPSON CO, A-34 EA. BLK/PL.

2 X 10 F.J. @ 16" O.C. W/ SIMPSON A-34 EA. JOIST/ PL.

2-2 X 6 LAP 48" MIN.

2 X 6 P.T. STUDS @ 12" O.C.

3/4" C-D EXT. 48/24 PLY LAID PERP TO STUDS CAULK ALL ' JOINTS.

SOLID BLK. @ PLY JOINTS

6" BATTS R-25 MIN

4" DIA. DRAIN IN 12" MIN. WIDE 3/4" GRAVEL

2 X 6 P.T. SILL OVER 2 X 10 P.T. SILL

4" CONC SLAB OVER 4" GRAVEL BED AND 6 MIL VAPOR BARRIER

WOOD WALL
1/2"═══ I'-0"

(3 / 13)

ASSUMED SOIL PRESSURE 30# PER CUBIC FOOT.

GENERAL NOTES:

WATER PROOF EXTERIOR SIDE OF WALL WITH 2 LAYER HOT ASPHALTIC EMULSION COVERED WITH 6 MIL. VAPOR BARRIER.

PROVIDE ALTERNATE BID FOR 2" RIGID INSULATION ON EXTERIOR FACE FOR FULL HEIGHT.

ALL MATERIAL BELOW UPPER TOP PLATE OF BASEMENT WALL TO BE PRESSURE PRESERVATIVELY TREATED IN ACCORDANCE WITH AWPA-C22 AND SO MARKED.

FIGURE 26.37 Stem walls and basement retaining walls can be framed using pressure-treated wood with no foundation. The size and spacing of members are determined by the loads being supported and the height of the wall.

Residential Designs

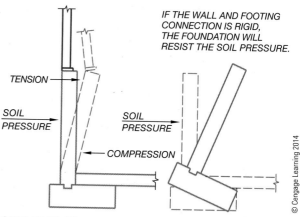

FIGURE 26.38 An 8' (2400 mm) high retaining wall may not be required on sloping lots. A partial restraining wall with wood-framed walls above it is often used.

© Cengage Learning 2014

IF THE WALL AND FOOTING CONNECTION IS RIGID, THE FOUNDATION WILL RESIST THE SOIL PRESSURE.

TENSION

SOIL PRESSURE

SOIL PRESSURE

COMPRESSION

© Cengage Learning 2014

FIGURE 26.39 When a wall is not held in place at the top, soil pressure will attempt to move the wall inward. The intersection of the wood and concrete walls is called a hinge point because of the tendency to move. The width of the footing must be increased and the hinge point must be rigid to resist overturning.

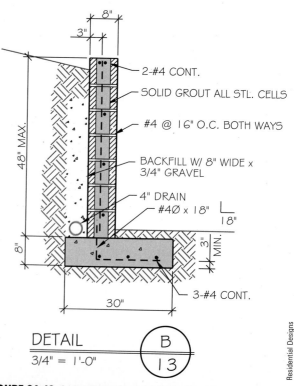

8"

3"

2-#4 CONT.

SOLID GROUT ALL STL. CELLS

#4 @ 16" O.C. BOTH WAYS

BACKFILL W/ 8" WIDE x 3/4" GRAVEL

4" DRAIN

#4Ø x 18"

18"

48" MAX.

8"

3" MIN.

30"

3-#4 CONT.

DETAIL
3/4" = 1'-0"

(B / 13)

Residential Designs

FIGURE 26.40 A detail must be drawn to explain the construction of a partial-height retaining wall.

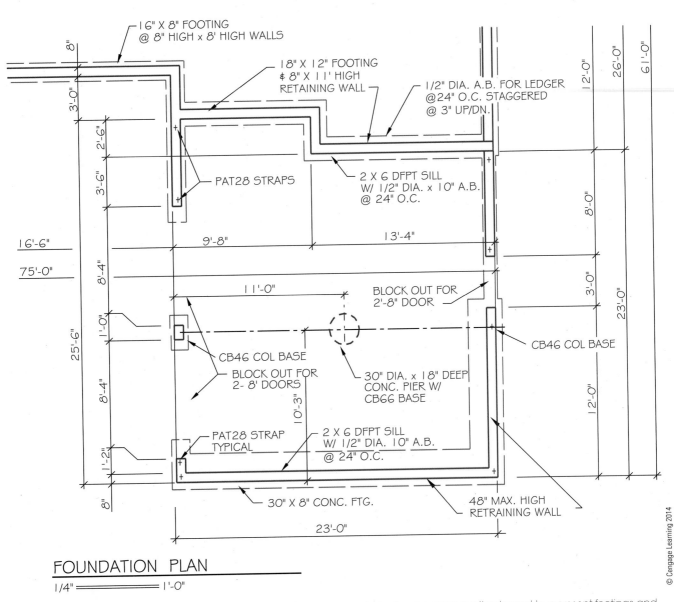

16" X 8" FOOTING
@ 8" HIGH x 8' HIGH WALLS

18" X 12" FOOTING
& 8" X 11' HIGH
RETAINING WALL

1/2" DIA. A.B. FOR LEDGER
@24" O.C. STAGGERED
@ 3" UP/DN.

PAT28 STRAPS

2 X 6 DFPT SILL
W/ 1/2" DIA. x 10" A.B.
@ 24" O.C.

BLOCK OUT FOR
2'-8" DOOR

CB46 COL BASE
BLOCK OUT FOR
2- 8' DOORS

30" DIA. x 18" DEEP
CONC. PIER W/
CB66 BASE

CB46 COL BASE

PAT28 STRAP
TYPICAL

2 X 6 DFPT SILL
W/ 1/2" DIA. 10" A.B.
@ 24" O.C.

30" X 8" CONC. FTG.

48" MAX. HIGH
RETRAINING WALL

16'-6" 75'-0" 9'-8" 13'-4" 11'-0" 10'-3" 25'-6" 23'-0"

FOUNDATION PLAN
1/4" = 1'-0"

FIGURE 26.41 Full-height and partial-height retaining walls are represented using the same methods used to represent footings and stem walls. Because of the added height, the width is typically specified on the foundation plan and the building components are specified in details or sections.

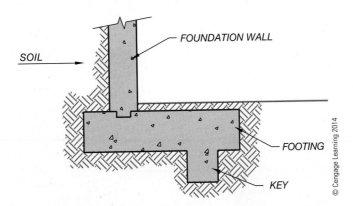

SOIL FOUNDATION WALL FOOTING KEY

FIGURE 26.42 Soil pressure will attempt to make the wall and footing slide across the soil. A key may be provided on the bottom of the footing to provide added surface area to resist sliding.

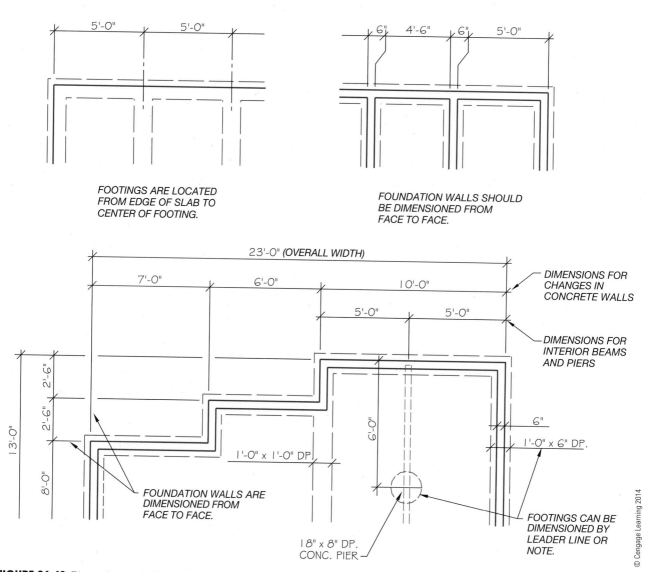

FOOTINGS ARE LOCATED
FROM EDGE OF SLAB TO
CENTER OF FOOTING.

FOUNDATION WALLS SHOULD
BE DIMENSIONED FROM
FACE TO FACE.

DIMENSIONS FOR
CHANGES IN
CONCRETE WALLS

DIMENSIONS FOR
INTERIOR BEAMS
AND PIERS

FOUNDATION WALLS ARE
DIMENSIONED FROM
FACE TO FACE.

1'-0" x 1'-0" DP.

FOOTINGS CAN BE
DIMENSIONED BY
LEADER LINE OR
NOTE.

18" x 8" DP.
CONC. PIER

1'-0" x 6" DP.

FIGURE 26.43 Dimensioning techniques for foundation plans. Always dimension to the outside edge of concrete walls and to the center of concrete piers.

© Cengage Learning 2014

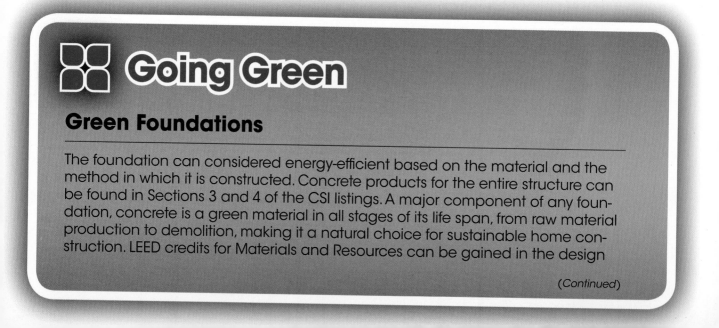

Going Green

Green Foundations

The foundation can considered energy-efficient based on the material and the method in which it is constructed. Concrete products for the entire structure can be found in Sections 3 and 4 of the CSI listings. A major component of any foundation, concrete is a green material in all stages of its life span, from raw material production to demolition, making it a natural choice for sustainable home construction. LEED credits for Materials and Resources can be gained in the design

(Continued)

of the foundation. Credits for Energy and Atmosphere and Indoor Environmental Quality can be gained when concrete is used for the entire structure. No matter the use, key sustainable qualities of concrete include the efficient use of a resource, durability, heat retention, reflectivity, and minimal waste.

- **Resource efficiency.** The predominant raw material for the cement in concrete is limestone, the most abundant mineral on earth. Concrete can also be made with fly ash, slag cement, and silica fume and other waste byproducts from power plants, steel mills, and other manufacturing facilities. This efficient use of natural resources produces long-lasting structures with life spans that can be double or triple the life of structures made from other common building materials.

- **Thermal mass.** Homes built with concrete walls, foundations, and floors can be highly energy-efficient if they are designed to take advantage of concrete's inherent thermal mass or ability to absorb and retain heat. The mass of concrete slows down heat's passage through the wall. With the same insulation as other types of construction, a concrete home stays warmer in the winter and cooler in the summer than a wood-frame home. By efficiently using concrete mass in the design of the structure, homeowners can significantly cut their heating and cooling bills and install smaller-capacity HVAC equipment.

- **Reflectivity.** With proper planning, concrete can also be used to reduce heat absorption in a structure and minimize the effects that produce urban heat islands. Light-colored concrete roofs absorb less heat and reflect more solar radiation than dark-colored materials, such as asphalt, reducing air-conditioning demands in the summer. Concrete can also be used to form the substructure for green roofs described in Section 4.

- **Minimal waste.** With proper planning, concrete can be produced in the quantities needed for each project, reducing waste. After a concrete structure has served its original purpose, the concrete can be crushed and recycled into aggregate for use in new concrete pavements or as backfill or road base.

Other areas of the foundation that gain LEED credits are the use of EPS foam blocks, wood foundations, and the use of insulation to protect the stem wall. Stem and retaining walls made of EPS blocks provide built-in insulation that will remain in place for the life of the structure. Adding wall insulation to the outside of the stem walls will allow the walls to act as a thermal mass and store heat from the living area. Insulating stem walls and eliminating the crawl space venting will allow the crawl space to be used as a plenum to circulate heated air to the living area of the home located above the crawl space.

Additional Resources

The following websites can be used as a resource to help you keep current with changes in foundation materials:

Address	Company or Organization
www.afmcorp-epsfoam.com	AFM Corporation®
www.concrete.org	American Concrete Institute
www.polysteel.com	American PolySteel®
www.arxx.com	Arxx™ Building Products
www.bluwood.com	BluWood USA, Inc.
www.bocciabros.com	Boccia Inc.
www.eco-block.com	Eco-Block
www.haenerblock.com	Haener Block Inc™. (mortarless interlocking system)
www.cement.org	Portland Cement Association
www.woodfoundations.com	Permanente Wood Foundation Systems
www.post-tensioning.org	Post-Tensioning Institute
www.rewardwalls.com	Reward Wall Systems
www.strongtie.com	Simpson Strong-Tie Company
www.smartvent.com	Smart Vent® Products, Inc.
www.soils.org	Soil Science Society of America
www.southernpine.com	Southern Pine Lumber
www.vobb.com	VOBB®—Verot Oaks Building Blocks

Foundation Systems Test

Follow these instructions to access and complete an electronic copy of the Chapter 26 Foundation Systems Test:

1. Go to cengagebrain.com
2. Enter the email address and password you used to register for the site (see Preface for full instructions).
3. Select the website from the **My Course & Materials** area of your home page. Select the chapter you want from the pull-down menu at the top of the page. Choose the resources for that chapter from the menu on the left.
4. Type your name, the chapter number, and the date at the top of the sheet.
5. Answer the following questions with short, complete statements using a word processor.

> ### NOTE:
> *The answers to some questions may not be contained in this chapter and will require you to do additional research using the Internet. Use your favorite search engine to search for specific professional companies or general categories of information.*

Questions

26.1. What are the major parts of a continuous foundation system?

26.2. What factors influence the size of footings?

26.3. List five forces that a foundation must withstand.

26.4. How can soil texture influence a foundation?

26.5. List the major types of material used to build foundation walls.

26.6. Why is steel placed in footings?

26.7. Describe when a stepped footing might be used.

26.8. What size footing should be used with a basement wall?

26.9. What influences the size of piers?

26.10. Describe the difference between a full-height retaining wall and a partial-height retaining wall.

26.11. Use the Internet to research and write a report on one of the following subjects relevant to your area.

   a. High winds and uplift affecting the foundation

   b. Soil classifications common to your area

   c. Flooding and the risk of foundation damage

26.12. After making an appointment, contact a contractor in your area and research common methods of forming foundation and basement walls for your area.

26.13. Research the greatest weather-related risk to structures in your area, and describe methods for reducing these dangers and how they affect the foundation.

26.14. Visit the website for your local building department and research local requirements for foundation support for braced wall panels.

26.15. Visit the website for your local building department and research local requirements for foundation reinforcement.

Problems

Unless your instructor gives other instructions, complete the following details for a one-level house. Use the skeleton drawings that are provided on the website in the Supplemental Drawing folder. Use a scale of 3/4" = 1'–0" with proper line weight and quality and provide notes required to label typical materials. Use four different line weights to distinguish between concrete, wood that has been cut by the cutting plane, wood that lies beyond the cutting plane, and steel. Provide dimensions based on common practice in your area. Omit insulation unless specified.

26.1 Show a typical foundation with poured concrete with a 2 × 4 key, 2 × 6 floor joists at 16" o.c., and 2 × 4 studs at 24" o.c. Provide steel reinforcement as required by local codes.

26.2 Show a typical post-and-beam foundation system. Show 4 × 6 girders at 48" o.c. parallel to the stem wall. Provide steel reinforcement as required by local codes.

26.3 Draw a foundation showing a concrete floor system. Use #10 × #10-4" × 4" welded wire mesh 2" down from top surface and (2) #4 bars centered in the footing 2" up and down. Use 2 × 4 studs at 16" o.c., for walls.

26.4   Draw a detail showing an interior footing for a concrete slab supporting a 2 × 4 stud-bearing wall. Anchor the wall with Ramset-type fasteners (or equal). Use the same slab reinforcing that was specified in problem 26.3.

26.5   Design a retaining wall for an 8' tall basement, using concrete blocks. Use 2 × 10 floor joists parallel to wall, with 5/8" diameter anchor bolts at 32" o.c. Show typical solid blocking and anchor rim joists with A-35 anchors at 16" o.c.

Show #5 @ 18" o.c., each way at 2" from tension side with (1) #5 in footing 2" up. Use a scale of 1/2" = 1'-0".

26.6   Show a detail of the intersection of a 48" high concrete retaining wall. Use a 30" wide footing with (2) #5 continuous 3" up at 12" o.c., and #5 at 24" o.c., in wall 2" from tension side. Use a 4" diameter drain in 8" × 30" gravel bed. Use 2 × 6 sill with 5/8" anchor bolts at 24" o.c. Use an 8' ceiling with 2 × 10 floor joists at 16" o.c. Cantilever 15" past wall with 1" exterior stucco. Use a scale of 1/2" = 1'-0".

Chapter 27
Floor Systems and Foundation Support

The foundation plan shows not only the concrete footings and stem walls but also the members used to form the floor system. Two common types of floor systems are used in residential construction: those built at grade level and those with a crawl space or basement below the floor system. Each has its own components and information that must be represented on a foundation plan.

Key Terms

Construction joint	Girder	Open-web truss	Sheathing
Contraction joint	Gusset	Post-and-beam	Solid blocking
Control joint	Isolation joint	Post-tensioning	Subfloor
Coverage	Joists	Rebar	Vapor barrier
Expansion joint	Ledger	Rim joist	Welded wire fabric
Flange	Monolithic	Rim track	

ON-GRADE FLOOR SYSTEMS

A concrete slab is often used for the floor system of residences in warm, dry climates. A concrete slab provides a firm floor system that requires little or no maintenance and generally less material and labor than a conventional wood floor system. The floor slab can be poured as an extension of the foundation in what is referred to as *monolithic* construction (see Figure 27.1). Other common methods of pouring a concrete foundation and floor system are shown in Figure 27.2. A 3 1/2" (90 mm) concrete slab is the minimum thickness allowed by the IRC for residential floor slabs. The slab is used only as a floor surface, not to support the weight of the walls or roof. If the floor slab must support load-bearing walls, it must be

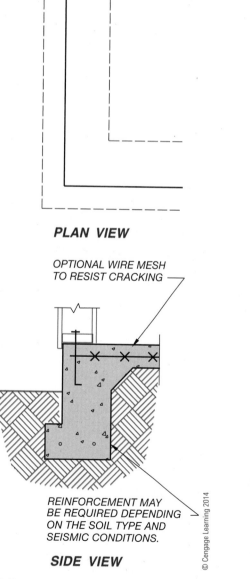

FIGURE 27.1 The foundation and floor system can often be constructed in one pour, saving time and money.

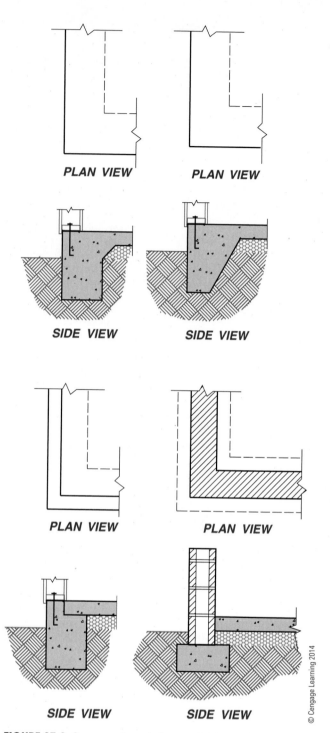

FIGURE 27.2 Common foundation and slab intersections. The upper two examples show monolithic pours and are often referred to as turned-down footings.

thickened, as shown in Figure 27.3. If a load is concentrated in a small area, a pier may be placed under the slab to help disperse the weight, as shown in Figure 27.4.

Slab Joints

Concrete tends to shrink approximately 0.66" per 100' (16.7 mm per 30 000 mm) as the moisture in the mix

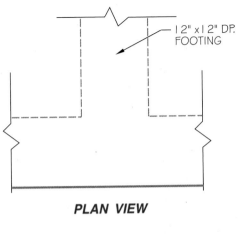

PLAN VIEW

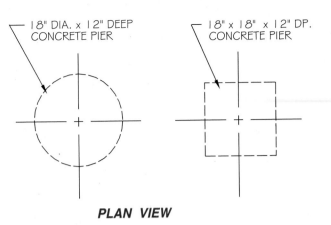

PLAN VIEW

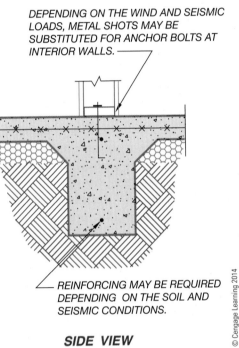

SIDE VIEW

FIGURE 27.3 A continuous footing is placed under an interior load-bearing wall.

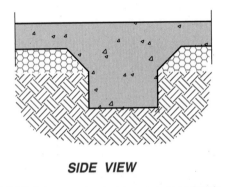

SIDE VIEW

FIGURE 27.4 A concrete pier is poured under loads concentrated in small areas. Piers are typically round or rectangular, depending on their location. Square piers are used when the exterior footing needs to be reinforced, or if the footing is so large that it must be framed with lumber. Round piers are used when the pier is placed inside the foundation and are typically dug by hand. The load to be supported and the soil bearing capacity determine the size of each pier.

hydrates and the concrete hardens. Concrete also continues to expand and shrink throughout its life, depending on the temperatures and the moisture in the supporting soil. This shrinkage can cause the floor slab to crack. To help control possible cracking, three types of joints can be placed in the slab: control, construction, and isolation joints (see Figure 27.5). The location of control and isolation joints must be referenced by the drafter, based on the designer's specifications.

Control Joints

As the slab contracts during the initial drying process, the lower surface of the slab rubs against the soil, creating tensile stress. The friction between the slab and the soil causes cracking, which can be controlled by a *control* or *contraction joint*. Such a joint does not prevent cracking, but it does control where the cracks will develop in the slab. Control joints are created by cutting the fresh concrete or sawing the concrete within 6 to 8 hours of placement. Joints are usually one-quarter of the slab depth. Because the slab has been weakened, any cracking due to stress will result along the joint. The American Concrete Institute (ACI) suggests that control joints be placed a distance in feet equal to about 2 1/2 times the slab depth in inches. For a 4" (100 mm) slab, joints would be placed at approximately 10' (3000 mm) intervals. The locations of control joints, their spacing, and the method of placement are usually specified in the foundation general notes.

Construction Joints

When concrete construction must be interrupted, a *construction joint* is used to provide a clean surface where work can be resumed. Because a vertical edge of one slab will have no bond to the next slab, a keyed joint is used to provide support between the two slabs. The key is typically formed by placing a beveled strip about one-fifth of the slab thickness and one-tenth of the slab thickness in

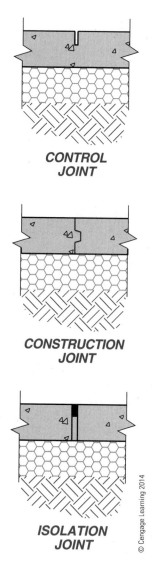

CONTROL JOINT

CONSTRUCTION JOINT

ISOLATION JOINT

© Cengage Learning 2014

FIGURE 27.5 Joints are placed in concrete to control cracking. A control joint is placed in the slab to weaken the slab and cause cracking to occur along the joint rather than throughout the slab. When construction must be interrupted, a construction joint is formed to increase bonding with the next day's pour. Isolation joints are provided to keep stress from one structural material from cracking another.

width to mold the slab. The method used to form the joint can be specified with other foundation notes, but the crew placing the concrete will determine the location.

Isolation Joints

An *isolation* or *expansion joint* is used to separate a slab from an adjacent slab, wall, or column or some other part of the structure. The joint prevents forces from an adjoining structural member from being transferred into the slab, causing cracking. Such a joint also allows for expansion of the slab caused by moisture or temperature. Isolation joints are typically between 1/4 and 1/2" (6 and 13 mm) wide. The location of isolation joints should be specified on

the foundation plan. Because of the small size of residential slabs, isolation joints are not usually required. Slabs subject to severe freezing conditions often have an isolation joint to separate the slab from the stem wall.

Slab Placement

The slab may be placed above grade, below grade, or at grade level.

Above-Ground Slabs

Residential slabs are often placed above grade for hillside construction to provide a suitable floor for a garage. A platform made of wood or steel materials can be used to support a lightweight concrete floor slab. Plywood floor sheathing, covered with 55-lb building paper, protects the wood from moisture in the concrete. Ribbed metal decks are also used for the heavier floors often found in multifamily construction. Concrete is considered lightweight depending on the amount of air that is pumped into the mixture during the manufacturing process. The components of an above-ground concrete floor should be noted on a framing plan but not drawn. The strength of the concrete and its weight should also be noted. The foundation plan shows the columns and footings used to support the increased weight of the floor. An example of a framing plan to support an above-ground concrete slab is shown in Figure 27.6. The foundation

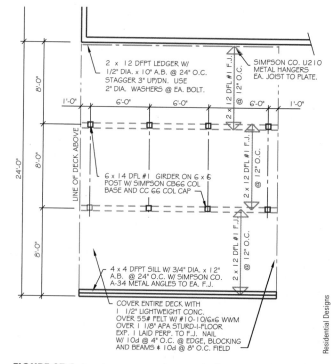

Residential Designs

FIGURE 27.6 An above-ground concrete floor is often used for high-end multifamily projects, and for a garage floor and driveway for hillside residential construction. The framing plan shows the framing of the platform used to support the concrete slab.

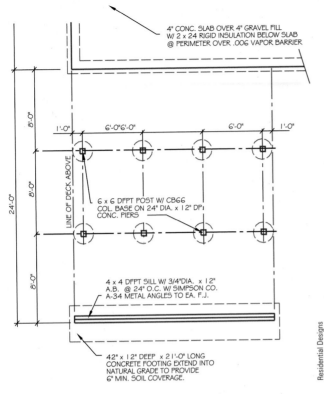

FIGURE 27.7 The foundation plan for an above-ground concrete slab shows the support piers for the framing platform.

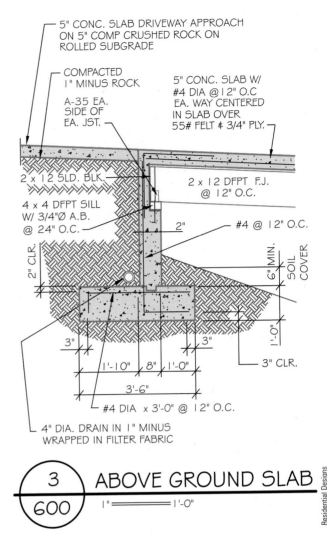

Residential Designs

$$\underset{\overline{600}}{3} \quad \text{ABOVE GROUND SLAB}$$

1" ════════════ 1'-0"

FIGURE 27.8 In addition to the framing and foundation plans, details are used to clarify the concrete reinforcement. This detail shows how the above-ground slab intersects the on-grade slab.

plan for the same area is shown in Figure 27.7. The construction process will also require details similar to those in Figure 27.8. Multilevel custom homes and multifamily projects may use precast hollow core slab units to help provide large open areas beneath the slabs. Figures 27.9a and 27.9b show premanufactured concrete floor panels being lifted into position for a residential addition.

At-Grade and Below-Grade Slabs

Slabs built below grade are most commonly used in basements. When used at grade, the slab is usually placed just above grade level. The IRC requires the slab to be 6" (150 mm) minimum above grade, but many municipalities require the top of the slab to be 8" (200 mm) above the finish grade to keep structural wood away from ground moisture.

Slab Preparation

When a slab is built at grade, approximately 8 to 12" (200 to 300 mm) of topsoil and vegetation are removed to provide a stable, level building site. Excavation usually extends about 5' (1500 mm) beyond the building edge to allow for the operation of excavating equipment needed to trench for the footings. Once forms for the footings have been set, fill material can be spread to support the slab. The IRC requires the slab to be placed on a 4" (100 mm) minimum base of compacted sand, gravel fill, or crushed stone.

FIGURE 27.9a Precast hollow core slab units are lifted into position for a residential addition.

Courtesy David P. Schulze, AIBD/CPBD, DPS-labs.com

FIGURE 27.9b Precast hollow core slab units were used to provide a large open space free of columns and beams at the lower floor level.

FIGURE 27.10a Concrete is poured in a semi-liquid state and pushed in to fill in all spaces. Notice in the background, a pumper truck is onsite. It was used to pump concrete that lies farthest from the concrete truck to save the labor cost associated with moving the concrete by hand in a wheelbarrow.

The availability of materials will dictate the type of fill material used. The fill material provides a level base for the concrete slab and helps eliminate cracking caused by settling of the ground under the slab.

The slab is required to be placed over 6-mil polyethylene sheet plastic to protect the floor from ground moisture. When a plastic *vapor barrier* is to be placed over gravel, a 1" (25 mm) layer of sand should be specified to cover the gravel fill to avoid tearing the vapor barrier. An alternative is to use 55-lb rolled roofing in place of the plastic. The fill material and the vapor barrier are not shown on the foundation plan but are specified with a note. A typical note to specify the concrete and fill material might read:

4" CONC. SLAB OVER .006 VISQUEEN OVER 1" SAND FILL OVER 4" COMPACTED GRAVEL FILL.

Figures 27.10a, 27.10b, and 27.10c show the process of a concrete slab being poured and finished.

Slab Reinforcement

When the slab is placed on more than 4" (100 mm) of uncompacted fill, *welded wire fabric* should be specified to help the slab resist cracking. Spacing and sizes of wires of welded wire fabric are identified by style and designations. A typical designation specified on a foundation plan might be:

$6 \times 12 — W16 \times W8$

where

6 = longitudinal wire spacing
12 = transverse wire spacing
16 = longitudinal wire cross sectional area
8 = transverse wire cross sectional area

FIGURE 27.10b While the two workers move the concrete into position, the center worker begins the process of smoothing the concrete and compacting the concrete to remove air pockets.

FIGURE 27.10c A worker uses a power trowel to provide a smooth finish to the concrete slab.

The letter W indicates smooth wire. D can be used to represent deformed wire. Typically a steel mesh of number 10 wire in 6" (150 mm) grids is used to reinforce residential floor slabs that are placed over fill. A note to specify reinforced concrete and fill material might read:

4" CONC. SLAB W/6 × 6 W12 × 12 WWM OVER .006 VISQUEEN OVER 1" SAND FILL OVER 4" COMPACTED GRAVEL FILL.

Figure 27.11a shows an example of the mesh used in concrete slabs. Steel reinforcing bars similar to those shown in Figure 27.11b can be added to a floor slab to prevent bending of the slab due to expansive soil.

Steel Rebar Placement in Floor Slabs

Although mesh is placed in a slab to limit cracking, steel reinforcement is placed in the concrete to prevent cracking due to bending. Steel reinforcing bars, or ***rebar***, can be laid in a grid pattern near the surface of the concrete that will be in tension from bending. The placement of the reinforcement in the concrete is important to the effectiveness of the reinforcement. The amount of concrete placed around the steel is referred to as ***coverage***. Proper coverage strengthens the bond between the steel and concrete and also protects the steel from corrosion if the concrete is exposed to chemicals, weather, or water. Proper coverage is also important to protect the steel from damage by fire. If steel is required to reinforce a residential

FIGURE 27.11a Welded wire mesh is often placed in concrete slabs to reduce cracking.

FIGURE 27.11b Steel reinforcing is used in place of welded wire mesh when the slab is placed over fill material.

concrete slab, an engineer will typically determine the size, spacing, coverage, and grade of bars to be used. As a general guideline to placing steel, the ACI recommends:

- For concrete cast against and permanently exposed to earth (footings): 3" (75 mm) minimum coverage.
- For concrete exposed to weather or earth such as basement walls: 2" (50 mm) coverage for #6–18 bars and 1 1/2" (38 mm) coverage for #5 and W31/D31 wire or smaller.
- For concrete not exposed to weather or in contact with ground: 1 1/2" (38 mm) coverage for slabs, walls, and joists; 3/4" (19 mm) coverage for #11 bars and smaller; and 1 1/2" (38 mm) coverage for #14 and #18 bars.

Wire mesh and steel reinforcement is not shown on the foundation plan but is specified by a note similar to that in Figure 27.6.

Post-Tensioned Concrete Floor Systems

The methods of reinforcement mentioned thus far assume that the slab will be poured over stable soil. Concrete slabs can often be poured over unstable soil by using a method of reinforcement known as ***post-tensioning***. This method of construction was originally developed for slabs that were to be poured at ground level and then lifted into place for multi-level structures. Adopted for the use of residential slabs, post-tensioning allows concrete slabs to be poured on grade over expansive soil. The technology has advanced sufficiently so that post-tensioning is now widely used even on stable soils.

For design purposes, a concrete slab can be considered as a wide, shallow beam supported by a concrete foundation at the edge. Although a beam may sag at the center from loads and gravity, a concrete slab can either sag or bow, depending on the soil conditions. Soil at the edge of a slab will be exposed to more moisture than soil near the center of the slab. This differential in moisture content can cause the edges of the slab to heave, creating tension in the bottom portion of the slab and compression in the upper portion. Center lift conditions can result as the soil beneath the interior of the slab becomes wetter and expands, as the perimeter of the slab dries and shrinks, or as a combination of these occurs. Heaving at the center of the slab creates tension in the upper portion of the slab with compression in the lower portion. Because concrete is very poor at resisting stress from tension, the slab must be reinforced with steel which has a high tensile strength. Steel tendons with anchors can be extended through the slab as it is poured. Usually between 3 and 10 days after the concrete has been poured, these tendons are stretched by hydraulic jacks, which place approximately 25, 000 lb of force on each tendon. The tendon force is transferred to the concrete slab through anchorage devices at the ends of the tendons. This process creates an internal compressive force throughout the slab, increasing the ability of the slab to resist cracking and heaving. Post-tensioning usually allows for a thinner slab than normally would be required to span over expansive conditions, elimination of other slab reinforcing, and elimination of most slab joints.

Two methods of post-tensioning are typically used for residential slabs: flat slab and ribbed slab. The flat-slab method uses steel tendons ranging in diameter from 3/8 to 1/2" (10 to 13 mm). The maximum spacing of tendons recommended by the Post-Tensioning Institute (PTI) are:

- 3/8" (9 mm) diameter: 5'-0"(1500 mm) spacing
- 7/16" (11 mm) diameter: 6'-10" (1800 mm) spacing
- 1/2" (13 mm) diameter: 9'-0" (2700 mm) spacing

An engineer determines the exact spacing and size of tendons based on the loads to be supported and the strength and conditions of the soil. When required, the tendons can be represented on the foundation plan, as shown in Figure 27.12. Details will also need to be provided to indicate how the tendons will be anchored as well as to show the exact locations of the tendons. Figure 27.13 is an example of a tendon detail. In addition to representing and specifying the steel throughout the floor system, the drafter will need to specify the engineer's requirements for the strength of the concrete at 28 days, the period when the concrete is to be stressed, as well as what strength the concrete should achieve before stressing.

A second method of post-tensioning an on-grade floor slab is with the use of concrete ribs or beams placed below the slab, similar to the foundation in Figure 27.14. These beams reduce the span of the slab over the soil and provide increased support. The engineer determines the width,

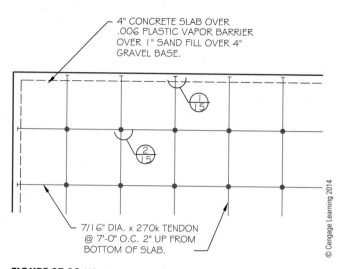

FIGURE 27.12 When a concrete slab is post-tensioned, the tendons and anchors used to support the floor slab must be represented on the foundation plan.

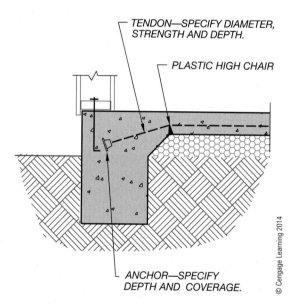

FIGURE 27.13 Tendon details should be drawn to reflect the design of the engineer.

FIGURE 27.14 The preparation for a post-tensioned on-grade floor slab is with the use of concrete ribs placed below the slab. These beams reduce the span of the slab over the soil and provide increased support. The width, depth, and spacing are determined by the engineer based on the strength and condition of the soil and the size of the slab.

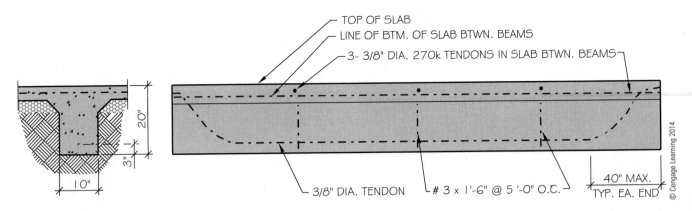

FIGURE 27.15 concrete beams can be placed below the floor slab to increase the effect of the slab tensioning. Details must be drawn to indicate how the steel will be placed in the beam, as well as how the beam steel will interact with the slab steel.

depth, and spacing based on the strength and condition of the soil and the size of the slab. Figure 27.15 shows an example of a beam detail that a drafter would be required to draw to show the reinforcing specified by the engineer. Figure 27.16 is an example of how these beams could be shown on the foundation plan.

Slab Insulation

Depending on the risk of freezing, some municipalities require the concrete slab to be insulated to prevent heat loss. The insulation can be placed under the slab or on the outside edge of the stem wall. When placed under the slab, a rigid insulation material at least 2 × 24" (50 × 600 mm)

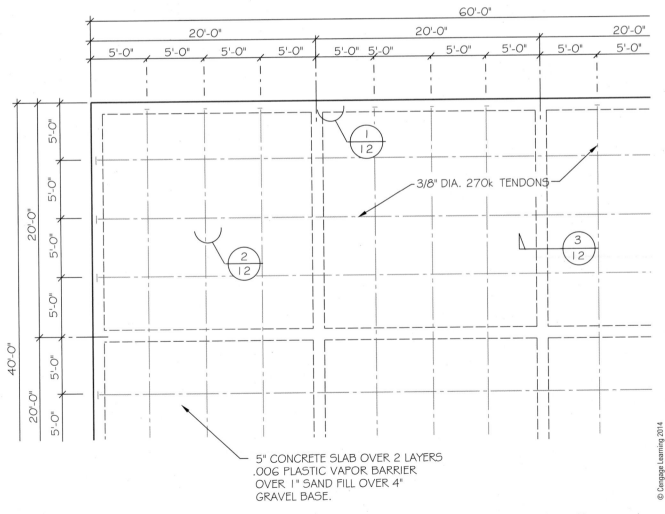

FIGURE 27.16 Beams located below the slab must be located on the foundation plan using the same methods used to represent an interior footing.

FIGURE 27.17 Rigid insulation added to the foundation wall prior to backfilling.

FIGURE 27.18 Plumbing must be placed prior to pouring the concrete slab.

should be used to insulate the slab. When placed on the exterior side of the stem wall, the insulation should extend past the bottom of the foundation. Care must be taken to protect exposed insulation on the exterior side of the wall. This is usually be done by placing a protective covering such as 1/2" (13 mm) concrete board over the insulation. Review Figures 4.20a and 4.20b for common methods of placing insulation to meet IRC/IECC requirements. Insulation is not shown on the foundation plan but is represented by a note on the foundation plan and specified in sections and footing details. Figure 27.17 shows an example of insulation placed on the exterior side of the stem wall.

Preparations for Plumbing and Heating

Plumbing and heating ducts must be placed under the slab before the concrete is poured. On residential plans, plumbing is usually not shown on the foundation plan. Generally the skills of the plumbing contractor are relied on for the placement of required utilities. Although piping runs are not shown, terminations such as floor drains are often shown and located on a concrete slab plan. Figure 27.18 shows the placement of plumbing materials prior to pouring the slab. If heating ducts will be placed under the slab, they are usually drawn on the foundation plan, as shown in Figure 27.19.

Changes in Floor Elevation

The floor level is often required to step down to meet the design needs of the client. A stem wall similar to that

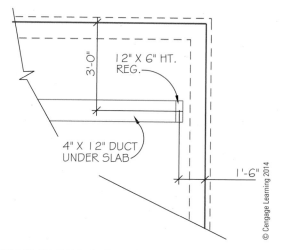

FIGURE 27.19 HVAC ducts and registers that are to be located in a concrete floor must be shown on the foundation plan.

shown in Figure 27.20 is formed between the two floor levels and should match the required width for an exterior stem wall. The lower slab is typically thickened to a depth of 8" (200 mm) to support the change in elevation. Steps between floors greater than 24" (600 mm) should be designed as a retaining wall and detailed using the methods described later in this chapter. Figure 27.21 shows how to represent a lowered slab. The step often occurs at what will be the edge of a wall when the framing plan is complete. Take great care to coordinate the dimensions of a floor plan with those of the foundation plan, so that the walls match the foundation.

Representing Materials for a Concrete Slab

Figure 27.21 shows an example of a foundation plan with a concrete slab floor system. Some materials must be drawn, located with dimensions, and referenced in a note. Other items are not drawn but are specified in a note. Use the following guidelines for placing items on a foundation plan.

Common Components Shown on a Slab Foundation

Each of the following materials are shown in Figure 27.21. The following items must be represented and dimensioned on the foundation plan:

- Outline of slab
- Interior footing locations
- Changes in floor level
- Floor drains

Exterior footing locations
Ducts for mechanical
Metal anchors
Patio slabs

Common Components Specified by Note Only

The specification for each of the following materials is shown in Figure 27.21. Do not draw, but reference with a note, the following items on the foundation plan:

Slab thickness and fill material	Reinforcing steel
Wire mesh	Anchor bolt size and spacing
Mudsill size	Insulation
Vapor barriers	Slab slopes
Pier sizes	Concrete strength
Assumed soil strength	

WOOD FLOOR SYSTEMS ABOVE A CRAWL SPACE

The crawl space is the area formed between the floor system and the ground. The IRC requires a minimum of 18" (450 mm) from the bottom of the floor decking to the ground and 12" (300 mm) from the bottom of girders to the ground. Two common methods of providing a crawl space below the floor are by using floor joists or the post-and-beam system. An introduction to each system is needed to complete the foundation. See Section 6 for a review of each type of floor system as it relates to the entire structure.

Joist Floor Framing

A common method of framing a wood floor is with repetitive wood members called *joists*. Floor systems made with joists are often used on sloping sites because the system requires less interior supports than with a post-and-beam system. Floor joists are used to span between the foundation walls. Three different common materials

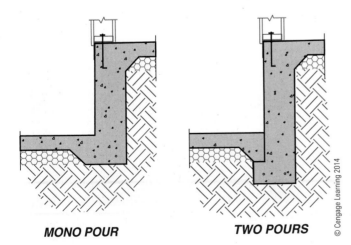

MONO POUR   **TWO POURS**

© Cengage Learning 2014

FIGURE 27.20 A stem wall is created between floor slabs when a change in elevation is required.

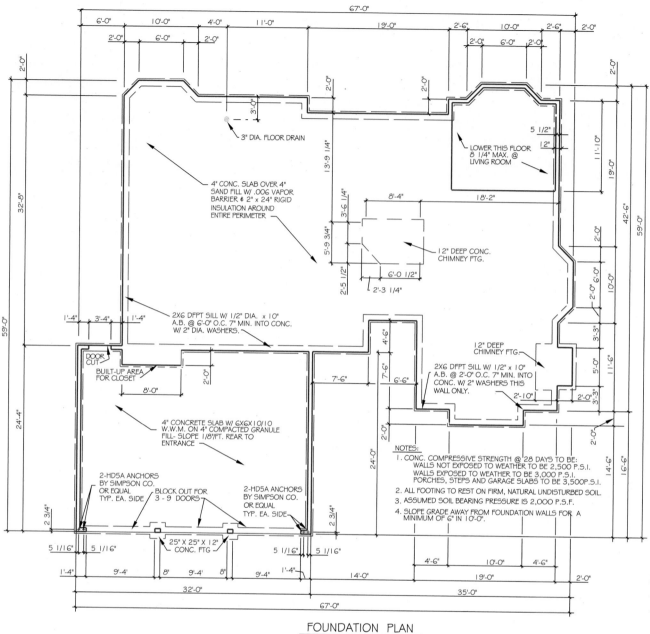

FOUNDATION PLAN
1/4" = 1'-0"

FIGURE 27.21 A foundation plan for a home with a concrete slab floor system.

are used for joists and each is shown in Figure 27.22. Sawn lumber ranging in size from 2 × 6 through 2 × 12 (50 × 150 to 50 × 300) are used to frame the floor platform. *Open-web trusses*, steel joists, and joists made from engineered lumber are also used to frame the floor system. Sawn floor joists are usually placed at 16" (400 mm) o.c., but the spacing of joists may change depending on the span, the material used, and the load to be supported.

Joist Floor Framing Methods

To construct a joist floor system, a pressure-treated sill is bolted to the top of the foundation wall with the anchor bolts that were placed when the foundation was formed.

FIGURE 27.22a A floor framed with sawn joists uses wood members ranging from 2 × 6 through 2 × 12 (50 × 150 to 50 × 300) to span between supports. Solid blocking is placed between the joists at 10'-0" (3000 mm) o.c.

FIGURE 27.22b Engineered lumber is a popular material for joist floor systems. Joists are typically placed at 16" (400 mm) o.c. Depending on the load to be supported, the allowable deflection, and the span, a 12 or 24" (300 or 600 mm) spacing may also be used.

FIGURE 27.22c Steel joists are also used to frame a floor system.

FIGURE 27.23 Although floor joists are normally placed above the sill, they can be mounted flush to the sill to reduce the distance from the finish floor to the finish grade. The weight of the joist is transferred to the sill using joist hangers.

Sawn, engineered, or open-web floor joists can then be nailed to the sill. A continuous *rim joist* (see Chapter 22) is nailed to the end of the joists, or *solid blocking* is placed between the ends of the joists to provide stability and to keep the joists from rolling over. Solid blocking is also placed at mid span for sawn joists longer than 10' (3000 mm). An alternative used to reduce the distance from the finished floor to the finish grade is to set the floor joists flush with the sill, as in Figure 27.23. This method requires the use of metal hangers to support the joists.

Steel joists are supported at the stem wall by a C-shaped *rim track*. The track is attached to a wood mudsill and then the joists slide into the track. The IRC requires the track to be connected to the sill with a 3" × 3" × 0.33 mil (75 × 75 mm × 0.33 mil) minimum steel plate and to also have #8 screws through the track *flange* at 24" (600 mm) o.c. to the mudsill. Each individual joist must also be attached to the mudsill with a metal L-bracket, a web stiffener, or a metal clip-angle attached to the sill with #8 screws. See Figure 27.24 for IRC

fastening requirements. Additional methods for fastening tracks and joists to the foundation can be seen in Section 505 of the IRC.

Supporting Floor Joists. When the distance between the foundation walls is too great for the floor joists to span, a girder is used to support the joists. A *girder* is a horizontal load-bearing member that spans between two or more supports at the foundation level. Typically either 4× or 6× (100× or 150×) sawn members are used, but depending on the span and the load to be supported, multiple 2× (50×) laminated wood, engineered wood products, or steel can be used for the girder. The IRC requires a minimum distance of 12" (300 mm) for clearance between the bottom of the girder and the soil. Girders may be drawn using a single bold line or pairs of thin lines similar to those in Figure 27.25. The girder is usually supported in a concrete beam pocket, where it intersects the foundation wall. Depending on the load to be supported and the area you are in, either wood, an engineered wood product, or a steel column may be used to support girder. In areas of seismic risk, the girder must be attached to the supporting post or column if support is needed as the girder spans between the stem walls. When wood members are used, a *gusset* attaches the post and girder together. A steel connector can also be used to make wood-to-wood connections or wood-to-steel connections. A steel girder may require no intermediate supports or can be welded to a steel column. Figure 27.26 shows the use of a steel girder to form the floor system over a basement.

TABLE R505.3.1(1)
FLOOR TO FOUNDATION OR BEARING WALL CONNECTION REQUIREMENTS[a, b]

FRAMING CONDITION	BASIC WIND SPEED (mph) AND EXPOSURE	
	85 mph Exposure C or less than 110 mph Exposure B	Less than 110 mph Exposure C
Floor joist to wall track of exterior wall per Figure R505.3.1(1)	2-No. 8 screws	3-No. 8 screws
Rim track or end joist to load-bearing wall top track per Figure R505.3.1(1)	1-No. 8 screw at 24 inches o.c.	1-No. 8 screw at 24 inches o.c.
Rim track or end joist to wood sill per Figure R505.3.1(2)	Steel plate spaced at 4 feet o.c. with 4-No. 8 screws and 4-10d or 6-8d common nails	Steel plate spaced at 2 feet o.c. with 4-No. 8 screws and 4-10d or 6-8d common nails
Rim track or end joist to foundation per Figure R505.3.1(3)	$^1/_2$ inch minimum diameter anchor bolt and clip angle spaced at 6 feet o.c. with 8-No. 8 screws	$^1/_2$ inch minimum diameter anchor bolt and clip angle spaced at 4 feet o.c. with 8-No. 8 screws
Cantilevered joist to foundation per Figure R505.3.1(4)	$^1/_2$ inch minimum diameter anchor bolt and clip angle spaced at 6 feet o.c. with 8-No. 8 screws	$^1/_2$ inch minimum diameter anchor bolt and clip angle spaced at 4 feet o.c. with 8-No. 8 screws
Cantilevered joist to wood sill per Figure R505.3.1(5)	Steel plate spaced at 4 feet o.c. with 4-No. 8 screws and 4-10d or 6-8d common nails	Steel plate spaced at 2 feet o.c. with 4-No. 8 screws and 4-10d or 6-8d common nails
Cantilevered joist to exterior load-bearing wall track per Figure R505.3.1(6)	2-No. 8 screws	3-No. 8 screws

For SI: 1 inch = 25.4 mm, 1 pound per square foot = 0.0479 kPa, 1 mile per hour = 0.447 m/s, 1 foot = 304.8 mm.

a. Anchor bolts are to be located not more than 12 inches from corners or the termination of bottom tracks (e.g., at door openings or corners). Bolts extend a minimum of 15 inches into masonry or 7 inches into concrete. Anchor bolts connecting cold-formed steel framing to the foundation structure are to be installed so that the distance from the center of the bolt hole to the edge of the connected member is not less than one and one-half bolt diameters.

b. All screw sizes shown are minimum.

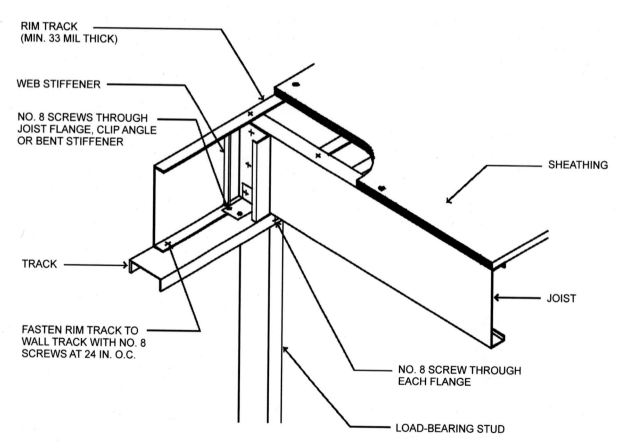

RIM TRACK (MIN. 33 MIL THICK)

WEB STIFFENER

NO. 8 SCREWS THROUGH JOIST FLANGE, CLIP ANGLE OR BENT STIFFENER

SHEATHING

TRACK

JOIST

FASTEN RIM TRACK TO WALL TRACK WITH NO. 8 SCREWS AT 24 IN. O.C.

NO. 8 SCREW THROUGH EACH FLANGE

LOAD-BEARING STUD

For SI: 1 mil = 0.0254 mm, 1 inch = 25.4 mm.

FIGURE 27.24 Required methods of attaching steel tracks and joists to the foundation.

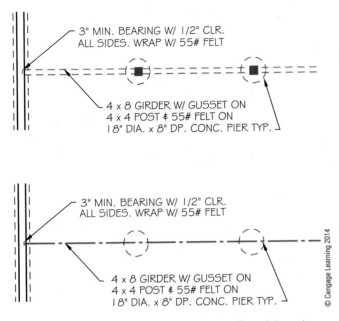

FIGURE 27.25 Common methods of representing girders, piers, and posts in plan view.

© Cengage Learning 2014

Courtesy Reward Wall Systems

FIGURE 27.26 Steel girders placed in preparation for the placement of joists for the floor system.

Girder Supports. A concrete pier is placed under the intermediate girder supports to resist settling. The post must be attached to the pier in some seismic zones. A metal rod inserted into a predrilled hole in the post can be used in areas of low seismic risk. A metal strap or post base may be required where high wind or seismic risk is greater. Figure 27.27 shows common connections that may be encountered when working with a joist floor system. Figure 27.25 shows methods of representing the girders, posts, piers, and beam pockets on the foundation plan.

Floor Sheathing. With the girders and floor joists in place, plywood floor *sheathing* is installed to provide a base for the finish floor. The size of the subfloor depends on the spacing of the floor joists and the floor loads that must be supported. The live load to be supported will also affect the thickness of the plywood to be used. The APA has span tables for plywood from 7/16 through 7/8" (11 through 22 mm) to meet the various conditions that might be found in a residence. A subfloor can also be made from 1" (25 mm) material such as 1 × 6 (25 × 150 mm) tongue-and-groove (T&G) lumber, although this method requires more labor. The floor sheathing is not represented on the foundation plan but is specified in a general note. Figure 27.28 shows common methods of drawing floor joists on the foundation plan.

Representing Materials for a Joist Floor System

Figure 27.29 shows a complete foundation plan using floor joists to support the floor. Some materials must be drawn, located with dimensions, and referenced in a note. Other items are not drawn but are specified in a note. The following guidelines can be used for placing items on a foundation plan.

Common Components Shown with a Joist Floor System. The following items must be represented on a foundation plan with a joist floor system. Unless marked with an asterisk, all of the components require dimensions to provide location information. The location of objects marked with an asterisk are specified in a note and do not require dimensions. Items that must be drawn include:

Foundation walls	Metal anchors
Door openings in foundation walls	Fireplace footings
Fireplace chimney	The outline of floor cantilevers
Floor joists	Interior piers
Girders (bearing walls and floor support)	Changes in floor levels
Girder pockets	Crawl access*
Exterior footings	Vents for crawl space*

Common Components Specified by Note Only. The specifications for each of the following materials are shown in Figure 27.29. The following materials are not drawn but must be referenced by a note on the foundation plan:

Floor joist size and spacing	Subfloor material
Anchor bolt size and spacing	Girder sizes
Insulation	Mudsill size
Crawl height	Vapor barrier
Assumed soil strength	Concrete strength
	Wood type and grade

Text in figures:

3" MIN. BEARING W/ 1/2" CLR. ALL SIDES. WRAP W/ 55# FELT

4 x 8 GIRDER W/ GUSSET ON 4 x 4 POST & 55# FELT ON 18" DIA. x 8" DP. CONC. PIER TYP.

3" MIN. BEARING W/ 1/2" CLR. ALL SIDES. WRAP W/ 55# FELT

4 x 8 GIRDER W/ GUSSET ON 4 x 4 POST & 55# FELT ON 18" DIA. x 8" DP. CONC. PIER TYP.

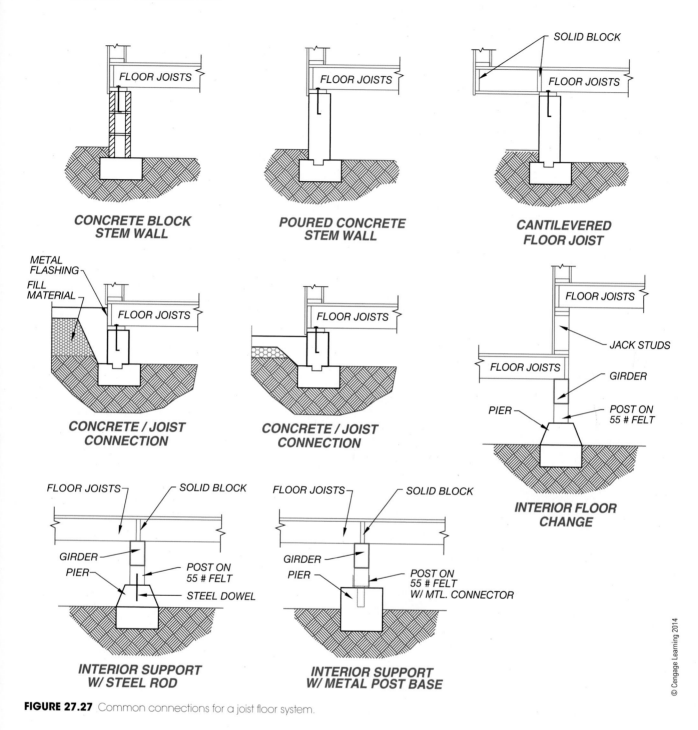

FIGURE 27.27 Common connections for a joist floor system.

Post-and-Beam Floor Systems

A *post-and-beam* floor system is built using a standard foundation system. It is a popular floor framing choice for flat or low-sloped building sites. Rather than having floor joists span between the foundation walls, a series of beams are used to support the *subfloor*, as shown in Figure 27.30. Once the mudsill is bolted to the foundation wall, the beams are placed so that the top of each beam is flush with the top of the mudsill. The beams are

placed at 48" (1200 mm) o.c., but the spacing can vary depending on the size of the floor decking to be used. The area of the country affects how the subfloor is made. Generally plywood with a thickness of 1 1/8" (28.5 mm) and an APA rating of STURD-I-FLOOR 2-4-1 with an exposure rating of EXP-1 is used to build a post-and-beam subfloor. When the subfloor is glued to the support beams, the strength and quality of the floor are greatly increased because squeaks, bounce, and nail popping are eliminated.

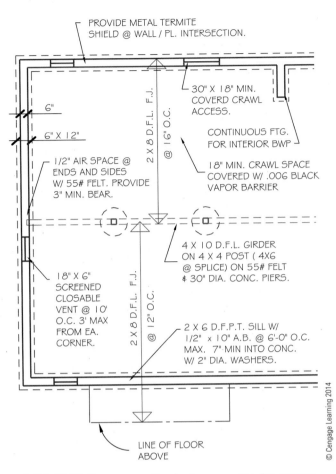

PROVIDE METAL TERMITE SHIELD @ WALL / PL. INTERSECTION.

30" X 18" MIN. COVERD CRAWL ACCESS.

CONTINUOUS FTG. FOR INTERIOR BWP

18" MIN. CRAWL SPACE COVERED W/ .006 BLACK VAPOR BARRIER

6"

6" X 12"

1/2" AIR SPACE @ ENDS AND SIDES W/ 55# FELT. PROVIDE 3" MIN. BEAR.

2 X 8 D.F.L. F.J. @ 16' O.C.

4 X 10 D.F.L. GIRDER ON 4 X 4 POST (4X6 @ SPLICE) ON 55# FELT & 30" DIA. CONC. PIERS.

18" X 6" SCREENED CLOSABLE VENT @ 10' O.C. 3' MAX FROM EA. CORNER.

2 X 8 D.F.L. F.J. @ 12' O.C.

2 X 6 D.F.P.T. SILL W/ 1/2" x 10" A.B. @ 6'-0" O.C. MAX. 7" MIN INTO CONC. W/ 2" DIA. WASHERS.

LINE OF FLOOR ABOVE

© Cengage Learning 2014

FIGURE 27.28 Common methods of representing the components of a joist floor system in plan view.

The following guidelines can be used for placing items on a foundation plan.

Common Components of a Post-and-Beam System. The following items must be represented on a foundation plan using a post-and-beam floor system. Unless marked with an asterisk, all of the components require dimensions to provide location information. The location of objects marked with an asterisk are specified in a note and do not require dimensions. Items that must be drawn include:

Foundation walls | Exterior footings
Openings in walls for doors | Metal anchors
Fireplace chimney | Fireplace footings
Girders (beams) | Piers
Girder pockets | Changes in floor levels
Crawl access* | Vents for crawl space*

Common Components Specified by Note Only. The specification for each of the following materials can be found in Figure 27.33. The following materials are not drawn but must be referenced by a note on the foundation plan:

Anchor bolt spacing | Girder sizes
Mudsill size | Vapor barrier
Insulation | Concrete strength
Minimum crawl height | Wood type and grade
Subfloor material | Assumed soil strength

An alternative to plywood is to use 2" (50 mm) material such as 2 × 6 (50 × 150) T&G boards laid perpendicular or diagonally to the girders.

Girder Support

The girders are supported by wooden posts as they span between the foundation walls. Posts are usually placed at 8' (2400 mm) o.c., but spacing can vary depending on the load to be supported and the size of the girder. A concrete pier similar to those shown in Figure 27.31 supports each post. Figure 27.32 shows common components of a post-and-beam floor system. Beams, posts, and piers are drawn on the foundation plan, as shown in Figure 27.25.

Representing Materials for a Post-and-Beam Floor System

Figure 27.33 shows an example of a foundation plan with a post-and-beam floor system. Some materials must be drawn, located with dimensions, and referenced in a note. Other items are not drawn but are specified in a note.

COMBINED FLOOR METHODS

Floor systems and foundation construction methods may be combined, depending on the building site. This is typically done on partially sloping lots when part of a structure may be constructed with a slab and part of the structure with a joist floor system, as shown in Figure 27.34. The slab is built in an area requiring little or no excavation, and the wood floor system eliminates the need for placing compacted fill to support a concrete slab. A residence with a basement is another example of construction that requires combined floor methods. A home with a partial basement will require the use of a concrete floor in the basement area, with either a joist or post-and-beam floor system over the crawl space. A joist floor for the crawl space is easier to match with the floor system that will be used above the basement area. Figure 27.35a shows a residence with a partial basement. The right portion of the plan uses a joist floor system over the crawl area. The left side of the structure has a basement with a concrete slab floor.

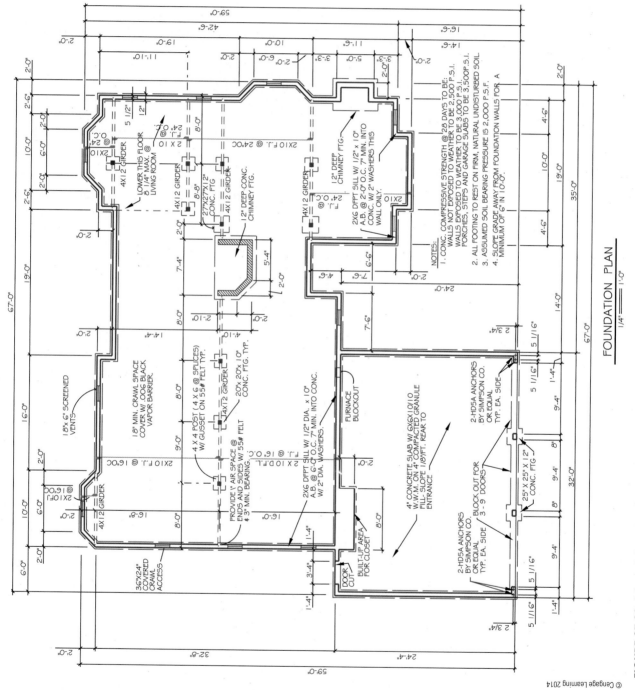

FOUNDATION PLAN
1/4" = 1'-0"

NOTES:
1. CONC. COMPRESSIVE STRENGTH @ 28 DAYS TO BE:
   WALLS NOT EXPOSED TO WEATHER TO BE 2,500 P.S.I.
   WALLS EXPOSED TO WEATHER TO BE 3,000 P.S.I.
   PORCHES, STEPS AND GARAGE SLABS TO BE 3,500P.S.I.
2. ALL FOOTING TO REST ON FIRM, NATURAL UNDISTURBED SOIL.
3. ASSUMED SOIL BEARING PRESSURE IS 2,000 P.S.F.
4. SLOPE GRADE AWAY FROM FOUNDATION WALLS FOR A
   MINIMUM OF 6" IN 10'-0".

FIGURE 27.29 A foundation plan for the home shown in Figure 25.1 with a joist floor system.

© Cengage Learning 2014

FIGURE 27.30 Girders are placed at 48" (1200 mm) o.c. with supports at 8'-0" (2400 mm) o.c. Additional girders can be added to provide support for braced wall panels. Blocking is used between girders to provide support for plumbing.

Figure 27.35b shows a residence with a full basement. The entire basement can be constructed using the methods that were introduced earlier, in the discussion of concrete floors. Figure 27.35c shows a residence with a daylight basement. The major difference between b and c is that the retaining wall does not totally enclose the basement. This type of basement is ideal for homes built on sloping sites. The basement is built on the low side of the site, allowing some exterior walls to be constructed of wood. Notice on each side of the foundation that a 48" (1200 mm) high retaining wall has been used. Careful grading allows the 8'-0" (2400 mm) high retaining wall to be reduced and eliminated for a portion of the basement. Depending on your area, the drawings for the basement may require an engineer's stamp. Your local building department can provide information on the maximum wall heights allowed without an engineer's stamp. Chapter 29 explores the drawing needed to detail the basement walls.

One component typically used when floor systems are combined is a ledger. A *ledger* is used to provide support

FIGURE 27.31 Posts for a wood floor system sit on a shingle or 55-lb felt placed above a concrete pier. The shingle is placed to stop moisture from being drawn into the post. A vapor barrier keeps moisture from passing from the soil into the crawl space. At the top of the post, a gusset is used to connect the girder to the post. Cross bracing between posts may be required, depending on the height of the post and the seismic zone.

for floor joists and the subfloor when they intersect the concrete. Unless felt is placed between the concrete and the ledger, the ledger must be pressure-treated lumber. The ledger can be shown on the foundation plan but is generally specified by note only.

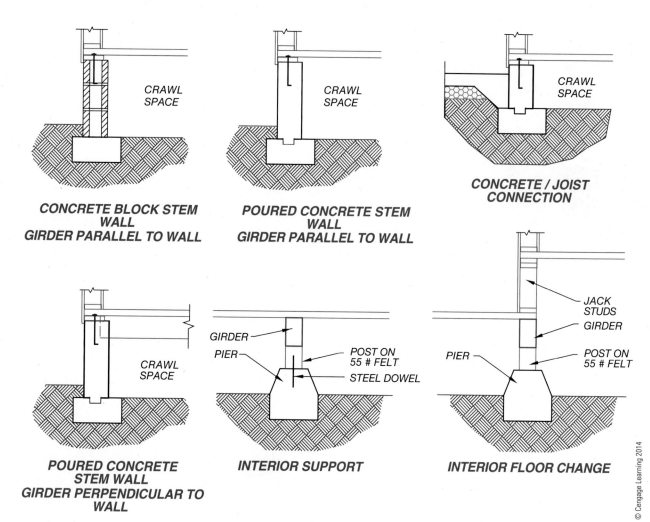

CRAWL SPACE

CRAWL SPACE

CRAWL SPACE

CONCRETE / JOIST CONNECTION

CONCRETE BLOCK STEM WALL GIRDER PARALLEL TO WALL

POURED CONCRETE STEM WALL GIRDER PARALLEL TO WALL

CRAWL SPACE

GIRDER

PIER

POST ON 55 # FELT

STEEL DOWEL

JACK STUDS

GIRDER

PIER

POST ON 55 # FELT

POURED CONCRETE STEM WALL GIRDER PERPENDICULAR TO WALL

INTERIOR SUPPORT

INTERIOR FLOOR CHANGE

© Cengage Learning 2014

FIGURE 27.32 Common connections for a post-and-beam floor system.

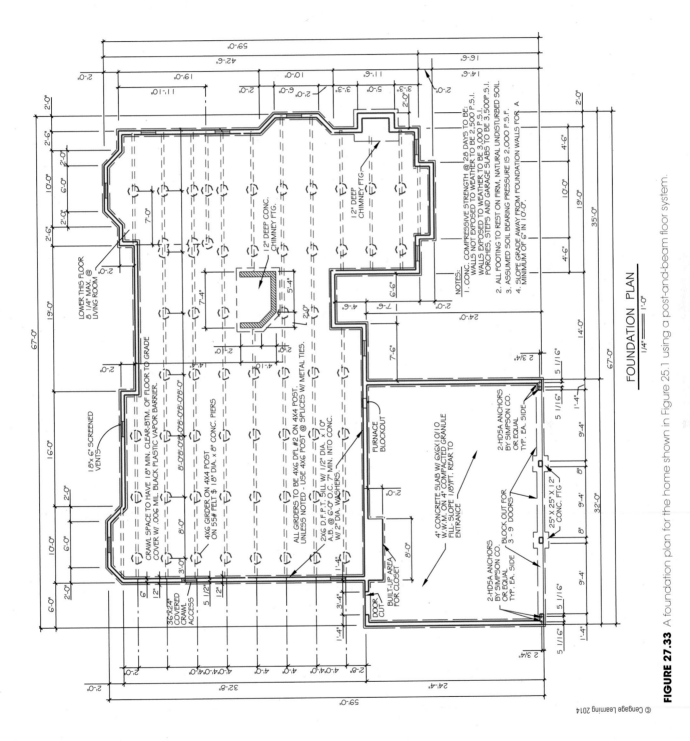

FIGURE 27.33 A foundation plan for the home shown in Figure 25.1 using a post-and-beam floor system.

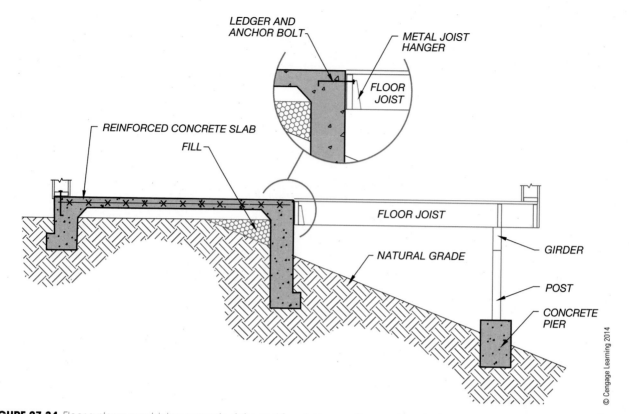

FIGURE 27.34 Floor systems combining concrete slabs and floor joists are often used on sloping sites to help minimize fill material. A ledger is used to provide anchorage to floor joists where they intersect the concrete slab. Metal joist hangers are used to join the joists to the ledger.

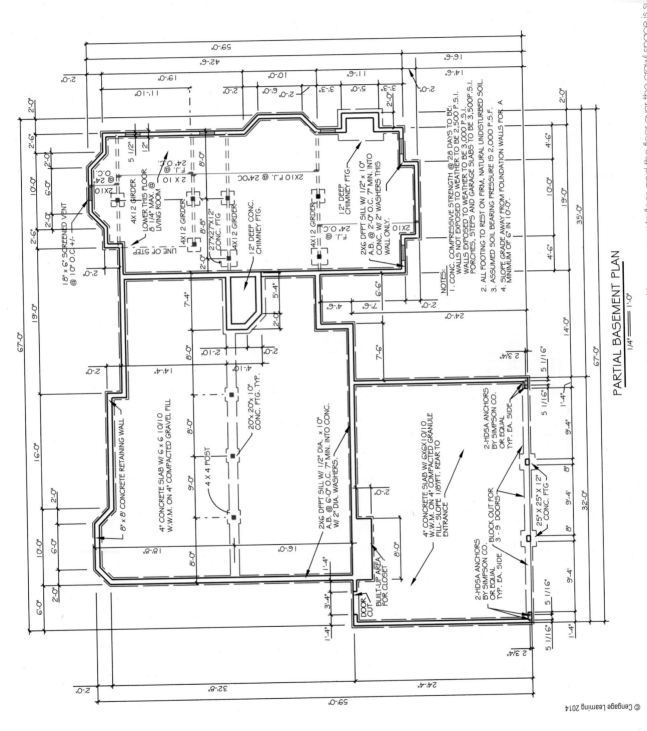

PARTIAL BASEMENT PLAN
1/4" = 1'-0"

NOTES:
1. CONC. COMPRESSIVE STRENGTH @ 28 DAYS TO BE:
   WALLS NOT EXPOSED TO WEATHER TO BE 2,500 P.S.I.
   WALLS EXPOSED TO WEATHER TO BE 3,000 P.S.I.
   PORCHES, STEPS AND GARAGE SLABS TO BE 3,500P.S.I.
2. ALL FOOTING TO REST ON FIRM, NATURAL UNDISTURBED SOIL.
3. ASSUMED SOIL BEARING PRESSURE IS 2,000 P.S.F.
4. SLOPE GRADE AWAY FROM FOUNDATION WALLS FOR A
   MINIMUM OF 6" IN 10'-0".

FIGURE 27.35a A foundation plan for a home shown in Figure 25.1 using a partial basement. The basement has a concrete floor, and the floor over the crawl space is supported by joists.

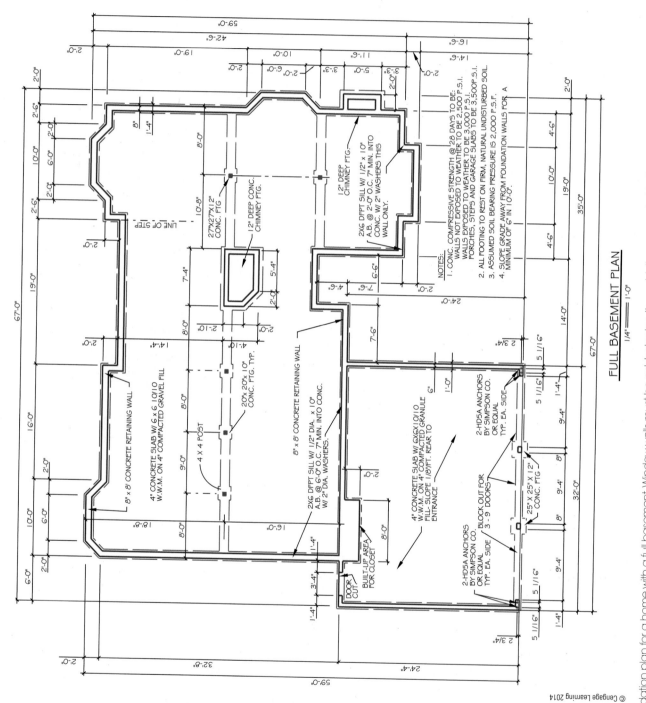

FULL BASEMENT PLAN
1/4" = 1'-0"

FIGURE 27.35b A foundation plan for a home with a full basement. Window wells must be added using the guidelines presented in Chapter 7 if habitable space is located in the basement.

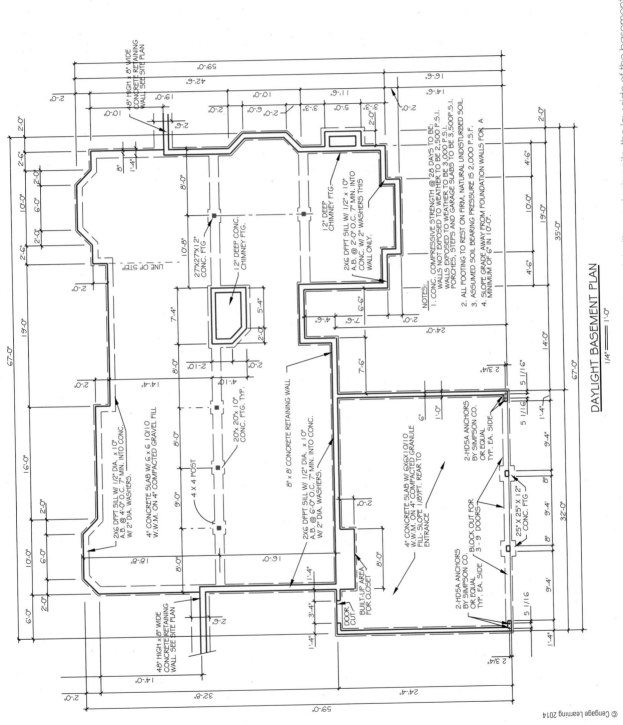

DAYLIGHT BASEMENT PLAN
1/4" = 1'-0"

NOTES:
1. CONC. COMPRESSIVE STRENGTH @ 28 DAYS TO BE: WALLS NOT EXPOSED TO WEATHER TO BE 2,500 P.S.I. WALLS EXPOSED TO WEATHER TO BE 3,000 P.S.I. PORCHES, STEPS AND GARAGE SLABS TO BE 3,500 P.S.I.
2. ALL FOOTING TO REST ON FIRM, NATURAL UNDISTURBED SOIL.
3. ASSUMED SOIL BEARING PRESSURE IS 2,000 P.S.F.
4. SLOPE GRADE AWAY FROM FOUNDATION WALLS FOR A MINIMUM OF 6" IN 10'-0".

© Cengage Learning 2014

FIGURE 27.35c A foundation plan for a home shown in Figure 25.1 using a daylight basement. When a home is built on a sloping site, the low side of the basement can be constructed using slab-on-grade construction methods. The 48" (1200 mm) retaining walls on each side of the home allow standard wood construction to be used for lower walls.

Going Green

Floor Systems

Even something as mundane as the floor framing can incorporate green qualities and gain LEED credits. Common materials used to form the floor system can be found in CSI listings for Division 3 Concrete; Division 5.21 Steel Framing; and Division 6 Wood. LEED credits can typically be gained in the areas of Material and Resources, Energy and Atmosphere, and Indoor Environmental Quality.

Concrete, wood, and engineered wood products can each gain credits if used properly. Concrete mixtures incorporating recycled content and Portland-cement-reducing admixtures such as fly ash also earn LEED credits. Recycled materials used in place of mined stone aggregate ease landfill burdens and can improve the concrete's strength-to-weight ratio and thermal properties.

Wood floor joists will receive LEED credits if they are milled in the area or if they come from a certified forest. Using reclaimed wood from demolished buildings is another method of gaining credits. Wood milled from disease-killed trees that have been recently been harvested or from logs that have been submerged for decades after sinking long ago during river-based log drives also provides a source of credits. The use of engineered floor joists and trusses is a much more popular method of gaining credits for use of sustainable products. Most engineered products are made from materials that come from a certified forest or from scrap content from making other products. Many of the products that are used to attach wood framing members are capable of gaining LEED credits because of their recycled content.

Although steel is an energy-intensive framing material to create, it gains credits for its recycled content. Because of its strength, the use of steel allows fewer floor joists and girders to be used. Heavy-gauge structural steel framing members often have greater than 90 percent recycled content. Lightweight steel framing used for joists typically contains 20 percent to 25 percent recycled material, although according to information provided by the Steel Joist Institute, some manufacturers have in excess of 90 percent recycled content. Steel framing members also gain credit for being recyclable at the end of the building's useful life.

Flooring materials can also gain LEED credits in the Energy and Atmosphere and Indoor Environmental Quality categories. Concrete floor slabs and walls gain credits because of their thermal mass. Wood, engineered framing members, and steel flooring assemblies gain credits based on the insulation placed in the framing cavities of each system.

Additional Resources 💻

The following websites can be used as a resource to help you keep current with changes in foundation materials. These links are also provided on the textbook's website where you can select a link and go automatically to the specified site.

Address	**Company, Product, or Service**
www.aci-int.org	American Concrete Institute
www.apawood.org	APA—The Engineered Wood Association
www.concreteconstruction.net	Concrete Construction Online
www.cement.org	Portland Cement Association
www.post-tensioning.org	Post-Tensioning Institute (PTI)
www.strongtie.com	Simpson Strong-Tie
www.steelframing.org	Steel Framing Alliance
www.steeljoist.org	Steel Joist Institute
www.ilevel.com	Weyerhaeuser (structural frames)

Floor Systems and Foundation Support Test

Follow these instructions to access and complete an electronic copy of the Chapter 27 Floor Systems and Foundation Support Test: 💻

1. Go to cengagebrain.com
2. Enter the email address and password you used to register for the site (see Preface for full instructions).
3. Select the website from the **My Course & Materials** area of your home page. Select the chapter you want from the pull-down menu at the top of the page. Choose the resources for that chapter from the menu on the left.
4. Type your name, the chapter number, and the date at the top of the sheet.
5. Answer the following questions with short, complete statements using a word processor.

➤ NOTE:

The answers to some questions may not be contained in this chapter and will require you to do additional research using the Internet. Use your favorite search engine to search for specific professional companies or general categories of information.

Questions

27.1. Why is a concrete slab called an on-grade floor system?

27.2. What is the minimum thickness for a residential slab?

27.3. Why are control joints placed in slabs?

27.4. What is the minimum amount of fill required under an on-grade concrete slab?

27.5. What thickness of vapor barrier is to be placed under a slab?

27.6. What are the minimum height limitations required in the crawl area?

27.7. What is the purpose of a girder?

27.8. How are floor joists attached to the foundation wall?

27.9. How are girders supported at the foundation wall?

27.10. What is a common spacing for beams in a post-and-beam floor system?

27.11. After making an appointment, visit a contractor who installs and sets foundation forms. Discuss and write a written report on common problems the contractor encounters that are caused by the poor drawing specifications.

27.12. Visit the website of your local building department and verify any differences in footing and stem wall sizes that were introduced in this chapter.

27.13. Visit the website of your local building department and determine the maximum required distance between foundation supports for braced wall lines.

27.14. Visit the Simpson Strong-Tie website and find at least five different types of anchors and straps used to resist uplift at the foundation.

27.15. After making an appointment, visit with a contractor who installs concrete foundations. Discuss and write a report on the most common type of foundation/floor system in your area. Discuss why the system is the most common, why other types of systems are not used as often in your area, and common costs associated with the most common system used in your area.

Section 8
Details and Sections

Chapter 29
Sectioning Basics

Sections are drawn to show the vertical relationships of the structural materials called for on the floor, framing, roof, and foundation plans. The sections show the methods of construction for the framing crew. Before drawing sections, it is important to understand the different types of sections, their common scales, and the relationship of the cutting plane to the section.

Key Terms

Cross section	Full section	Stock details
Cutting plane	Longitudinal section	Transverse section
Details	Partial section	Viewing plane

CAD Commands and Tools

Other than the basic drawing, editing, text, and dimensioning commands, no new AutoCAD commands, tools, or concepts are necessary for you to understand and complete the CAD problems referenced in this chapter.

SECTION ORIGINATION

Building sections are the result of passing the ***viewing plane*** (see Chapter 3) through a structure to reveal the construction methods being used. Material that was in front of the viewing plane has been removed and cannot be seen. Material that is behind the viewing plane is projected to the plane and reproduced in the section. Think of it as a giant saw slicing through the structure, dividing it into two sections. One portion is removed to allow viewing of the portion that remains. Using the saw analogy, the viewing plane is referred to as a ***cutting plane***. The location of the cutting plane is shown on the floor or framing plan using symbols similar to those shown in Figure 29.1. Notice that with each symbol, an arrow indicates the portion of the structure that is being viewed. Figure 29.2 shows an example of a framing plan with section markers. Figure 29.3 shows the section that is specified by the section marker AA/3. Notice that material the cutting plane passes through on the floor plan is represented on the section. Material in the background, such as doors, windows, and cabinets, has been omitted, but can be shown depending on office practice.

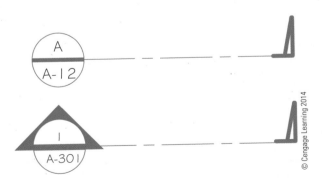

© Cengage Learning 2014

FIGURE 29.1 The location of a section is shown on the floor plan by the use of a cutting plane. The upper text represents the specific section, and the lower text represents the page number where the detail can be found.

Section Alignment

In drawing sections, as with other parts of the plans, the drawing is read from the bottom or right side of the page. The cutting plane on the framing plan shows the view of the section. The arrows of the cutting plane should be pointing to the top or left side of the paper, depending on the area of the building being sectioned (see Figure 29.4). Where possible, the cutting plane should extend through the entire structure. The cutting plane can be broken for notes or dimensions to maintain clarity. On complex structures, the cutting plane can be jogged to show material clearly and avoid having to draw a second section.

TYPES OF SECTIONS

Three types of sections may be drawn for a set of plans: full sections, partial sections, and details.

Full Sections

A ***full section*** is a view that results from passing the cutting plane through the entire structure. Full sections, either longitudinal or transverse, are meant to provide an overall view of a specific area of the structure. A ***transverse section*** results when the cutting plane is parallel to the short axis of the structure (section A in Figure 29.4), and it is often referred to as a ***cross section***. The cutting plane for a transverse section is usually parallel to the materials for framing the roof, ceiling, and floor systems, and it generally provides a better view of the structure's shape.

A ***longitudinal section*** (section B in Figure 29.4) results when the cutting plane is parallel to the long axis of the structure. It is generally perpendicular to most structural materials for framing the roof, ceiling, and floor systems. Because the framing members are perpendicular to the cutting plane, they are seen as if they had been cut. Longitudinal sections are rarely drawn in residential construction.

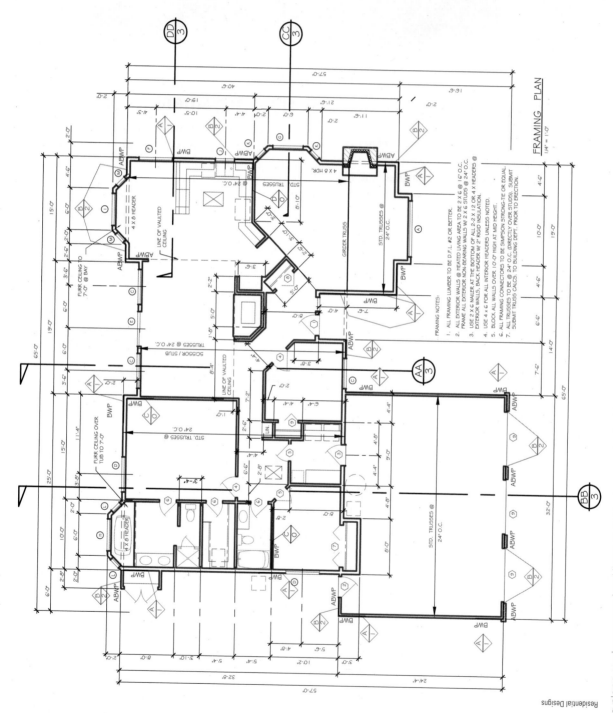

FRAMING PLAN
1/4" = 1'-0"

FRAMING NOTES:

1. ALL FRAMING LUMBER TO BE D.F.L. #2 OR BETTER.
2. ALL EXTERIOR WALLS @ HEATED LIVING AREA TO BE 2 X 6 @ 16" O.C. FRAME ALL EXTERIOR NON-BEARING WALLS W/ 2 X 6 STUDS @ 24" O.C.
3. USE 2 X 6 NAILER AT THE BOTTOM OF ALL 2-2 X 12 OR 4 X HEADERS @ EXTERIOR WALLS. BACK HEADER W/ 2" RIGID INSULATION.
4. USE 4 X 6 FOR ALL INTERIOR HEADERS UNLESS NOTED.
5. BLOCK ALL WALLS OVER 10'-0" HIGH AT MID HEIGHT.
6. ALL FRAMING CONNECTORS TO BE SIMPSON STRONG-TIE OR EQUAL.
7. ALL TRUSSES TO BE @ 24" O.C. (DIRECTLY OVER STUDS). SUBMIT TRUSS CALCS. TO BUILDING DEPT. PRIOR TO ERECTION.

Residential Designs

FIGURE 29.2 Cutting-plane markers may extend through a structure, may be broken at a text or dimensions to provide clarity, or may be jogged to eliminate a second section. A full section shows framing members used in a specific area of a structure.

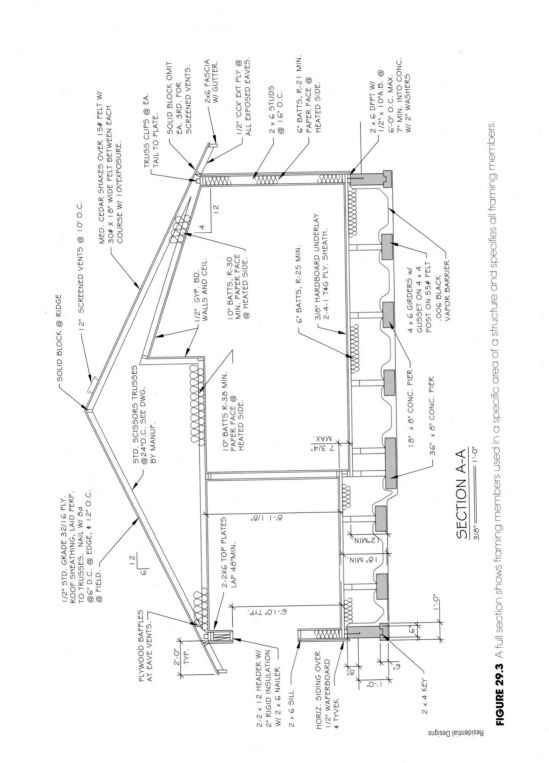

FIGURE 29.3 A full section shows framing members used in a specific area of a structure and specifies all framing members.

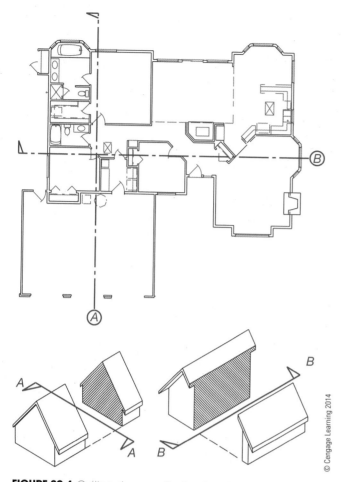

© Cengage Learning 2014

FIGURE 29.4 Cutting planes on the framing plan show the direction from which the section is to be viewed. Always try to keep the cutting-plane arrows pointing to the left or to the top of the page.

Regardless of the type of section, the NCS-V5 recommends that a building section should include the following components:

- Room names and numbers of the areas cut by the cutting plane.
- Floor-to-floor dimensions.
- Finish elevations.
- Ceilings and partitions that are cut by the cutting plane.
- Major materials, symbols, and lists of abbreviations.
- Other building section references that intersect the building section.

Figure 29.3 shows a full section. It is necessary to draw and specify each major structural material and provide the vertical dimensions. Notice that the roof is framed with standard/scissor trusses, the exterior walls are framed with 2×6 (50×150) studs, and the floor system is post-and-beam with a 7 3/4" (195 mm) step. Vertical relationships for the roof pitch, wall height, window and door header heights, foundation, and crawl heights are also provided. For a simple home,

only one section might be required to fully explain the types of construction. For a more complex structure, more than one section may be required to specify each major type of construction. Some offices use a combination of partial and full sections to explain the required construction procedures.

An alternative method of drawing full sections is to use the drawing as a reference map, including dimensions to explain various heights and room titles to explain the rooms being viewed. Very little text is provided to explain materials, and details markers are placed on the section to reference related details that explain all materials. Figure 29.5 shows a section with minimal information. Notice the information in the background is also represented. Figure 29.6 shows two of the supporting details for the section.

Plotting Scales for Sections

To make the sections easier to read, sections have become somewhat standardized in several areas, including scales and alignment. The NCS-V5 recommends using 1/2" = 1'-0" or 3/4" = 1'-0" (1:10 for metric drawings) for plotting sections. Smaller scales may be used for supplemental sections requiring little detail. Several factors influence the choice of scale in drawing sections:

1. Size of the drawing sheet.
2. Size of the project.
3. Purpose of the section.
4. Placement of the section.

Factors 1 and 2 need little discussion. The floor plan determines the size of the project. Once the sheet size is selected for the floor plan, that size should be used throughout the entire project. The placement of the section as it relates to other drawings should have only a minor influence on the scale. It may be practical to put a partial section in a blank corner of a drawing, but don't let space dictate the scale.

The most important factor is the purpose of the section. If the section is to merely show the shape of the project, a plotting scale of 1/8" = 1'-0" (1:96) is fine. Residential drawings rarely require this type of section but it is often used in drawing multiunit residential projects. When it is used for residential projects, this type of section is used as a reference map to locate structural details. Figure 29.7 provides an example of a shape section for a shear wall in a multilevel apartment project.

A common practice in many residential offices is to plot the primary section at a scale of 3/8" = 1'-0" (1:32). This scale provides benefits for both the print reader and the CAD technician. The main advantage is the ease of distinguishing each structural member. At a smaller scale, separate members, such as the finished flooring

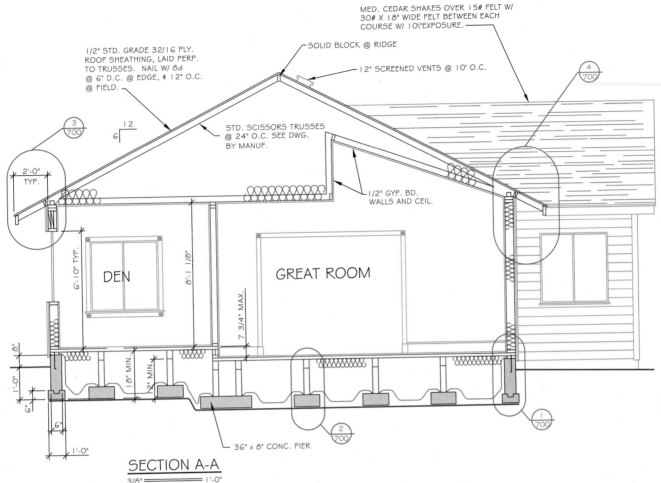

MED. CEDAR SHAKES OVER 15# FELT W/
30# X 18" WIDE FELT BETWEEN EACH
COURSE W/ 10\"EXPOSURE.

1/2" STD. GRADE 32/16 PLY.
ROOF SHEATHING, LAID PERP.
TO TRUSSES. NAIL W/ 8d
@ 6" D.C. @ EDGE, & 12" O.C.
@ FIELD.

SOLID BLOCK @ RIDGE

12" SCREENED VENTS @ 10' O.C.

STD. SCISSORS TRUSSES
@ 24" O.C. SEE DWG.
BY MANUF.

1/2" GYP. BD.
WALLS AND CEIL.

2'-0"
TYP.

6'-10" TYP.

8'-1 1/8"

7 3/4" MAX.

DEN

GREAT ROOM

8"

1'-0"

6"

6"

1'-0"

18" MIN.

2" MIN.

36" x 8" CONC. PIER

SECTION A-A
3/8" = 1'-0"

FIGURE 29.5 Some offices use a full section to show the framing members used in a specific area of a structure as well as materials that lie beyond the cutting plane. Notes are kept to a minimum, with most information placed on details referenced to the section.

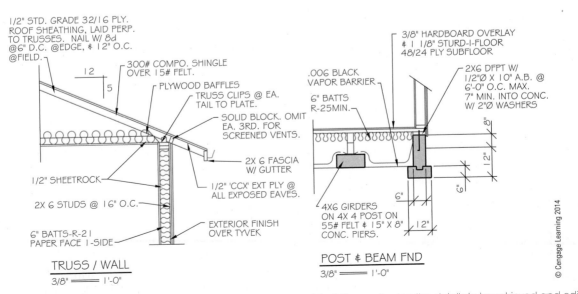

1/2" STD. GRADE 32/16 PLY.
ROOF SHEATHING, LAID PERP.
TO TRUSSES. NAIL W/ 8d
@6" D.C. @EDGE, & 12" O.C.
@FIELD.

12
5

300# COMPO. SHINGLE
OVER 15# FELT.

PLYWOOD BAFFLES

TRUSS CLIPS @ EA.
TAIL TO PLATE.

SOLID BLOCK. OMIT
EA. 3RD. FOR
SCREENED VENTS.

1/2" SHEETROCK

2X 6 FASCIA
W/ GUTTER

2X 6 STUDS @ 16" O.C.

1/2" 'CCX' EXT PLY @
ALL EXPOSED EAVES.

6" BATTS-R-21
PAPER FACE 1-SIDE

EXTERIOR FINISH
OVER TYVEK

3/8" HARDBOARD OVERLAY
& 1 1/8" STURD-I-FLOOR
48/24 PLY SUBFLOOR

.006 BLACK
VAPOR BARRIER

2X6 DFPT W/
1/2"Ø X 10" A.B. @
6'-0" O.C. MAX.
7" MIN. INTO CONC.
W/ 2"Ø WASHERS

6" BATTS
R-25MIN.

8"

12"

6"

6"

12"

4X6 GIRDERS
ON 4X 4 POST ON
55# FELT & 15" X 8"
CONC. PIERS.

TRUSS / WALL
3/8" = 1'-0"

POST & BEAM FND
3/8" = 1'-0"

FIGURE 29.6 Details that were created for a previous job are saved in a block library allowing the details to be retrieved and edited for other jobs requiring the same type of construction. The details of the standard roof truss/top plate connection and the wall/post-and-beam foundation along with other standard connection details were used to form the base for this section.

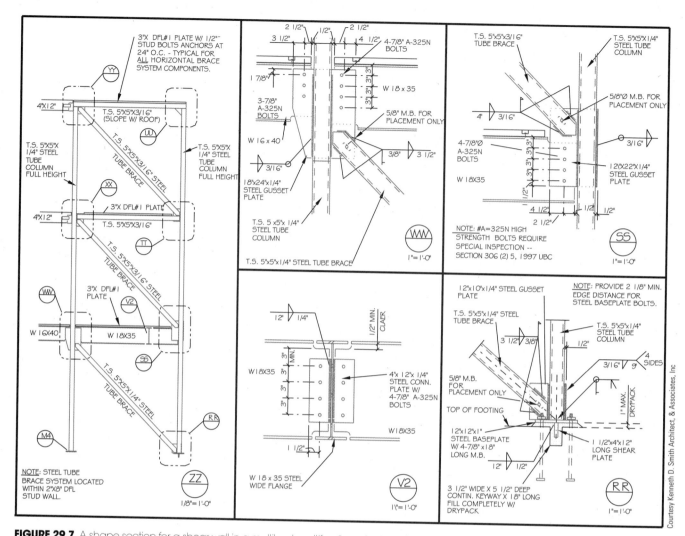

FIGURE 29.7 A shape section for a shear wall in a multilevel, multifamily project serves as a reference map for detail markers. Notice that section shows no specific details of an intersection but relies instead on details to show how the assembly will be created.

and the rough flooring, are difficult to draw and read. Without clarity, problems could arise at the job site. At 3/8" (1:32) scale, you'll have a bigger drawing on which to place the notes and dimensions.

A scale of 1/2" = 1'-0" (1:24) produces great clarity, but the sections are so large that a great deal of drawing sheets will be required to complete the project. Often, if drawing more than one section, plot the primary section at 3/8" = 1'-0" (1:32) and the other sections at 1/4" = 1'-0" (1:48). By combining drawings at these two scales, typical information can be placed on the larger section and the smaller sections are used to show variations with little detail.

Partial Wall Sections

A *partial section* is a view that does not cut completely through the structure. The partial or wall section is used to supplement the full sections and to show construction materials for specific areas of the structure that are not

visible in other sections. Figure 29.8 is an example of a partial section. For a more complex residence, more than one section may be required to specify each major type of construction. Some offices use a combination of partial and full sections to explain the required construction procedures. A partial section shows only typical roof, wall, floor, and foundation information for one typical wall rather than the full structure. A partial section may be plotted at a scale of 3/8" = 1'-0", 1/2" = 1'-0", or 3/4" = 1'-0" (1:20, 1:32, 1:24, or 1:16), depending on office procedure and the amount of detail to be represented in the detail.

The partial section is typically supplemented with full sections plotted at a scale of 1/4" = 1'-0" or 3/8" = 1'-0" (1:48 or 1:32). Only material that has not been specified on the partial section is noted on the full sections. The use of partial sections is popular in many professional offices because of the use of computers. Several different partial sections can be created to reflect major types of construction such as one- or two-level construction, truss or stick

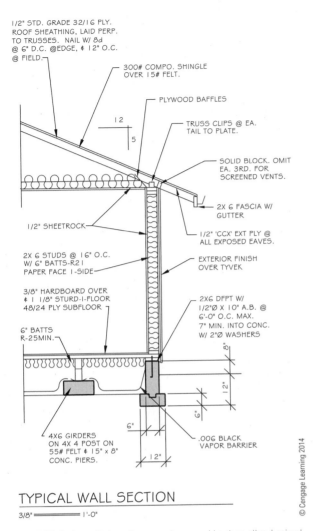

1/2" STD. GRADE 32/16 PLY.
ROOF SHEATHING, LAID PERP.
TO TRUSSES. NAIL W/ 8d
@ 6" D.C. @EDGE, # 12" O.C.
@ FIELD.

300# COMPO. SHINGLE
OVER 15# FELT.

PLYWOOD BAFFLES

TRUSS CLIPS @ EA.
TAIL TO PLATE.

SOLID BLOCK. OMIT
EA. 3RD. FOR
SCREENED VENTS.

2X 6 FASCIA W/
GUTTER

1/2" SHEETROCK

1/2" 'CCX' EXT PLY @
ALL EXPOSED EAVES.

2X 6 STUDS @ 16" O.C.
W/ 6" BATTS-R21
PAPER FACE 1-SIDE

EXTERIOR FINISH
OVER TYVEK

3/8" HARDBOARD OVER
1 1/8" STURD-I-FLOOR
48/24 PLY SUBFLOOR

2X6 DFPT W/
1/2"Ø X 10" A.B. @
6'-0" O.C. MAX.
7" MIN. INTO CONC.
W/ 2"Ø WASHERS

6" BATTS
R-25MIN.

4X6 GIRDERS
ON 4X 4 POST ON
55# FELT # 15" X 8"
CONC. PIERS.

.006 BLACK
VAPOR BARRIER

6"

12"

TYPICAL WALL SECTION

3/8" = 1'-0"

© Cengage Learning 2014

FIGURE 29.8 A partial section can be used to show the typical roof, wall, floor, and foundation construction materials of a specific structure. The partial section was created by assembling the two details shown in Figure 29.6. The MIRROR command was used to place the section in the proper orientation for creating the section shown in Figure 29.3.

roof, concrete slab, post-and-beam or joist foundations, and various wall coverings. These partial sections can be stored in a library and inserted into each set of plans as needed. Partial sections can also be used on complex structures to serve as a reference for details of complicated areas. The partial section shown in Figure 29.8 was assembled from the two stock details shown in Figure 29.6.

Details

Details are enlargements of specific areas of a structure such as Figure 29.6, and are typically drawn where several components intersect or where small members are required. Figure 29.9 shows a partial section of a hillside residence built on a piling foundation. Rather than showing just one specific wall, this is a longitudinal section that only shows the lower portion of the hillside home.

Figure 29.10 shows two details that relate to the partial section in Figure 29.9. The NCS-V5 recommends using scales ranging from 1/2" = 1'-0" through 3" = 1'-0" for plotting details depending on the complexity of the drawing. NCS recommends 1:20 or 1:5 if metric scales are to be used for plotting.

Stock Details

Most offices have a library of *stock details*. These are details of items such as footings that remain the same. Common stock foundations might include:

- One-level concrete slab.
- One-level concrete slab with masonry veneer.
- One-level concrete slab with exterior insulation flush wall.
- One-level concrete slab with exterior insulation projected wall.

The same details would typically exist for two-level construction, for post-and-beam construction, and for joist construction. Using a computer, the typical detail can be drawn with all required dimensions and all notations added. Once complete, copies can be made for each required detail, each copy can be edited and saved. The first detail may take an hour to complete, the second detail may take just a few minutes for editing. Figure 29.11 shows a detail created by editing the master detail. By combining the information on the framing plans and the sections and details, the contractor should be able to make accurate estimates of the amount of material required and the cost of completing the project.

Choosing the Type of Drawing to Use

The architectural team must draw sections to comply with the building permit application process and to explain to the construction crew each type of construction method to use on the project. Many municipalities will accept a partial section as sufficient to meet the demands for the building permit. Most architects and designers provide far more sections explaining each type of construction and changes in shape or size of the structure. Although not specifically required for a building permit, details may also be provided to explain the intersections of structural materials, changes in levels, and the application of materials. Details for the home started in Chapter 12 would include:

- Site-related work.
- Construction and reinforcing of footings.

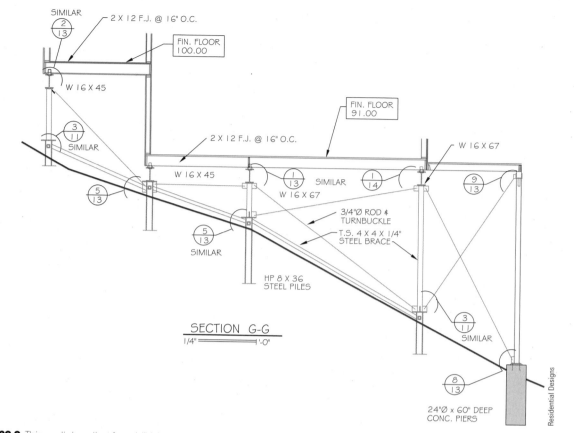

SECTION G-G
1/4" = 1'-0"

FIGURE 29.9 This partial section for a hillside residence is used to provide supplemental information about one specific area of the structure.

- Lateral supports and connections between floors.
- The foundation retaining wall.
- Interior trim details.

REPRESENTING AND LOCATING MATERIALS

The type of section drawn dictates the amount of information to be displayed and how the material will be represented. The smaller the plotting scale, the less information will be presented and the fewer number of linetypes will be used. In addition to using larger plotting scales, details require more attention to line contrast and the use of more varied line weights. Careful consideration must also be given to how materials will be represented.

Adding Layers

Before starting details, create layers to separate information by material and by lineweight and linetypes. Layers should start with a prefix of *DETL* and information should be named with a modifier listed in Appendix F. Sub-names of *ANNO, DIMN, FOOT, OUTL,* and *SYMB* will always be needed. As with any other drawing, create additional layers as needed to ensure that only layers that will be used are added to the drawing.

Using Line Contrast

Although standards vary, some details require a minimum of four different lineweights to provide contrast between materials. Unfortunately there is no standard of "*always use this lineweight.*" Instead, lineweights vary depending on the plotting scale of the detail and the materials being represented. To provide contrast between thin and thick lines, use .0 (default) for thin lines and .60 lines as a starting point for all details. When drawing foundation details to be plotted at a scale of 3/8" = 1'-0" (1:32), a thickness of 0.90 can be used to represent the outline of concrete and a weight of 1.00 to represent the finished grade.

> ### NOTE:
> *The goal of any detail is to clearly represent material. Because there is no set standard for lineweight, draw a few lines using varied lineweights and then make a test plot. Line thickness should be thick enough to provide contrast, but not so thick that it bleeds into other objects.*

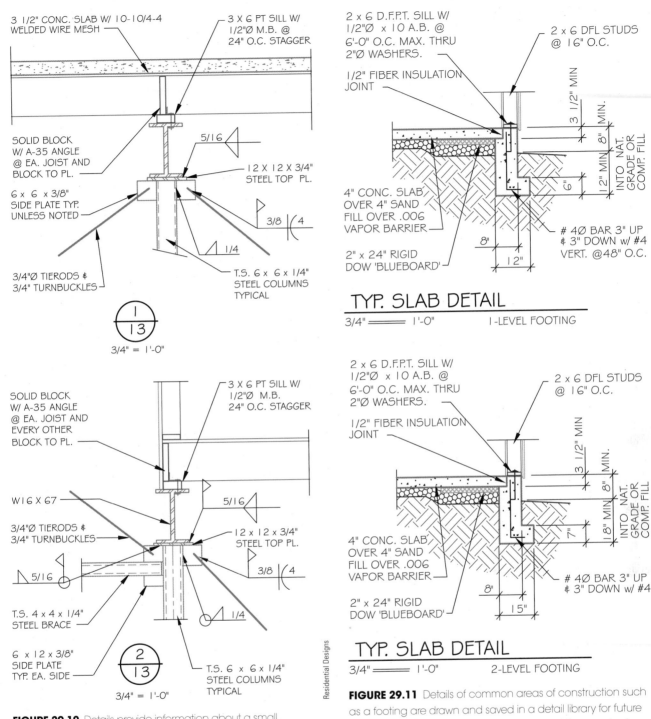

FIGURE 29.10 Details provide information about a small, complicated area of a structure, such as the intersection of various materials. These details are referenced to the partial section in Figure 29.9.

FIGURE 29.11 Details of common areas of construction such as a footing are drawn and saved in a detail library for future use. The detail at the top was edited to meet the needs of a one-level project.

Once the lineweights have been selected, a method will need to be selected on how to assign lineweights. Two common methods include:

- Assign and name layers such as *THIN, THICK, VERY THICK,* and *MEGA THICK.*

- Assign layers names based on materials such as *WOOD, STEEL, CONCRETE,* or *SOIL.* Then

assign lineweights to objects on those layers using the PROPERTIES command. See the guidelines for naming layers on the student website.

In plotting, use a gray scale to provide contrast to existing and new materials. For example, assign gray to existing materials and black to new materials.

Representation of Material

The method for representing each material varies depending on the scale that is used. Different methods are also used to represent materials that are continuous and are cut by the cutting plane or are intermittent and beyond the cutting plane. Although the method may vary with each office, it is critical to distinguish each material from other materials. Figure 29.12 shows common materials displayed in section. Do not spend more time than is necessary detailing materials. If a product is delivered to the site ready for installation, it requires minimal detail. If a component must be constructed at the job site, the drawings must provide enough information for all of the different trades, depending on the drawings.

Wood, Timber, and Engineered Products

Notice in Figure 29.11 that thin lines represent studs that lie beyond the cutting plane and thick lines represent the plates. On small-scale sections, the lumber and timber products can be drawn using their nominal sizes. Thin materials, such as the plywood in Figure 29.12K, may have to be exaggerated so that they can be clearly represented. Represent trusses perpendicular to the cutting plane with thick lines showing the shapes of the trusses. When parallel to the cutting plane, represent the chords and webs with thin lines similar to those in Figure 29.12V.

In partial sections and details, represent the actual size of lumber and timber. In addition to using thick lines to outline members shown in end views, several methods can be used to represent the material. Figures 29.12P and 29.12S show common methods to represent materials such as plates, ledgers, and beams. Represent plywood, sheetrock, and other finishes with hatch patterns similar to those shown in Figures 29.12A, K, and L.

Steel

The size of the drawing affects how sectioned steel members are represented. At small scale, a solid, thick line represents the desired shape of steel members (see Figure 29.12Q). As the scale increases, pairs of lines can represent the desired shapes of sectioned members. In details, pairs of thin lines (ANSI 32) represent sectioned steel with a hatch pattern consisting of pairs of parallel diagonal lines (see Figure 29.12R). Thin lines represent the nominal thickness for steel columns, beams, or trusses that are beyond the cutting plane. Represent steel trusses using methods similar to those used with wood trusses.

Unit Masonry

Methods of representing brick and masonry products vary as the scale of the drawing increases. In small-scale sections, units are typically hatched with diagonal lines

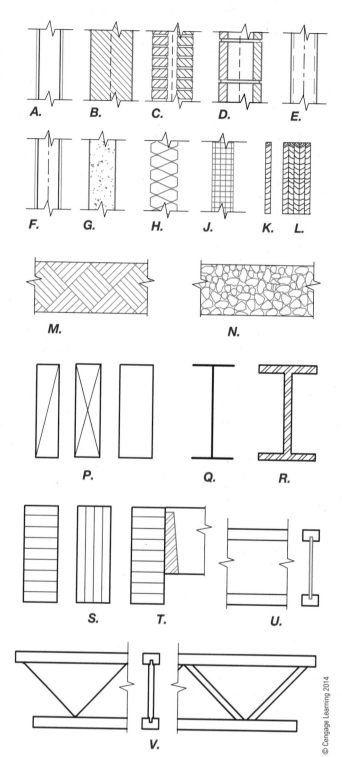

FIGURE 29.12 Common symbols for representing materials in sections and details. Materials include (A) wood-framed wall; (B) small-scale masonry; (C) double-wythe brick wall; (D) concrete masonry units; (E) steel tubes; (F) steel I or W shapes; (G) poured concrete walls; (H) batt insulation; (J) rigid insulation; (K) small-scale plywood; (L) large-scale plywood; (M) soil; (N) gravel; (P) wood and timber in end view (blocking and two methods of showing continuous members); (Q) small-scale steel shapes in end view; (R) large-scale steel shapes in end view; (S) laminated timbers in end view; (T) wood member supported by a metal hanger in side view on a laminated member in end view; (U) solid-web trusses in side and end view; and (V) open-web trusses in side and end views.

and no attempt is made to represent cavities or individual units. As the size of the drawing increases, individual units are represented, as well as cavities within the unit and grouting between the units. Use individual hatch patterns to differentiate between the masonry unit and the grout. Represent steel reinforcing with either a hidden or continuous polyline. Figures 29.12B, C, and D show an example of a wall section representing unit masonry and brick veneer.

Concrete

The edges of poured members are represented by thick lines and a hatch pattern consisting of dots and small triangles (see Figure 29.12G). Because of the complexity of concrete construction, the section depends on many details to show construction of each concrete member.

Glazing

Glass is represented in sections using a single line or pairs of lines depending on the drawing scale. In full and partial sections, glass is generally represented by thin lines, with little attention given to intersections between the glazing and window frames. As the drawing scale increases, the detail in representing the glass and the frame also increases.

Insulation

The type of insulation dictates how it is drawn. Batt insulation is generally represented as shown in Figure 29.12H. Depending on the complexity of the section, the insulation may be shown across its entire span or in only one portion of the section. When only a portion of the insulation is drawn, include notes that clearly define the limits of the insulation. Represent rigid insulation as shown in Figure 29.12J with the same considerations used to show batt insulation. As the scale increases, show insulation throughout the entire detail.

Locating Materials with Dimensions

Dimensions are an important element of full, partial, and wall sections. Both vertical and horizontal dimensions may be placed on sections, while partial sections and details generally show only vertical dimensions. On small-scale sections, the use of dimensions depends on the area being represented.

Vertical Dimensions

Represent vertical heights by using typical dimension methods or elevation symbols from a known point. Each type of dimension is usually placed on the outside of the section. Dimensions are generally given from the bottom

of the sole plate to the top of the top plate for wood frame structures. This dimension also provides the height from the top of the plywood floor to the bottom of the framing member used to frame the next level. A common alternative is to provide a height from the top of the floor sheathing to the top of the next level of floor sheathing. Other common vertical exterior dimensions include:

- Steel stud walls: from plate to top of channel.
- Structural steel: to top of steel member.
- Masonry units: to top of unit with distance and number of courses provided.
- Concrete slab: from top of slab or panel.

The job captain generally provides the exact dimensions for inexperienced drafters on a check print. Once the major shapes of the structure have been defined, provide dimensions to define openings, floor changes, or protective devices. Locate openings by providing a height from the top of the floor decking or sheathing to the bottom of the header. Changes in floor height and the height of landings are dimensioned in a similar method as changes in height between floor levels. Other common interior dimensions that should be provided include height of railings, partial walls, balconies, planters, and decorative screens. When possible, group interior dimensions together.

Horizontal Dimensions

The use of horizontal dimensions on full sections varies greatly for each office. With the exception of footing widths, horizontal dimensions are not usually placed on partial sections or details. When provided, horizontal dimensions generally are located from grid lines to the desired member using the following guidelines:

- Reference exterior wood and concrete members to their edges.
- Reference interior wood members to a centerline.
- Reference interior concrete members to an edge.
- Reference steel members to their centers.

The distance for roof overhangs and balcony projections also may be placed on sections.

Drawing Symbols

The sections use symbols that match those of the floor, roof, and elevation drawings to reference material. Symbols that might be found on the section include:

- Grid markers
- Elevation markers
- Section markers

- Detail markers
- Room names and numbers

Examples of each are shown in Figure 29.13. Grid markers should match in both style and reference symbol to those used on other drawings so the sections can be easily matched to other drawings. Elevations that are specified on the floor plan and elevation drawings should also be referenced on the section using a datum line or by placing an elevation over a leader line.

Reference each section and detail to other drawings using a section marker, which defines the page the section is drawn on and which section is being viewed. With a reference such as B over A-12, the B represents a specific detail on page A-12. The smaller the scale used to draw the section, the more likely it is that section and detail markers will be used to reference other drawings to the section. Detail markers are especially prevalent on sections where enlarged views of intersections are provided.

Drawing Notations

Use annotation on each type of section to specify materials and explain special installation procedures. As with other drawings, place notes as either local or keyed notes. Most offices use local notes with a leader line that

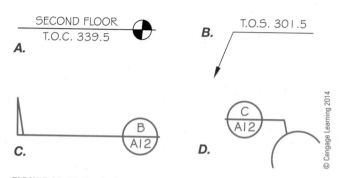

FIGURE 29.13 Symbols used on sections and details are common to other architectural drawings and include (A) elevation marker; (B) elevation marker; (C) section marker; and (D) detail markers.

© Cengage Learning 2014

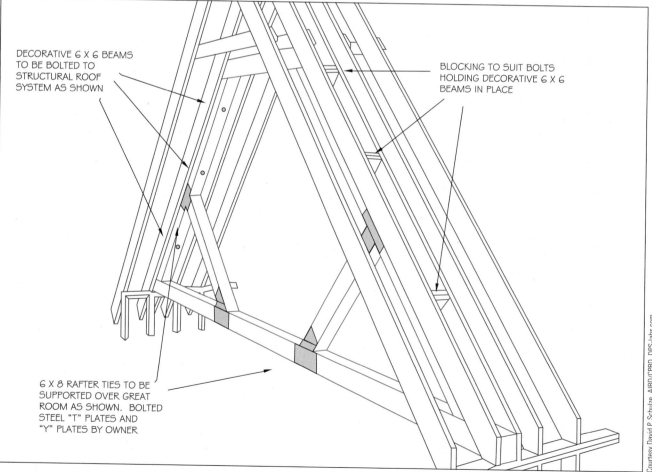

FIGURE 29.14a The use of computers, and specifically 3D drawing programs, has greatly aided the development of 3D drawings for construction details. This 3D drawing shows the placement of a timber truss in a vaulted ceiling.

Courtesy David P. Schulze, AIBD/CPBD, DPS-labs.com

connects the note to the material. To aid the print reader, align local notes so they are parallel to the drawing. On full sections, place notes neatly throughout the entire drawing. Wherever possible, place notes on the exterior of the building. For wall sections, aligned notes can greatly add to drawing neatness.

The smaller the scale, the more generic the notes tend to be on a section. For instance, on a full section, roofing that might be specified as:

300# COMP. ROOF SHINGLES OVER 15# FELT
OVER 1/2" OSB

would be referenced by complete notes for the roofing, insulation, and roof sheathing in the roofing details. Group related notes together within the same area of a section.

3D Details

Throughout this text, information has been presented using orthographic projections, not because it's the best way, but because it's just the way the construction industry has represented objects for the last 100 years. Using computers, and specifically 3D drawing programs, greatly aids the development of 3D drawings for construction details. Figure 29.14a shows a 3D drawing depicting the placement of a timber truss in a vaulted ceiling. A 3D drawing offers an excellent view of how major components relate to each other. Figure 29.14b shows a 3D rendering of the truss placement, and Figure 29.14c shows the placement of the truss at the job site.

FIGURE 29.14b A 3D rendering helps the owners visualize how the loft ceiling will appear when completed.

FIGURE 29.14c The results of the detail shown in Figure 29.14a.

Additional Resources

More so than any other drawings, creating details requires the use of vendor catalogs. Use the following websites as resources to help you keep current with building materials.

Address	Company or Organization
www.confast.com	Concrete Fastening Systems
www.nationalcadstandard.org	National CAD Standards-V5
www.strongtie.com	Simpson Strong-Tie
www.woodbywy.com	Weyerhaeuser

Sectioning Basics Test

Follow these instructions to access and complete an electronic copy of the Chapter 29 Sectioning Basics Test:

1. Go to cengagebrain.com.
2. Enter the email address and password you used to register for the site (see Preface for full instructions).
3. Select the website from the **My Course & Materials** area of your home page. Select the chapter you want from the pull-down menu at the top of the page. Choose the resources for that chapter from the menu on the left.
4. Type your name, the chapter number, and the date at the top of the sheet.
5. Answer the following questions with short, complete statements using a word processor.

NOTE:

The answers to some questions may not be contained in this chapter and will require you to do additional research using the Internet. Use your favorite search engine to search for specific professional companies or general categories of information.

Questions

29.1. What is a full section?

29.2. When could a partial section be used?

29.3. What is a stock detail and when is it used?

29.4. From which drawings does a drafter get the information needed to draw a section?

29.5. What is the most common scale for drawing full sections?

29.6. What factors influence the scale of a detail?

29.7. What is a cutting plane and how does it relate to a section?

29.8. In which directions should the arrows on a cutting plane be pointing?

29.9. What type of section might be drawn at a scale of 1/8" = 1'-0"?

28.10. What factors influence the choice of scale for the section?

28.11. Visit the website of your local building department and determine their requirements for building sections to obtain a permit.

28.12. After making an appointment, visit two different residential design professionals and interview them about common problems new employees seem to encounter when drawing sections. Find out what they expect of their CAD technicians with various levels of experience regarding drawing sections and details. Discuss and provide a written report on what you find.

28.13. After making an appointment, visit two different residential design professionals to research and report on how they set up their drawing libraries of details and partial sections. Get examples of what they expect new CAD technicians to do regarding this area of the working drawings. Write a report on your findings.

28.14. Use the Internet to locate at least five companies that provide products that would be referenced on a foundation plan in your area.

29 15. Use the Internet to locate and download a minimum of five national companies that provide stock details of products that would be referenced to the foundation plan. Download at least two details from each of these companies and report on how these details relate to foundations common to your area.

Drawing Problems

The following details will be completed as generic details. They are not drawn for a specific project but will be saved in a library for use on future projects. Once needed, the detail can be edited to meet the needs of a specific project. Use the following minimum sizes and materials to complete the drawings.

Minimum Drawing Standards

Unless noted, prepare all details for plotting at a minimum scale of 1/2" = 1'-0". Bigger is OK; smaller is not:

- NO ISOMETRIC DRAWINGS ARE TO BE DRAWN. Convert isometric drawings to 2D details using the appropriate lineweight. Save each drawing as an individual drawing file. Use the problem number as the file name.

- Format all text as StylusBT or another architectural style font with 1/8" text.

- Place leaders with a shoulder using the leader command. Keep arrows approximately the same size as text.

- Place text inside of details where space allows. Maintain 3/4" clearance between the drawing and dimensions or text. Never label material twice when more than one view is provided.

- Use dimensions for locations where possible rather than notes.

- Use side-by-side fractions (1/2), not top-over-bottom.

- Provide detail marker with 1/4" text (detail # over page #). Your text should fit neatly inside the circle without touching the circle. The detail number should match the problem number.

- Provide a title (1/4" text) over the scale (at 1/8" text) for all details. Provide a block reference for all details (detail number from book).

- Draw all material sizes to meet or exceed IRC minimum requirements.

- Assume all floor joists are 2 × 10 and all I joists to be 9 1/2" TJI pro 150 joists by Weyerhaeuser. Assume all trusses to have 2 × 4 cords. Use appropriate Simpson hangers for each type of joist. Specify floor joists with a generic note, such as:

  - FLOOR JOISTS—SEE FOUNDATION PLAN FOR SIZE AND SPACING

- Provide #4 diameter steel 3" up from bottom of the footing and 3" down from top of stem wall with #4 vertical bars placed at 48" o.c. maximum from the footing to the stem wall.

- Assume all rafters are 2 × 6 at 24" o.c. with 24" overhangs and 2 × 8 fascias and barge rafters and all ceiling joists are 2 × 6 at 16" o.c. Provide minimum required bearing for rafters at plate connection. Specify rafters and ceiling joists with generic notes such as:

  - 2× RAFTERS—SEE ROOF FRAMING PLAN FOR SIZE AND SPACING

  - 2× CEIL. JSTS—SEE FRAMING PLAN FOR SIZE AND SPACING

- Assume all beams are 4 ×12 DFL #2 unless noted.

- Assume all girders are 4 × 8 on 4 × 4 post (4 × 6 at splices) on 15"Ø × 8" deep concrete piers.

- Provide 18" minimum below floor joists and 12" minimum below girders to grade.

- Floor decking over floor joists is 3/4" plywood. Decking for post-and-beam systems is 1 1/8" Sturd-I-Floor.

- Provide all insulation to meet minimum code standards.

- Use a distance of 3/4" for the OFFSET command when representing 1/2" material or smaller.

- Show and specify finishing materials with generic notes such as:

  - EXTERIOR SIDING—SEE ELEVATION

  - INTERIOR FINISH—SEE FINISH SCHEDULE

- Show and specify a lightweight roofing material over solid roof sheathing.

Foundation Problems

Unless told otherwise by your instructor, base all foundation sizes on the minimum sizes required by the IRC. See Table 26.4a & b for required foundation sizes. Create a drawing template suitable for all foundation details using appropriate layers, lineweight, text, and dimension sizes. Place all annotation and dimensions to explain all construction. Show and specify required insulation.

Concrete Slab Details

29.1. Use the attached sketch to create a detail showing the foundation for a one-level concrete floor system. Show and specify # 10 × 10, 4 × 4 welded wire mesh 2" down from the top of the slab. Provide steel as required for your seismic zone. Show a wall framed with 2 × 6 studs at 16" o.c.

29.2. Use the drawing created in Problem 29.1 to create a detail showing the foundation for a two-level concrete floor system.

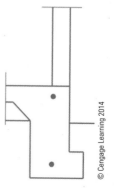

29.3. Use Figure 26.14f as a guide and draw a detail showing a monolithic footing for a one-level residence. Assume a 2 × 6 stud wall with Hardiplank siding over 1/2" OSB underlayment.

29.4. Edit the drawing created in Problem 29.3 to create a detail showing the foundation for a one-level concrete floor system. Provide 2" rigid insulation on the outer side of the foundation. Cover the insulation with 1/2" concrete board and use metal flashing to protect the concrete board. Show a 6"-wide wood-framed wall flush with the edge of the concrete. Make a second copy showing a two-level footing.

29.5. Create a detail showing the foundation for a one-level concrete floor system. Provide 2" rigid insulation on the outer side of the foundation. Cover the insulation with 1/2" concrete board and use metal flashing to protect the insulation. Show a 6"-wide wood-framed wall with a 2" projection past the slab edge. Make a second copy showing a two-level footing. Save the drawings for future use.

29.6. Use Figure 26.14d as a guide to draw a detail showing monolithic footing for a one-level residence with a 4" thick independent slab. Assume a 2 × 4 stud wall with 1" exterior stucco.

29.7. Use the attached sketch to create a detail showing an interior one-level concrete floor system. Show a 4" stud wall anchored to the concrete

with (Ramset®) Red-head type fasteners. Select a strike anchor that will have a 1 1/2" minimum embedment. Make a second copy showing a two-level footing. Save the drawings for future use.

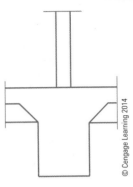

© Cengage Learning 2014

29.8. Use the left portion of Figure 27.20 as a guide to draw a detail of a concrete slab with a 7 3/4" step. Provide a minimum concrete thickness of 8" at the step. Provide WWM set 2" down from the top of the upper slab. Show a 2 × 4 stud wall bolted to the upper slab.

29.9. Use the drawing created in Problem 29.1 to create a detail showing a one-level concrete footing supporting 4"-wide brick veneer. Extend the footing to be 16" wide. Edit the detail to create a two-story footing.

Floor Joist Details

29.10. Use the attached sketch to create a detail showing a one-level concrete T footing supporting a joist floor system. Show and specify a 2 × 6 stud wall with double-wall construction and generic finishing materials. Provide steel as required for your seismic zone. Save the drawing for future use.

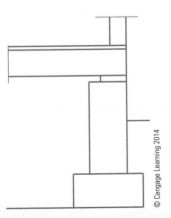

© Cengage Learning 2014

29.11. Use the drawing created in Problem 29.10 to create a detail showing the foundation for a two-level footing for a joist floor system.

29.12. Use the drawing created in Problem 29.10 to create a detail showing a one-level footing for a joist floor system constructed using engineered lumber.

29.13. Create a detail showing a two-level footing for a joist floor system constructed using engineered lumber.

29.14. Create a detail showing a one-level concrete footing with a 6" wide CMU stem wall supporting a joist floor system. Show and specify a 2 × 4 stud wall with double-wall construction and generic finishing materials. Provide steel as required for your seismic zone.

29.15. Create a detail showing a two-level concrete footing with an 8" wide CMU stem wall supporting a joist floor system. Show and specify a 2 × 6 stud wall with double-wall construction

29.16. Use Figure 27.27 as a guide to draw a detail showing a joist floor system supported on an interior girder and a concrete pier.

29.17. Use Figure 27.27 as a guide to draw a detail showing a joist floor system with an 18" step between floor levels. Support each floor with a girder placed below the lower floor level.

29.18. Use Figure 27.27 as a guide to draw a detail showing a joist floor system with a 7 3/4" maximum step between the floor levels. Support the upper floor joists on the girder and hang the lower joists from the girder. Use appropriate joist hangers for the lower joists.

29.19. Use Figure 27.27 as a guide to draw a detail showing a joist floor system intersecting a 4" concrete garage slab. Assume the top of the slab is 8" below the wood floor level. Use 26-gauge flashing to protect the floor framing. Thicken the slab as required at the edge.

29.20. Use Figure 27.27 as a guide to draw a detail showing a joist floor system with an 18" cantilever measured from the outside edge of the wall to the outside edge of the stem wall. Show a 2 × 6 stud wall with double-wall construction.

29.21. Create a detail showing an engineered joist floor system with an 18" cantilever measured from the outside edge of the wall to the outside edge of the stem wall. Show a 2 × 6 stud wall with double-wall construction.

29.22. Create a detail showing a two-level concrete footing with an 8" wide CMU stem wall supporting engineered floor joists. Show and specify a 2 × 6 stud wall with double-wall construction and generic finishing materials. Provide rebar as required for your seismic zone. Increase the footing as required to support 4" brick veneer that extends 48" above the finish grade.

29.23. Use Figure 27.34 as a guide to draw a detail showing the intersection of a joist floor system and a concrete slab. Extend the concrete footing 24" into the grade. Use a 3 × 10 DFPT ledger bolted to the concrete with 1/2" anchor bolts at 32" o.c. staggered 3" up/down. Specify appropriate metal joist hangers. Reinforce the slab with the appropriate WWM and specify steel in the footing and stem wall as per minimum standards presented earlier.

29.24. Use Problem 29.10 as a base to draw a detail showing the floor joists parallel to the stem wall. Show at least three joists.

29.25. Create a detail showing engineered floor joists parallel to the stem wall. Show at least three joists.

29.26. Use Problem 29.10 as a base to draw a detail showing the top of the floor joists set flush with the top of the mudsill. Use appropriate metal hangers to hang the floor joists from the top of the ledger.

29.27. Create a detail showing the top of the engineered floor joists set flush with the top of the mudsill. Use appropriate metal hangers to hang the floor joists from the top of the mudsill.

29.28. Use the attached sketch to create a detail showing the intersection of a wood deck with a wood floor supported on a concrete stem wall. Frame the floor using sawn lumber. Use a continuous rim joist with solid blocking between the floor joists. Set the top of the deck so it is 2" below the finish floor level of the residence. Build the deck using 2 × 4 decking laid flat with a 1/4" gap supported on 2 × 8 treated floor joists. Hang the floor joists from a 2 × 10 treated ledger. Attach the ledger to the residence using nailing from the standard nailing schedule.

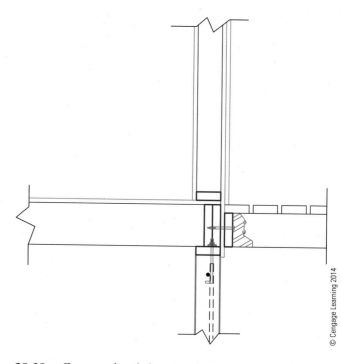

© Cengage Learning 2014

29.29. Create a detail showing the intersection of a wood deck with a wood floor supported on a concrete stem wall. Frame the floor using engineered lumber. Use a continuous rim joist with solid blocking between the floor joists. Set the top of the deck 2" below the finish floor level of the residence. Build the deck using 1 1/2" lightweight concrete over 30# felt over 3/4" plywood decking supported on 2 × 10 treated floor joists. Hang the floor joists from a 3 × 10 treated ledger. Attach the ledger to the residence using 3/8" Ø lag bolts set at 24" o.c. staggered 3" up/down.

Post-and-Beam Details

29.30. Use the attached sketch to create a detail showing a one-level concrete T footing supporting a post-and-beam floor system. Show the beams parallel to the stem wall. Show and specify a 2 × 6 stud wall with double-wall construction and generic finishing materials. Provide steel as required for your seismic zone.

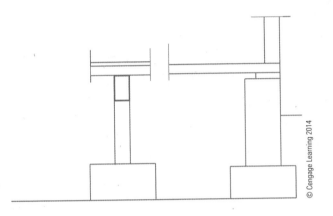

© Cengage Learning 2014

29.31. Create a detail showing a one-level concrete footing with a 6" CMU stem wall supporting a post-and-beam floor system. Show the beams parallel to the stem wall. Show and specify a 2 × 4 stud wall with single-wall construction and generic finishing materials. Provide steel as required for your seismic zone.

29.32. Create a detail showing a two-level concrete T footing supporting a post-and-beam floor system. Show the beams parallel to the stem wall. Show and specify a 2 × 6 stud wall with double-wall construction and generic finishing materials. Provide steel as required for your seismic zone.

29.33. Create a detail showing a two-level concrete footing with an 8" CMU stem wall supporting a post-and-beam floor system. Show the beams parallel to the stem wall. Show and specify a 2 × 6 stud wall with double-wall construction and generic finishing materials. Provide steel as required for your seismic zone.

29.34. Create a detail showing a one-level concrete T footing supporting a post-and-beam floor system. Show the beams perpendicular to the stem wall. Show and specify a 2 × 6 stud wall with double-wall construction and generic finishing materials. Provide steel as required for your seismic zone.

29.35. Create a detail showing a two-level concrete T footing supporting a post-and-beam floor system. Show the beams perpendicular to the stem wall. Show and specify a 2 × 6 stud wall with double-wall construction and generic finishing materials. Provide steel as required for your seismic zone.

29.36. Use Figure 27.32 as a guide and show a post-and-beam floor with a 7 3/4" maximum step.

Retaining Walls

29.37. Use the attached drawing as a guide to draw a detail of an 8' high retaining wall made of CMUs to support a floor and upper level wood wall made of 2 × 6 studs. Show the use of sawn lumber joists that are perpendicular to the retaining wall for the upper floor system and use a 4" concrete slab with no WWM for the lower floor. Provide a 4" Ø French drain at the footing in a 12" wide gravel bed. Reinforce the wall with #5 vertical rebar set 2" clear of the interior face. Extend a #5 × 18" L rebar from the footing into the wall at 48" o.c. Provide (2) #5 continuous rebar 3" up from the bottom of the footing. Reinforce the wall with #5 horizontal rebar at 16" o.c. with (2) #5 at mid-height of wall, and (4) #5 at the top of the wall. Provide #5 vertical rebar at 48" o.c. Attach the mudsill to the wall with 1/2" Ø A.B. at 24" o.c. and use Simpson Company A-34 anchors at each joist-to-plate connection. Provide two layers of hot asphaltic emulsion on the exterior face of the wall.

29.38. Use Figure 26.33 as a guide to draw a detail of an 8' high retaining wall made of poured concrete to support a floor and upper level wood wall made of 2 × 6 studs. Use engineered floor joists that are parallel to the retaining wall for the upper floor system and a 4" concrete slab with no WWM for the lower floor. Show at least four joist spaces and solid blocking between the joists. Place the blocks at 48" o.c. and show them extending 48" out

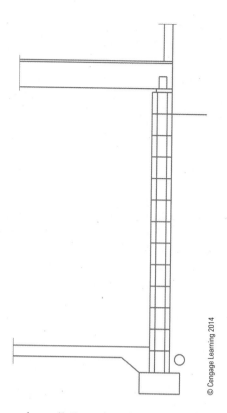

© Cengage Learning 2014

from the wall. Provide a 4" Ø French drain at the footing in a 12" wide gravel bed. Reinforce the wall with #5 vertical rebar set 2" clear of the interior face. Extend a #5 × 18" L rebar from the footing into the wall at 48" o.c. Provide (2) #5 continuous rebar 3" up from the bottom of the 16" × 12" footing. Provide #5 horizontal rebar at 16" o.c. with (2) #5 at mid-height of wall, and (4) #5 at the top of the wall. Provide #5 vertical rebar at 48" o.c. Attach the mudsill to the wall with 1/2" Ø A.B. at 24" o.c. and use a Simpson Company A-34 anchor at 16" o.c. along the rim joist to the plate. Provide two layers of hot asphaltic emulsion on the exterior face of the wall. Cover the exterior wall with 2" rigid insulation and protect the insulation with 1/2" concrete board to a depth of 18". Extend the protection to the mudsill and protect with 26-gauge flashing.

29.39. Use the wall detail drawn in Problem 29.38 as a base to show the intersection of an engineered joist floor system resting on a poured concrete retaining wall. Show a concrete slab intersecting the retaining wall. Show the slab 8" below the top of the wood floor. Thicken the slab to be 12 × 12 at the edge and provide a #5 Ø 18 × 18 L at 32" o.c. from the slab to the retaining wall. Provide (2) #5 continuous bars, 3" up from the bottom of the slab. Provide 26-gauge flashing for any wood exposed to the slab.

29.40. Use the attached sketch to create a detail showing the intersection of a 48" poured concrete retaining wall and a 2 × 4 stud wall. The height of the wall (48" max.) is determined from the top of the 4" concrete floor slab to the line of the finish grade. Extend the wall 6" above the finish grade. Provide a 30" wide × 8" deep footing with (2) #5 Ø continuous bars 3" up from the bottom of the footing. Provide a #5 Ø 15" × 18" L at 18" o.c. extending from the footing into the wall. Reinforce the wall with #5 Ø at 18" o.c. 2" from the tension side of the wall. Provide a 4" Ø drain in an 8 × 30" gravel bed. Use a 2 × 6 DFPT sill with 1/2" A.B. placed at 24" o.c. Show the wood wall supporting an engineered joist floor system with a 12" cantilever. Cover the exterior wood with 1" exterior stucco, and cover the wood at the lower level with 5/8" type X gypsum board.

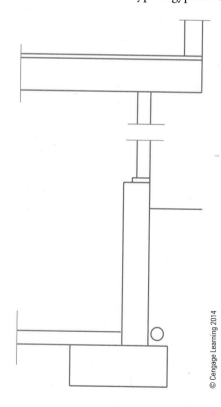

© Cengage Learning 2014

Wall Details

29.41. Use Figure 21.13 as a guide to draw the header over an opening in a 2 × 6 stud wall with double top plates, a 4 × 8 header, and a 2× nailer. Assume that the top of the top plate is set at 8' and the bottom of the header is set at 6'-8".

29.42. Use Figure 21.13 as a guide to draw the header over an opening in a 2 × 6 stud wall with double top plates, (2) 2 × 12 headers, and a 2 × 6 nailer. Provide 2" rigid insulation on the interior side of the wall.

29.43. Use Figure 21.12 as a guide to draw a plan view of an exterior corner formed with (3) 2 × 6 studs. Show the exterior side using single-wall construction.

29.44. Use Figure 21.12 as a guide to draw a plan view of an exterior corner formed with (2) 2 × 6 studs. Show the exterior side using double-wall construction.

29.45. Use Figure 21.12 as a guide to draw a plan view of a 2 × 4 interior wall intersection with an exterior wall formed with (2) 2 × 6 studs. Use a flat stud intersection. Show the exterior side using double-wall construction.

29.46. Use Figure 21.12 as a guide to draw a plan view of a 2 × 4 interior wall intersection with an exterior wall formed with (2) 2 × 6 studs. Use a ladder-backed intersection. Show the exterior side using double-wall construction.

29.47. Use Figure 21.12 as a guide to draw a plan view of a 2 × 4 interior wall intersection with an exterior wall formed with (2) 2 × 6 studs. Use a one-stud intersection with the interior finish supported with metal drywall clips placed at 16" o.c. Show the exterior side using double-wall construction.

29.48. Use Figure 22.31 as a guide to draw an elevation and a section of (2) 2 × 6 king studs and a single trimmer supported on a 4 × 6 post at the lower level. Frame the upper wall with 2 × 6 studs resting on a joist floor system that is supported on a lower wall made of 2 × 6 studs. Tie the trimmers to the post below with a Simpson Company HD-5A connector. (Show just enough framing to explain the connection from the upper to lower floor.)

29.49. Use the information from Chapter 25 and the rough draft on the student website to draw an elevation and a section of one side of a portal frame adjacent to a garage opening.

29.50. Use the information from Chapter 25 to draw an elevation and a section of one side of a braced wall panel.

29.51. Use the information from Chapter 25 to draw an elevation and a section of one side of an alternative braced wall panel.

29.52. Use the information from Figure 25.45 to draw an elevation and a section of one side of the intersection of an upper braced wall panel to a lower braced wall panel.

29.53. Use the information from Figure 25.45 to draw an elevation and a section of one side of the intersection of an upper alternative braced wall panel to a lower alternative braced wall panel.

Roof-to-Wall Connections

29.54. Use Figure 21.14 as a guide to draw a detail showing the intersection of a standard truss with a 6/12 pitch to a 2 × 6 stud wall.

29.55. Draw a detail showing the intersection of a standard truss with a 6/12 pitch to a 2 × 6 stud wall. Show an enclosed soffit using 1 × 4 T&G cedar. Create a cornice detail using at least three pieces of trim.

29.56. Use Figure 21.20 as a guide to draw a detail showing the intersection of a standard truss with a 6/12 pitch to an 8" CMU wall. Use a 2 × 6 DFPT sill with 1/2" Ø A.B. at 48" o.c.

29.57. Use Figure 21.14 as a guide to draw a detail showing the intersection of a standard truss with a 6/12 pitch to a 2 × 6 stud wall. Provide enclosed soffits. Use advanced framing techniques and assume the use of an 8' plate height and a 9' top chord height. Provide solid blocking between the top chords.

29.58. Draw a gable-end wall truss resting on a 2 × 4 stud wall covered with double-wall construction. Assume a 12" overhang and a 2 × 6 barge rafter.

29.59. Draw the intersection of a scissor truss with a 6/12 pitch to a 2 × 6 stud wall. Show the bottom chord with a 4/12 pitch.

29.60. Use Figure 21.5 as a guide to draw a detail showing the intersection of rafters placed at a 6/12 pitch to the top plate of a 2 × 6 stud wall. Assume the use of ceiling joists.

29.61. Draw a detail showing the intersection of rafters placed at a 4/12 pitch to a 2 × 6 top plate on an 8" CMU wall. Assume the use of ceiling joists.

29.62. Draw a detail showing the intersection of 2 × 12 rafters/ceiling joists set at an 8/12 pitch with the top plate of a 2 × 6 stud wall.

29.63. Draw a detail showing the intersection of 2 × 12 rafters/ceiling joists set at a 7/12 pitch with the top plate of a 2 × 6 stud wall. Use an enclosed eave with a 2 × 6 fascia. Cut the rafter tails as required.

29.64. Draw a detail showing the intersection of 2 × 12 rafters/ceiling joists set at a 7/12 pitch with a 2 × 6 stud wall built with double-wall construction. Support the rafter/ceiling joists with the appropriate metal hangers and with a 2 × 12 ledger laid over the OSB sheathing. Provide 26-gauge flashing.

29.65. Draw a detail showing 2 × 12 rafters/ceiling joists that are parallel to a 2 × 6 stud wall built with double-wall construction. Use a 2 × 12 ledger laid over the OSB sheathing and flash with 26-gauge flashing.

29.66. Draw a gable-end wall showing the rafters and ceiling joists resting on a 2 × 6 stud wall covered with double-wall construction. Assume a 12" overhang and a 2 × 6 barge rafter.

29.67. Draw a detail showing the intersection of 2 × 12 rafters/ceiling joists set at a .25/12 pitch with the top plate of a 2 × 6 stud wall. Notch the rafter tails to 3 1/2" and provide a plumb cut. Do not provide a fascia.

29.68. Draw a detail showing the intersection of 2 × 6 rafters with a gable-end wall and a flush barge rafter.

29.69. Draw a detail showing two options for the intersection of 2 × 12 rafters/ceiling joists to a 6 × 14 ridge beam. Show one option with the rafters resting on the top of the ridge beam. Provide solid blocking between each rafter and provide screened roof vents for each third rafter. Notch each rafter 1 1/2" deep × 3" for airflow. Draw a second option with the rafter/ceiling joists hung from the ridge beam using appropriate metal joist hangers.

Partial Wall Sections

Use a foundation detail and a roof detail to create a partial wall section. Assume the plate to be 8'-1 1/8" above the finish floor. Edit notes so wall materials are only specified once per detail.

29.70. Create a partial wall section showing a one-level concrete slab floor system supporting a standard truss roof.

29.71. Create a partial wall section showing a two-level concrete slab floor system supporting a truss roof. Show each wall framed with 2 × 6 studs. Show a window 48" deep in one of the walls. Provide a header framed with (2) 2 × 12s. Show the upper floor framed with engineered joists and provide an 18" cantilever. Frame the roof using standard trusses.

29.72. Create a partial wall section showing a one-level T footing supporting sawn floor joists and 2 × 6 studs supporting a standard truss roof.

29.73. Create a partial wall section showing a one-level T footing supporting engineered floor joists and 2 × 6 studs supporting a scissor truss roof.

29.74. Create a partial wall section showing a one-level footing with a 6" wide stem wall made with CMUs supporting engineered floor joists and 2 × 6 studs supporting a standard truss roof.

29.75. Create a partial wall section showing a one-level T footing supporting a post-and-beam floor system with the girders parallel to the stem wall. Show a 2 × 4 stud wall supporting a standard truss roof.

Chapter 31
Stair Construction and Layout

More than a means of traveling from floor to floor, stairs similar to those in Figure 31.1 can provide an elegant focal point to a home. Section 3 provides a minimal introduction to stairs so that they can be represented on floor plans. This chapter introduces methods for drawings stairs in section. Using commands such as ARRAY, OFFSET, TRIM, and FILLET can quickly reproduce repetitive elements of the stair. These commands are introduced as the step-by-step instructions are given. Steps are provided to aid in the planning, layout, and drawing of straight-run, open, and L- and U-shaped stairways.

This chapter assumes the use of AutoCAD to draw the stair section. A stair section is even easier to draw with a parametric CAD system. With parametric systems, the user provides the starting point of the stairs, the type of stair construction, rise and run, and the stair width and direction and the program automatically calculates the rise of each step. You provide handrails with or without balusters and the program gives you several options for handrail ends. Once you key in all of the necessary information, the stair section is drawn automatically.

Key Terms

Balusters	Headroom	Run	Tread
Banister	Kick block	Spiral stairs	Walkline
Circular stairs	Kicker	Stair jack	Winders
Finial	Landing	Stairwell	
Flight	Newel post	Stringer	
Guardrail	Nose or Nosing	Total rise	
Handrail	Riser	Total run	

CAD Commands and Tools

In addition to basic drawing, editing, text, and dimensioning commands, the following AutoCAD commands and tools are concepts that you should be familiar with to successfully understand and complete the CAD skills referenced in this chapter.

ARRAY   DIVIDE   OFFSET
CHAMFER   FILLET   TRIM

STAIR TERMINOLOGY

There are several basic terms you must be familiar with to work with stairs. Many of these terms are shown in Figure 31.2; others will be defined as you work your way through the chapter. To help understand the general construction of stairs, the terms are divided into the categories describing the general areas where the stairs are placed, the construction of the stairs, and the rails which provide safe usage.

Describing Where the Stair Is Built

Six terms are often used in describing the general area around the stairs including flight, stairwell, walkline, headroom, total rise, and total run. The term *flight* describes an uninterrupted series of steps between two different levels. The hole that is made in the upper floor to provide room for a flight of stairs is the *stairwell*, which can be thought of as the imaginary shaft that extends vertically between floors where the stairs will be placed. The stairwell can be enclosed with walls and with a door at each level to control the spread of sounds and heat, or it can be left open, allowing heat to easily move between floors and creating an open feeling.

The term *walkline* describes an imaginary line indicating the path people tend to walk as they use the stairs. The IRC defines the minimum allowable step size at the walkline but the size varies depending on how the stairs are constructed. The IRC also regulates the minimum required space above each portion of the stairs by defining the *headroom*. This size also varies based on the type of stair to be constructed.

FIGURE 31.1 In addition to being a key component in the traffic flow of a home, stairs can be used to add elegance.

Courtesy Alan Mascord, AIBD. Alan Mascord Design Associates, Inc. Bob Greenspan Photographer http://houseplans.com

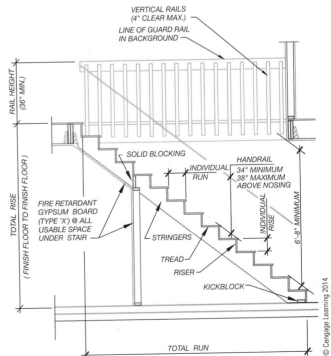

FIGURE 31.2 Common terms used to describe stairs.

© Cengage Learning 2014

The final two terms that describe the area where the stairs are placed are the total run and total rise. The **total run** describes the total length of the stair (see Figure 31.2). The **total rise** refers to the height from floor to floor that the flight of stairs will connect.

Describing Stair Construction

One of the key supports for a flight of stairs is the **stringer** or **stair jack** which supports the other components of the stair. A 2 × 12 (50 × 300) notched stringer is typically used for enclosed stairs. For an open stair, a 4 × 14 (100 × 350) is common, but sizes vary greatly. Double floor joists support the stringer at the top of the run. Metal joist hangers connect each stringer to the floor joists. A **kick block** or **kicker** keeps the bottom of the stringer from sliding on the floor when downward pressure is applied to the stringer.

Once the stringers are in place, treads are attached to the stringers. A **tread** is the horizontal step of the stairs. It is usually made from 1" (25 mm) material on enclosed stairs and 2" (50 mm) material on open stairs. The IRC requires a minimum tread depth of 10" (254 mm) for the individual tread **run** but this size varies based on the type of construction and the walkline location. The vertical backing between the treads is the **riser**. The IRC regulates the individual riser height to a maximum rise of 7 3/4" (196 mm) but the height varies based on the type of construction. A riser is usually made from 1" (25 mm) material for enclosed stairs and is not used on open stairs. The outer edge of the tread that extends over the riser beneath it is the **nose** or **nosing**. The tread width is the measurement from the face of the riser to the nosing.

When the flight of stairs changes direction, a horizontal platform—the **landing**—supports each stair run. The IRC requires a landing in every flight of stairs in which the height between floor levels exceeds 12' (3658 mm). Figure 31.3 shows stringers, risers, treads, and a landing.

Describing Safety and Decorative Features

Handrails are required for each continuous run of treads with four or more risers. A **handrail** is the rail fixed to the wall or posts that you hold on to for support as you walk up or down the stairs. The IRC requires the handrail to be mounted at a height between 34 and 38" (864 and 965 mm). For stairways that are enclosed between two walls, a handrail is only required on one side of the stair. For open stairs, a handrail is required on each open side. A **newel post** is a vertical handrail support at each end of an open stair run. Depending on the architectural style of the home, the newel post is often topped with a decorative cap called a **finial**.

FIGURE 31.3 Stairs with the lower stringers, treads, and risers in place, ready for the upper portion of the run.

© Cengage Learning 2014

A **guardrail** is required for any change in floor elevation of 30" (762 mm) or greater. If the stairwell is not enclosed, a guardrail must be placed around the open sides of the stairwell, except where the steps are entered. The horizontal part of the guardrail is referred to a **banister**. The verticals that support the guardrail are **balusters** and must to be spaced so that a 4" (102 mm) sphere will not pass through them.

DETERMINING RISE AND RUN

The IRC dictates the maximum rise of the stairs. Table 31.1 shows common sizes for various components of a stair. To determine the actual rise, the total height from floor to floor must be known (see Chapter 31 for a review). The total rise can be found by adding the floor-to-ceiling height, the depth of the floor joists, and the depth of the floor covering. The total rise can then be divided by the maximum allowable rise to determine the number of steps required, as shown in Table 31.2. Once the required rise is determined, this information should be stored in your memory for future reference. Of the residential stairs you will lay out in your career, 99% will probably have the same rise. So with a standard 8'-0" (2400 mm) ceiling, you will always need 14 risers.

TABLE 31.1 Basic Stair Dimensions Required by the IRC

STAIR TYPE	IRC
Straight stair	
Max. rise	7 3/4" (195 mm)
Min. run	10" (250 mm)
Min. headroom	6'-8" (2000 mm)
Min. tread width	3'-0" (900 mm)
Handrail height	34" (850 mm) min. 38" (950 mm) max.
Guardrail height	36" (900 mm) min.
Winders	
Min. tread depth	6" (150 mm) min. 10" (250 mm) @ 12" (300 mm)
Spiral	
Min. width	26" (650 mm)
Min. tread depth	7 1/2" (190 mm) @ 12" (300 mm)
Max. rise	9 1/2" (240 mm)
Min. headroom	6'-6" (1950 mm)

Portions of this publication reproduce excerpts from the 2012 International Residential Code® for One- and Two-Family Dwellings®, International Code Council®, Inc., Washington, D.C. Reproduced with permission. All rights reserved. www.iccsafe.org

TABLE 31.2 Determining the Rise and Run Needed for a Flight of Stairs

Step 1. Determine the total rise in inches.

3/4	19	plywood
9 1/4	235	floor joist
3	76	top plates
92 5/8	2353	studs
1 1/2	38	bottom plate
107.125"	2721 mm	total rise

Step 2. Find the number of risers required. Divide the total rise of 107.125" (2721 mm) by the maximum individual riser height of 7 3/4" (197 mm).

$$7\ 3/4\overline{)107.125}\quad\overset{13.8}{}\qquad 197\overline{)2721}\quad\overset{13.8}{}$$

Because you cannot have .8 risers, the number will be rounded up to 14 risers.

Step 3. Find the number of treads required. Number of treads equal Rise − run.
14 − 1 = 13 treads required.

Step 4. Multiply the length of each tread by the number of treads to find the total run.

© Cengage Learning 2014

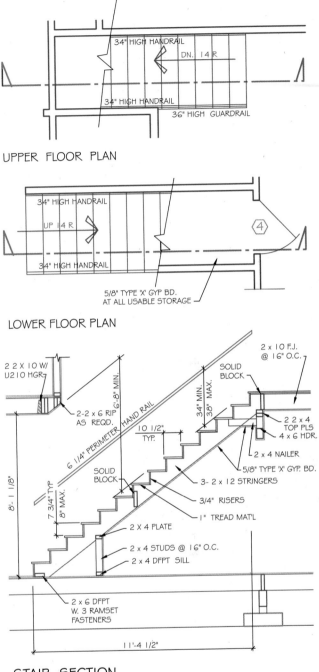

UPPER FLOOR PLAN

LOWER FLOOR PLAN

STAIR SECTION
3/8" = 1'-0"

FIGURE 31.4 The plan and section views for a straight-run enclosed flight of stairs.

Once the number of risers is known, it is easy to calculate the required number of treads, since there will always be one less tread than the number of risers. Thus, a typical stair for a house with 8'-0" (2400 mm) ceilings has 14 risers and 13 treads. If each tread is 10 1/2" (267 mm) wide, the total run can be found by multiplying 10 1/2" (267 mm) (the width) by 13 (the number of treads required). With this basic information, you are ready to draw the stairs. The following is the layout for a straight stairway.

© Cengage Learning 2014

STRAIGHT STAIR LAYOUT

The straight-run stair goes from one floor to another in one straight run (see Figure 31.4). Figure 31.5 shows the stair section for the same house with the basement option. Complete each stair using the four steps of layout, drawing construction, adding dimensions, and annotation.

Stair Planning

The objects drawn during this stage will not be displayed on the completed drawings. Objects can be frozen or placed on non-plotting layers. Place the following steps on the *DETL OUTL* layer unless noted, using thin, continuous lines. See Figure 31.6 for Steps 1–4.

Step 1. Draw walls that may be near the stairs.
Step 2. Draw lines to represent each floor level.
Step 3. Draw a line to represent one end of the stairs. If no dimensions are available on the framing plans, scale your drawing.
Step 4. Determine the required risers and treads. Use the OFFSET command to represent the total run for the flight of stairs.

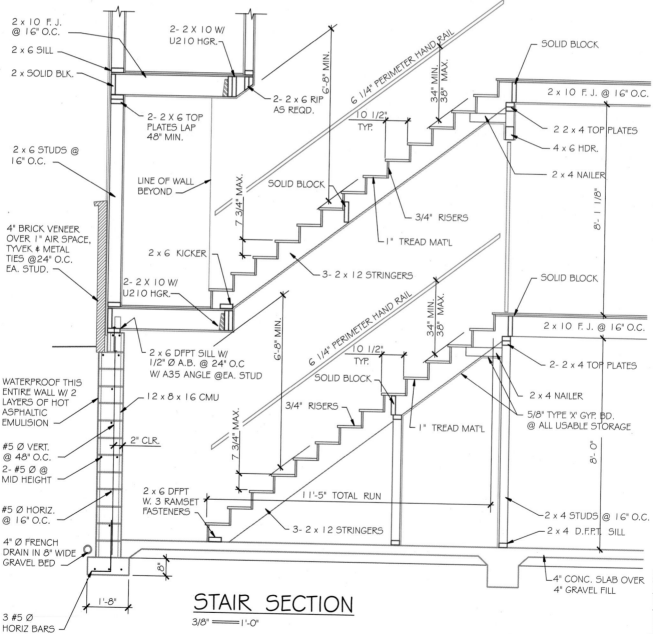

STAIR SECTION
3/8" = 1'-0"

FIGURE 31.5 Straight-run stairs for a multilevel home.

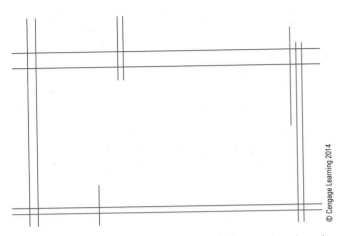

FIGURE 31.6 Draw lines to represent the walls, floor, and each end of the stairs using the *DETL OUTL* layer.

Step 5. Draw a line from floor to floor and use the DIVIDE command to determine the required risers. See Figure 31.7.

Step 6. Draw a line from one end of the stair to the other and use the DIVIDE command to determine the required treads. See Figure 31.7.

Step 7. Draw a line that passes through the nose of each step. Use the OFFSET command to represent the bottom of the stringer.

Step 8. Use the FILLET, CHAMFER, and OFFSET commands to represent the outline of the treads and risers, as shown in Figure 31.8.

Stair Construction

Once the locations of the basic materials have been represented, lay out the objects necessary to complete the drawing. Use the *DETL WOOD* layer to draw the stairs unless otherwise noted. See Figure 31.9 for Steps 9–12.

Step 9. Use the grid that was just created to draw a line representing the location of each tread and riser.

Step 10. Use the OFFSET command and the line created in Step 7 to represent the bottom side of the stringer. Assume a depth of 12" (300 mm).

Step 11. Draw the upper stringer support or support wall where the stringer intersects the floor. Use thick lines to accent any structural wood that the cutting plane has passed through. Place thick lines on the *DETL MCUT* layer.

Step 12. Use the *DETL MBND* layer to draw metal hangers if there is no support wall.

See Figure 31.10 for Steps 13–18. Place each item on the *DETL MBND* layer unless otherwise noted.

Step 13. Draw any intermediate support walls.

Step 14. Draw the gypsum board in all usable storage below the stairs. The IRC requires gypsum (GYP.) board that is 1/2" (13 mm) thick for enclosing all usable storage space under the stairs.

Step 15. Draw any floors or walls that are over the stairs.

Step 16. Draw the handrail and any guardrails, newel post, and balusters that may be in the background.

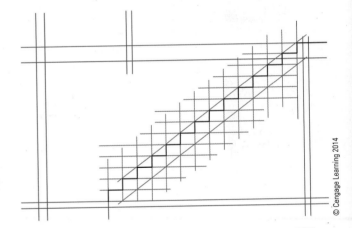

FIGURE 31.8 Outline the treads, stringer, and risers on the *DETL OUTL* layer.

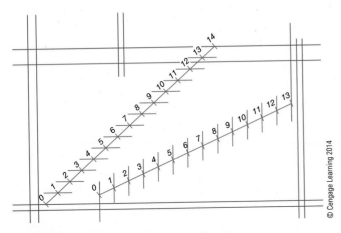

FIGURE 31.7 Determining the risers and treads.

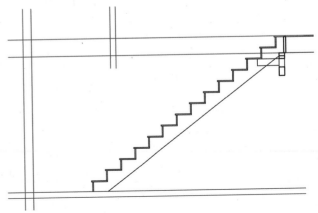

FIGURE 31.9 Representing the treads, risers, and the stringer with the layout grid frozen.

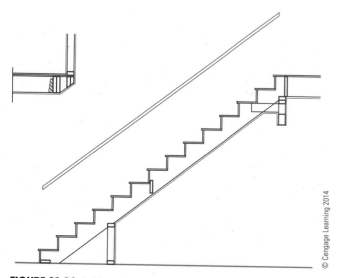

FIGURE 31.10 Add materials such as the kick block, support walls, blocking, fire-rated gypsum board, and handrails.

Step 17. Draw the kick block with bold lines on the *DETL MCUT* layer.

Step 18. Draw solid blocking on the *DETL MCUT* layer.

Adding Dimensions

Table 31.1 shows common stair dimensions based on the IRC requirements. Use the *DETL DIMS* layer to locate all of the following material. See Figure 31.11 for Steps 19–24. Place the required leader and dimension lines to locate the following dimensions:

Step 19. Total rise

Step 20. Total run

Step 21. Rise

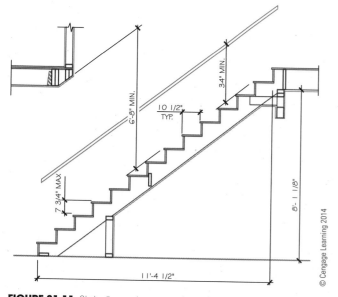

FIGURE 31.11 Stair dimensions are placed on the *DETL DIMS* layer to show the individual and total rise and run, the location of the handrail, and the height between floors.

Step 22. Run

Step 23. Headroom

Step 24. Handrail

Adding Annotation

See Figure 31.12 for typical notes placed on stair sections using the *DETL ANNO* layer. Verify local variations with your instructor. Common materials that must be represented include:

- The size and type of the stringer, tread material, and riser material.
- The upper floor framing members.
- The kick block size and method of attachment to the floor.
- Any stair blocking.
- The handrail.
- Fire protection below the stairs.

OPEN STAIRWAY LAYOUT

An open stairway is similar to a straight enclosed stairway. It goes from one level to the next in a straight run. As seen in Figure 31.13, the major difference is that with the open stair, there are no risers between the treads. This allows for viewing from one floor to the next, creating an open feeling. Use the *DETL WOOD* layer to draw the following materials unless otherwise noted. See Figure 31.14 for Steps 1, 2, and 3.

Step 1. Start the drawing by following Steps 1–6 of the previous stair layout.

Step 2. Draw the 3 × 12 (75 × 300) treads.

Step 3. Draw the 14" (360 mm) deep stringer centered on the treads.

See Figure 31.15 for Steps 4–9:

Step 4. Draw the treads on the *DETL MCUT* layer.

Step 5. Draw the stringer on the *DETL MBND* layer.

Step 6. Draw the upper stringer supports on the *DETL MCUT* layer.

Step 7. Draw the metal hangers for the floor and stringer on the *DETL MBND* layer.

Step 8. Draw any floors or walls that are near the stairs on the *DETL MBND* layer.

Step 9. Draw the handrail on the *DETL MBND* layer.

Step 10. Place the required leader and dimension lines to provide the needed dimensions on the *DETL DIMS* layer. See Steps 19–24 of the enclosed stair layout for a guide to the needed dimensions. See Figure 31.16.

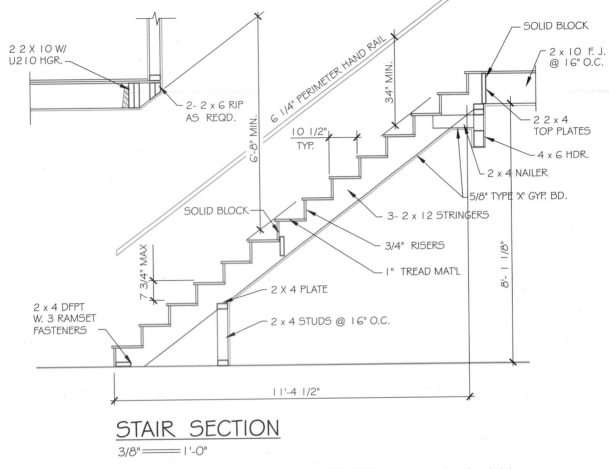

STAIR SECTION
3/8" = 1'-0"

FIGURE 31.12 The stair drawing is completed by adding notes on the *DETL ANNO* layer to describe all materials.

FIGURE 31.13 Open tread stairs supported between steel stringers.

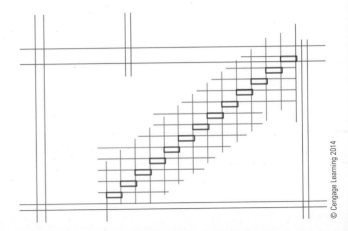

FIGURE 31.14 Layout of Steps 1 through 3 for an open tread stair.

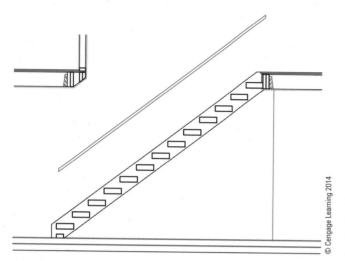

FIGURE 31.15 Representing the structural materials for an open tree stair.

Step 11. Place the required notes on the section on the *DETL MBND* layer. Use Figure 31.16 as a guide. Have your instructor specify local variations.

L- AND U-SHAPED STAIRS

An L- or U-shaped stair similar to Figure 31.17 is often used in residential design. Rather than going up a whole flight of steps in a straight run, this stair layout introduces a landing. The landing is usually located at the midpoint of the run, but it can be offset, depending on the amount of room allowed for stairs on the floor plan. The stairs may be either open or enclosed, depending on the location. The layout is similar to the layout of the straight-run stair but requires a little more planning in the layout stage because of the landing. Lay out the distance from the start of the stairs to the landing based on the floor plan measurements.

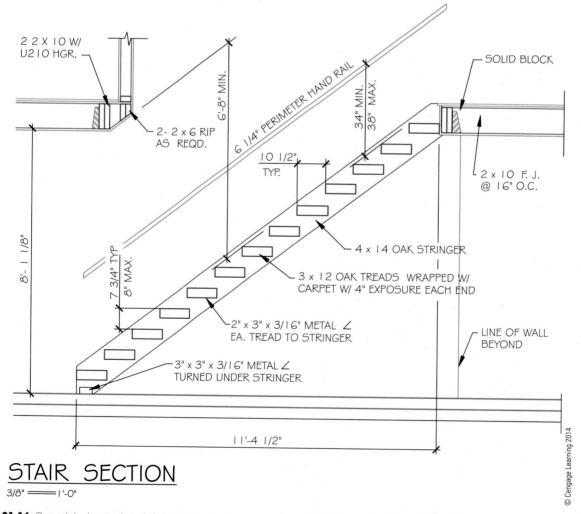

STAIR SECTION
3/8" = 1'-0"

FIGURE 31.16 Completed open tread stair with dimensions and notes added.

FIGURE 31.17 A multilevel, L-shaped open stair.

Then proceed using a method similar to that used to draw the straight-run stair. See Figure 31.18 for the initial layout of a U-shaped section. Figure 31.19 shows what a U-shaped stair looks like on the floor plan and in section.

STAIRS WITH NON-PARALLEL EDGES

The stairs introduced to this point are usually constructed with treads that have parallel edges. Three common tread options include winders, circular, and spiral stairs.

Winding Stairs

The IRC defines winding stairs similar to the stair in Figure 31.20 as stairs that have treads with non-parallel edges. **Winders** are often incorporated into L- or U-shaped

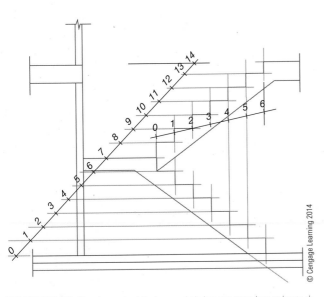

FIGURE 31.18 The layout of U-shaped stair runs requires a layout process similar to that used with a straight-run flight of stairs.

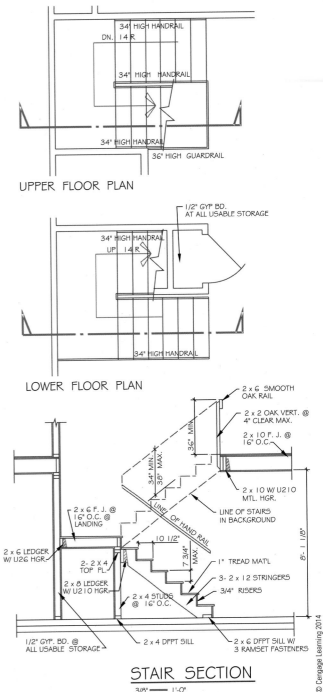

UPPER FLOOR PLAN

LOWER FLOOR PLAN

STAIR SECTION
3/8" = 1'-0"

FIGURE 31.19 A U-shaped stair in plan view and section.

stairs to eliminate the length of the overall run. Rather than having one landing with a uniform height, winders replace the landing with steps. Because of the risk of falling, winders may not be permitted in all areas. The IRC requires that winder treads have a minimum depth of 6" (152 mm) at the inner edge of the tread and a minimum depth of 10" (254 mm) at the walkline. The IRC defines walkline for winding stairs as a point 12" (305 mm) from the narrow side of the treads. Specify minimum

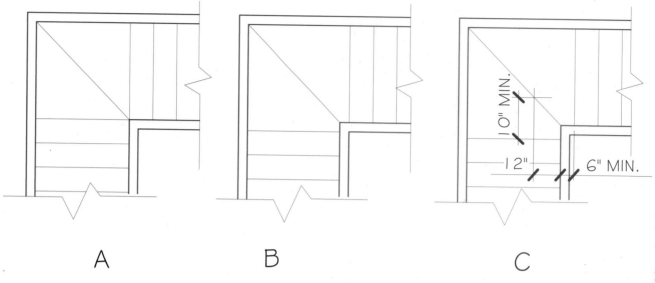

A   B   C

FIGURE 31.20 Winding stairs are defined by the IRC as stairs that have treads with non-parallel edges. Winders are often incorporated into L- or U-shaped stairs to eliminate the length of the overall run. Examples A and B show common methods of representing winders in plan view. Example C shows IRC minimum size requirements.

distances for stair construction in general notes referenced to a stair section or shown on an enlarged plan view where the winders occur.

Circular Stairs

Circular stairs or curved stairs similar to Figure 31.21 add a focal point to an entry and are often found in custom homes. A key consideration in representing circular stairs is to define the center point for the stair radius. Indicate the center point on the framing plan or provide an enlarged floor plan showing the stair layout. Figure 31.22 shows a partial framing for the area surrounding a circular stair. A detail showing the rise and run information is used to supplement the plan view.

Spiral Stairs

Spiral stairs are typically premanufactured stairs with treads with non-parallel edges that are formed around a center support. They get the name from the spiral pathway created between the floor levels they connect. They are often used as a means of access to a loft or other private areas. Although they provide access between floors while using very little floor space, they are difficult to use for moving furniture between floors. Figure 31.23 shows a custom spiral stair. Spiral stairs must have a minimum clear width at and below the handrail of 26" (660 mm). Each tread must have a minimum tread depth of 7 1/2" (190 mm) at a distance 12" (914 mm) from the narrow edge. Verify with your local building code if spiral stairs are an acceptable means of egress in your area.

FIGURE 31.21 A curved or circular stairway is often used as a focal point in an entry.

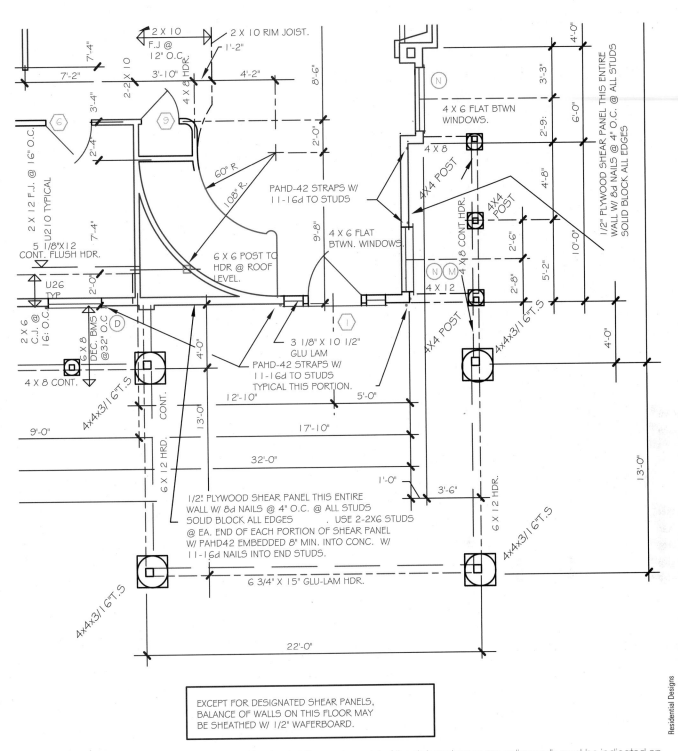

FIGURE 31.22 A partial framing plan showing a circular stair. The center point of the stair and any surrounding walls must be indicated on the framing plan.

EXTERIOR STAIRS

It is often necessary to draw sections of exterior stairs on multilevel homes. Figure 31.24 shows two different types of exterior stairs. Although there are many variations, these two options are common. Both can be laid out by following the procedure for straight-run stairs.

There are some major differences in the finishing materials. Notice that there is no riser on the wood stairs and the tread is thicker than the tread of an interior step. Usually the deck and the tread are made from the same material. In many parts of the country, a nonskid material must cover the treads. The concrete stair can also be laid out by following the procedure for straight-run stairs.

FIGURE 31.23 Premanufactured spiral stairs made of wood or steel are often used as a secondary means of access.

Once the risers and run have been marked off, the riser can be drawn. Notice that the riser is drawn on a slight angle. It can be drawn at about 10° and does not have to be labeled. This is something the flatwork crew will determine at the job site, depending on their forms.

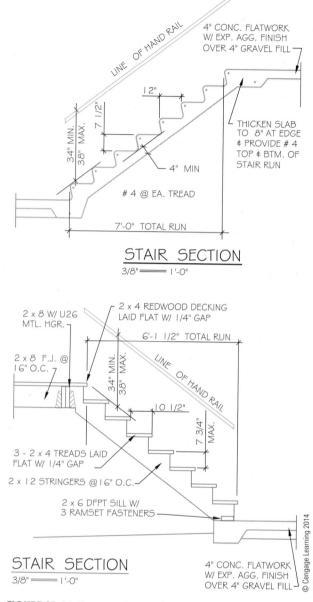

FIGURE 31.24 Common types of exterior stairs.

Additional Resources

Use the following websites as resources to help you keep current with changes in stair materials.

Address	Company or Organization
www.arcways.com	Arcways
www.stair.com	Stair & Millwork Co.
www.stairwaysinc.com	Stairways Inc.
www.southernstaircase.com	Southern Staircase™
www.theironshop.com	The Iron Shop®
www.yorkspiralstair.com	York Spiral Stair

Stair Construction and Layout Test

Follow these instructions to access and complete an electronic copy of the Chapter 31 Stair Construction and Layout Test:

1. Go to cengagebrain.com
2. Enter the email address and password you used to register for the site (see Preface for full instructions).
3. Select the website from the **My Course & Materials** area of your home page. Select the chapter you want from the pull-down menu at the top of the page. Choose the resources for that chapter from the menu on the left.
4. Type your name, the chapter number, and the date at the top of the sheet.
5. Answer the following questions with short, complete statements using a word processor.

NOTE:

The answers to some questions may not be contained in this chapter and will require you to do additional research using the Internet. Use your favorite search engine to search for specific professional companies or general categories of information.

Questions

31.1. What is a tread?

31.2. What is the minimum headroom required for a residential stair?

31.3. What is the maximum individual rise of a step?

31.4. What member is used to support the stairs?

31.5. What is the maximum spacing allowed between the verticals of a railing?

31.6. Describe the difference between a handrail and a guardrail.

31.7. How many risers are required if the height between floors is 10' (3000 mm)?

31.8. Sketch a section for three common stair types.

31.9. If a run of 10" (250 mm) is to be used, what will be the total run when the distance between floors is 9' (2700 mm)?

31.10. What is a common size for treads in an open-tread layout?

31.11. Use the Internet to determine what area limitations your local building code places on the use of spiral stairs.

31.12. Use the Internet to gather information from three different manufacturers of spiral stairs. Research the range of available diameters and the required range of space for a stair that spans 9' from floor to floor.

31.13. Visit construction sites and, with permission of the site supervisor, photograph the construction of three different types of stairs.

31.14. Use the Internet to find three companies that manufacture wood stair components such as newel post, balusters, and finals. Save the names of these companies as well as prints of samples of the type of materials they supply.

31.15. Use the Internet to research companies that make custom stair assemblies. Make an appointment to visit the site and to find out what the company does, common materials it uses, and how CAD technicians are utilized at their company. Write a report on your findings.

Problems

If the home you started in Chapter 12 contains a stairway, draw a section to document its design and construction. Using the guidelines in this chapter and information from your local building department website, create the required drawings to obtain a permit.

Project Planning

After reviewing the drawing criteria for this project on the student website, either verbally or in a written memo demonstrate to your client your understanding of the project, along with the amount of time you expect the drawing to take, and any resources you require to complete it. Respond verbally to any questions your client might have for you, and let the client know when the project will be complete. Ask for clarification of any questions you have regarding the drawing criteria. If you plan to present your project preview verbally, be prepared with your questions written down so that you can ask relevant questions in a professional manner and be prepared to take notes regarding your client's comments.

Once you have the criteria and direction to begin the project, make a plan to get it done. Using the guidelines presented in this chapter, include the minimum contents as well as an estimate of the time you require to complete each aspect of the drawing:

Research.

Major steps to complete the drawing.

Applicable codes that will apply to this drawing.

Applicable local requirements that apply to the drawing.

Adjusting drawing templates to set plotting standards, text heights, dimensions, and linetypes.

Completing all required annotation and dimensioning.

Evaluation.

Track the amount of time.

Compare the estimated completion time for each aspect of the project with the actual required time.

Use the appropriate checklist from the student website prior to submitting your drawing to your instructor.

Chapter 35
Renovations, Remodeling, and Additions

Many clients request modifications to be made to existing structures. The changes may come in the form of alterations, renovations, remodeling, or additions. The IRC requires any alteration, repair, or addition to comply with all aspects of the prevailing codes that apply to new structures. Most codes require that when the proposed changes affect more than 50 percent of the existing structure, the entire structure be made to comply with the current building codes. Always verify local requirements prior to starting a project.

Key Terms

Alteration

Building permits

Inclinometer

Legal description

Remodel

Renovation

CAD Commands and Tools

Other than the basic drawing, editing, text, and dimensioning commands, no additional CAD commands are required to successfully complete the CAD skills referenced in this chapter.

DETERMINING THE TYPE OF PROJECT

Nonstructural changes, such as removing or replacing cabinets, are examples of *alterations*. The IRC does not require a building permit for nonstructural changes. The code specifically excludes such projects as painting, papering, paneling, tiling, carpeting, cabinets, countertops, or other finishing projects.

Renovations

A *renovation* usually involves removing and replacing nonstructural materials, such as cabinets, and may include minor electrical or mechanical repairs. Permits are not required to do the following minor repairs and maintenance on one- or two-family dwellings:

- Painting buildings that are not historic landmarks.
- Blowing insulation into existing homes.
- Installing storm windows.
- Installing window awnings not more than 54" deep (not in a design zone) that are supported by exterior walls and do not project beyond the property line.
- Replacing interior wall, floor, or ceiling coverings, such as wallboard or sheet vinyl.
- Putting up shelving and cabinets.
- Installing gutters and downspouts. (A plumbing permit may be required for storm water disposal.)
- Replacing or repairing siding on walls that are 3' or more from a property line.
- Replacing or repairing roofing, excluding the replacement of sheathing. (A maximum of three layers of roofing is allowed.)
- Replacing doors or windows that don't require widening existing openings. In some areas, replacing windows requires a permit due to energy considerations. Verify with the local municipality prior to replacing window of equal size.

- Building a fence up to 6' high.
- Paving a walkway.
- Building a patio or deck that is not more than 30" above grade.

While the IRC allows work on these projects without building permits, drawings are helpful to aid in communication between the owner and the contractors who will complete the work.

Remodels

A *remodel* involving moving, adding, or removing walls requires a building permit. Most building departments require a building permit even if the remodel consists of nonbearing walls within the limits of the existing structure. An addition is defined by the IRC as any change in the size of an existing structure caused by increasing the existing floor area or by increasing or altering the height of a structure. A permit is required to construct, enlarge, alter, move, or demolish any one- or two-family dwelling or similar structure. Examples of projects requiring permits include:

- Adding a room.
- Building, demolishing, or moving a carport, garage, or shed of more than 200 sq ft (18.58 m²).
- Finishing an attic, garage, or basement for additional living space.
- Cutting a new window or door opening or widening existing openings.
- Moving, removing, or adding walls.
- Applying roofing when removing all of the old roofing and installing new sheathing.
- Building a stairway.
- Building a retaining wall more than 4' (1200 mm) high.
- Building a deck more than 30" (750 mm) above grade.
- Putting up a fence more than 6' (1800 mm) high.
- Moving any amount of cut or fill on sites affected by waterways or slope hazards.

PERMIT REQUIREMENTS

Building departments require plans that clearly define the location, nature, and extent of the work to be completed. Drawings must contain sufficient detail to allow construction to conform to the existing code. *Building permits* required for remodels or additions include structural, electrical, plumbing, and mechanical permits. Some municipalities require the permits to be obtained by the property owner or by the licensed contractor who will complete the work. They do not allow the project designer to obtain the permits, but a member of the design team may prepare the necessary paperwork. If it is legal in your area for the designer to obtain the permits, working with the building department can be a valuable learning experience that will improve your drawings.

Structural Permits

To obtain a structural permit, drawings must be submitted that include:

- The address and *legal description* of the property.
- A description of the work proposed.
- The owner's name, address, and phone number. If a contractor will do the work, provide the contractor's name, address, phone number, and state license number.

Obtaining structural permits typically requires three sets of plans clearly showing all work on the building and where the building sits on the property. The local building department determines the exact requirements. Plans for a residential addition normally include a site plan, floor plan, framing plan, foundation plan, exterior elevations, and cross sections showing construction details. In addition to these drawings, written specifications for major equipment and materials, energy documentation, structural calculations, and required fire-protection equipment must be provided. Requirements for each of these drawings are discussed later in this chapter.

> ## NOTE:
> The building department of many larger municipalities provides standard details to guide construction. Retaining walls, partial wall sections, and other standard construction details are available for the homeowner to ensure compliance with the current codes and building requirements. Verify with your local building department the availability of standard details that may provide a homeowner with significant savings.

Electrical Permits

An electrical permit is required to perform the following work:

- Installing or altering any permanent wiring or electrical device.
- Running any additional wiring, putting in an electrical outlet or light fixture, installing a receptacle for a garage-door opener, or converting from a fuse box to circuit breakers.
- Installing or altering low-voltage systems such as security alarms.

Your area's building department issues permits for electrical work. Drawings are not usually necessary to get a permit for residential electrical work, but you must know the structure's square footage, the panel's amperage, and the number of circuits needed to complete the necessary electrical forms. Fees charged for the permit are based on these figures.

Plumbing Permits

A plumbing permit is required to perform the following work:

- Replacing water heaters and altering piping inside a wall or ceiling or beneath a floor.
- Doing emergency repair, alteration, or replacement of freeze-damaged or leaking concealed piping if new piping exceeds 3' (900 mm).
- Relocating existing plumbing while remodeling or adding to a one- or two-family dwelling. This includes the installation of building sewers, water service, and rain drains outside the building.

Your area's building department issues permits for plumbing. Drawings are not usually necessary to get a permit for residential plumbing work, but you must know the number of fixtures being added. Fees charged for the permit are based on the size and complexity of the plumbing work. Some municipalities base the plumbing fees on the number of fixtures, or the number of feet of water and sewer lines or the number of rain drains to be added. Some municipalities require a one-line diagram showing pipe sizes for fresh- and wastewater lines. The plumbing contractor, not the CAD drafter, usually provides these drawings.

Mechanical Permits

A mechanical permit is required to perform the following work:

- Installing or changing any part of a heating or cooling system that must be vented into any kind of chimney, including unvented decorative appliances.

- Installing a woodstove, fireplace insert, pellet stove, or related venting.

- Installing, altering, or repairing gas piping between the meter and an appliance (indoors or outdoors).

- Installing bath fans, dryer exhausts, kitchen range exhausts, and appliances that must be vented.

While drawings generally are not required to obtain permits for mechanical work on a dwelling, you must briefly describe the work proposed. For example, you must indicate if a specific appliance or a new vent or ductwork will be installed. If installing new gas piping, you must specify the number of outlets (future gas appliances).

Fire Protection

Depending on the municipality governing the construction site, a sprinkler system may be required when working on a large addition or renovation. Municipalities under the jurisdiction of the **NFPA (National Fire Protection Association)** may require fire protection above what the IRC requires. Homes larger than 3500 sq ft may require sprinkler systems. If your building department has adopted the 2012 IRC, all new homes, regardless of size, require sprinkler systems. Review Chapter 5 for placement requirements and limitations. The designer must verify with the building and fire departments regarding specific requirements. Typically NFPA requirements are based on the proximity of existing fire protection, access to the site, distance to the nearest fire hydrant, and the size of the structure. While a house the size of the one in this chapter would normally require sprinklers, they are not necessary in this case because two fire hydrants are adjacent to the property.

DRAWING CONSIDERATIONS FOR AN ADDITION

When remodeling a home or adding space, the building department requires the same types of drawings necessary for new construction. The minimum drawings to obtain a building permit include site, floor, foundation plans, sections, and exterior elevations. Electrical, framing, roof plans, and interior elevations may also be required depending on the complexity of the structure. The major difference in requirements for new construction and for a remodel or addition is the need to clearly distinguish between types of construction. Another major difference is in the project's starting point.

Defining Construction Types

It is extremely important to define major types of construction on each of the drawings explaining the alterations. Major types of construction include:

- New material.
- Existing material to remain.
- Existing material to be removed.
- Future work.
- Items to be relocated.
- Material not in the contract.

The drawing affects how it is represented. Figure 35.1 shows an example of a floor plan with several types of construction. Because the symbols representing each type of construction vary with each office, you must provide a legend clearly distinguishing each material used. Common symbols are discussed as each drawing type is

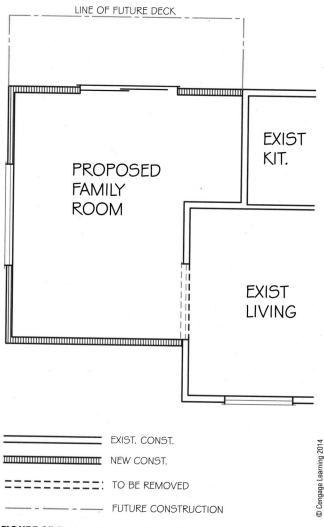

FIGURE 35.1 Varied lineweights and linetypes should be used to distinguish between types of construction.

© Cengage Learning 2014

introduced. Common methods for representing varied materials include:

- Using color if drawings are to be plotted in color.
- Using a plot style of gray scale, represent new materials in black and existing materials in gray.
- Using AutoCAD color numbers 8 or 9.
- Using dashed lines to represent materials for removal.
- Using black dashed lines to represent structural materials for removal.
- Using gray dashed lines to represent nonstructural materials for removal.

Defining a Project

The first step to overcome for a remodel or addition is determining the extent that the existing structure will be affected by the proposed project. To complete the site plan, determine the dimensions for each exterior surface to draw the footprint of the structure on the site plan. Only the existing rooms affected by the new construction must be represented on other drawings. Before considering any dimensions, the scope of the jobsite must be determined.

Basic Site Information

The street and legal description of the property are major pieces of information needed to start a remodel or addition. The client will provide the street address and a legal description of the jobsite during the initial contact. See Chapter 9 for a review of the different types of legal descriptions. If the owner is unable to provide the legal description, you can obtain it from a local title company. Obtain the name of a title company in your area from the Internet. The customer service department of the title company can provide you with four valuable pieces of information about the proposed jobsite for free. These include a map with a legal description, a deed showing current ownership, a printout describing the property, and a record of the tax history. You should have the map in your possession prior to making the initial site visit. Obtain this information on the Internet if the street address is known using sites such as Google Earth, Zillow, or the website for the governing zoning department.

The site map provides the size of the proposed jobsite and helps you determine the property lines. If you know that a site is 50' (15 000 mm) wide and the structure is 38' (11 400 mm) wide, you know that 12' (3600 mm) of side yard is available. If you find you have 14' (4200 mm) at the jobsite, you know you either have the wrong lot on the map or you've made a mistake in your measurements.

Once you have the street address, obtain the setbacks for construction from the zoning department governing the site. This information may also be available by visiting the website of the appropriate zoning department. Request the following information when making contact with the zoning department:

- Zoning of the proposed jobsite.
- Types of uses (occupancy) allowed for this property.
- Building department requirements for construction.
- Sizes of the front, side, and rear yards.
- Size limitations for existing and new structures.
- Height limitations.
- Whether certain materials, such as overhangs, decks, or masonry chimneys, extend into the setbacks.
- Minimum drawings required by the municipality to obtain a permit.

Once you have this information, you're ready for the initial site visitation.

Initial Site Visitation

As you prepare to visit the site, consider the needed materials or equipment, the measurements that must be made, and the measuring methods you will use.

Materials. Take the following basic equipment with you to the jobsite:

- Measuring tapes, camera, and clipboard.
- Writing equipment such as pens (felt/ball, multicolor) and pencils.
- Flashlight.
- Ladder/step stool.
- Compass.
- Inclinometer.

A 100' (30 000 mm) and a 25' (7500 mm) tape will be useful in making measurements. Use the 100' (30 000 mm) tape to measure overall sizes of the structure, setbacks, and the width of the street from curb to curb. In rural areas, a 200' (60 000 mm) tape will prove useful. Regardless of its length, the tape should be flexible so it won't be damaged if run over by a car. The short tape should be wide enough to extend about 10' (3000 mm) in a vertical direction without bending. The shorter tape will be useful to take most interior dimensions and to determine the vertical dimensions on the outside of the structure. Just as important as the tools is the measuring system you will use. The best results will be achieved if you are consistent in how measurements are written in your notes. Write dimensions as feet and inches (14'-6") or in inches (174"). Do not mix feet and inch measurements and inch only measurements. At the risk of seeming anal, you must be consistent in recording distances to ensure that you'll understand your notes after they've sat for a few days.

Take a digital camera or cell phone with you to capture images of the jobsite, the surrounding view, each side of the existing structure, and important interior features. Take photos that identify the locations of every major feature on the exterior of the structure, all of the structure's surfaces—even the ones that will not be affected by the new construction. A photo of an unaltered side may be useful to determine angles or sizes of features on an affected side. Figure 35.2 shows the exterior of the structure to be altered in this chapter.

A clipboard is a useful tool for support while sketching and placing field notes. In adverse weather, bring a piece of plastic to protect your sketches. Writing equipment should include a combination of pens and pencils. Working in multiple colors or mediums will help keep the structure separate from the dimensions and notes explaining the structure. Depending on the weather, ballpoint pens may be better than felt pens because the ink from most felt pens runs if exposed to rain. A flashlight is a useful for taking measurements in the attic or crawl space. The ladder will provide safe access into the attic. An *inclinometer* is an instrument for measuring angles of slope. It measures positive slopes, as seen by an observer looking upward. See Chapter 16 for converting angles to roof pitch. It can also be used to measure negative slopes, as seen by an observer looking downward, which will be helpful in determining ground slopes. Review Chapter 9 for ground slopes.

FIGURE 35.2 The northeast elevation of this structure will be remodeled. The deck and porch roof will be removed to provide space for a new kitchen and family room.

Gathering Information

Gathering information about the project begins before getting out of your car. Take notes about the existing roof shape and major materials, such as roofing or siding, and approximate the roof pitch. Even though you will take measurements, making a note to yourself may help when you are back at a workstation trying to guess what you've written. After you talk to the client and walk around the jobsite, obtain the following information:

- Sketch the building footprint on a site plan.
- Use a compass to determine north and record it on your site sketch.
- Indicate material on each side at property line (objects on a neighbor's property may obstruct views) such as trees, fences, hedges, open spaces, using abbreviations such as **F, RS, LS,** and **R** or compass directions to represent each side of the structure.
- Determine the distance from the structure to existing fences. A fence may not be exactly on a property line, but it is a good guide for locating the property edge.
- Locate sewer cleanouts and plumbing stacks on the plan.

Obtain dimensions to complete specific drawings for the site, elevations, floor, and sections. Express dimensions as feet and inch measurements (12'-0") or as inch units (144"), depending on your preference for entering units at a computer.

Site. Gather the following information to locate each major feature that the building department may require for a building permit including:

- **Overall length of each side of the structure.** This information is necessary for drawing the building footprint. These sizes are determined by taking total length measurements of each surface of the existing foundation wall, or by taking measurements from one opening to the next and adding the totals.
- **Driveway location relative to the structure and the street.** Note the driveway material. Measure the length and the width of the driveway.
- **Sidewalk locations.** For homes on acreage, this may be only an estimate or it may not apply. For city lots, measure from curb to curb to determine the street width, from the face of the curb to the exterior edge of the sidewalk, and then the sidewalk width. For many municipalities, the property line is within a few inches of the interior edge of the sidewalk.
- **Each side yard distance to the structure.** On paper you'll dimension from the structure to a line that

© Cengage Learning 2014. Courtesy Matthew Jefferis

Professional Perspective

If the foundation wall is not easily accessible, measure the length of each side of the building from the edge of the siding. Remember that typically the wood walls align with the foundation. If you use this method, be sure to measure how far the siding extends past the foundation wall at a location where you can get to the foundation. This will allow you to accurately describe the wall locations on the foundation.

does not exist at the jobsite. Look for a fence or a row of shrubs that may indicate the property edge. If you're working on a city lot, measure to a neighboring structure and then split the distance to get the approximate location. If the house is near the side yard setback, but the location can't be determined, draw the home at the property line and list the minimum required distance. On rural property, an approximation such as 300' ± is adequate.

- **Distance from any other structures to the proposed structure.** Locate other structures on the site such as a detached garage, barn, or pump house.

- **Size of other structures on the property.** Determine the overall dimensions of other buildings on the property to locate the footprint of each building on the site plan.

- **Location and diameter of trees or other obstructions near where the alteration will occur.** As shown in Figure 35.3, locate a tree by taking measurements from three different locations and the diameter of the trunk. Measure the distances from known locations on the exterior of the structure. At your workstation, the three locations become the center point and the lengths become the radius. The arcs will intersect at the location of the tree.

- **Locations of water and sewer lines or the septic tank and drain field.** Sewer is usually provided in the street for most city sites. Usually a sewer cleanout is located outside of a bath or kitchen to indicate the location of the sewer. Where public sewers are not available, a cleanout is often located in a rear or side yard near a bath or kitchen. If there is a septic tank, a recessed area can often be found about 10' from the cleanout. The property owner typically has the map that was required to obtain the original building permit. Such a map is useful for approximating the location of the tank and the drainage field. Keep in mind that most building departments need only the approximate location of the septic system.

It is generally the contractor's responsibility during the initial excavation to verify that the new addition will not be built over or within 10' of a septic tank.

If public water is provided, locate the main supply line by the location of the water meter. For rural sites, the well location must also be considered in relation to the septic system. Most municipalities require at least 100' (30 000 mm) between the well and the septic system.

- **Location of all exterior openings in the portion of the structure to be remodeled.** Locate the sizes of all exterior openings in the affected rooms. Locate doors or windows even if they will be removed. Attach a tape measure on one end of a structure and then determine the distance to each edge of an opening to locate all doors and windows on the drawings. Although you must know the size of the trim when drawing the elevations, it is not necessary to locate

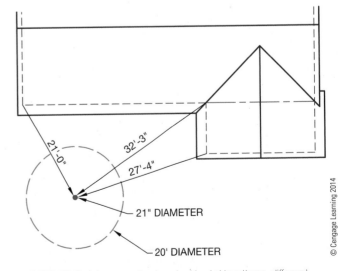

© Cengage Learning 2014

FIGURE 35.3 A tree can be located by taking three different dimensions from known locations and obtaining the diameter of the trunk. Once back at your workstation, you make the three locations the center point and each distance becomes a radius. The circles will intersect at the location of the tree.

> **NOTE:**
>
> *The siding, corner trim, and wall sheathing add inches that distort your measurements. Taking measurements at the foundation eliminates this accumulation. On a sketch show the location of the ridge and how it relates to windows or doors. While determining the overall size of the structure, take a measurement to locate the ridge. Since you know that it should be in the center of the two exterior walls, this measurement will help determine the overall size and to complete the roof plan.*

the windows on the floor plan. In addition to locating the openings on the outside of the structure, locate them from interior walls. This dual measuring serves as a method to cross check dimensions and increase the accuracy of your drawings.

Elevations. Once you take the measurements to locate the footprint of the house, gather information to complete the elevations. First draw the elevations for the existing structure, and then draw the elevations for the addition. Gather the information to create the exterior elevations of the existing structure from the interior and exterior of the structure.

Exterior Measurements. Make a sketch of each surface of the house that will be affected by the new addition and place the following information on the sketch.

- Finished floor location. Measure the distance from the doorsill to the finished grade. Because the grade will not be level, take this measurement at each exterior door. Be sure to count the number of steps and their heights.

- Vertical locations of all openings. This requires measuring the height of each opening and the height of the sill above the bottom of the siding. The actual height of the window above the floor can easily be determined when measuring the interior. Comparing interior dimensions with exterior dimensions will accurately locate the bottom of the siding to the floor line. While measuring windows, don't forget to make note of the window type.

- Siding reveal. If horizontal siding is used, measure the exposure of several pieces of siding. If you measure four pieces of siding and determine exposures of 6, 6.125, 5 7/8, and 6", use the average height of 6" to estimate vertical distances that are too high to measure with your tape measure.

- Heights of exterior walls.

- Measurement from the bottom of the siding to the top of the wall at the eave.

- Measurement from the top of the windows to the top of the wall at the eave. Count the total number of pieces of horizontal siding from the bottom to the top of the wall at the eave.

- Ridge height. Measure this distance from the top of the wall to the ridge. If there is a window in a gable end, measure the height of the window, the height of the window above the lower wall, and the distance from the top of the window to the bottom of the roof at the ridge.

- Height of trim above ground level. Determine the size and location of any exterior trim.

- Overhang size. Measure all overhangs and note the size of the rafter or truss tails. Note if the eaves are covered with plywood or individual pieces of wood such as 1 × 4s. If the eaves are enclosed make note of the venting method.

Interior Measurements. When you move inside the structure to gather information, gather the following key pieces of information to complete the exterior elevations:

- Height of the ceiling above the finished floor.

- Heights of the top and bottom of windows above finished floor.

Although each of these measurements has been recorded in measuring outside, recording these measurements from the inside provides a means to check other measurements.

Floor Plan. Create the floor plan from both external and internal measurements. Start the drawing with the external measurements taken to determine the overall footprint. The internal measurements serve as a check when placing the openings in exterior walls and provide information needed to locate the internal walls. It is important to remember that when you work with new construction, you typically use walls 6" and 4" (150 mm and 100 mm) wide. When you draw an existing floor plan, these sizes do not apply. Measure at an opening to determine the exact width of exterior and interior walls.

Interior Measurements. Key information to be determined inside the home related to the floor plan includes:

- Overall size of each room. Determine the measurements needed to draw the size of rooms by laying the tape measure on the floor, by hooking the beginning end under door or window trim, or by having a friend hold the other end of the tape. If help is available, have your assistant read the dimension to you so that you can write the dimension on the sketch.

Say the dimension back to your assistant as you write it down to ensure accurate recording. Although only the rooms affected by the addition or remodel must be drawn, it is best to measure all of the rooms. If the scope of the job is altered, it is not necessary to make an additional trip to the jobsite.

- Location of all doors and windows in rooms that may be affected by the proposed changes. Work through the house room-by-room and locate all door and window openings. Note the size of each opening as well as the location in the room.

- Location of all outlets, switches, and heating vents. While you should note the location of each electrical fixture on your sketch, there is no need to provide exact measurements. Noting that a plug is under the left side of a window allows you to locate the plug if you need to update the electrical drawing. Lighting fixtures for each room as well as the location of each switch that controls the fixtures for the room will also aid in drawing the new electrical plan. For homes heated by forced air, note the location and the size of all heat registers and the cold air returns.

- Location and size of the existing crawl access and attic access.

Sections. The sections are drawn using measurements taken for the site, floor, and elevations. The only two measurements to complete the sections are the height of the attic at the ridge and the height from the bottom of the floor to the ground in the crawl space. The height of the attic is determined from the top of the ceiling joists to the bottom of the ridge board. On newer homes, determine the height of the ridge by measuring the height between the chords. Be sure to note the following information while you are in the attic:

- Rafter (truss chord) size/spacing.

- Ceiling joist (truss chord) size/spacing.

- Height from top of ceiling joists to the bottom of the ridge (chord to chord).

When measuring the crawl space, determine the following information:

- Construction type (floor joists or post-and-beam).

- Size and spacing of floor joists, if any.

- Crawl height from decking to ground/beam to ground.

- Placement of access and ventilation.

- Girder size, locations, and direction.

DRAWING THE EXISTING STRUCTURE

Once the initial measurements are obtained, these sketches can be used to create the preliminary working drawings. Drawings to be started include the site plan, floor plan, foundation plan, elevations, sections, and details. Throughout this chapter, the development of plans for a family room/kitchen/pantry will be explored. The project includes removing the existing kitchen and nook areas and expanding the kitchen and providing a new walk-in pantry in the spaces occupied by the current kitchen and family room. A new nook and family room will be added to the north face of the home.

Before starting the project, consider how to create the drawings. Just as with new construction, assemble drawings by placing all plan views in one drawing file or by using externally referenced drawings. Since one office will create the drawings without the help of consultants, layers will be used on this project to separate each drawing.

Drawing the Site Plan

The site plan for a remodel or an addition is similar to a site plan for new construction. The plan must show the size of the jobsite, the street, easements, setbacks, and the footprint of the existing structure, including decks. Once the existing structure is drawn, determine the space for the addition. For the addition used in this chapter, the home is in a rural setting and is not located near any setbacks. The existing home is near the top edge of a steep slope that will dictate the size of the addition.

Start the site plan using an existing drawing template or create a template based on the information in Chapter 10. In addition to the layers required for a new site plan, create layers for the following information:

SITE ANNO EXIST	(thin black lines)
SITE DIMS EXST	(thin black lines)
SITE OUTL EXST	(thick gray continuous lines)
SITE PROP	(thin black phantom lines)
SITE PROP BEAR	(thin black lines)
SITE UTIL	(gray, varied linetypes and weights)

Common items to be represented on a site plan include:

- Sizes specified on the map provided by the owner or title company.

- North arrow.

- Site orientation to the street, showing access to the residence including walks, driveway, front door, and garage.

- Centerline of the street or access road.
- All setbacks and obstructions to the proposed alterations.
- Footprint of the existing structure in bold lines.
- Existing grade elevations at the property corners and at the corners of the existing structure that the proposed project will affect.
- Existing landscaping that the proposed project will affect.
- Existing fencing, decorative walls, and decking that the project will affect.
- Deck walkways, pools, spa, and fountains that the project may affect.

Use the guidelines in Chapter 10 to complete the initial layout of the site plan. Figure 35.4 shows the existing features for the proposed project. This drawing will serve as a starting point as the project develops and will become the base for the final site plan to be submitted to obtain a building permit.

Drawing the Floor Plan

The complexity of the project determines how the floor plan will be drawn. On a simple project, the existing structure, material to be removed, and new material can be shown on the same floor plan using methods similar to those shown in Figure 35.5. If all information is combined in one floor plan, the print reader will have quick access to all needed information. On complex alterations, separate plans are often used to separate the material to be removed from the new work to be completed. Regardless of the method used to display the materials, the drawings are started in the same way. On the project for this chapter, the designer placed the existing material on a separate plan from the floor plan showing the new construction.

Start the existing floor plan using the dimensions from the jobsite. Use the drawing file that contains the site plan and create new layers to contain the floor material. Use the guidelines in Chapter 12 to create new layers for the floor information. Create layers for the following information:

FLOR CABS EXST (thin gray continuous lines)
FLOR DOOR EXST (thin gray continuous lines)
FLOR WALL EXST (thick gray continuous lines)
FLOR WALL REMV (thick gray hidden lines)
FLOR WALL PATT (thin gray lines)
FLOR GLAZ EXST (thin gray continuous lines)

Using the footprint of the structure on the site plan as a base, draw the existing walls based on the field notes. Draw each room touched by the addition. Figure 35.6 shows the drawing of the existing family room, kitchen, dining room, and exterior deck created from the field notes. Knowing that the owner intends to enlarge the kitchen into the existing family room and add a new family room on the north side of the home allows you to ignore the rooms on the south side of the home. Because the plans will document the removal and addition of the kitchen, large amounts of detailing are required to document the project. To clarify information for each of the construction crews, a separate demolition and floor plan will be provided. Separate plans will also be required to document the electrical and framing information.

After creating the base floor plan, alter it to show material that will remain or be removed. As you begin the new plans, it is wise to keep an unaltered copy of the existing floor plan in case the drawing suffers major changes during the design process. The unaltered, original drawing provides a reference point for additional design options. Figure 35.7 shows the demolition plan created using the existing drawing as a base.

Figure 35.8 shows the proposed new floor plan. It was created using the same drawing with the demolition layers frozen and the new construction layers displayed. Notice that there is only minimal information on both plans because the drawings are still in the preliminary stages, and are subject to many changes as the client works with the designer. Once the owner confirms the design, the drawings can be completed.

Drawing the Exterior Elevations

Start the existing elevations by drawing the view that shows the best contour of the existing roof. Use the guidelines that were presented when elevations were explored. Drawing the existing elevations is similar to drawing the exterior elevations for new construction with

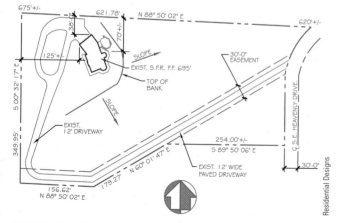

FIGURE 35.4 Using the guidelines from Chapter 10 and field notes, the initial layout of the site plan can be started. This drawing will provide a base for the design process.

Residential Designs

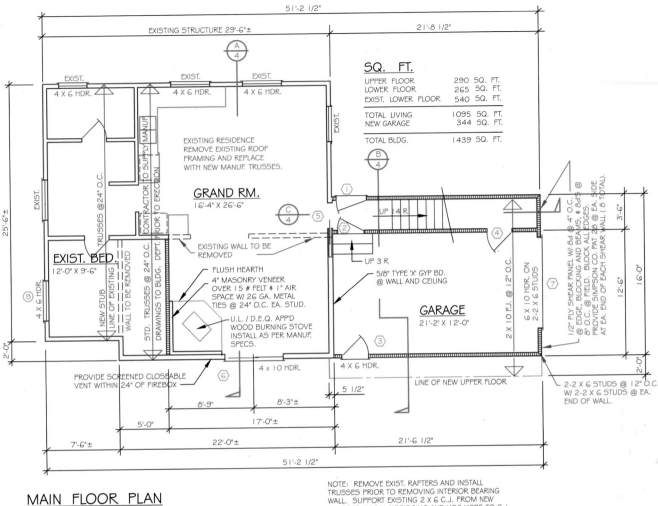

SQ. FT.

UPPER FLOOR	290	SQ. FT.
LOWER FLOOR	265	SQ. FT.
EXIST. LOWER FLOOR	540	SQ. FT.
TOTAL LIVING	1095	SQ. FT.
NEW GARAGE	344	SQ. FT.
TOTAL BLDG.	1439	SQ. FT.

MAIN FLOOR PLAN
1/4" = 1'-0"

NOTE: REMOVE EXIST. RAFTERS AND INSTALL TRUSSES PRIOR TO REMOVING INTERIOR BEARING WALL. SUPPORT EXISTING 2 X 6 C.J. FROM NEW TRUSSES W/ 2 X 4 BRIDGING AND U26 HGRS TO C.J.

FIGURE 35.5 The proposed floor plan for a garage addition and a new upper floor over an existing one-level residence. The complexity of the project will determine how the floor plan will be drawn. On a simple project, the existing structure, material to be removed, and new material can be shown on the same floor plan using methods presented in Chapter 11. Combining all information in one floor plan gives the print reader quick access to all needed information.

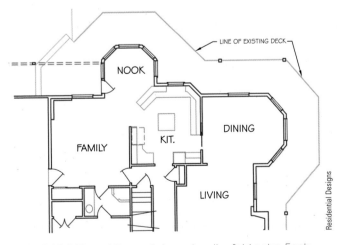

FIGURE 35.6 The existing walls based on the field notes. Each of the rooms that will be touched by the addition will need to be drawn. Knowing that the owner intends to enlarge the kitchen and add a new family room on the north side of the home allows the rooms on the south side of the home to be ignored.

two exceptions. Knowing that some of the structure will be either removed or covered by the new addition, don't spend time representing siding, roofing, or other exterior details. A second difference is the relationship of the structure to the soil elevations. Keep the drawings simple and show only the following features:

- Shapes of major features of the existing structure.
- Existing openings such as doors, windows, and skylights.
- Existing chimneys.
- Existing porches, decks, and railings.
- The slope of the finished grade.

Use the guidelines in Chapter 18 to begin the initial layout of the existing elevations. Because these elevations will eventually be used to show the intersections of existing and new material, it will be helpful to establish

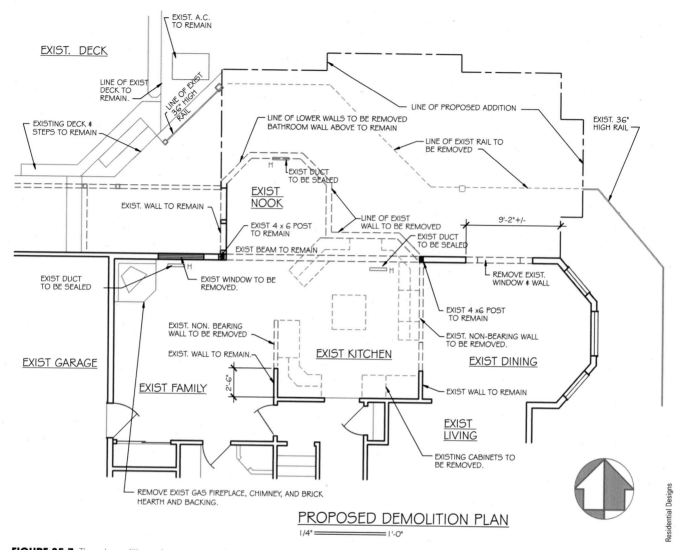

FIGURE 35.7 The demolition plan was created by using the existing drawing as a base, indicating material that will be removed, and then showing the outline of what will be added.

separate layers to represent the existing and new materials. To represent the existing materials, use layer titles such as:

ELEV ANNO EXST   (thin black lines)
ELEV DIMS EXST   (thin black lines)
ELEV FND EXST   (thin gray dashed lines)
ELEV OUTL EXST   (thin gray lines)
ELEV PATT EXST   (thin gray lines)
ELEV WALL EXST   (thin gray continuous lines)

Figure 35.9 shows the three exterior elevations that the proposed project will affect.

Drawing the Foundation Plan

The foundation plan shows the intersection of the existing and new foundation and floor systems. The shape of the foundation is drawn using the outline of the existing floor plan. Use the guidelines presented in Chapter 28 to start the layout of the existing materials. If the loads over the existing foundation will not change, you'll only need to show only the general pattern and type of the existing floor system. If new loads will be imposed over the existing construction, eventually new support must be represented on the foundation plan. For now, concentrate on representing the existing materials. Use the sketches from the jobsite and the guidelines presented in Chapter 27 to lay out the existing floor system and foundation material. The drawing should show all of the existing materials that the new addition will affect, including:

- Footings and stem walls.
- Floor system members.
- Crawl access.
- Vents.
- Material that must be removed.

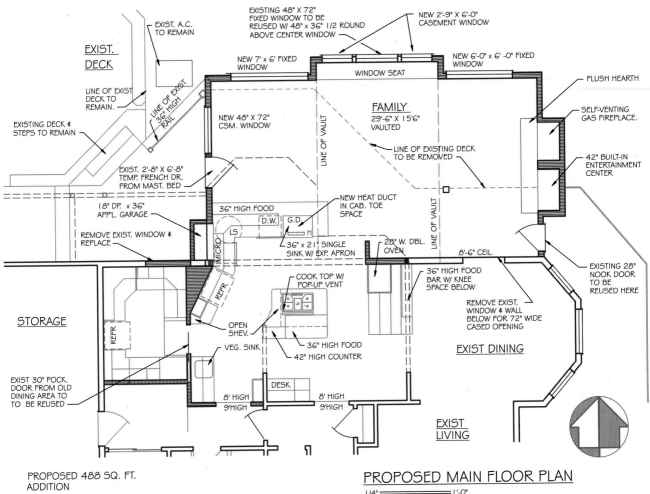

PROPOSED MAIN FLOOR PLAN

PROPOSED 488 SQ. FT. ADDITION

FIGURE 35.8 The proposed new floor plan was created using the same drawing shown in Figure 35.7 with the demolition layers frozen and the new construction layers displayed. Only a minimum of information has been placed on the plan because it is still in the preliminary stage and requires the owner's approval.

EAST ELEVATION

NORTH ELEVATION

WEST ELEVATION

FIGURE 35.9 The existing exterior elevations will serve as a base for the design of the proposed project.

Create the foundation plan in the drawing file that contains the site as well as the floor plans. Use layers to separate the foundation material from the other plan views and to separate the existing and new foundation materials. Use layer titles such as:

FNDN ANNO EXST   (black lines)
FNDN BEAM EXST   (thin gray lines, hidden)
FNDN DIMS EXST   (black lines)
FNDN FOOT EXST   (thin gray dashed lines)
FNDN JSTS EXST   (thin gray continuous lines)
FNDN WALL EXST   (thick gray lines)

Figure 35.10 shows an example of the foundation plan showing existing construction.

Drawing Sections

A section of the existing structure is useful for planning intersections between new and existing materials. Use the field notes from the site visit to draw a section of the existing structure. Pass the cutting plane through an area of the existing structure that the proposed addition will affect. Since the existing framing is generally not exposed during the site visitation, represent materials you expect to find. Structures built after the 1940s are likely made using western platform construction. Homes built prior to the 1940s are usually built using balloon framing. Refer to previous chapters for reviews of each type of construction. Confirm the existing roof construction by looking in the attic to determine the sizes of rafters and ceiling joists and whether trusses were used. Confirm the floor construction by entering the crawl space. The preliminary section should show the following existing materials:

- Foundation and relationship to the finish grade.
- Floor framing.
- Wall framing.
- Roof and ceiling construction.

Use the guidelines from Chapter 30 to begin the initial layout of the sections. Because these drawings will

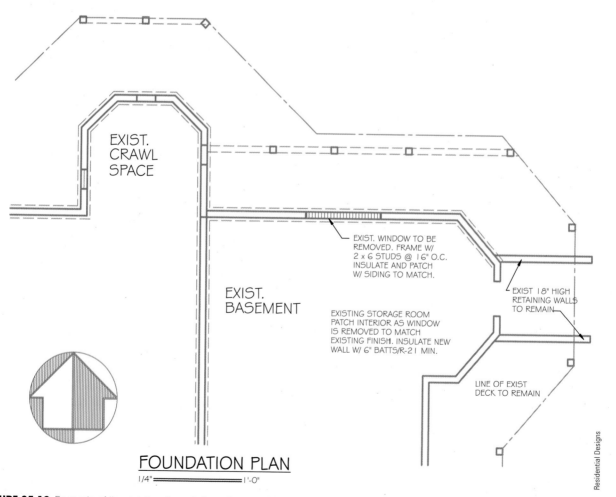

FOUNDATION PLAN
1/4" = 1'-0"

EXIST. CRAWL SPACE

EXIST. BASEMENT

EXIST. WINDOW TO BE REMOVED. FRAME W/ 2 x 6 STUDS @ 16" O.C. INSULATE AND PATCH W/ SIDING TO MATCH.

EXISTING STORAGE ROOM PATCH INTERIOR AS WINDOW IS REMOVED TO MATCH EXISTING FINISH. INSULATE NEW WALL W/ 6" BATTS/R-21 MIN.

EXIST 18" HIGH RETAINING WALLS TO REMAIN

LINE OF EXIST DECK TO REMAIN

Residential Designs

FIGURE 35.10 Enough of the existing foundation plan must be drawn to show any new loads that must be supported, as well as how new loads will be supported.

eventually be used to show the intersections of existing and new material, it is helpful to establish separate layers to represent existing and new materials. Use layer titles such as:

SECT EXST ANNO (thin black lines)
SECT EXST DIMS (thin black lines)
SECT EXST PATT (thin gray lines)
SECT EXST THIN (thin gray lines; show material behind the cutting plane)
SECT EXST THCK (thick gray lines; material cut by the cutting plane)

Figure 35.11 shows one of the sections used to show existing construction. This project required the following sections:

- One section showing how the addition will tie into the two-story portion of the house.

- A second section showing how the new project will tie into the structure where the lower floor is removed and the second level remains.

- A third section showing a longitudinal view of the new construction and is not started at this point.

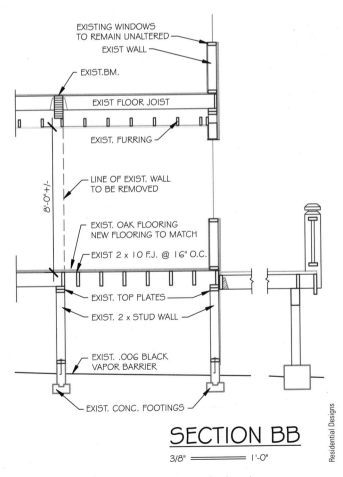

EXISTING WINDOWS
TO REMAIN UNALTERED
EXIST WALL
EXIST.BM.
EXIST FLOOR JOIST
EXIST. FURRING
8'-0"+/-
LINE OF EXIST. WALL
TO BE REMOVED
EXIST. OAK FLOORING
NEW FLOORING TO MATCH
EXIST 2 x 10 F.J. @ 16" O.C.
EXIST. TOP PLATES
EXIST. 2 x STUD WALL
EXIST. .006 BLACK
VAPOR BARRIER
EXIST. CONC. FOOTINGS

SECTION BB
3/8" = 1'-0"

Residential Designs

FIGURE 35.11 Sections must be drawn to show how new construction will tie in with existing construction.

REPRESENTING THE PROPOSED CHANGES

Once the existing materials have been drawn, represent the new construction on each drawing. Complete the new material using methods similar to those introduced in the previous chapters. The biggest difference in working on an addition or renovation is that you must clearly define the new material on each drawing. Because gray was used to represent the existing material on each of the drawings, plot the new material using black lines. Materials are drawn using any color if a black pen is assigned to the color for plotting purposes. See the AutoCAD Help menu for adjusting plot styles.

Completing the Site Plan

The site plan must show the size of the jobsite as well as the street, easements, setbacks, and footprint of the existing structure, including decks. Indicate the footprint of the new construction in a manner that clearly distinguishes between old and new construction. Although a complete topographic plan is rarely required, indicate the slope of the site to ensure proper drainage. Site plans for rural settings may also require the location of wells, septic tanks, and utilities to be represented. Complete the drawing using the existing site plan as a base. Notice the modifier NEWW (new work) has been added to many of the layer titles. Materials to be included can be controlled using layer titles such as:

SITE ANNO NEWW (thin black lines)
SITE DIMS NEWW (thin black lines)
SITE MATL NEWW (thin black lines)
SITE OUTL NEWW (thick black continuous lines)
SITE PATT NEWW (thin black lines)

In addition to the materials shown on the existing site plan, represent the following items:

Drawing

Represent the following new materials on the site plan:

- Footprint of new structure in bold lines.

- New walks and driveways.

- Outline of the new roof.

- New grade elevations for each corner of the addition.

- New fencing or decorative walls.

- New deck walkways, pools, spa, and fountains.

Provide two different hatch patterns to distinguish between the existing and new construction.

Required Text

Specify the following information on the site plan:

- Insert the legal description.
- Label the existing residence as an existing single-family residence (SFR).
- Label the addition as PROPOSED ADDITION.
- Provide the square footage of the existing and the new construction.
- List the finish floor elevation of the proposed construction.
- Label the street, sidewalks, driveways, decks, fencing, grade elevations, concrete flatwork, stairs, patios, walkways, decks, and rails.

Dimensions

Provide dimensions to locate the following:

- Lot size
- All setbacks

- Easements
- Centerline of road
- Location of the existing residence and the new construction to each property line

Figure 35.12 shows the complete site plan for the residential addition used throughout this chapter.

Completing the Floor-Related Plans

The floor plan for the project in this chapter shows all new materials. The demolition plan shows material to be removed, and electrical information is shown on a separate electrical plan. Cabinet notes, reference symbols, and framing information are each shown on separate plans. When the floor plan is complete, drawing symbols and notes should clearly define all new materials. Include a legend or a note explaining symbols that define existing and new walls. In addition to defining the existing and new portions of a project, complete the floor plan using the guidelines presented in Chapter 12.

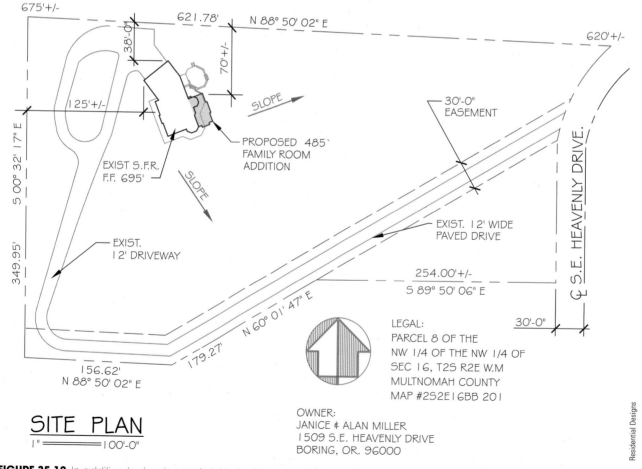

FIGURE 35.12 In addition to showing material typically represented on a site plan, the plan must clearly represent and distinguish between existing and new materials.

Complete the drawing using the existing floor plan as a base. Materials to be included can be controlled using layer titles such as:

FLOR ANNO NEWW (thin black lines)
FLOR CABS NEWW (thin black continuous lines)
FLOR CABS SYMB (thin black continuous lines)
FLOR DOOR NEWW (thin black continuous lines)
FLOR WALL EXIST (thick lines, gray, continuous)
FLOR WALL NEWW (thick black continuous lines)
FLOR WALL PATT NEWW (thin black lines)
FLOR GLAZ NEWW (thin black continuous lines)

Figure 35.13 shows the completed floor plan for the project. Notice that existing walls are drawn with gray lines and new walls have been hatched with a series of thin parallel lines. By using the floor plan with the demolition plan, the owner, contractor, and building officials should have a clear understanding of the new project. Because the floor plan relates to information that will be placed on several different plan views, be sure to:

- Provide a north arrow to reference the floor plan to other plan views.
- Display all plan views in the same orientation. Don't rotate a plan to crowd in additional information.

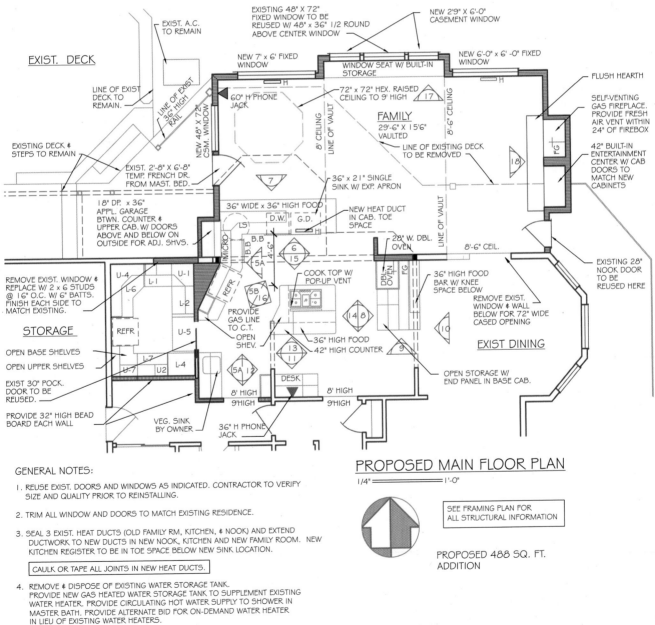

FIGURE 35.13 The floor plan must show portions of the existing plan that will be affected by the addition as well as all new construction.

Residential Designs

- Always show the same amount of the existing structure to help the print reader switch between plan views.

Completing the Demolition Plan

The demolition plan shows the existing walls and materials to be removed to prepare the site for the new project. On the project used in this chapter, part of the existing deck, walls, windows, doors, plumbing, and HVAC will be removed or altered in some manner. Existing electrical service will also be affected, but it will be indicated on the electrical plan. Use the existing floor plan as a base for the demolition plan. Materials to be included can be controlled using layer titles such as:

FLOR DEMO ANNO	(thin black lines)
FLOR DEMO CABS	(thin gray dashed lines)
FLOR DEMO DIMS	(thin black lines)
FLOR DEMO MISC REMV	(thin gray dashed lines)
FLOR DEMO WALL REMV	(thick gray dashed lines)
FLOR DEMO WALL REMN	(thick gray continuous lines)

Represent the following materials on a demolition plan:

- Existing walls, doors, windows, and cabinets to remain.
- Existing walls, doors, windows, and cabinets to be removed.
- Indicate material to be removed and reused.
- Indicate material to be removed and discarded.
- Notes specifying all materials to be altered.

Notice in Figure 35.14 that continuous green lines represent existing materials that will remain; materials to be removed are indicated by dashed brown lines. The outline of the deck to be removed is shown with dashed lines and a phantom line indicates the boundary of the proposed project. Figures 35.15a and b show the results of the demolition plan.

Completing the Electrical Plan

The electrical plan for a renovation, addition, or remodel is similar to the plan required for new construction introduced in Chapter 13. Use the completed floor plan as a base and freeze all the floor-related materials except for the walls, windows, doors, cabinets, appliances, and plumbing symbols. Indicate new fixtures, switches, and plugs on the plan. The plan should also show existing switches, fixtures, or plugs that must be removed or altered in any way. Use a note to explain what is to be removed or altered. It is not necessary to represent existing fixtures, plugs, and switches that do not require alteration on the plan. It is not necessary to indicate existing and new circuits on the drawings. The electrician will design the circuits to support the indicated fixtures and plugs. In addition to the layers describing the existing and new features of the floor plan, control materials using layer titles such as:

ELEC ANNO	(thin black lines)
ELEC SCHD	(thin black continuous lines)
ELEC SYMB	(thin black continuous lines)
ELEC WIRE	(thin black dashed lines)

Represent the following materials on the electrical plan:

- Existing and new walls, doors, windows, and cabinets.
- New electrical fixtures including lights, plugs, and switches.
- Notes to explain all new electrical work for the electrician to perform.

Figure 35.16a shows the electrical plan for the proposed addition and some of the resulting work. Figure 35.16b shows the installation of an electrical feature.

Completing the Framing Plan

The framing plan for a remodel is similar to the framing plan required for new construction that was introduced in Chapter 25. Use the completed floor plan as a base and freeze all of the floor-related materials except for the walls, windows, doors, cabinets, appliances, and plumbing symbols. As with other plan views, this drawing must clearly represent new features, existing materials, and material to be removed. The drawing must also clearly show all new and existing framing members. Be sure to distinguish between walls to be removed and new beams and headers. Be careful in using layers and colors since beams and removed materials are generally represented by hidden or dashed lines on a framing plan. In addition to the layers describing the existing and new features of the floor plan, materials can be controlled using layer titles such as:

FRAM ANNO	(thin black lines)
FRAM BEAM	(thin black dashed lines)
FRAM DIMS	(thin black lines)
FRAM JSTS (or TRUS)	(thin black continuous lines)
FRAM LATL	(thin black continuous lines)
FRAM LATL SCHD	(thick black continuous lines)
FRAM SECT PLAN	(thin black phantom lines)

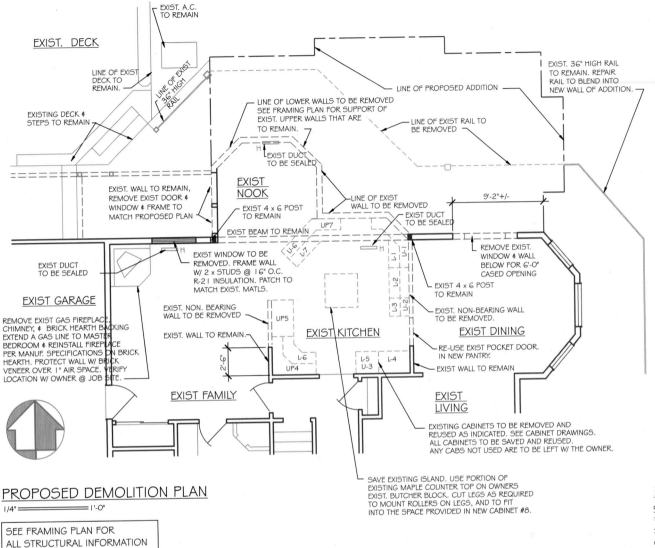

EXIST. A.C.
TO REMAIN

EXIST. DECK

LINE OF EXIST
DECK TO
REMAIN.

LINE OF EXIST 36 HIGH RAIL

EXISTING DECK &
STEPS TO REMAIN

LINE OF LOWER WALLS TO BE REMOVED
SEE FRAMING PLAN FOR SUPPORT OF
EXIST. UPPER WALLS THAT ARE
TO REMAIN.

LINE OF PROPOSED ADDITION

EXIST. 36" HIGH RAIL
TO REMAIN. REPAIR
RAIL TO BLEND INTO
NEW WALL OF ADDITION.

EXIST DUCT
TO BE SEALED

LINE OF EXIST RAIL TO
BE REMOVED

EXIST
NOOK

EXIST. WALL TO REMAIN,
REMOVE EXIST DOOR &
WINDOW & FRAME TO
MATCH PROPOSED PLAN

EXIST 4 x 6 POST
TO REMAIN

LINE OF EXIST
WALL TO BE REMOVED

9'-2"+/-

EXIST BEAM TO REMAIN

UP7

EXIST DUCT
TO BE SEALED

REMOVE EXIST.
WINDOW & WALL
BELOW FOR 6'-0"
CASED OPENING

EXIST DUCT
TO BE SEALED

EXIST WINDOW TO BE
REMOVED. FRAME WALL
W/ 2 x STUDS @ 16" O.C.
R-21 INSULATION. PATCH TO
MATCH EXIST. MATLS.

EXIST GARAGE

REMOVE EXIST GAS FIREPLACE,
CHIMNEY, & BRICK HEARTH BACKING
EXTEND A GAS LINE TO MASTER
BEDROOM & REINSTALL FIREPLACE
PER MANUF. SPECIFICATIONS ON BRICK
HEARTH. PROTECT WALL W/ BRICK
VENEER OVER 1" AIR SPACE. VERIFY
LOCATION W/ OWNER @ JOB SITE.

EXIST. NON. BEARING
WALL TO BE REMOVED

EXIST. WALL TO REMAIN.

UP5

2'-6"

UP4

L-6

EXIST 4 x 6 POST
TO REMAIN

EXIST. NON-BEARING WALL
TO BE REMOVED.

EXIST KITCHEN

EXIST DINING

RE-USE EXIST POCKET DOOR.
IN NEW PANTRY.

EXIST WALL TO REMAIN

L-5
U-3

L-4

EXIST FAMILY

EXIST
LIVING

EXISTING CABINETS TO BE REMOVED AND
REUSED AS INDICATED. SEE CABINET DRAWINGS.
ALL CABINETS TO BE SAVED AND REUSED.
ANY CABS NOT USED ARE TO BE LEFT W/ THE OWNER.

PROPOSED DEMOLITION PLAN
1/4" = 1'-0"

SAVE EXISTING ISLAND. USE PORTION OF
EXISTING MAPLE COUNTER TOP ON OWNERS
EXIST. BUTCHER BLOCK. CUT LEGS AS REQUIRED
TO MOUNT ROLLERS ON LEGS, AND TO FIT
INTO THE SPACE PROVIDED IN NEW CABINET #8.

SEE FRAMING PLAN FOR
ALL STRUCTURAL INFORMATION

Residential Designs

FIGURE 35.14 The demolition plan shows the existing walls and materials to be removed to prepare the site for the new project. On a simple project, this information can be placed on the floor plan.

© Cengage Learning 2014. Courtesy David Jefferis

FIGURE 35.15a The results of the demolition plan with the deck removed and the wall prepared for removal. The wall will not be removed until the new shell is in place.

© Cengage Learning 2014

FIGURE 35.15b The kitchen cabinets have been removed (see outline in floor) and the existing wall between the kitchen and the family room is prepped for demolition. All existing electrical and plumbing must be rerouted to allow the wall to be removed.

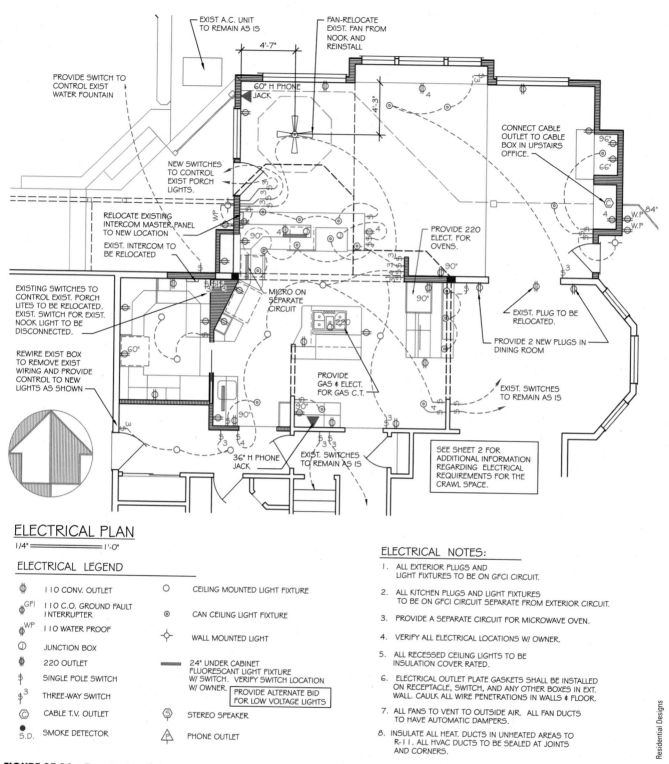

ELECTRICAL PLAN
1/4" ══════════ 1'-0"

ELECTRICAL LEGEND

Symbol	Description	Symbol	Description
⌀	110 CONV. OUTLET	○	CEILING MOUNTED LIGHT FIXTURE
⌀GFI	110 C.O. GROUND FAULT INTERRUPTER	◎	CAN CEILING LIGHT FIXTURE
⌀WP	110 WATER PROOF	-◇-	WALL MOUNTED LIGHT
①	JUNCTION BOX	▬	24" UNDER CABINET FLUORESCANT LIGHT FIXTURE W/ SWITCH. VERIFY SWITCH LOCATION W/ OWNER.
⌀	220 OUTLET		PROVIDE ALTERNATE BID FOR LOW VOLTAGE LIGHTS
$	SINGLE POLE SWITCH		
$³	THREE-WAY SWITCH	Ⓢ	STEREO SPEAKER
©	CABLE T.V. OUTLET	△	PHONE OUTLET
● S.D.	SMOKE DETECTOR		

ELECTRICAL NOTES:

1. ALL EXTERIOR PLUGS AND LIGHT FIXTURES TO BE ON GFCI CIRCUIT.

2. ALL KITCHEN PLUGS AND LIGHT FIXTURES TO BE ON GFCI CIRCUIT SEPARATE FROM EXTERIOR CIRCUIT.

3. PROVIDE A SEPARATE CIRCUIT FOR MICROWAVE OVEN.

4. VERIFY ALL ELECTRICAL LOCATIONS W/ OWNER.

5. ALL RECESSED CEILING LIGHTS TO BE INSULATION COVER RATED.

6. ELECTRICAL OUTLET PLATE GASKETS SHALL BE INSTALLED ON RECEPTACLE, SWITCH, AND ANY OTHER BOXES IN EXT. WALL. CAULK ALL WIRE PENETRATIONS IN WALLS & FLOOR.

7. ALL FANS TO VENT TO OUTSIDE AIR. ALL FAN DUCTS TO HAVE AUTOMATIC DAMPERS.

8. INSULATE ALL HEAT. DUCTS IN UNHEATED AREAS TO R-11. ALL HVAC DUCTS TO BE SEALED AT JOINTS AND CORNERS.

FIGURE 35.16a The electrical plan must show all new fixtures and switches as well as existing electrical features to be moved.

Materials that should be represented on the framing plan include:

- Existing and new walls, doors, windows, and cabinets.
- Framing members, including beams and joists (or trusses).
- Framing fasteners and connectors.
- Lateral bracing requirements.
- Dimensions to locate all walls, openings, and beams.
- Notes to describe all new framing materials and procedures to be completed.

Figure 35.17a shows the framing plan for the proposed addition. Notice that existing walls are represented

FIGURE 35.16b Electricians use the electrical plan to determine how new features will be located.

© Cengage Learning 2014. Courtesy Michael Jefferis

by gray lines in order to provide a stark contrast with new materials. Figure 35.17b shows the results of the information placed on the framing plan.

Completing the Elevations

The exterior elevations for a remodel are similar to the elevations required for new construction introduced in Chapter 19. Use the drawings of the existing home as a base and a copy of the new floor plan to project all new features onto the existing drawing. Create a block of the floor plan that includes all features affecting the exterior of the project. Freeze all layers containing interior material. Once the block is created, insert the block into the drawing containing the existing exterior. Insert and rotate the block as described in Chapter 19 to aid projection of the new material. In addition to the layers describing the existing material, create layers to describe new materials using layer titles such as:

ELEV NEWW	(thin black continuous lines)
ELEV ANNO NEWW	(thin black lines)
ELEV DIMS NEWW	(thin black lines)
ELEV FINH	(thin black continuous lines)
ELEV FNDN NEWW	(thin black dashed lines)
ELEV LATL	(thin black continuous lines)
ELEV OUTL NEWW	(thin black lines)
ELEV PATT NEWW	(thin black lines)
ELEV SIDG NEWW	(thin black continuous lines)
ELEV WALL NEWW	(thin black continuous lines)

Represent the following materials on the exterior elevations:

- Existing walls, openings, and roofs that are affected by the new construction.
- Outlines of all new construction including roofs, walls, and foundations.
- All new openings including skylights, windows, and doors.
- All new decks, required supports, and railings.
- Notation explaining demolition, repairs, and remaining material.
- Notation explaining all new construction.
- Dimensions explaining roof pitch, chimney heights, and floor and ceiling heights.
- Lateral bracing requirements (optional but helpful to represent material specified on the framing plan).

Figure 35.18a shows the completed elevations for this project. As with other drawings, the existing construction is shown in gray and all new materials are shown in black. Figure 35.18b shows the completed project.

Representing Interior Elevations

Draw the interior elevations for an addition, renovation, or remodel using the methods presented in Chapter 20. Review the step-by-step instructions to complete the drawings. The only difference from new construction is that some materials must be specified as existing construction. Represent existing walls or openings with gray lines. Since the majority of the interior elevations show only new cabinets, existing materials are usually not important. Materials to be shown on the interior elevations can be controlled using layer titles such as:

I ELEV ANNO	(thin black lines)
I ELEV DIMS	(thin black lines)
I ELEV SYMB	(thin black continuous lines)
I ELEV THCK	(thick black continuous lines)
I ELEV THIN	(thin black continuous lines)

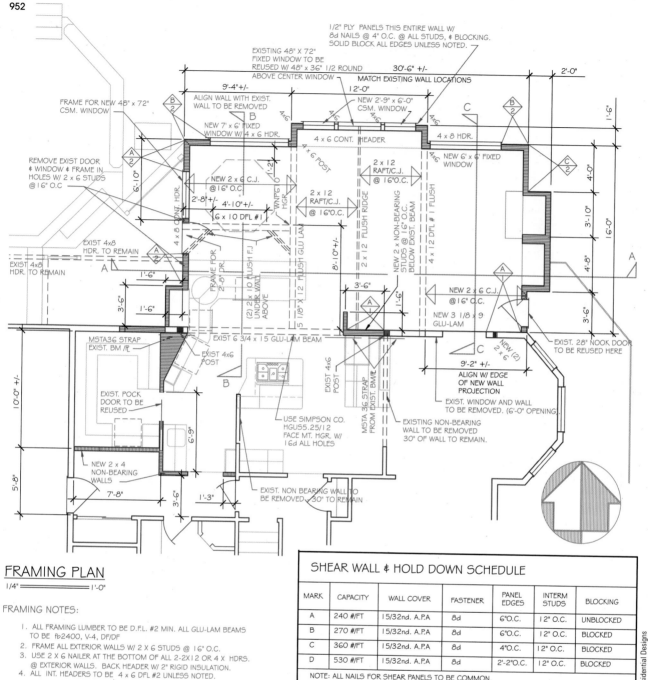

FRAMING PLAN

1/4" = 1'-0"

FRAMING NOTES:

1. ALL FRAMING LUMBER TO BE D.F.L. #2 MIN. ALL GLU-LAM BEAMS TO BE fb2400, V-4, DF/DF
2. FRAME ALL EXTERIOR WALLS W/ 2 X 6 STUDS @ 16" O.C.
3. USE 2 X 6 NAILER AT THE BOTTOM OF ALL 2-2X12 OR 4 X HDRS. @ EXTERIOR WALLS. BACK HEADER W/ 2" RIGID INSULATION.
4. ALL INT. HEADERS TO BE 4 x 6 DFL #2 UNLESS NOTED.

SHEAR WALL & HOLD DOWN SCHEDULE

MARK	CAPACITY	WALL COVER	FASTENER	PANEL EDGES	INTERM STUDS	BLOCKING
A	240 #/FT	15/32nd. A.P.A	8d	6"O.C.	12" O.C.	UNBLOCKED
B	270 #/FT	15/32nd. A.P.A	8d	6"O.C.	12" O.C.	BLOCKED
C	360 #/FT	15/32nd. A.P.A	8d	4"O.C.	12" O.C.	BLOCKED
D	530 #/FT	15/32nd. A.P.A	8d	2'-2"O.C.	12" O.C.	BLOCKED

NOTE: ALL NAILS FOR SHEAR PANELS TO BE COMMON.

Residential Designs

FIGURE 35.17a The framing plan for an addition shows the location and sizes of all new structural materials.

© Cengage Learning 2014, Courtesy Sara Jefferis

FIGURE 35.17b Based on the information on the framing plan, the floor, walls, and roof framing is placed. Compare the work shown in this photo with the home in Figure 35.15a.

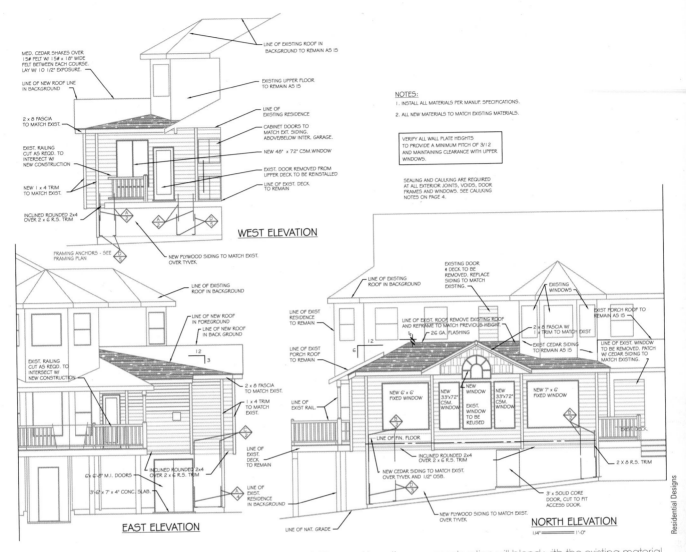

FIGURE 35.18a The elevations will show each side of the addition and how the new construction will blend with the existing material.

Represent the following materials on the interior elevations:

- Outlines of new and existing walls, ceilings, and floors.
- All new and existing openings such as doors and windows.
- All appliances and fixtures.
- All cabinet doors, drawers, and open shelves.
- Outlines of all cabinets.
- All counters and backsplashes.
- Notation explaining all materials, appliances, and fixtures.
- Dimensions explaining all the heights and widths of cabinets and appliances.

Reference the interior elevations on the floor plan to show the viewing plane for each elevation. Figure 35.13 shows the elevation reference symbols. Figure 35.19a

FIGURE 35.18b The completed exterior based on the exterior elevations.

shows a portion of the completed interior elevations for the kitchen renovation/family room addition. Figures 35.19b and 35.19c shows a portion of the completed cabinets. Figures 20.26, 20.27, and 20.28 show the drawings for the food bar (drawing 10) that extends into the existing dining room. Unlike other drawings for this project, all existing and new materials are plotted in black. Because the existing kitchen cabinets are still in good condition, they will be removed and reused in the new pantry that will occupy the old family room.

Completing the Foundation Plan

The foundation plan shows the intersection of the new foundation and floor systems with the existing structure. The drawing is completed using the guidelines presented in Chapter 28 and the existing foundation drawing.

A key consideration for an addition is joining the new concrete to the existing concrete. Steel reinforcing bars are often used to tie the new stem wall to the existing

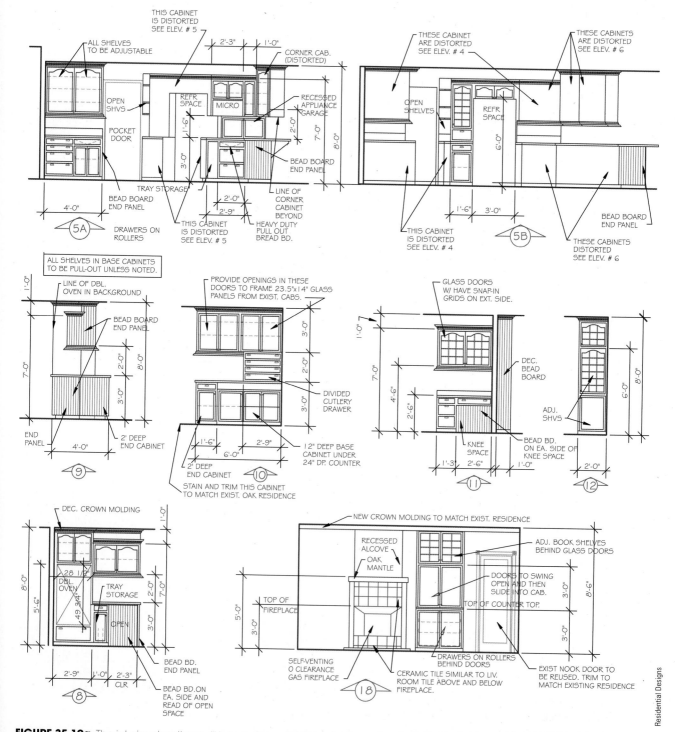

FIGURE 35.19a The interior elevations will be used by each trade to complete its work.

Residential Designs

FIGURE 35.19b The completed cabinets based on the interior elevations.

FIGURE 35.19c The view from the family room looking into the kitchen.

concrete. Holes are drilled into the existing concrete and held in place by epoxy cement.

Other considerations for an addition include crawl space access and ventilation. Although both are considered when drawing a new foundation, reevaluate each to ensure that new construction will not block airflow or access to the existing crawl space. On this particular project, a door at each end of the addition provides access. New vents will be provided along the perimeter of the addition and existing vents remain to provide airflow to the existing crawl space. The existing crawl access for this project is from the existing basement, so no additional access is required. If the access had been altered, a hole could be cut in the existing stem wall to provide access from one crawl space to the other.

Although not required for this project, loads from new construction are often imposed over existing floor systems. If a load is transferred into an existing wood floor system, support must be provided to transfer the load into the

soil. By placing a concrete pier with a wood post below the existing floor, the load is transferred from the floor to the soil. An alternative is to place a girder below the new load that spans between existing supports. If a new load is applied to an existing concrete slab, a portion of the slab must be removed to place a concrete pier below the slab. The slab can then be patched to match the existing floor level. A similar situation occurs when imposing a new load over an existing stem wall and footing. If the load is greater than the assumed design load for the soil or the concrete, provide a new footing under the existing footing. A new footing is not required on this project because the engineer determined the loads to be applied to the existing retaining wall could safely be distributed into the existing footing.

Draw the foundation plan in the file containing the existing foundation plan. Create additional layers including all the new material that must be represented. Using Chapter 28 as a guide, create layers for the foundation and floor material using titles such as:

FNDN ANNO NEWW (thin lines, black)
FNDN BEAM NEWW (thin hidden black lines)
FNDN DIMS NEWW (black lines)
FNDN FOOT NEWW (thin dashed black lines)
FNDN JSTS JSTS (thin continuous black lines)
FNDN LATL (thin continuous black lines)
FNDN LATL SCHD (thick black continuous lines)
FNDN WALL NEWW (thick black lines)

Represent the following materials on the foundation plan:

- Existing stem walls and footings.
- Existing material that will be removed.
- New footings and stem walls.
- New floor system members.
- New crawl access.
- New vents.
- New hold down and connectors required for lateral bracing.
- Dimensions locating the edges of all new concrete and connections for lateral bracing.
- Dimensions locating all new beams, floor cantilevers, and spot piers and footings.
- Notes describing all existing materials.
- Notes describing all new materials and conditions provided at the foundation level.

Figure 35.20a shows the foundation plan for the addition and how it ties into the existing foundation.

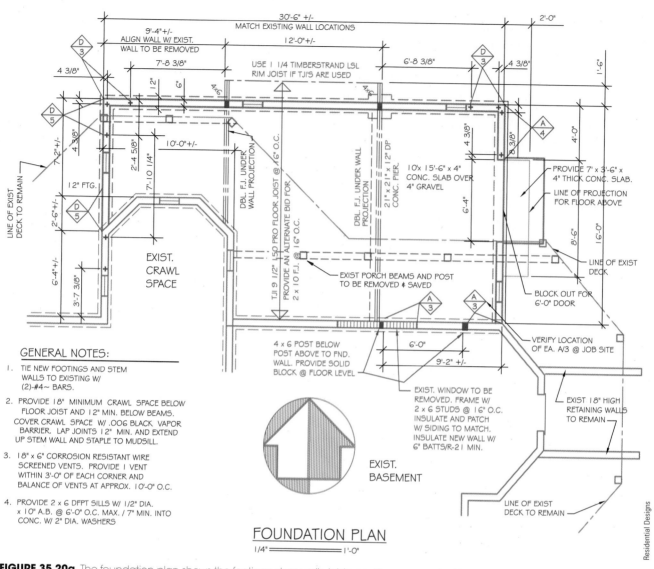

GENERAL NOTES:

1. TIE NEW FOOTINGS AND STEM WALLS TO EXISTING W/ (2)-#4~ BARS.

2. PROVIDE 18" MINIMUM CRAWL SPACE BELOW FLOOR JOIST AND 12" MIN. BELOW BEAMS. COVER CRAWL SPACE W/ .006 BLACK VAPOR BARRIER. LAP JOINTS 12" MIN. AND EXTEND UP STEM WALL AND STAPLE TO MUDSILL.

3. 18" x 6" CORROSION RESISTANT WIRE SCREENED VENTS. PROVIDE 1 VENT WITHIN 3'-0" OF EACH CORNER AND BALANCE OF VENTS AT APPROX. 10'-0" O.C.

4. PROVIDE 2 x 6 DFPT SILLS W/ 1/2" DIA. x 10" A.B. @ 6'-0" O.C. MAX. / 7" MIN. INTO CONC. W/ 2" DIA. WASHERS

FOUNDATION PLAN
1/4" ========== 1'-0"

FIGURE 35.20a The foundation plan shows the footings, stem walls, joists, and beams required to support the new loads.

Figure 35.20b shows the placement of stem walls and footings based on the foundation plan.

Completing the Sections and Details

The sections originally showing the existing structure will be used to show how the new project will merge with existing structure. Use the guidelines presented in Chapter 30 for drawing sections for new construction to represent new materials for an addition. Use dashed lines to represent existing materials that will be removed. Use gray lines to draw existing materials that will remain. To represent new material on the existing sections, use layer titles such as:

SECT ANNO NEWW (thin black lines)
SECT DIMS NEWW (thin black lines)
SECT PATT NEWW (thin gray lines)

FIGURE 35.20b The completed concrete work based on the foundation plan.

Residential Designs

SECT THIN NEWW (thin gray lines to show material behind the cutting plane)

SECT THCK NEWW (thick gray lines to show material cut by the cutting plane)

Represent the following materials on the sections:

- Typical construction of the existing structure.
- Typical construction of the new walls, floor, ceiling, and roof.

- Intersections of the new and old floor.
- Intersections of the new and old roof construction.
- Notes specifying all existing and new materials.
- Dimensions specifying the heights of all existing and new constructions.

As the existing structure was shown in section, it is mentioned that three sections are required for this project. Section AA (Figure 35.21a) shows how the walls

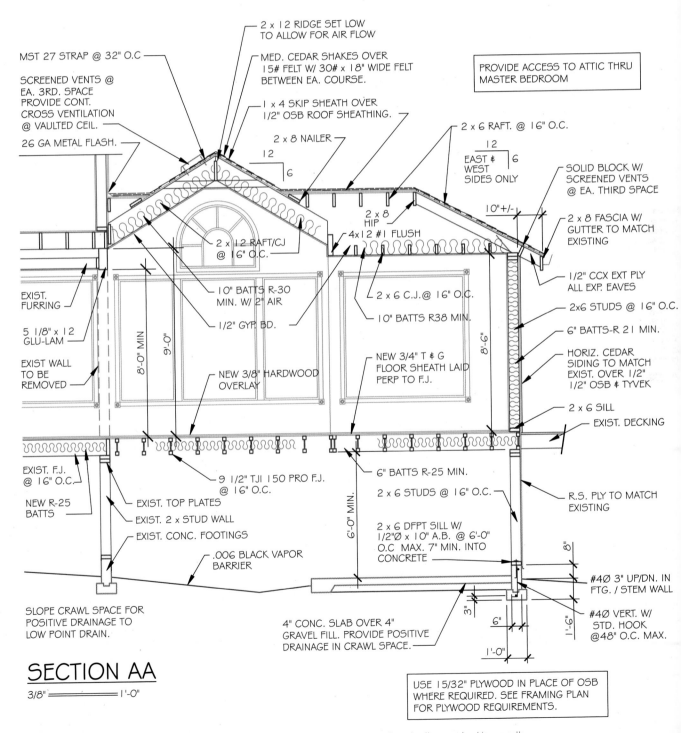

SECTION AA
3/8" = 1'-0"

FIGURE 35.21a A section through the new family room and existing upper floor bathroom looking north.

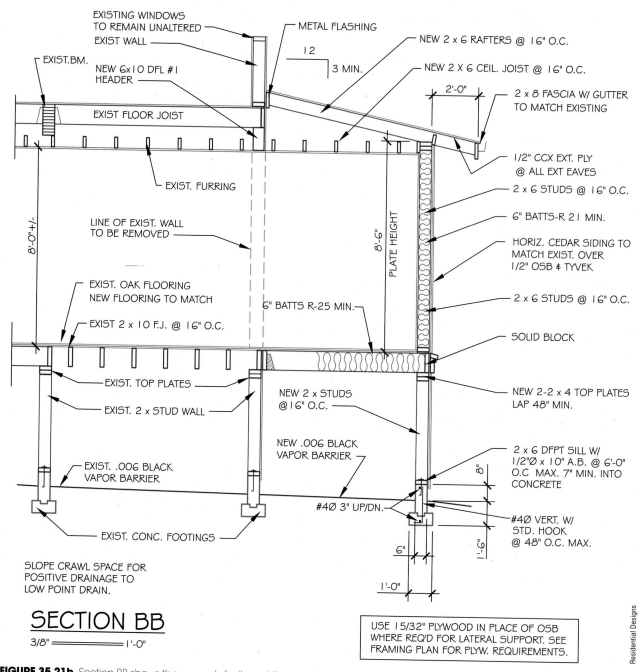

EXISTING WINDOWS TO REMAIN UNALTERED

EXIST WALL

METAL FLASHING

NEW 2 x 6 RAFTERS @ 16" O.C.

12 | 3 MIN.

NEW 2 X 6 CEIL. JOIST @ 16" O.C.

EXIST.BM.

NEW 6x10 DFL #1 HEADER

2'-0"

2 x 8 FASCIA W/ GUTTER TO MATCH EXISTING

EXIST FLOOR JOIST

1/2" CCX EXT. PLY @ ALL EXT EAVES

2 x 6 STUDS @ 16" O.C.

EXIST. FURRING

6" BATTS-R 21 MIN.

HORIZ. CEDAR SIDING TO MATCH EXIST. OVER 1/2" OSB & TYVEK

LINE OF EXIST. WALL TO BE REMOVED

8'-0"+/-

8'-6" PLATE HEIGHT

2 x 6 STUDS @ 16" O.C.

EXIST. OAK FLOORING NEW FLOORING TO MATCH

6" BATTS R-25 MIN.

SOLID BLOCK

EXIST 2 x 10 F.J. @ 16" O.C.

EXIST. TOP PLATES

NEW 2 x STUDS @ 16" O.C.

NEW 2-2 x 4 TOP PLATES LAP 48" MIN.

EXIST. 2 x STUD WALL

NEW .006 BLACK VAPOR BARRIER

EXIST. .006 BLACK VAPOR BARRIER

2 x 6 DFPT SILL W/ 1/2"Ø x 10" A.B. @ 6'-0" O.C MAX. 7" MIN. INTO CONCRETE

8"

#4Ø 3" UP/DN.

#4Ø VERT. W/ STD. HOOK @ 48" O.C. MAX.

EXIST. CONC. FOOTINGS

1'-6"

6"

SLOPE CRAWL SPACE FOR POSITIVE DRAINAGE TO LOW POINT DRAIN.

1'-0"

SECTION BB
3/8" = 1'-0"

USE 15/32" PLYWOOD IN PLACE OF OSB WHERE REQ'D FOR LATERAL SUPPORT. SEE FRAMING PLAN FOR PLYW. REQUIREMENTS.

Residential Designs

FIGURE 35.21b Section BB shows the supports for the existing upper floor and how the new addition will blend with the existing materials. Additional sections were also provided to show how the new addition will tie into the existing basement and upper bedroom window.

surrounding the nook will be removed and how the vaulted ceiling ties into the flat ceilings. This section also shows how the new floor ties into the existing floor system and how the partial floor slab will be placed. Section BB (Figure 35.21b) shows how the new walls and ceilings tie into the existing construction at the nook and second floor bathroom. Section CC (not shown) shows how the new floor, ceiling, and roof will intersect with the existing structure. This section also shows the new beam that will support the upper floor once the north wall of the existing dining room is removed.

Additional Resources

Address	Company or Organization
www.home-improvement-guides.com	Home Improvement Guides
www.interiordec.about.com	About Interior Decorating
www.improvementnet.com	Improvement Net
www.letsrenovate.com	LetsRenovate.com (home remodeling center)
www.nahb.org	National Association of Home Builders (NAHB)
www.nari.org	National Association of the Remodeling Industry® (NARI®)
www.nkba.org	National Kitchen & Bath Association (NKBA)
www.renovatorsplace.com	Renovators Place
www2.remodeling.hw.net	Remodeling Online
www.roomadditions.com	Room Additions
www.updaterenovate.com.au	Update Renovate

Renovations, Remodeling, and Additions Test

Follow these instructions to access and complete an electronic copy of the Chapter 35 Renovations, Remodeling, and Additions Test:

1. Go to cengagebrain.com
2. Enter the email address and password you used to register for the site (see Preface for full instructions).
3. Select the website from the **My Course & Materials** area of your home page. Select the chapter you want from the pull-down menu at the top of the page. Choose the resources for that chapter from the menu on the left.
4. Type your name, the chapter number, and the date at the top of the sheet.
5. Answer the following questions with short, complete statements using a word processor.

NOTE:

The answers to some questions may not be contained in this chapter and will require you to do additional research using the Internet. Use your favorite search engine to search for specific professional companies or general categories of information.

Questions

35.1. What are the major differences between a renovation, a remodel, and an addition?

35.2. Which of the three types of projects presented in this chapter require drawings to obtain a building permit?

35.3. What permits are required for a remodel in the municipality where you live?

35.4. What drawings are required to obtain a building permit for the structural portion of a remodel in the municipality where you live?

35.5. How can you obtain a site map of a prospective remodeling project in your area?

35.6. List three pieces of equipment that are useful in measuring a jobsite.

35.7. List five common limitations that may influence a remodeling project.

35.8. Explain how to measure the setbacks at a jobsite.

35.9. Explain how to determine the height of an existing structure.

35.10. How can the existing materials be determined in drawing a section of the existing structure?

Problems

Use a floor plan for any project from Chapter 12 and the corresponding site plan from Chapter 10 to complete the following project.

35.1 Redesign the existing kitchen/family room to be suitable for a family that likes to entertain. Provide seating at a food bar for four to six people. Assume that the existing roof is framed with trusses so that interior walls may be altered, but keep the footprint of the house as is (as the owners have requested). Complete the drawings required by the building department that governs your area.

35.2 Use the elevations from any project in Chapter 19 to design two different exterior renovations.

35.3 Design a single-level addition that includes the removal and redesign of a new kitchen and the addition of a bedroom suite, bathroom, and family room that blends in with the structure from Chapter 12. Reuse the existing kitchen and bedroom space needed to meet the needs of the new owner. Include an island in the kitchen with seating for four. Include a new masonry fireplace and chimney in the family room.

35.4 Design an addition above the existing main floor living area including a den and a master bedroom suite and master bath. Determine a suitable area for a stair to access the upper floor.

35.5 Design an addition of a family room, bathroom, and one bedroom that will be sited in a daylight basement below the existing main floor living area. Determine a suitable area for a stair to access the lower floor. Assume that the roof over the main level is a truss roof. Blend all materials to match.

In addition to the previous instructions provided for this chapter, complete one of the remodeling projects as a team project using the team requirements and goals listed in Chapter 12.

Project Planning

After reviewing the design criteria, either verbally or in a written memo demonstrate to your client your understanding of the project, along with the amount of time you expect the drawings to take, and any resources you require to complete the project. Respond verbally to any questions your client might have for you, and let the client know when the project will be complete. Ask for clarification of any questions you have regarding the drawing criteria. If you plan to present your project preview verbally, be prepared with your questions written down so that you can ask relevant questions, in a professional manner, and be prepared to take notes regarding your client's comments.

Once you have the criteria and direction to begin the project, make a plan to get it done. Using the guidelines presented in this text and the local building requirements to obtain a building permit, include the minimum contents as well as an estimate of the time you require to complete each aspect of the required drawings:

Research.

Major steps to complete the drawing.

Applicable codes that will apply to this drawing.

Applicable local requirements that apply to the drawing.

Adjusting drawing templates to set plotting standards, text heights, dimensions, and linetypes.

Completing all required annotation and dimensioning.

Evaluation.

Track the amount of time.

> *Compare the estimated completion time for each aspect of the project with the actual required time.*
>
> *Use the appropriate checklist from the student website prior to submitting your drawing to your instructor.*

Acronyms

AAC: Autoclaved aerated concrete

AAMA: American Architectural Manufacturers Association

ACCA: Air Conditioning Contractors of America

ACH: Air exchange per hour

ACI: American Concrete Institute

ADA: Americans with Disabilities Act

ADDA: American Design & Drafting Association

AEC: Architecture, Engineering and Construction

AF&PA: American Forest and Paper Association

AFF: American Forest Foundation

AFT: Advanced framing techniques

AIA: The American Institute of Architects

AIBD: American Institute of Building Designers

AISC: American Institute of Steel Construction

AITC: American Institute of Timber Construction

ANSI: American National Standards Institute

APA: The Engineered Wood Association (formerly the American Plywood Association)

APMM: Association of Professional Model Makers

ASAI: The American Society of Architectural Illustrators

ASCE: American Society of Civil Engineers

ASHRAE: American Society of Heating, Refrigerating, & Air-Conditioning Engineers

ASID: American Society of Interior Designers

ASLA: American Society of Landscape Architects

ASME: American Society of Mechanical Engineers

ASTM: American Society for Testing and Materials International

BIM: Building Information Modeling

BLM: Bureau of Land Management

BOCA: Building Officials and Code Administrators International, Inc.

BTU: British thermal unit

CAD: Computer-aided design

CADD: Computer-aided drafting and design

CC&R: Covenants, Conditions, and Restrictions

CFCs: Chlorofluorocarbons

CID: Certified Interior Decorators

CKD: Certified Kitchen Designer

CMKBD: Certified Master Kitchen & Bathroom Designer

CMU: Concrete masonry units

CPA: Composite Panel Association

CSA: Canadian Standards Association

CSI: The Construction Specifications Institute

DOC: U.S. Department of Commerce

EERE: U.S. Department of Energy's Office of Energy Efficiency and Renewable Energy

EPA: U.S. Environmental Protection Agency

EPS: Expanded polystyrene foam

FEMA: Federal Emergency Management Agency

FHA: Federal Housing Administration

FSC: Forest Stewardship Council

FTC: Federal Trade Commission

GS: Green Seal

HDF: High density fiberboard

HGTV: Home & Garden Television

HPVA: Hardwood Plywood & Veneer Association

HUD: U.S. Department of Housing and Urban Development

IBC: International Building Code

ICBO: International Conference of Building Officials

ICC: International Code Council

ICF: Insulated concrete form

IECC: International Energy Conservation Code

IgCC: International Green Construction Code

IRC: International Residential Code

ISO: International Organization for Standardization

KCMA: Kitchen Cabinet Manufacturers Association

LCCA: Life-cycle cost analysis

LRFD: Load reduction factor design standards

LSL: Laminated strand lumber

LVL: Laminated veneer lumber

MBI: Modular Building Institute

MDF: Medium density fiberboard

MEL: Mechanically evaluated lumber

NAHB: National Association of Home Builders

NAHBRC: NAHB Research Center

NBS: National Bureau of Standards
NCBDC: National Council of Building Design Certification
NCDC: National Climate Data Center
NCIDQ: National Council for Interior Design Qualification
NCMA: National Concrete Masonry Association
NCSEA: National Council of Structural Engineers Associations
NDS: National Design Specification
NFPA: National Fire Protection Association
NFRC: National Fenestration Rating Council
NGBS: National Green Building Standard
NIBS: National Institute of Building Sciences
NIST: National Institute of Standards and Technology
NKBA: National Kitchen & Bath Association
NMHC: National Multi Housing Council
NSPE: National Society of Professional Engineers
OSB: Oriented strand board
OSHA: Occupational Safety & Health Administration
PF: Portal frame
PSL: Parallel strand lumber
PTI: Post-Tensioning Institute
PVC: Polyvinyl chloride

RFCI: Resilient Floor Covering Institute
SBC: Standard Building Code
SBCCI: Southern Building Code Congress International, Inc.
SFI: Sustainable Forestry Initiative Inc.
SFPA: Southern Forest Products Association
SHGC: Solar heat gain coefficient
SIPs: Structural insulated panels
SPIB: Southern Pine Inspection Bureau
SRCC: Solar Rating and Certification Corporation
T&G: Tongue and groove
TCIA: Tree Care Industry Association
TLC: The Learning Channel
TS: Tube steel
UBC: Uniform Building Code
UL: Underwriters Laboratories LLC
USGBC: U.S. Green Building Council
USMA: U.S. Metric Association
VA: U.S. Department of Veterans Affairs
VOC: Volatile organic compound
WDMA: Window and Door Manufacturers Association
WWPA: Western Wood Products Association

Abbreviations

Drafters and designers use many abbreviations to conserve space. Using *standard* abbreviations ensures that drawings are interpreted accurately. Here are common guidelines for proper use:

1. A period is used only when the abbreviation may be confused with a word.
2. Several words use the same abbreviation; use is defined by the location within the drawings.

access panel	ap	basement	basm	built-in	blt-in
acoustic	ac	bathtub	bt	buzzer	buz
acoustic plaster	ac pl	batten	batt.	by	×
actual	act.	beam	bm	cabinet	cab.
addition	add.	bearing	br	cast iron	c.i.
adhesive	adh	benchmark	B.M.	catalog	cat.
adjustable	adj	bending moment	M	catch basin	C.B.
aggregate	aggr	better	btr	caulking	calk
air conditioning	a.c.	between	btwn	ceiling	clg
alternate	alt	beveled	bev	ceiling diffuser	c.d.
alternating current	ac	bidet	bdt	ceiling joist	c.j. or ceil jst
aluminum	alum.	block	blk	cement	cem
amount	amt	blocking	blkg	center	ctr
ampere	amp	blower	blo	center line	CL
anchor bolt	a.b.	board	bd.	center to center	c/c
angle	/	board feet	bd ft	centimeter	cm
approved	appd	both sides	b.s.	ceramic	cer
approximate	approx	both ways	b.w.	chamfer	cham.
architectural	arch.	bottom	btm	channel	c
area	a.	bottom of footing	b.f.	check	chk
asbestos	asb.	boulevard	blvd	cinder block	cin blk
asphalt	asph	brass	br	circuit	cir
asphaltic concrete	asph conc	brick	brk	circuit breaker	cir bkr
at	@	British thermal unit	Btu	class	cl
automatic	auto.	bronze	brz	cleanout	c.o.
avenue	ave	broom closet	bc	clear	clr
average	avg	building	bldg	cold water	c.w.
balcony	balc	building line	BL	column	col.

combination	comb.	drawing	dwg	forced air unit	FAU
common	com.	dryer	D	foundation	fnd
composition	comp.	drywall	D.W.	front	fnt
computer-aided drafting	CAD	each	ea	full size	fs
		each face	E.F.	furnace	furn
concrete	conc	each way	E.W.	furred ceiling	fc
concrete masonry unit	cmu	elbow	el.	future	fut
		electrical	elect.	guage	ga
conduit	cnd	elevation	elev	gallon	gal.
construction	const	enamel	enam	galvanized	galv
continuous	cont	engineer	engr	galvanized iron	g.i.
contractor	contr	entrance	ent	garage	gar.
control joint	c.j.	equal	eq	gas	g.
copper	cop.	equipment	equip.	girder	gird.
corridor	corr	estimate	est.	glass	gl
corrugate	corr	excavate	exc	glue laminated	glu-lam
countersink	csk	exhaust	exh	grade	gr
courses	c.	existing	exist.	grating	grtg
cubic	cu.	expansion joint	exp jt	gravel	gvl
cubic feet	cu ft	exposed	expo.	grille	gr
cubic feet per minute	cfm	extension	extn	ground	gnd
		exterior	ext.	ground fault circuit interrupter	GFCI or GFI
cubic inch	cu in	fabricate	fab.		
cubic yard	cu yd	face brick	f.b.	grout	gt
damper	dpr	face of studs	f.o.s.	gypsum	gyp
damp proofing	dp	Fahrenheit	F	gypsum board	gyp bd
dead load	dl	feet / foot	' or ft	hardboard	hdb
decibel	db	feet per minute	fpm	hardware	hdw
decking	dk	finished	fin.	hardwood	hdwd
deflection	d.	finished floor	fin fl	head	hd.
degree	° or deg	finished grade	fin gr	header	hdr
design	dsgn	finished opening	f.o.	heater	htr
detail	det.	firebrick	fbrk	heating	htg
diagonal	diag	fire hydrant	F.H.	heating/ventilating/ air conditioning	hvac
diameter	Ø or dia	fireproof	f.p.		
diffuser	dif	fixture	fix.	height	ht
dimension	dimen	flammable	flam.	hemlock	hem.
dining room	dr	flashing	fl	hemlock-fir	hem-fir
dishwasher	d/w	flexible	flex.	hollow core	h.c.
disposal	disp	floor	flr	horizontal	horiz
ditto	" or do	floor drain	f.d.	horsepower	h.p.
division	div.	floor joist	fl jst	hose bibb	h.b.
door	dr	floor sink	f.s.	hot water	h.w.
double	dbl	fluorescent	fluor	hot water heater	h.w.h.
double hung	dh	folding	fldg	hundred	c
Douglas fir	df	foot	(') ft	illuminate	illum.
down	dn	footcandle	fc	incandescent	incan.
downspout	d.s.	footing	ftg	inch	" or in.
drain	d	foot pounds	ft lb	inch pounds	in. lb.

incinerator	incin.	mile	mi.	position	pos
inflammable	infl.	minimum	min	pound	# or lb
inside diameter	i.d.	minute	(') min	pounds per square	
inside face	i.f.	mirror	mirr	foot	psf
inspection	insp	miscellaneous	misc	pounds per square	
install	inst	mixture	mix.	inch	psi
insulate	ins	model	mod	prefabricated	prefab
insulation	insul	modular	mod	preferred	pfd
interior	int.	molding	mldg	preliminary	prelim.
iron	i	mullion	mull.	pressure treated	p.t.
jamb	jmb.	natural	nat	property	prop.
joint	jt.	natural grade	nat. gr.	pull chain	p.c.
joist	jst.	noise reduction		pushbutton	p.b.
junction	jct.	coefficient	n.r.c.	quality	qty
junction box	J-box	nominal	nom	quantity	qty
kiln dried	k.d.	not applicable	n.a.	radiator	rad.
kilowatt	kW	not in contract	N.I.C.	radius	r or rad.
kilowatt hour	kWh	not to scale	N.T.S.	range	r
Kip (1,000 lb)	K	number	# or no	receptacle	recp
kitchen	kit.	obscure	obs	recessed	rec.
knockout	k.o.	on center	O.C.	redwood	rdwd
laboratory	lab.	opening	opg	reference	ref.
laminated	lam.	opposite	opp	refrigerator	refr
landing	ldg	ounce	oz	register	reg
laundry	lau	outside diameter	O.D.	reinforcing	reinf
lavatory	lav	outside face	O.F.	reinforcing bar	rebar
length	lgth	overhead	ovhd	required	reqd
level	lev.	painted	ptd	return	ret.
light	lt	pair	pr	revision	rev.
linear feet	lin ft	panel	pnl	ridge	rdg
linen closet	lin	parallel	// or par.	riser	ris
linoleum	lino	part	pt	roof drain	R.D.
live load	LL	partition	part.	roofing	rfg
living room	Liv	pavement	pvmt	room	rm
long	lg	penny	d	rough	rgh
louver	lv	perforate	perf	rough opening	r.o.
machine bolt	m.b.	perimeter	per.	round	Ø or rd
manhole	m.h.	permanent	perm.	safety	saf
manufacturer	manuf	perpendicular	' or perp.	schedule	sch
marble	mrb	pi (3.1416 . . .)	p	screen	scrn
masonry	mas	plaster	pls.	screw	scr
material	matl	plasterboard	pls. bd.	second	sec.
maximum	max	plastic	plas	section	sect.
mechanical	mech	plate	pl	select	sel
medicine cabinet	m.c.	platform	plat.	select structural	sel. st.
medium	med.	plumbing	plmb	self-closing	s.c.
membrane	memb	plywood	ply	service	serv
metal	mtl	polyethylene	poly	sewer	sew
meter	m	polyvinyl chloride	pvc	sheathing	shtg

sheet	sht	synthetic	syn	vertical	vert.
shower	sh	system	sys	vertical grain	vert gr
siding	sdg	tangent	tan.	vinyl	vin.
sill cock	s.c.	tee	T	vinyl asbestos tile	v.a.t.
similar	sim	telephone	tel	vinyl base	v.b.
single hung	s.h.	television	tv	vinyl tile	v.t.
soil pipe	s.p.	temperature	temp.	vitreous	vit
solid block	sol. blk.	terra-cotta	t.c.	vitreous clay tile	v.c.t.
solid core	S.C.	terrazzo	tz	volt	v
Southern pine	SP	thermostat	thrm	volume	vol
specifications	specs	thickness	thk	wainscot	wsct
spruce-pine-fir	SPF	thousand	m	wall vent	w.v.
square	sq	thousand board		washing machine	wm
square feet	sq ft	feet	MBF	waste stack	w.s.
square inch	sq in.	threshold	thr	water closet	w.c.
stainless steel	sst.	through	thru	water heater	w.h.
standard	std	toilet	tol	waterproof	w.p.
standpipe	st. p.	tongue and		watt	W
steel	stl	groove	T&G	weatherproof	wp
stirrup	stir	top of wall	t.o.w.	weather stripping	ws
stock	stk	total	tot.	weep hole	wh
storage	sto	tread	tr	weight	wt
storm drain	S.D.	tubing	tub.	welded wire fabric	wwf
street	st	typical	typ	welded wire mesh	wwm
structural	str	unfinished	unfin	white pine	wp
structural clay		utility	util	wide flange	W
tile	S.C.T.	V-joint	v-jt	width	w
substitute	sub.	valve	v	window	wdw
supply	sup.	vanity	van.	with	w/
surface	sur	vapor barrier	v.b.	without	w/o
surface four sides	S4S	vapor proof	v prf	wood	wd
surface two sides	S2S	ventilation	vent.	wrought iron	w.i.
suspended ceiling	susp clg	vent pipe	vp	yard	yd
switch	sw	vent stack	v.s.	yellow pine	yp
symbol	sym	vent through roof	v.t.r.	zinc	zn

Glossary

A

Accessibility Ability to go in, out, and through a building and its rooms with ease regardless of disability.

Accessible route The walking surface from the exterior access through the residence that is required to connect all spaces of the dwelling unit. If there is only one route, it cannot pass through a bathroom, closet, or similar space.

Accordion door Often used as a room divider, this type of door has multiple folding panels.

Acoustics The science of sound and sound control.

Active solar system A system that uses mechanical devices to absorb, store, and use solar heat.

Addenda An item of additional material used to amend a building contract during the bidding process—prior to the awarding of the contract.

Adobe A heavy clay used as a building material in many southwestern states to make sun-dried bricks.

Advanced framing techniques Framing methods that use less structural lumber than those used with typical platform construction, producing greater energy savings.

A-frame A method of framing walls and a system of framing roofs.

Aggregate Stone, gravel, cinder, or slag used as one of the components of concrete.

Air-dried lumber Lumber that has been stored in yards or sheds for a period of time after cutting. Building codes typically assume a 19% moisture content for determining joist and beam sizes of air-dried lumber.

Air duct A pipe, typically made of sheet metal or flexible foil-covered fiberglass, that carries air from a source such as a furnace or air conditioner to a room within a structure.

Air-to-air heat exchanger A heat recovery and ventilation device that pulls polluted air from the building envelope and transfers the heat by pulling fresh air into the house.

Air trap A U-shaped pipe placed in wastewater lines to prevent backflow of sewer gas.

Alcove A small room adjoining a larger room, often separated by an archway.

Aligned text Text that is rotated so it can be read when looking from the right side of the drawing page.

Alteration Nonstructural changes made to a structure.

Alternative braced wall panel (ABWP) A method of bracing a braced wall line that uses panels with a minimum length of 2'-8" (800 mm) to resist lateral loads.

Ambient light Light that comes from all directions.

Ambient temperature The temperature of the air surrounding a heating or cooling device.

American Design & Drafting Association A national association of designers and CAD drafters from many different fields of the design professionals.

American Foursquare A home style that is recognizable for the simplicity of its design that features a two-story, simple box shape with an attic and a full basement. Each floor generally has four rooms.

American Institute of Architects An association of licensed architects in the United States who work to promote high-quality professional standards.

American Institute of Building Designers A national association of designers and CAD technicians who are certified as knowledgeable in the field of residential design.

Ampere (amp) A measure of electrical current.

Anchor A metal tie or strap used to tie building members to each other.

Anchor bolt An L-shaped threaded bolt used to fasten wood structural members to masonry or concrete.

Angle iron A structural piece of steel shaped to form a 90° angle.

Angle of repose The slope of a cut or fill bank measured by comparing the horizontal run to the vertical rise. With an angle of repose of 3:1, one vertical unit of elevation change can occur in three horizontal units.

Annotation Used in architectural CAD applications to refer any text, notes, dimensions, and text symbols on a drawing.

Antebellum Latin for "before the war," the term refers to the elegant plantation homes built in the American South preceding the Civil War.

Apron The inside trim board placed below a windowsill. The term is also used to describe a curb around a driveway or parking area.

Architect A licensed professional who is responsible for the design of a structure and the way the building relates to the environment.

Architect's scale A tool for measuring distance with divisions based on 1/16" for full scale. Other divisions are based on common fractions such as 1/8" = 1'-0", 1/4" = 1'-0", and 3/4" = 1'-0".

Architrave In trim designed to mimic classical architecture, it is the lowest part of the trim placed at the wall/roof intersection, often resting directly on columns and providing support to the frieze and the cornice.

Archive Drawings that are no longer in use and are stored for reference.

Areaway A subsurface enclosure to admit light and air to a basement; sometimes called a window well.

Art deco A style of architecture originating in the 1920s that features geometric, streamlined shapes and includes materials such as aluminum, stainless steel, lacquer, and in-laid wood.

Asbestos A mineral that does not burn or conduct heat; it is usually used for roofing material.

Ash dump An opening in the hearth for dumping ashes.

Ashlar masonry Squared masonry units laid with a horizontal bed joint.

Ash pit An area in the bottom of the firebox of a fireplace for collecting ash.

Asphalt An insoluble material used for making floor tile and for waterproofing walls and roofs.

Asphalt shingle Roof shingles made of asphalt-saturated felt and covered with mineral granules.

Asphaltic concrete A mixture of asphalt and aggregate that is used for driveway surfaces.

Assessed value The value assigned by governmental agencies for calculating the value of a structure or land for tax purposes.

Asymmetrical Shapes that are not equal, lacking in symmetry.

Atrium An inside courtyard of a structure that may either be open at the top or covered with a roof.

Attic The area formed between the ceiling joists and rafters.

Awning window A window that is hinged along the top edge.

Axonometric A drawing projection method that shows an image as if were viewed from a skewed direction in order to reveal more than one side of the object.

B

Backfill Earth, gravel, or sand placed in the trench around the footing and stem wall after the foundation has cured.

Baffle A shield, usually made of scrap material, for keeping insulation from plugging eave vents or a sound-deadening device for preventing the spread of wind or sound in a particular direction. The term is also used to describe the feeling some students have after taking a test for which they were unprepared.

Balance A principle of design dealing with the relationships between the various areas of a structure as they relate to imaginary centerlines.

Balcony An aboveground deck that projects from a wall or building with no additional supports.

Balloon framing (eastern framing) A construction method that has vertical wall members extending uninterrupted from the foundation to the roof.

Balusters One of a series of closely spaced ornamental vertical supports for a railing.

Balustrade A low ornamental railing used on the roofs of Georgian and Federal style homes to surround a flattened central area of a low-pitched hipped roof, forming what is often referred to as a "widow's walk" (from which sea captains' wives supposedly watched for their husbands' ships). Balustrades on Federal style houses are usually found above the exterior walls.

Band joist (rim joist) A joist set at the edge of the structure that runs parallel to the other joists.

Banister A handrail beside a stairway.

Barge rafter The inclined trim that hangs from the projecting edge of a roof rake.

Baseboard The finish trim where the wall and floor intersect.

Baseboard heater An electric heater that extends along the floor.

Base cabinets Cabinets that sit on the floor.

Base course The lowest course in brick or concrete masonry unit construction.

Baseline A reference line in mapping.

Basement A level of a structure that is built either entirely below grade level (full basement) or partially below grade level (daylight basement).

Basement wall The portion of a wall that is partially or totally below grade and encloses a basement.

Basic wind speeds The wind speed values that can be expected in an area measured in three-second gust speeds and listed in miles per hour.

Bath, full A room with a lavatory, toilet, and tub or a combination tub-and-shower unit.

Bath, half A room with a lavatory and water closet (toilet).

Bath, suite A room attached to the master bedroom, typically featuring a full bath with separate adjoining areas for a toilet, tub or spa, and shower.

Bath, three-quarter A room that includes a shower, toilet, and lavatory, but no tub.

Batt insulation Material, usually made of fiberglass, used between framing members for insulating buildings.

Batten A board used to hide the seams when other boards are joined together.

Battlement A parapet wall with open spaces once intended for shooting.

Bay window A window placed in a projection of an exterior wall that extends all the way down to the foundation. In plan view, the wall projection may be rectangular, polygonal, or curved. *See also* Oriel window.

Beam A horizontal structural member used to support roof or wall loads, often called a header.

Beamed ceiling A ceiling with exposed support beams.

Bearing plate A support member, often a steel plate, used to spread weight over a larger area.

Bearings Directions related to site boundaries referencing one quadrant of the compass.

Bearing wall A wall that supports vertical loads in addition to its own weight.

Benchmark A reference point used by surveyors to establish grades and construction heights.

Bending One of three major forces acting on a beam, it is the tendency of a beam to bend or sag between its supports.

Bending moment A measure of the forces that cause a beam to break by bending; represented in math formulas by the letter M.

Berm A raised area of soil.

Beveled siding Siding that has a tapered thickness.

Bibb An outdoor faucet that is threaded for attaching a hose. (Represented by H.B. on floor plans.)

Bidet A basin-like plumbing fixture used for personal hygiene of one's private areas.

Bifold door A set of two or more doors that fold to open—either with two doors folding to one side or with four doors splitting in the center of the opening (with two doors folding back to each side).

Bill of material Part of a set of plans listing all of the material needed for a project.

Bird block (eave blocking) A block placed between rafters or trusses to maintain uniform spacing and to keep animals out of the attic.

Bird's mouth A notch cut into a rafter to provide a bearing surface where the rafter intersects the top plate.

Blind nailing Driving nails in such a way as to conceal heads from view.

Blocking (bridging) Framing members, typically of wood, placed between joists, rafters, or studs to provide rigidity.

Board and batten A type of siding using vertical boards with small wood strips (battens) that cover the joints of the boards.

Board foot The volume of a piece of lumber that is 1" thick by 12" wide by 12" long (25 × 300 × 300 mm).

Bolt A fastening device made of metal, with a threaded shaft that connects to what is typically a hexagonal head.

Bolt, anchor An L-shaped bolt used to connect wood members to concrete.

Bolt, carriage A bolt with a rounded head and threaded shaft for connecting steel and other metal members as well as timber connections.

Bolt, drift A steel rod that has been threaded to span between two different structural members, such as posts, to form an X for lateral bracing.

Bolt, expansion A bolt with a special expanding sleeve that surrounds the bolt shaft to increase the bolt's holding power once it is inserted into a hole.

Bolt, machine A bolt with a hexagonal head and a threaded shaft for attaching steel to steel, steel to wood, or wood to wood.

Bolt, toggle A bolt with a nut that expands so it can't be removed once it is inserted through a hole.

Bond A legal document ensuring that the contractor will provide the goods or services represented in a contract agreement; the mortar joint between two masonry units; or a pattern in which masonry units are arranged. Also used to describe the top-secret spy (007) Bond, James.

Bond beam A reinforced concrete beam used to strengthen masonry walls.

Boolean operators Words such as AND, OR, NOT, and NEAR that are used with special symbols that can be used to ensure an Internet search is as intended.

Bottom chord The lower, usually horizontal, member of a truss used to support ceiling material.

Bounds Limitation or restriction specified in a legal description.

Bow window An arc-shaped bay window.

Box beam A hollow, built-up beam made of individual boards with a hollow center, to resemble a solid beam.

Boxed eave Rafter or truss tails enclosed by either plywood or 1× material.

Boxed soffit *See* Eave, boxed.

Braced wall line Each exterior surface of a residence.

Braced wall panel A method of reinforcing a braced wall line using 48" (1200 mm) wide panels to resist lateral loads.

Branch lines Water feeder lines that branch off the main line to supply fresh water to fixture groups in the home.

Breaker An electrical safety switch that automatically opens the circuit when excessive amperage occurs in the circuit.

Break lines Lines used to indicate an unimportant portion of an object has been removed so that it will fit into a specific space.

Breezeway A covered walkway with open sides between two different parts of a structure.

Bridging Cross-blocking between horizontal members used to add stiffness; also called *blocking*.

British thermal unit (BTU) A unit of measurement of heat; each BTU is the amount of heat required to raise the temperature of 1 lb (0.454 kg) of water 1° Fahrenheit. The measurement also assumes that the heating is done at a constant pressure of one atmosphere (air pressure at sea level).

Bubble drawings Freehand sketches used to determine room locations and relationships.

Building code Legal requirements designed to protect the public by providing guidelines governing the structural, electrical, plumbing, and mechanical areas of a structure. *See also* International Residential Code.

Building designer A restricted term in many states used to specify someone who has had formal training in home design and who has passed a competency test.

Building envelope The portion of a building that encloses the treated environment, including the walls, ceiling or roof, and floor.

Building line An imaginary line determined by the zoning department to specify the limits where a structure may be built; also known as *setback*.

Building paper A waterproofed paper used to prevent the passage of air and water into a structure.

Building permit A permit to build a structure issued by a governmental agency after the plans for the structure have been examined and the structure is found to comply with all building code requirements.

Built-up beam A beam built of smaller members that are bolted or nailed together.

Built-up roof A roof composed of three or more layers of felt, asphalt, pitch, or coal tar.

Bullnose Rounded edges of cabinet trim.

Bungalow A 1½ story home popular in America between 1900 and 1920 and featuring open and balanced, but nonsymmetrical, floor plans.

Butler's pantry An auxiliary kitchen area with additional preparation and storage areas located near the main kitchen.

Butt joint The junction where two members meet in a square-cut joint, end-to-end or edge-to-edge.

Buttress A projection from a wall often located below roof beams to provide support to the roof loads and to keep long walls in the vertical position.

C

Cabinet work The interior finish woodwork of a structure, especially cabinetry.

CAD technician A person who uses a computer for completing drawings that were once drawn manually by drafters.

Café door Doors that swing in two directions.

Camber A curve built into a laminated beam to increase the support for a load.

Cantilever Construction material that extends past its supports.

Cant strip A small built-up area between two intersecting roof shapes to divert water.

Cape Cod A style of home developed in New England during the seventeenth and eighteenth centuries, typically described as a small, one-level home with a steep gabled roof and a central chimney.

Carbon footprint The measure of impact that human activities have on the environment, in terms of the amount of greenhouse gases produced, measured in units of carbon dioxide.

Carbon neutral The reduction of emissions from all greenhouse gas sources to produce a neutral result through energy efficiency, renewable energy purchases and carbon-offset purchases.

Carbon offsets The lessening of carbon emissions through the development of alternative energy projects, such as solar or wind energy.

Carport A covered, but not fully enclosed automobile parking structure.

Carriage The horizontal part of a stair stringer that supports the tread.

Carriage bolt A bolt used for connecting wood to steel or other metal members.

Casement window A hinged window that swings outward around a vertical axis.

Casing The metal, plastic, or wood trim around a door or window.

Catch basin An underground reservoir for water drained from a roof before it flows to a storm drain.

Cathedral ceiling A vaulted ceiling.

Cathedral window A window with an upper edge that is parallel to the roof pitch.

Caulking A soft, waterproof material used to seal seams and cracks in construction.

Cavity wall A masonry wall formed with two wythes with an airspace between each face.

CC&Rs (covenants, conditions, and restrictions) The name given to an agreement between two or more property owners that is recorded on the deed of each property. It consists of a covenant or binding agreement; a condition or statement of what is required as part of an agreement; and a restriction or principle limiting the extent of something.

Ceiling joists The horizontal members of the roof used to resist the outward spread of the rafters and to provide a surface for installing the finished ceiling.

Cement A powder of alumina, silica, lime, iron oxide, and magnesia pulverized and used as an ingredient in mortar and concrete.

Centerlines Lines used to locate the center axis of circular features such as drilled holes, bolts, columns, and piers.

Central heating A heating system that delivers heat throughout a structure from a single source.

Cesspool An underground catch basin for the collection and dispersal of sewage.

Chain A unit of measure used in survey work that is equal to 66' (19 800 mm).

Chair rail A molding placed horizontally on the wall at the height where chair backs would otherwise damage the wall.

Chamfer A beveled edge formed by removing the sharp corner of a piece of material.

Channel A standard form of structural steel with three sides at right angles to each other forming the letter *C*.

Chase A recessed area formed between structural members that conceal electrical, mechanical, or plumbing materials.

Check Lengthwise cracks in a board caused by natural drying.

Check valve A valve in a pipe that permits flow in only one direction.

Chimney An upright structure connected to a fireplace or furnace that passes smoke and gases to outside air.

Chimney cap The sloping surface on the top of the chimney.

Chimney hood A covering placed over the flue to keep the elements from entering the flue.

Chimney liner A fire clay or terra-cotta liner built into a chimney to provide a smooth surface to the chimney flue.

Chord The upper and lower members of a truss that are supported by the web.

Cinder block A block made of cinder and cement used in construction.

Circuit The various conductors, connections, and devices found in the path of electrical flow from the source through the components and back to the source.

Circuit breaker A safety device that opens and closes an electrical circuit.

Circular stair A curved stair formed using a uniform radius.

Circumference The distance around the perimeter of a circle.

Civil engineer A licensed professional who is responsible for the design and supervision of the land drawings such as a topography map, grading plans, street design, and other land-related improvements.

Civil engineer's scale A tool used to measure distance with divisions based on one-tenth of an inch equals one foot, or one inch equals one foot, ten feet, or 100 feet. Other scales include 20, 30, 40, 50, and 60 divisions per inch which can also be used to equal one, ten or 100 feet.

Clapboard A tapered board used for siding that overlaps the board below it.

Cleanout A fitting with a removable plug put in plumbing drainage lines to allow access for cleaning out the pipe.

Clearance A clear space between building materials to allow for airflow or access.

Clerestory A window or group of windows placed above the normal window height, often with the top edge parallel to the rake of the roof.

Code A performance-based description of the desired results, with wide latitude allowed to achieve the results, that is adopted by a municipality to govern construction.

Code of ethics A formal document stating an organization's values and the rules and principles that employees are expected to follow.

Coffered ceiling A ceiling formed using beams and trim to create a pattern of recessed panels or grid-like compartments.

Collar tie Horizontal ties placed between rafters near the ridge to help resist the tendency of the rafters to separate.

Colonial A style of architecture and furniture adapted from the American colonial period.

Column A vertical structural support, usually made of steel.

Combustion air Outside air supplied to a fireplace or a gas- or oil-burning furnace for fuel combustion.

Common rafter Rafters that span and support the roof loads from the ridge to the top plate.

Common wall The partition that divides two different dwelling units.

Complex beam A beam with a non-uniform load at any point on it that has supports that are not located at its ends.

Composition shingles Roofing shingles typically made of fiberglass backing and covered with asphalt and a filler with a coating of finely crushed particles of stone.

Compression A force that crushes or compacts.

Concentrated load A load centralized in a small area; the weight supported by a post results in a concentrated load.

Concrete A building material made from cement, sand, gravel, and water.

Concrete blocks Blocks of precast concrete with a standard size of 8 × 8 × 16".

Concrete form masonry unit (CFMU) Construction that features a hybrid design blending unit masonry construction and cast-in-place concrete construction into a composite wall system.

Concrete masonry units (CMUs) Precast blocks made from concrete that are typically 8" high × 8" wide × 16" long.

Condensation The formation of water on a surface when warm air comes in contact with a cold surface.

Conditional use A use of a property prohibited by zoning regulations unless allowed on a case-by-case basis, if certain conditions are met.

Conduction The process of transferring heat energy between molecules within an object or between the molecules of two or more objects that are in contact.

Conductor Any material that permits the flow of electricity or a drainpipe that diverts water from the roof (a downspout).

Conduit A bendable metal, fiber pipe, or tube used to enclose one or more electrical wires.

Coniferous Cone-bearing trees such as cedars, cypresses, Douglas-firs, firs, junipers, larches, pines, redwoods, and spruces that have year-round, long, thin, and needle-like leaves.

Construction documents Drawings and written specifications prepared by design professionals for communicating the design of a project and administering the construction.

Construction estimator A person who develops the cost information that companies use to bid on construction contracts and to decide on the profitability of a proposed new project.

Construction joint A joint used when a concrete pour must be interrupted; provides a clean surface when work is resumed.

Continuous beam A single beam supported by more than two supports.

Continuously sheathed braced panel Braced wall reinforcing that is composed of the sheathing used for double-wall construction with additional nailing based on IRC requirements.

Contour lines Lines placed on a topography map or grading plan to represent all points with a specific elevation.

Contour A line that represents land formations.

Contraction joint An expansion joint in a masonry wall or slab formed to control where cracking will occur. *See also* Control joint.

Contractor The manager of an entire construction project or one specific phase of it.

Control joint (contraction joint) An expansion joint in a masonry wall formed by raking mortar from the vertical joint.

Control-point survey A survey method that establishes elevations that are recorded on a map.

Convection The transfer of heat from a heated surface to a fluid moving over the heated surface, or heat that is transferred by molecules in a fluid from one heated molecule to another.

Convenience outlet An electrical receptacle through which current is drawn for an appliance.

Cool roof A roof featuring light colors and highly reflective materials that help reduce the surface temperature of the roofing materials.

Coping A masonry cap placed on top of a block or brick wall to protect it from water penetration.

Corbel A ledge formed in a wall by building out successive courses of masonry.

Cornice The uppermost portion of molding (entablature) along the top of the wall just below the roof.

Counter flash A metal flashing used under normal flashing to provide a waterproof seam.

Course A continuous row of building material such as shingles, stone, or brick.

Court An exterior space that is at grade level and is enclosed on three or more sides by walls or buildings; it is open and unobstructed to the sky.

Cove lighting Lighting concealed behind a cornice or other ceiling features that direct light upward.

Craftsman-style A style of home popular in America in the early twentieth century with floor plans that usually consist of asymmetrical, free-flowing, two-story layouts with upper levels that are often cantilevered over the lower levels.

Crawl space The area between the floor joists and the ground.

Cricket A diverter built to direct water away from an area of a roof where it would otherwise collect, as behind a chimney.

Cripple stud A wall stud, sometimes called a jack stud, that is cut at less than full length.

Cross bracing Boards fastened diagonally between structural members, such as floor joists, to provide rigidity.

CSI (Construction Specification Institute) An organization that provides guidelines for written specifications for the construction industry. This CSI has nothing to do with crime scene investigators.

Cubic foot An area of space that is one foot wide, one foot deep, and one foot high.

Cubic yard An area defined as 3' wide × 3' deep × 3' tall or 27 cubic feet.

Cul-de-sac A dead-end street with a circular turnaround.

Culvert An underground passageway for water, usually part of a drainage system.

Cupola A short windowed tower or dome typically located in the center of a flat or low-sloped roof on traditional homes to provide light or ventilation.

Cure The process of concrete drying to its maximum design strength, usually taking 28 days.

Cut material Removing soil to lower the original ground elevation.

Cutting-plane line A line on a floor or framing plan showing the location of a cut to create a sectional view at the specified location.

D

Damper A movable plate that controls the amount of draft for a woodstove, fireplace, or furnace.

Damp proof Preparing a wall to slow the infiltration of moisture.

Datum A reference point for starting a survey.

Daylight The point represented on a grading plan that represents the intersection between cut and fill.

Daylight basement A basement that allows egress from the ground level, directly from the basement floor.

Deadening board A material used to control the transmission of sound.

Dead load The weight of building materials or other immovable objects in a structure.

Deciduous Broad-leafed trees that lose their leaves seasonally.

Deck An exterior floor supported on at least two opposing sides by adjoining structures, posts, or piers.

Decking A wood material used to form a floor or roof, typically used in 1" and 2" thicknesses.

Deflection The tendency of a structural member to bend under a load due to gravity.

Degree day A measurement of heating or cooling needed for a building using 65 degrees as a baseline.

Dehumidifier An appliance used to remove excessive moisture from a building's interior.

Demand factor An assumption based on NEC standards that not all lights will be on at the same time, so the lighting load can be reduced.

Density The number of people allowed to live in a specific area of land or to work in a specific area of a structure.

Dentil Molding made from a series of closely spaced rectangular blocks. It is typically found below the cornice along the roofline of a building, but may be used as a decorative band anywhere on a structure.

Designer Someone with formal training who has passed a competency test to design and draw residences but is not licensed as an architect. This definition varies by state.

Details Enlargements of specific areas of a structure that are drawn where several components intersect or where small members are required.

Diameter The distance across an arc or circle passing through the center.

Diaphragm A rigid plate-like surface located in roof, wall, or floor assemblies used to keep a plane in its true shape.

Diffuser The outlets that supply treated air from the HVAC system into a room.

Dimension line A line that extends between two extension lines to show the length of a specific feature.

Dimension lumber Lumber ranging in thickness from 2" to 4" (50 to 100 mm) and having a moisture content of less than 19%.

Dimensions Measurements placed on construction drawings to locate or describe the size of a product or assembly.

Dimmer switch An electrical switch used to vary the amount of current flowing through a fixture.

Direct gain A passive solar heating method that directly heats the inside of a building by the sun's rays as they pass through large areas of south-facing glass.

Direct solar gain Heat created by the sun and absorbed by a structure.

Direct-vent fireplace A prefabricated fireplace unit that vents through an exterior wall.

Discipline designator A two-character code representing the discipline that originates the drawings.

Distribution panel Panel where the conductor from the meter base is connected to individual circuit breakers that are connected to separate circuits for distribution to various locations throughout the structure.

Diverter A metal strip used to divert water.

Dormer A structure that projects from a sloping roof to form another roofed area, typically used to provide a surface to install a window.

Double-acting door A door that swings in two directions.

Double glazing Glazing in a door or window that is constructed from two layers of glazing.

Double hung window A type of window that allows the upper and lower halves to slide past each other, thus providing an opening at the top and bottom of the window.

Double-wall construction A method of construction used in cold climates that places the exterior finishing material over sheathing, which is then placed over a water-resistant membrane which is placed over the wall studs.

Downspout A pipe that carries rainwater from the gutters of the roof to the ground.

Drafter The person who uses the proper line properties, dimension, and text styles to create the drawings and details for another person's creations.

Drain A collector for a pipe that carries wastewater from each plumbing fixture to the waste line of the building drainage system.

Drainage grate A metal cover that lets water flow into a catch basin without allowing anyone to fall in.

Drawing area modules Areas on a drawing template that are defined by non-plotting lines that form horizontal rows identified with letters, and vertical columns identified by a number to aid in describing the contents of a page.

Dressed lumber Lumber that has been surfaced by a planing machine to give the wood a smooth finish.

Drift bolt A steel rod that has been threaded to span between two different structural members such as posts to form an X for lateral bracing.

Dry rot A type of wood decay caused by fungi that leave the wood a soft powder.

Drywall An interior wall covering installed in large sheets made of gypsum board.

Dry well A shallow well used to disperse water from the gutter system.

Duct Pipes, typically made of sheet metal, used to conduct hot or cold air of the HVAC system.

Duplex outlet A standard electrical convenience outlet with two receptacles.

Dutch Colonial A home style that has a broad gambrel roof with flaring eaves that are slightly rounded into barn-like gambrel shapes.

Dutch door A door divided horizontally in the center so that each half may be opened separately.

Dutch hip A type of roof shape that combines features of a gable and a hip roof.

Dynamic load The loads imposed on a structure from a sudden gust of wind or from an earthquake.

E

Earth-bermed Structures that are built into the ground or have soil pushed against the walls and roof.

Easement A right to make limited use of another's real property that is recorded on the deed and survives any sale of the property for use as a public right-of-way, such as a utility easement that grants access to private land to place or maintain a utility.

Eave The lower part of the roof that projects from the wall. *See also* Cornice.

Eave, boxed An eave with a covering applied directly to the bottom side of the rafter or truss tails.

Effluent Treated sewage from a sewage treatment plant or septic tank.

Egress A means of access.

Elastic limit The extent to which a material can be bent and still return to its original shape.

Elastomeric coatings A liquid roofing material that when applied creates a rubber-like protective membrane.

Elbow An L-shaped plumbing pipe.

Electrical conduit A metal or fiber pipe or tube used to enclose electrical wiring.

Electrical engineer A licensed professional responsible for the design of lighting and communication systems, surround-sound systems, security features, and requirements for computer networking.

Elevation The height of a specific point in relation to another point. The exterior views of a structure.

Eminent domain The right of a government to condemn private property so that it may be obtained for public use.

Enamel A paint that produces a hard, glossy, and smooth finish.

Engineered lumber Structural components made by turning small pieces of wood into framing members such as joists, studs, and rafters.

Engineered studs Structural vertical wall components made by turning small pieces of wood into framing members.

Engineers Licensed professionals who apply mathematical and scientific principles to the design and construction of structures. They include structural, electrical, mechanical, and civil engineers.

Entablature In classical architecture, the upper portion of a building that is above the columns and below the roof; comprised of the architrave, frieze and cornice.

Entourage The surroundings of a rendered building including ground cover, trees, people, and automobiles.

Envelope The exterior shell of a structure enclosing heated and cooled air of the living space.

Environmentally friendly construction Designing and constructing buildings with renewable materials and recycled products.

Equity The value of real estate in excess of the balance owed on the mortgage.

Ergonomics The study of human space and movement needs as they relate to a given work area, such as a kitchen.

Excavation The removal of soil for construction purposes.

Expanded polystyrene forms (EPFs) Wall forms that snap together, which are filled with concrete and left in place to create a super-insulated concrete wall system.

Expansion bolt A bolt with a special expanding sleeve that surrounds the bolt shaft to increase the bolt's holding power.

Expansion joint A joint installed in concrete construction to reduce cracking and to provide workable areas.

Extension lines Thin lines showing the limits of a dimension.

Exterior insulation and finishing systems (EIFS) A type of siding installed over rigid insulation board that is used as a base for a fiberglass-reinforced base coat.

F

Fabrication Work done on a structure away from the jobsite.

Facade The exterior covering of a structure.

Face brick Brick used on the visible surface of a structure to cover other masonry products.

Face grain The pattern in the visible veneer of plywood.

Fanlight A semicircular or semi-elliptical non-opening transom window with a horizontal sill; in the Federal style of home, it is placed above a door or another window typically above the main entry door.

Farmhouse A home style featuring two-story construction usually surrounded by a covered wraparound porch. The roof ridge runs parallel to the front surface of the home while a steep roof with dormers usually covers the home with a shallow pitch at the porch.

Fascia A horizontal board nailed to the ends of rafters or trusses to conceal those ends.

Federal Housing Administration (FHA) A governmental agency that insures home loans made by private lending institutions.

Federal style A home style that combines Georgian architecture with classic Roman and Greek styles, including curved lines and decorative flourishes, such as swags, garlands, and elliptical windows.

Felt A tar-impregnated paper used for water protection under roofing and siding materials. Sometimes used under concrete slabs for moisture resistance.

Fenestration Windows or doors located in the building envelope.

Fiber bending stress (F_b) The measurement of structural members used to determine their stiffness.

Fiberboard Fibrous wood products that have been pressed into a sheet. Typically used for the interior construction of cabinets and to cover the subfloor.

Field weld A weld performed at the jobsite.

Fill Material used to raise or level an area for construction, typically gravel or sand.

Filled insulation Insulation material blown or poured into place in attics and walls.

Fillet weld A weld between two surfaces that butt at 90° to each other, with the weld filling the inside corner.

Finial A decorative cap placed on a newel post for some home styles.

Finished floor The flooring material above the subfloor.

Finished grade The shape of the ground once all excavation and movement of earth have been completed.

Finished lumber Wood milled to a smooth finish, suitable for trim and other finish work.

Finished size Also known as *dressed size*, it represents the actual size of lumber after all milling operations and is typically about 1/2" (13 mm) smaller than the nominal size (size of lumber before planing).

Nominal Size (inches)	Finished Size (inches)
1	3/4
2	1 1/2
4	3 1/2
6	5 1/2
8	7 1/2
10	9 1/2
12	11 1/2
14	13 1/2

Firebox The area of a fireplace where combustion occurs.

Fire cut An angular cut on the end of a joist or rafter that is supported by masonry; allows the wood member to fall away from the wall without damaging a masonry wall when wood is damaged by fire.

Firebrick Refractory brick capable of withstanding high temperatures; used for lining fireplaces and furnaces.

Fire door Door used between different types of construction that has been rated as being able to withstand fire for a certain amount of time.

Fireplace insert Metal fireplace inserted into a masonry fireplace and vented using the existing chimney; to control drafts and increase heat production.

Fireplace opening The open area between the side and top faces of the fireplace.

Fireproofing Non-combustible material covering structural materials; used to increase the fire rating.

Fire rating A rating given to building materials specifying the amount of time the material can resist damage caused by fire.

Fire-stop Blocking placed between studs or other structural members to resist the spread of fire.

Fire suppression system A system, such as home sprinklers, for controlling or stopping the spread of an interior fire.

Firewall A wall constructed of materials that will resist fire before structural damage will occur.

Fitting A standard pipe or tubing joint, such as a tee, elbow, or reducer, used to join two or more pipes.

Fixed window A window designed without hinges so it cannot be opened.

Flagstone Flat stones used for floor and wall coverings.

Flange The top and bottom horizontal surfaces of a steel beam.

Flashing Metal used to prevent the leakage of water through surface intersections.

Flat roof A roof with a minimal roof pitch, usually about 1/4" per 12" (6 per 25 mm).

Flight An uninterrupted series of steps between two different floor levels or between a floor and a landing.

Flitch beam A built-up beam consisting of steel plates bolted between wood members.

Floor joists Repetitive, horizontal structural members of the floor framing system that are used to span between the stem wall or girders to provide support to the subfloor.

Floor plan Architectural drawing of a room or building as seen from above.

Floor plug A 120-V convenience outlet located in the floor.

Flue A passage inside of the chimney to conduct smoke and gases away from a firebox to outside air.

Flue liner A terra-cotta pipe used to provide a smooth flue surface so unburned materials will not cling to the flue.

Folk Victorian Homes developed for less affluent consumers during the period of 1870–1910 that were much simpler than the traditional Victorian home.

Foot-candle The amount of light a candle casts on an object 12" (300 mm) away.

Footing The lowest member of a foundation system used to spread the loads of a structure across supporting soil.

Forced-air system A system that blows treated air through ducts using a fan located in the heating or cooling device.

Formal balance Symmetrical arrangement of space so that one side of the structure or room matches the opposite side.

Form of Agreement Included in a project manual, it is a legal contract that includes the who, what, how much, and when of the project.

Foundation The system used to support a building's loads consisting of the stem walls, footings, and piers. It is referred to in many areas as *footing*.

Foyer A room located by the main entry that serves as a place to meet and greet guests and as a funnel to other living areas.

Frame The structural skeleton of a building.

French doors Exterior or interior doors that have glass panels and swing into a room.

French Normandy Homes patterned after homes in Normandy and the Loire Valley of France that feature a turret with living space.

French Plantation A two-level home style that incorporated French, West Indies, and Caribbean features into homes suited for the hot wet climates of the Mississippi valley.

French Provincial Two-level brick or stucco homes recognized by their balance and symmetry that had their origins in the style of the rural manor homes or chateaus built by French nobles during the mid-1600s.

Frieze A horizontal band decorated with designs or carvings that runs above doorways or windows or below the cornice.

Frost line The average depth to which soil will freeze.

Full sections A drawing view resulting from passing the cutting plane through the entire structure that provides an overall view of a specific area of the structure.

Furnace A unit that produces heat by burning fuel oil or natural gas or by using electric heating coils or heat pumps.

Furring Wood strips attached to structural members used to provide a level surface for finishing materials when different sized structural members are used.

G

Gable A type of roof with two sloping surfaces that intersect at the ridge of the structure.

Gable-end wall The triangular wall that is formed at each end of a gable roof between the top plate of the wall and the rafters.

Galley kitchen A kitchen arrangement in which all cabinets are on two parallel walls.

Galvanized Steel products that have zinc applied to their exterior surfaces to provide protection from rusting.

Gambrel A type of roof formed with two planes on each side of the ridge. The lower pitch is steeper than the upper portion of the roof.

Garden window A 90-degree bay window that extends beyond the exterior wall with a glass front, sides, and roof to allow in additional natural light.

Garrison style A design style that combines saltbox and Georgian styles with the construction methods of log buildings.

General Conditions of the Contract Part of a project manual that specifies the relationship of each party signing the contract and how the contract will be administered.

General contractor The person responsible for working directly with the design professional or property owner to complete a project.

General notes Notes that apply to the overall project.

General sheet notes Notes that provide sheet-specific information or instructions.

Georgian Named for the kings of England, this architectural style follows the classic principles of design of ancient Rome.

Geothermal From the Greek words *geo* (earth) and *thermo* (heat) to describe heat from within the earth.

Geothermal reservoir Naturally occurring, large areas of hydrothermal resources found deep underground.

Geothermal system Heating and cooling systems that use the constant, moderate ground temperature for space heating and cooling; or domestic hot water, by placing a heat exchanger in the ground, or in wells, lakes, rivers, or streams.

Girder A horizontal support beam used at the foundation level to support the floor joists. In a post-and-beam system, a girder supports the floor decking.

Glazing All areas that let in natural light, including windows, clerestories, skylights, glass doors, glass block walls, and glass portions of doors.

Glued-laminated beam (glu-lam) A structural member made up of layers of lumber that are glued together.

Gothic A style of architecture that originated during the medieval period, typically seen in cathedrals, that features pointed arches, ribbed vaults, and flying buttresses (exterior wing walls used to resist the outward thrust of arches).

Gothic Victorian An asymmetrical style of architecture popular in America in the period of 1840–1880.

Grade The designation of the quality of a manufactured piece of lumber.

Grade beam A reinforced concrete beam placed under the soil below the stem wall that spans between stable supports (pilings or stable soil).

Grading Moving soil to change the elevation of land at a construction site.

Grading plan A drawing used to show the finished soil configuration of the building site.

Graphic scale A scale used on drawings that resembles a small ruler with divisions representing increments of measure that can be easily applied to the drawing.

Gravel stop A metal strip used to retain gravel at the edge of built-up roofs.

Gravity Uniform force that affects all structures due to the gravitational force from the Earth.

Gravity load Loads from each building component causing a downward motion.

Gravity system A heating system that allows warm air to rise naturally, without a fan.

Gray water Wastewater from a shower or bath, washing machines, and rain runoff collected from roof gutters for reuse.

Greek Revival A home style with a large, rectangular, and very boxlike shape, including bold, simple lines that reflect classic proportions and decorations of classic Greek architecture

Green board A type of water-resistant gypsum board designed for use in a high-moisture area, such as behind a shower enclosure.

Green Construction Code Published by the ICC, the code mandating certain environmental construction requirements.

Green home A home that uses less energy, water, and natural resources; creates less waste; and is healthier and more comfortable for the occupants.

Green lumber Lumber that has not been kiln-dried and still contains moisture.

Greenhouse effect Atmospheric heating caused by solar radiation being readily transmitted inward through the Earth's atmosphere but long wave radiation less readily transmitted outward, due to absorption by certain gases in the atmosphere.

Greenhouse gases Gases, such as water vapor, methane, carbon dioxide, and ozone, that absorb global radiation and contribute to the greenhouse effect.

Green roof A roof that is covered in plants to reduce building temperatures, filter pollution, and lessen water runoff.

Ground An electrical connection to the Earth by means of a rod.

Ground fault circuit interrupter (GFCI or GFI) A 120-V convenience outlet with a built-in circuit breaker for use within 60" of any water source.

Ground snow load The amount of snow expected in a specific area of a state.

Grout A mixture of cement, sand, and water used to fill joints in masonry and tile construction.

Guardrail A horizontal protective railing used around stairwells, balconies, and changes of floor elevation greater than 30".

Gusset A metal or wood plate used to strengthen the intersection of structural members.

Gutter A device mounted on the eave for the collection of rainwater from the roof to downspouts.

Gypsum board An interior finishing material made of gypsum and fiberglass covered with paper; it is installed in large shapes.

H

Habitable room Areas used for sleeping, living, cooking, or dining.

Half bath *See* Bath, half.

Half-hot receptacle A conventional outlet with one receptacle that is always hot and a second that is connected to a wall switch for controlling the flow of power through the receptacle.

Half-timber A frame construction method that fills spaces between exposed wood members with masonry.

Handrail A railing placed on the open side of a stair to prevent injury.

Hanger A metal support bracket used to attach two structural members.

Hardboard Sheet material formed of compressed wood fibers.

Hard conversions Metric conversions calculated close to or exactly the same as the inch equivalent. A hard conversion of 12" is 25.4 × 12" = 305 mm.

Head The upper portion of a door or window frame.

Header A horizontal structural member used to support other structural members over openings, such as doors and windows.

Header course A horizontal masonry course with the end of each masonry unit exposed.

Headroom The clearance over a stairway measured vertically from the tread nosing to the obstruction.

Hearth Fire-resistant floor extending in front and to the side of the firebox.

Heartwood The inner core of a tree trunk.

Heat loss The speed of heat moving through the building envelope, measured in BTUs per Hour (BTUH).

Heat pump A unit designed to produce forced air for heating and cooling.

Hidden lines Thin lines used in drawings to represent a surface or object that is hidden from view.

Hip A traditional roof shape formed by four or more inserting planes. The term also describes an exterior edge formed by two sloping roof surfaces.

Hip roof A roof shape with four sloping sides.

Hopper window A window that is hinged at the bottom and swings inward.

Horizon line A line drawn parallel to the ground line to represent the intersection of ground and sky.

Horizontal shear (F$_v$) One of three major forces acting on a beam; the tendency of the fibers of a beam to slide past each other in horizontal direction.

Hose bibb A water outlet that is threaded to receive a hose.

Hue A color or shade.

Humidifier A mechanical device that controls the amount of moisture inside of a structure.

Hurricane ties Metal connectors used to connect roof members to wall members to resist uplift.

Hydroelectric power Electricity generated by the conversion of the energy created by falling water.

Hydronic system A method of heating that passes heated liquid through tubes buried in the floor.

Hydrostatic vent A vent placed in the stem wall of structures located in areas prone to flooding; it allows floodwaters into the crawl space to equalize pressure on both sides of the stem wall.

I

I beam The generic term for a wide-flange or American standard steel beam with a cross section in the shape of the letter *I*.

I-joist Engineered joists in the shape of the letter *I*.

Illustration board A durable cardboard material with surfaces suitable for most types of drawing materials.

Illustrator A person with a background in art and architecture who produces drawings showing proposed, realistic structures.

Inclinometer A tool used to measure angles for determining roof pitch or ground slope.

Included angle The angle formed between the center and the endpoints of the arc.

Indirect gain A method of passive solar heating that places a thermal mass between the sun and the interior of the residence.

Indirect lighting Mechanical or artificial lighting that is reflected off a surface.

Infill sites Intercity lots created by dividing established sites into smaller sites than normally required.

Infiltration The flow of air through building intersections.

Informal balance Nonsymmetrical placement achieved by placing shapes of different sizes in various positions around the imaginary centerline.

Insulated concrete form (ICF) An energy-efficient wall framing system made by placing poured concrete in polystyrene forms that are left in place to create a super insulated wall.

Insulated glass Two or more panes of glass with a sealed space between.

Insulation Material used to restrict the flow of heat, cold, or sound from one surface to another.

Intensity The brightness or strength of a specific color.

Interior decorator A person who decorates the interiors of buildings with the aim of making rooms more attractive, comfortable, and functional.

Interior designer A person who works with the structural designer to optimize and harmonize the interior design of structures in regard to how a space will be used, the amount of light required, acoustics, seating, storage, and work areas.

Intermittent bracing Wall reinforcement for braced wall lines placed at specific intervals based on IRC standards.

International Building Code (IBC) A national building code for multifamily, commercial, and other large structures involving public occupancy.

International Residential Code (IRC) A national building code for one- and two-family dwellings.

Interpolation A combination of rounding off and guessing based on known points. If you know that two points have a change of elevation of 12" (25 mm), you can identify a point halfway between these two points and assign it an elevation representing a 6" (13 mm) difference in height.

Inverter Part of a photovoltaic system that monitors the output of the solar modules and transforms DC into AC electricity.

Invitation to Bid A portion of a project manual including a summary of the project's bidding and construction procedures.

Irrigation plan A drawing usually completed by a technician working for landscape architect that shows how landscaping will be maintained.

Island A stand-alone cabinet and counter, normally found in the middle of a U-shaped kitchen.

Isolation joint *See* Expansion joint.

Isometric drawings 3D drawings showing three surfaces of an object in one view.

Italianate-style Symmetrical style homes with large rectangular wood-framed structure emphasizing vertical proportions and elaborate decorations.

J

Jack rafter A rafter cut shorter than the other rafters to allow for an opening in the roof.

Jack stud (cripple) A wall member cut shorter than other studs to allow for an opening, such as a window.

Jalousie window A type of window made of thin horizontal panels that can be rotated between the open and closed position.

Jamb The vertical members of a door or window frame.

Joist A horizontal structural member used in repetitive patterns to support floor and ceiling loads.

Junction box Also known as a *J-box,* it protects electrical wiring splices in conductors or joints in runs and provides a mounting surface for switches and fixtures.

K

Key A concrete member on the bottom side of the foundation that keeps the foundation from sliding across the soil.

Keynotes Notes identifying objects in a drawing and showing how those objects relate to specific sections in the written specifications.

Keyway An indentation made in the topside of the foundation. A key in the stem wall fits into the foundation keyway to keep the stem wall from sliding across the footing.

Kick block (kicker) A block used to keep the bottom of the stringer from sliding on the floor when downward pressure is applied to the stringer.

Kiln dried Lumber dried in a kiln or oven. Kiln-dried lumber has a lower moisture content than air-dried lumber.

King stud A full-length stud placed at the end of a header and beside the trimmer stud supporting the header.

Kip Used in some engineering formulas to represent 1000 lbs.

Knee wall A wall of less than full height.

Knot A branch or limb of a tree that is cut through in the process of manufacturing lumber.

L

Lag screw A screw used for wood-to-wood or wood-to-steel connections.

Lally column A vertical steel column used to support floor or foundation loads.

Laminated Several layers of material glued together under pressure.

Laminated strand lumber (LSL) Structural members created by assembling small sections of wood into larger members.

Laminated veneer lumber (LVL) Structural members created by stacking thin veneers of wood peeled from a log and cutting them into lumber-sized members.

Landing A platform between two flights of stairs.

Landscape plan A drawing showing the location, type, size, and quantity of all vegetation required for a project as well as hard scaping, such as patios, walkways, fountains, pools, sports courts, and other landscaping features.

Latent heat gain Moisture added to the air inside the building envelope that evaporates from the occupants' skin as well as the moisture from their breath.

Lateral Sideways motion in a structure caused by wind or seismic forces. It is also the pipe that connects the construction site to the public sewer pipe.

Lateral force (load) A load resulting from wind or earthquakes that pushes a structure sideways.

Lath Wood or sheet metal strips attached to the structural frame to support plaster.

Latitude The angular distance between an imaginary line around the earth parallel to and including the equator.

Lattice A grille made by crisscrossing strips of material.

Lavatory A bathroom sink or a room that is equipped with a washbasin.

Leach lines Waste drain lines placed in an absorbent soil to disperse liquid material from a septic system.

Leader line A line connecting a note to a feature in a drawing.

Ledger A horizontal 2× member attached to the side of wall members to provide support for rafters or joists.

LEED (Leadership in Energy and Environment Design) A certification system developed by U.S. Green Building Council to help improve the quality of buildings and to minimize their impact on the environment.

Legal description The description of a parcel of land for legal purposes, such as the recording of a deed of ownership.

Legends A type of drawing used to explain symbols on a specific drawing project.

Let-in brace A diagonal member (typically a 1 × 4) placed in a notch in the wall studs to keep them vertical.

Linear foot A straight-line measurement of length expressed in feet.

Lintel A horizontal steel member used to provide support for masonry over an opening.

Lintel block A long rectangular stone block that spans a door or window opening to support the weight of the structure above the opening.

Lisp A programming language used to customize CADD software.

Live load The load from all movable objects within a structure including loads from furniture and people. External loads from snow and wind are also considered live loads.

Living area The living, dining, and family rooms, den, and breakfast nook.

Load-bearing wall A support wall that holds floor or roof loads in addition to its own weight.

Load path The route used to transfer the roof loads into the walls, then into the floor, and then to the foundation.

Local notes Drawing notes that refer to a specific material or area of a project.

Longitude Imaginary lines on a map, also called *meridians,* which run north and south.

Longitudinal section A section produced by a cutting plane that is parallel to the long axis of the structure and perpendicular to most structural materials used to frame the roof, ceiling, and floor systems.

Lookout Bracing between the wall and sub-fascia or end cap to which the soffit is attached. Also a beam used to support eave loads.

Loose-fill insulation Fibers or granules used for insulation made from cellulose, fiberglass, rock wool, cotton, or other materials and blown into position.

Lot and block A system of describing land, including individual site and blocks within incorporated cities.

Louver An opening with horizontal slats for ventilation.

Low-e glass Low-emission glass with transparent coating on its surface acting as a thermal mirror.

Lux The metric equivalent of a foot-candle—the amount of light a candle casts on an object 12" (300 mm) away.

M

Magnetic declination The difference between true north and magnetic north.

Magnetic north The point on a compass that the needle points to as north.

Main The water supply line extending from the water meter into the home to deliver potable water.

Major group code A four-character code that identifies a building component specific to the defined layer.

Manifold A distribution center between the main, branch, and riser lines.

Mansard A four-sided, steep-sloped roof used to enclose the upper level of a structure.

Mantel A decorative shelf above the opening of a fireplace.

Manual drafting Traditional pencil or ink drafting.

Market value The amount for which property can be sold.

Masonry The use of brick, stone, or concrete blocks to construct a wall.

Masonry veneer Construction using a thin layer of stone or brick on a wood-framed structure.

Mass wall An above-grade wall, according to the IRC, made of brick (excluding brick veneer), concrete, concrete block, earth (compressed earth blocks and rammed earth) insulated concrete form (ICF), masonry cavity, and solid timber/logs.

MasterFormat A list of numbers and titles for organizing information into a standard sequence relating to construction requirements, products, and activities.

Master switch An electrical switch used to override all other circuits in a structure from one location.

Mechanical engineer A licensed professional responsible for the sizing and layout of heating, ventilation, and air-conditioning (HVAC) systems and other plans for routing treated air throughout the project.

Mediterranean A home style featuring low-pitched gable roofs covered with colored roof tiles and walls covered in stucco finishes.

Meridians Imaginary lines on a map, also called *longitude,* which run north and south.

Mesh A metal reinforcing material placed in concrete slabs and masonry walls to help resist cracking.

Metal tie A manufactured piece of metal for joining two structural members.

Metal wall ties Corrugated metal strips used to bond brick veneer to its support wall.

Meter A device for measuring the use of electricity or water.

Metes Property measurements expressed in feet, yards, rods, or surveyor's chains.

Metes-and-bounds A legal description of a parcel of land by its metes (measurements) and bounds (bearings).

Metric measurement hard conversions Made by using a mathematical formula to change a value of one system (e.g., 1") to the equivalent value in another system (e.g., 25.4 mm). A 6" distance would be 152 mm (6 × 25.4).

Metric measurement soft conversions Conversions made using a mathematical formula to change a value from one system (e.g., 1") to a rounded value in another system (e.g., 25 mm). A 6" distance is 150 mm.

Metric scale A tool used to measure distance, with the millimeter used as the basic unit of measurement.

Millwork Finished woodwork manufactured in a milling plant, including window and door frames, mantels, moldings, and stairway components.

Mineral wool An insulating material made of fibrous foam.

Minor group code A four-letter code used to define subgroups to the major group.

Modular cabinet Prefabricated cabinets constructed in specific sizes called modules, usually available in 3" (75 mm) widths.

Modular home An engineered method of constructing a home or building components, usually inside in a temperature controlled environment, in an efficient and cost-effective manner.

Module A standardized unit of measurement.

Modulus of elasticity (E) The degree of stiffness of a beam.

Moisture barrier A material used to restrict moisture vapor from penetrating a structure.

Molding Decorative strips, usually wood, used to conceal the seam in other finishing materials.

Moment The tendency of a force to rotate around a certain point.

Monolithic Concrete foundation construction with the footing and slab or the footing and stem wall created in one pour.

Monument A point established by the U.S. Geological Society (USGS) that is marked by a steel rod or a benchmark, it is the true point of beginning in a metes-and-bounds legal description.

Mortar A combination of cement, sand, and water used to bond masonry units.

Motion-detection switch An electrical control that emits an electrical beam, that when reflected back to the switch from a person or animal allows electricity to flow through the switch and light fixtures.

Moving loads Loads that are not stationary, such as those produced by automobiles and construction equipment.

Mudroom A room or utility entrance for removing soiled clothing or shoes before entering the main portion of the residence.

Mudsill (base plate) The horizontal wood member that rests on concrete to support other wood members.

Mullion A horizontal or vertical divider between sections of a window.

Muntin A horizontal or vertical divider within a section of a window.

N

Nailer A wood member bolted to concrete or steel members to provide a nailing surface for attaching other wood members.

National CAD standard CAD guidelines established by the National Institute of Building Sciences to ensure uniform drawings.

National Council of Building Designers Certification A professional group that provides third-party testing, accreditation, and certification of AIBD design professionals.

National Council for Interior Design Qualification (NCIDQ) The board that regulates the standards for becoming a professional interior designer.

National Kitchen & Bath Association (NKBA) An organization created to ensure quality among kitchen and bath designers.

Natural grade Soil in its unaltered state.

Neoclassical Buildings inspired by the classical architecture of ancient Greece and Rome, containing some of the main features.

Nested joists The practice of placing a steel joist around another joist to double the strength of the joist.

Net size Final size of wood after planing.

Net-zero energy A home that generates as much or more energy as the occupants consume through the course of a year.

Neutral axis The axis formed where the forces of compression and tension in a beam reach equilibrium.

Newel The end post of a stair railing.

Nominal size An approximate size achieved by rounding the actual material size to the nearest larger whole number.

Non-bearing wall A wall that supports no loads other than its own.

Nonferrous metal Metal, such as copper or brass, that contains no iron.

Non-habitable room Areas including closets, pantries, bath or toilet rooms, hallways, utility rooms, storage spaces, garages, darkrooms, and other similar spaces.

Nosing The rounded front edge of a tread that extends past the riser.

O

Object lines Continuous lines used to describe the shape of an object or to show changes in the distance from the surface of an object to the viewing plane.

Obscure glass Glass that is not transparent.

On center (o.c.) A measurement taken from the center of one member to the center of another member.

One-pipe heating system A heating system that circulates heated water through a continuous pipe loop.

One-point perspective A drawing method where all lines that would have been horizontal in an elevation merge at a single vanishing point on the horizon line.

Oriel window A window placed in a projection of an exterior wall that does not extend all the way to the foundation. In plan view, the wall projection may be rectangular, polygonal, or curved. *See also* Bay window.

Orientation The locating of a structure on a property based on the sun's location, prevailing winds, view, and noise.

Oriented strand board (OSB) Typically used in place of plywood, it is typically a 4 × 8' sheet of material made of layers of wood chips laminated together with glue under extreme pressure.

Orthographic projection The projection of the features of an object onto an imaginary plane called a plane of projection; the projection of the features of the object is made by lines of sight that are perpendicular to the plane of projection.

Outlet The location in the circuit where electrical devices are connected.

Outrigger A support for roof sheathing and the fascia that extends past the wall line perpendicular to the rafters.

Overhang The horizontal measurement of the distance the roof projects from a wall.

P

Palladian window A large window, divided into three parts typical of classical architectural styles, such as Georgian and Federal. The arched center section is larger than the two rectangular side sections. A typical location for a Palladian window is above the front door.

Parapet wall A portion of wall that extends above the edge of the roof.

Parallel strand lumber Engineered wood products laminated from veneer strips peeled from the outer layers of trees.

Parametric A feature of some CAD programs that allows information to be displayed in 2D or 3D such as stairs, to be represented on the floor plan, but also allow the drawings to be used to create stair sections.

Parging A thin coat of plaster used to smooth a masonry surface.

Parquet flooring Wood flooring arranged in patterns.

Partial section A section used to show construction materials that are not seen in other sections.

Partition An interior wall.

Party wall A wall dividing two adjoining spaces such as apartments or offices.

Passive solar system System that uses natural architectural means to store and radiate solar heat without the use of mechanical or electronic devices.

Patio A ground-level exterior entertainment area made of concrete, stone, brick, or treated wood.

Pediment A low-pitched triangular gable based on the Greek Revival style of architecture; it is placed over a door or window or on the front of a building.

Peninsula A kitchen arrangement that provides cabinets and workspace by adding one additional leg to an L-shaped or U-shaped kitchen.

Penny The length of a nail represented by the lowercase letter *d*; "10d" is read as "ten penny."

Percolation test A test used to determine whether the soil can accommodate a septic system.

Permit plans Plans required by a government agency for permission to build a structure.

Perspective A drawing method that provides the illusion of depth by the use of vanishing points.

Phantom lines Lines used to show motion or to show an alternative position of a moving part.

Photoelectric switch An electrical switch that allows the circuit to be regulated based on a specific amount of natural light.

Photovoltaic A field of technology and research related to the application of solar cells for energy by converting sunlight directly into electricity.

Pictorial drawing A drawing that shows an object in a three-dimensional format.

Picture plane The theoretical plane that a surface of an object is projected onto for viewing.

Picture window A large, rectangular, fixed panel of glass.

Pier A concrete or masonry foundation support.

Pilaster A reinforcing column built into or against a masonry wall.

Piling A vertical foundation support driven into the ground to provide support on stable soil or rock.

Pitch A description of roof angle comparing the vertical rise to the horizontal run.

Plank Lumber that is 1 1/2" to 2 1/2" thick.

Planned unit development A flexible approach to land development that can include residential areas, recreational areas, open spaces, schools, libraries, churches, or convenient shopping facilities within the development.

Plaster A mix of sand, cement, and water used to cover walls and ceilings.

Plat A map of an area of land showing the boundaries of individual lots.

Plate Horizontal pieces of wood used at the top and bottom of a wall to keep the studs in position.

Platform framing (western platform) A building construction method where each floor acts as a platform in the framing.

Plenum An enclosed air space for transporting air from the HVAC system. The air pressure in the plenum is greater than the pressure in the structure, causing air to flow from the furnace through the plenum and into the residence.

Plot A parcel of land. Also used to refer to the process of making a paper copy of a CAD drawing.

Plumb True vertical.

Plumbing fixture A unit used to supply and contain water, and discharge waste such as sinks, lavatories, showers, tubs, and water closets.

Plumbing system The system that provides all the piping and fixtures for fresh and wastewater distribution.

Plumbing wall A wall larger than normal-sized walls surrounding vent and waste pipes.

Plywood Wood composed of three or more layers bonded with glue, with the grain of each layer placed at 90° to the next.

Pocket door A door that slides into a pocket built into the wall.

Point of beginning Fixed location on a plot of land where the survey begins.

Polyester film Also known as *Mylar,* it is often used in presentation drawings due to its durability and the ease of correcting errors.

Porch A roofed entrance to a structure that is open to the air and supported on one side by the structure with the remaining sides supported by columns or arches.

Portal frame (PF) A method of reinforcing a braced wall line that uses two panels with a minimum width of 22 1/2" (570 mm). The panels are connected by a header to resist lateral loads.

Porte cochere A roofed area covering a driveway at the entrance to a structure that is large enough for vehicles to pass through and provides shelter while entering or leaving a vehicle.

Portico A roofed area leading to the structure's main entrance. It is open to the air on one or more sides and is supported on one side by the structure and on the others by columns or arches. Porticos are common on Federal, Early Classical Revival, and Greek Revival homes.

Portland cement A hydraulic cement made of silica, lime, and aluminum, it is the most common cement used in the construction industry due to its strength.

Post A vertical wood structural member usually 4" × 4" or larger.

Post-and-beam A framing method that places larger framing members at greater distances from each other than other traditional framing methods.

Post-tensioning A process of reinforcing concrete slabs that are poured over unstable soil using reinforcement placed in tension.

Potable Water that is free of impurities and suitable for drinking.

Power-driven studs Smooth bolt-like fasteners driven by a powder-actuated fastening tool to attach wood members to concrete or steel members.

Prairie-style Houses that were popular in the Midwest between 1900 and 1920, are recognizable for their low horizontal lines, one-story projections, low-pitched hipped roofs, and large overhanging eaves designed to blend the home into the landscape.

Precast A concrete component that has been cast in a location other than where it will be used.

Prefabricated units Buildings or components that are built away from the jobsite and transported there, ready to be used.

Preliminary drawings Drawings made from bubble drawings used to plan basic design concepts of a structure; such drawings comprise the site, the floor, the front elevation, and a typical cross section.

Presentation drawing Drawings used to convey basic design concepts.

Prestressed concrete A concrete component placed in compression as it is cast to help resist deflection.

Prevailing winds Winds identified by the direction from which they most frequently blow in a given area of the country.

Profile Vertical section of the surface of the ground and/or of underlying earth that is taken along any desired fixed line.

Project manual A manual designed to supplement the working drawings containing written documents and specifications related to a specific construction project.

Proportion A pleasing relationship in both size and balance. Rectangles using the proportions 2:3, 3:5, and 5:8 have long been considered pleasing.

Punch out A hole in the web of a steel framing member allowing for the installation of plumbing, electrical, and other trade components.

Purlin A horizontal roof member laid perpendicular to rafters to help limit deflection.

Purlin brace A support member that extends from the purlin down to a load-bearing wall or header.

Pyramidal roof A hipped roof that lacks a ridge. The four isosceles-triangular planes of the roof meet at a common apex resembling a pyramid. Low-slope pyramidal roofs are common on Greek Revival houses.

Q

Quad A courtyard surrounded by the walls of buildings.

Quarry tile An unglazed, machine-made tile.

Quarter round Wood molding that has the profile of one-quarter of a circle.

Quatrefoil window A round window common in Moorish, Gothic, and Mission style architecture. The window is composed of four equal lobes, like a four-petaled flower.

Queen Anne Victorian Named after the eighteenth-century English queen, this style of architecture is characterized by elaborate bric-a-brac, a complicated roofline, expansive porches that wrap around the front and side of the house, and usually a round tower, turret, or large round bay window.

Quoins Heavy blocks of stone, originally designed to reinforce masonry wall at the corners of a brick building. They are often found on Georgian and some Federal and Greek Revival houses. In newer construction, the quoins of a brick house usually consist of granite blocks, but may also be formed from bricks and painted in the trim color. Wood quoins are made to imitate stone and are strictly ornamental features.

R

Rabbet A rectangular groove cut on the edge of a board.

Radiant barrier Material made of aluminum foil with backing used to stop heat from radiating through an attic.

Radiant heat Heat emitted from a particular material such as brick, electric coils, or a hot water pipe without use of air movement.

Radius The distance from the center of an arc or circle to the circumference.

Radius windows A fixed window made in the shape of a half-round arc.

Radon A naturally occurring radioactive gas; usually found in a basement, it breaks down into carcinogenic compounds when it is inhaled over a long period of time.

Rafter The inclined structural member of a roof system designed to support roof loads.

Rafter/ceiling joist An inclined structural member that supports both the ceiling and the roof materials.

Rafter, common A rafter that extends the full length between the support wall and the ridge board.

Rafter, hip A rafter placed at the intersection of two roof planes that forms a sloping ridge (an exterior roof corner).

Rafter, jack A rafter that spans from the supporting wall to a hip or valley rafter so that the jack rafter is not the full length of a common rafter.

Rafter, valley A rafter placed at the intersection of two roof planes that forms an interior roof intersection.

Rake A roof extension projecting over an end wall that follows the slope of the roof.

Rake joint A recessed mortar joint.

Ranch style A popular home from the Southwest defined by a one-story, rambling layout.

Reaction The upward forces acting at the supports of a beam.

Rebar Reinforcing steel used to strengthen concrete.

Receptacle The device in the outlet box where the electrical component is actually attached.

Reference bubble A symbol used to designate the origins of details and sections.

Register An opening in a duct for the supply of heated or cooled air.

Reinforced concrete Concrete with steel rebar inside it to resist tension.

Reinforcing Steel used to strengthen concrete; also called *rebar*.

Relative humidity The amount of water vapor in the atmosphere compared to the maximum possible amount at the same temperature.

Remodel A construction project that involves moving, adding, or removing structural members.

Rendering An artistic process applied to a drawing or a drawing created using the perspective layout method.

Renovation The altering or removal and replacement of nonstructural materials such as cabinets as well as the making of minor electrical or mechanical repairs.

Retaining wall A wall, usually made of masonry, designed to resist soil loads.

Review boards Committees made up of residents who determine what may or may not be built in a neighborhood

R-factor A unit of thermal resistance applied to the insulating value of a specific building material.

Rheostat An electrical control device or dimmer switch used to regulate the current reaching a light fixture.

Rhythm A principle of design related to the repetitive elements that provide order and uniformity.

Ribbon A structural wood member framed into studs to support joists or rafters.

Ridge The uppermost area of two intersecting roof planes.

Ridge beam A beam located at the ridge used to support the roof framing members or a beam used as a decorative member at an interior ridge.

Ridge blocks Blocks that are placed between trusses at the ridge to maintain a uniform spacing and provide a nailing surface for the roof sheathing.

Ridge board The horizontal member at the ridge that runs perpendicular to the rafters. The rafters are aligned against the ridge to resist the downward force of the rafters.

Ridge brace A support member used to transfer the weight from the ridge board to a bearing wall or beam. The brace is typically spaced at 48" o.c. and may not exceed a 45° angle from vertical.

Rim joist Sometimes referred to as a *band* or *header,* this joist at the perimeter of a structure runs parallel to the other floor joist.

Rim track A metal track installed over the ends of steel floor joists to support the ends and close off the space between them.

Rise The amount of vertical distance between one tread and another or the angle of the roof based on 12 horizontal units.

Riser The vertical member of stairs between the treads or a water supply pipe that extends vertically one or more stories to carry water to fixtures.

Rod A unit of measurement for land surveys equal to 16.5' (4950 mm); also used to describe a favorite of all fishermen.

Roll roofing Roofing material of fiber or asphalt shipped in rolls.

Roof drain A receptacle for removal of roof water.

Roof framing plan A plan created to shows the size and direction of the construction members required to frame the roof.

Roof plan A drawing created to show the shape of the roof—the equivalent to the top view of the structure.

Rough floor The subfloor, usually plywood, that serves as a base for the finished floor.

Rough-in To add framing for a feature such as a door or window that will be installed at a future date. The opening is covered with the finish materials until the door or window is needed. The term is also used to describe the HVAC, plumbing, or electrical work that is done in the joist or stud space prior to adding the finish material.

Rough lumber Lumber that has not been surfaced but has been trimmed on all four sides.

Rough opening The unfinished opening provided between framing members to allow for the placement of doors, windows, or skylights.

Rowlock A pattern for laying masonry units so that the ends of the units are exposed.

Run The horizontal distance of a set of steps or the measurement describing the depth of one step. Also used to describe the horizontal measurement from the outside edge of the wall to the centerline of the ridge.

R-value Measurement of thermal resistance used to indicate the effectiveness of insulation.

S

Saddle A small gable-shaped roof used to divert water from behind a chimney.

Saltbox A home style that maintains the symmetry of the Georgian style excluding much of the detailing.

Sanitary sewer A sewer line that carries sewage without any storm, surface, or groundwater.

Sash An individual frame around a window.

Sawn lumber Lumber that has been cut from logs without being altered by engineering.

Scab A short member that overlaps the butt joint of two other members used to fasten those members.

Scale A ratio that is used to reduce or enlarge the size of a drawing for plotting. *Scale* is also used to refer to a measuring tool.

Schedule A written list of similar components such as windows and doors.

Sconce A wall-mounted light fixture that provides indirect lighting by directing light either up or down, depending on the shape of the sconce.

Scratch coat The first coat of stucco that is scratched to provide a good bonding surface for the second coat.

Seasoning The process of removing moisture from green lumber by either air (natural) or kiln drying.

Second Empire A type of Victorian style home inspired by French architecture featuring high mansard roofs covered with patterned slate shingles.

Section A type of drawing showing an object as if it had been cut through to show interior construction. In mapping, this is an area of land that is one mile square; 36 sections comprise a township.

Section lines A pattern placed in an object to indicate the portion of the object cut by the cutting plane.

Seismic design zone One of seven categories of the IBC defining the risk of seismic damage including zones A (least risk) B, C, D_0, D_1, D_2, and E (highest risk of damage).

Seismic loads (forces) Loads affecting a structure resulting from earthquake-related forces.

Self-drilling screws A fastener with a drilling point that is able to penetrate heavy-gauge metal.

Sensible heat gain The heat gain of a structure associated with the temperature of the outside air that leaks in due to infiltration and water that evaporates from the occupants' skin.

Septic system A sewage disposal system consisting of a storage tank and an absorption field. Sewage is stored in the septic tank and the liquid waste is dispersed into the drainage field.

Septic tank A tank in which sewage is decomposed by bacteria and dispersed by drain tiles.

Series-loop system A heating system that uses a continuous loop of pipes containing hot water.

Service area A major area of a residence, such as the baths, kitchen, utility rooms, and the garage.

Service connection The wires that run to a structure from a power pole or transformer.

Service entry A means of entry into a home that links the garage, kitchen, utility room, bathrooms, and patios or decks.

Setback The minimum distance required between the structure and the property line.

Shake A hand-split wooden roof shingle.

Shear The stress that occurs when two forces from opposite directions act on the same member. Shearing stress tends to cut a member just as scissors cut paper.

Shear panel A wall panel designed by an engineer to resist wind or seismic forces.

Shear wall A wall designed by a design professional to resist specific lateral loads caused by wind or seismic forces.

Sheathing A thin covering that is usually made of OSB or plywood with a thickness of between 3/8" and 3/4" (9.5 and 19 mm); it is placed over walls, floors, and roofs to serve as a backing for the finish materials.

Shim A piece of material used to fill a space between two surfaces.

Shiplap A siding pattern of overlapping rabbeted edges.

Sidelight A window or a series of small fixed panes arranged vertically and found on either side of the main entry door of many Federal and Greek Revival style homes.

Sill A horizontal wood member placed at the bottom of walls and openings in walls.

Simple beam Beam with a uniform load evenly distributed over its entire length and supported at each end.

Single hung window A type of window with a fixed upper half and a lower half that slides up and down.

Single-ply roof A method of protecting low-sloped roofs that is applied as a thin liquid or sheet.

Single-pole switch An electrical switch used to control one or more fixtures from one location.

Single-wall construction A construction method used in temperate climates that places the exterior finishing material directly over a water-resistant membrane and the wall studs.

Site orientation Placement of a structure on a property with certain environmental and physical factors taken into consideration.

Site plan A part of the working drawings for a structure that is used to describe property for the building site.

Sketching Freehand drawing created without the aid of drafting equipment.

Sketch paper A thin, inexpensive paper often used for the initial layout stages of presentation.

Skip sheathing Material such as 1 × 4s (25 × 100s) that are laid perpendicular to the rafters to support roofing such as wood shingles and concrete or clay tiles.

Skylight An opening in the roof to allow light and ventilation, usually covered with glass or plastic.

Sky window An opening in the wall and roof that combines features of a skylight and a window using glazing on a wall that extends to meet glazing on a portion of the roof.

Slab A concrete floor system typically poured at ground level or supported on a wood or steel ribbed decking.

Slab-on-grade A concrete floor system poured at grade level.

Slate shingles Roof shingles made from ancient metamorphic rock.

Sleepers Strips of wood placed over a concrete slab for attaching other wood members.

Smoke chamber The portion of the chimney located directly over the firebox that acts as a funnel between the firebox and the chimney.

Smoke shelf A shelf located at the bottom of the smoke chamber to prevent down-drafts from the chimney from entering the firebox.

Soffit A lowered ceiling, typically found in kitchens, halls, and bathrooms to allow for recessed lighting or HVAC ducts. The term is also used to describe an enclosed area below the overhangs to protect the rafter or truss tails from the elements.

Soft conversion The preferred metric conversions for construction drawings rounds off dimensions to convenient metric modules. Twelve inches equal 300 mm using soft conversions (12" × 25 mm = 300 mm).

Softwood Wood that comes from cone-bearing trees.

Soil line Disposal lines in the wastewater system.

Soil pipe A pipe that carries the discharge of water closets or other similar fixtures.

Soil stack The main vertical wastewater pipe.

Soil vent A vent that runs up a wall and vents out the roof, allowing vapor to escape and ventilate the system.

Solar access The availability of direct sunlight to a structure or construction site.

Solar collectors Assemblies that catch sunlight and convert it to energy.

Solar gain The increase in temperature in a building that results from solar radiation.

Solar heat Heat that comes from energy generated from sunlight.

Solar heat gain Heat generated by the sun that is transmitted through the fenestration and energy that is absorbed radiation.

Solar heat gain coefficient Represented by the letters SHGC, it is a ratio of the solar heat gain entering the space inside the envelope through the fenestration to the incident solar radiation.

Solarium Glassed-in porch on the south side of a house that is directly exposed to the sun's rays.

Solar orientation Orientating the glazing of home so that it can take advantage of heat gain.

Solar panel Solar cells that convert sunlight into electricity.

Solar reflectance The measure of the amount of sunlight that a surface reflects.

Soldier A masonry unit laid on end with its narrow surface exposed.

Sole plate The plate placed at the bottom of a wall.

Solid sheathing Usually OSB or plywood used to cover large areas for roof, walls, or floors.

Sound deadening board Specially designed drywall composed of gypsum, elastic polymers, and sound isolation layers used to absorb mechanical and plumbing sounds near living and sleeping areas.

Spackle The covering of sheetrock joints with joint compound.

Span The horizontal distance between two supporting members.

Spark arrester A screen placed at the top of the flue to prevent combustibles from leaving the flue.

Specification writer A person who provides written specifications to supplement the working drawings regarding the quality of materials to be used and labor to be supplied.

Specifications A written statement that describes the characteristics of a particular aspect of a project, such as a description of materials or equipment, construction systems, standards, and workmanship.

Specifications, cash allowance A type of specification that is used when the information regarding quality or quantity has not been determined.

Specifications, descriptive The most detailed type of specification, it is used when the architect assumes total responsibility for the performance of a system

Specifications, performance Specifications that define the desired results of a product or system.

Specifications, proprietary Specifications that call for materials by their trade name and model name.

Specifications, reference Specifications that list a minimum standard for quality or performance established by recognized testing authorities.

Spiral stairs Typically premanufactured, spiral stairs have treads with non-parallel edges that are formed around a center support.

Splice Two similar members joined together in a straight line, usually by nailing or bolting.

Split-level A house that has two levels, one about half a level above the other.

Spot grade A contour elevation determined by a survey team of a specific location at the jobsite.

Spread footing A foundation composed of a continuous concrete footing to support a stem wall typically made of poured concrete, concrete blocks, ICF, EPS, or treated wood.

Square An area of roofing covering 100 sq ft.

Square foot An area that is 12" wide × 12" deep.

Stack Vertical drain lines that carry waste from the home to the sewer main.

Stack line The vertical drain line that carries waste from the home to the sewer main.

Stair jack *See* Stringer.

Stairwell The opening in the floor where a stair will be framed.

Standpipe The plumbing system that fire hoses connect to. It is a dry system until a fire truck connects to it and pumps water through the system for fire suppression.

Station point The position of the observer's eye in a perspective drawing.

Stations Numbers given to the horizontal lines of a grid survey.

Status code An optional single-character code used to define the status of either a major or minor layer group.

Steam heating system A heating system that uses a boiler to make steam that is transported through pipes to radiators and baseboard heaters, producing heat through convection.

Stick framing Framing one member at a time on the jobsite instead of raising prefabricated units.

Stiffener plate A flat piece of plywood, OSB, or steel used to reinforce the intersection of two structural members.

Stile A vertical member of a cabinet, door, or decorative panel.

Stirrup A U-shaped metal bracket used to support wood beams.

Stock Common sizes of building materials.

Stock plans Houses with several different options designed to appeal to a wide variety of people.

Stop A wooden strip used to hold a window in place.

Storm sewer A municipal drainage system used to dispose of groundwater, rainwater, surface water, or other nonpolluting waste separately from sewage.

Stress A live or dead load acting on a structural member. Stress results as the fibers of a beam resist an external force.

Stressed-skin panel A hollow built-up member typically used as a beam.

Stretcher A course of masonry laid horizontally with the end of the unit exposed.

Stringer (stair jack) The inclined support member of a stair that supports the risers and treads.

Strong back A beam used to support ridge and ceiling loads. It is placed above the ceiling joists when perpendicular to the joists and between the joists when it is parallel to the joists.

Structural insulated panels (SIPs) A method of energy-efficient construction using panels composed of a continuous core of rigid foam insulation laminated between two layers of structural board.

Structural masonry Also referred to as *reinforced masonry*, it is normally a blend of materials manufactured at high temperatures and generally with higher compressive strength than concrete block or poured concrete.

Stub walls Short walls that do not go all the way across the room.

Stucco A type of plaster made from Portland cement, sand, water, and a coloring agent that is applied to exterior walls.

Stud The vertical repetitive framing members of a wall that are usually 2 × 4 (50 × 100) or 2 × 6 (50 × 150) in size.

Subdivision Also called a *plat*, it is an area of land divided into individual lots for development.

Subfloor The flooring surface placed on top of the floor joists to serve as a base layer for the finished floor.

Subsill A sill located between the trimmers and bottom side of a window opening. It provides a nailing surface for interior and exterior materials.

Sump A recessed area in a basement floor that collects water so that it can be removed by a pump.

Sun tunnel A skylight that delivers light into a room using a reflective, flexible tunnel to connect the roof opening with an opening in the ceiling. A diffuser is mounted at the ceiling end of the tunnel to disperse the light.

Supplementary conditions Special conditions listed in a project manual that are used to address the elements that are special to a specific project that do not fit into other sections of the contract.

Surfaced lumber Lumber that has been smoothed on at least one side.

Survey map Map of a property showing its size, boundaries, and topography.

Sustainable roof A roof system that includes the five E's of design including energy, environment, endurance, economics, and engineering.

Swale A recessed area formed in the ground to divert ground water away from a structure.

Symmetry Objects that are in perfect balance matching in shape on both sides of a centerline.

T

Tamp To compact soil or concrete.

Template drawing A base drawing that contains standard components, values, and settings that are used for most drawings.

Temporary load Loads that must be supported for a limited time.

Tensile strength The resistance of a material or beam to the tendency to stretch.

Tension Forces that cause a material to stretch or pull apart.

Termite shield A strip of sheet metal used at the intersection of concrete and wood surfaces near ground level to prevent termites from entering the wood.

Terra cotta Hard-baked clay typically used as a liner for chimneys.

Terrain The shape and character of a given stretch of land.

Thermal break Material used to prevent or reduce the direct transmission of heat or cold between two surfaces.

Thermal conductivity The rate of heat flow through 1 sq ft (0.0929 m^2) of homogeneous material 1" (25 mm) thick with a temperature difference of 1°F (217.2°C) between the opposite sides of the material.

Thermal conductor A material suitable for transmitting heat.

Thermal emittance A measurement that describes how efficiently a surface cools itself by emitting thermal radiation.

Thermal mass Material in a home that absorbs heat from the sun and later radiates the heat back into the air.

Thermal resistance Represented by the letter R, resistance measures the ability of a material to resist the flow of heat.

Thermal storage walls Walls constructed of any good heat-absorbing material such as concrete, masonry, or water-filled cylinders.

Thermostat A mechanical device for controlling the output of HVAC units.

Three-way switches Electrical switches that are named from the number of wires required for the circuit to work; they are used in pairs to control one or more fixtures from two locations.

Threshold The beveled member directly under a door.

Throat The narrow opening to the chimney just above the firebox where the damper is placed.

Timber Lumber with a cross-sectional size of 4×6 (100×150 mm) or larger.

Title block An area of a drawing that contains information about the originator, the client, and the sheet number and contents.

Toenail Nails driven into a member at an angle.

Toggle bolt A bolt with a nut that expands so it can't be removed once it is inserted through a hole.

Ton With regard to air conditioning, one ton is 12,000 BTUH and is derived from the number of BTUs absorbed by a ton of ice melting in 24 hours.

Tongue-and-groove A joint where the edge of one member fits into a groove in the next member.

Top chord The upper member of a truss that supports the roof sheathing and the finished roofing.

Topographical survey The measurement of a property that provides the contour of the land surface, with the grades measured in relation to sea level.

Topography Physical description of land surface showing its variation in elevation and location of features such as rivers, lakes, or towns.

Top plate A horizontal structural member located on top of the studs used to hold the wall together.

Top-venting fireplace A fireplace that requires a vent through the top of the assembly.

Township A six-square-mile parcel of land referenced to a baseline or meridian.

Track A U-shaped member used for applications such as top and bottom track for walls and rim track for floor joists.

Traffic flow The route people follow as they move from one area of a residence to another, using hallways or portions of a room.

Transformer An electrical device that either raises or lowers the voltage of electricity.

Transom window A shallow window located immediately above a door. Originally the term was used to denote a horizontal crossbar in a window and later came to mean a window positioned above such a crossbar.

Transverse section A section produced by a cutting plane parallel to the short axis of the structure, often referred to as a cross section.

Trap A U-shaped vented fitting below plumbing fixtures that provides a liquid seal to prevent the emission of sewer gases without affecting the flow of sewage or wastewater.

Tray ceiling A ceiling constructed with sides angling at approximately 45° or curving to a higher flat ceiling so that it resembles an inverted tray.

Tread The horizontal member of a stair on which the foot is placed.

Tributary width The accumulation of loads directed to a structural member. It is always half the distance between the beam to be designed and the next bearing point.

Trimmer A stud of less than full height that is used to support a header. The term is also used to describe a joist or rafters used to frame an opening in a floor, ceiling, or roof.

Trombe wall A wall that uses dense materials such as masonry or water containers to store heat.

True north Geographic north or the North Pole.

True point of beginning The known starting point in a legal description.

Truss A prefabricated or job-built construction member formed of triangular shapes used to support a roof or floor loads over long spans.

Truss, cantilevered A truss used where one must extend past its support to align with other roof members.

Truss clip A clip used to tie the roof framing members to the wall. *See also* Hurricane ties.

Truss, girder A truss used to hold trusses that are perpendicular to the girder truss.

Truss, header Similar to the function of a girder truss, it has a flat top used to support stub trusses.

Truss, hip A truss with a top chord that is parallel to the floor and is used to form a hip roof. Each succeeding truss increases in height until the full height of the roof is achieved and standard trusses can be used.

Truss, mono A single pitched truss used to form shed or to form the outer edges of a hip roof.

Truss, stub A truss that does not extend the full length of other trusses because there will be an opening in the roof or because the roof must be interrupted.

Tudor A masonry or stucco home modeled after English manor homes built in the 1500s during the Tudor period in England.

Turbine A machine used for producing continuous power in which a wheel or rotor is turned to rotate a generator to produce electricity.

Turned-down footing A concrete foundation system that combines a thickened floor slab at the edge, the stem wall, and footing into one component that is made monolithically.

Two-point perspective A drawing method that takes lines that would have been horizontal in an elevation drawing and places them on angles that merge at two points on the horizon line.

U

U-factor A measure of heat flow through material.

Ultimate strength The unit stress within a member just before it breaks.

Underlayment Thin material, usually plywood, wafer board, or hardboard 3/8 or 1/2" (9 or 13 mm) thick, used to provide a smooth, impact-resistant surface on which to install the finished flooring.

Unified Soils Classification System The system used to describe the texture and grain size of soil in engineering and geology disciplines.

UniFormat An arrangement of construction information based on physical parts of a facility called systems and assemblies.

Unit stress The maximum permissible stress a structural member can resist without failing.

Unity A principle of design related to the common design or decorating pattern that ties a structure together.

Uplift The tendency of structural members to move upward due to wind or seismic pressure.

U-value The coefficient of heat transfer expressed as BATU sq ft/°F of surface area.

V

Valley The internal corner formed between two intersecting roof structures.

Valley rafter A rafter placed at an incline to form a valley between two intersecting roof planes.

Value The darkness or lightness of a hue.

Valve A fitting used to control the flow of fluid or gas to a fixture or appliance.

Vanity A bathroom lavatory fixture that is freestanding or in a cabinet.

Vapor barrier Material used to block the flow of water vapor into a structure—typically 6-mil (0.006") black plastic.

Varge rafter *See* Barge rafter.

Variance A legal request by a property owner to allow a modification from a standard or requirement of the zoning code.

Vault An inclined ceiling area.

Vellum A type of paper specifically designed to accept graphite or ink for drafting.

Veneer A thin outer covering or non-load-bearing masonry face material.

Vent-free fireplace A premanufactured fireplace unit that does not require a venting system.

Ventilation The process of supplying and removing air from a structure.

Vent pipes Pipes that allow air into the waste lines to facilitate drainage. Each plumbing fixture is connected to a vent stack.

Vent stack A vertical pipe of a plumbing system used to equalize pressure within the system and vent sewer gases.

Vent system The system that allows for a continuous flow of air through the system so that gases and odors can dissipate and bacteria do not have an opportunity to develop.

Vertical shear A stress acting on a beam that causes a beam to drop between its supports.

Vestibule A small entrance or lobby.

Vicinity map A map that shows major roads and landmarks surrounding a specific area.

Victorian style A home style that often borrows elements from many other styles of architecture, including partial mansard roofs, arched windows, and towers.

Viewport A CAD option that allows you to see the drawing created in model space and to display the drawing in the layout for plotting.

Villa An upper-class country home.

Virtual reality A computer-simulated world that appears to be real.

Volatile organic compounds (VOCs) Organic chemicals such as formaldehyde that are dangerous to human health or cause harm to the environment.

Volt A unit of measurement of electrical force or potential that makes electricity flow through an electrical wire. For a specific load, the higher the voltage, the more electricity will flow.

W

Wainscot Paneling applied to the lower portion of a wall.

Wallboard Large, flat sheets of gypsum, typically 3/8", 1/2", or 5/8" (9.5, 13, or 16 mm) thick, used to finish interior walls.

Warp Variation from true shape.

Waste pipe A pipe that carries only liquid waste, free of fecal material.

Waste stack A vertical pipe that runs one or more floors and carries the discharge of fixtures other than water closets and similar fixtures.

Water closet A toilet.

Waterproof Material or a type of construction that prevents the absorption of water.

Watt A unit of power measurement based on the potential and the current, determined by multiplying the current (amps) by volts (potential).

Weathering The risk of damage from severe weather.

Weather strip A fabric or plastic material placed along the edges of doors, windows, and skylights to reduce air infiltration.

Web Interior members of the truss that span between the top and bottom chord. On wood I-joists and steel beams, the web is the vertical member between the flanges.

Web stiffener Additional material attached to the web of a steel W- or C-section member to strengthen the member against web crippling.

Weep hole An opening in the bottom course of masonry to allow for drainage.

Weld A method of providing a rigid connection between two or more pieces of steel.

Wet-bulb temperature A measurement of the environment that reflects the physical properties of the surrounding air based on the use of a thermometer that has its bulb wrapped in cloth and draws moisture from the surrounding air.

Wetland Lowland areas such as marshes, swamps, and bogs that in their normal condition are saturated with moisture and therefore provide the natural habitat for certain wildlife.

Wide flange A structural steel beam in the shape of the letter *I*.

Widow's walk A deck above the highest level of the roof from which sea captains' wives supposedly watched for their husbands' ships.

Winders A step that is incorporated into the landing of L- or U-shaped stairs to eliminate the length of the overall run.

Window well A surround placed around the outside of a window that is below or partially below the finish grade to keep the soil from falling against the window. The well also provides a means of egress through the window.

Winter design temperature The average outdoor temperature used to determine a structure's heat loss.

Winter inside design temperature The desired temperature for the inside of the house during winter.

Wire gauge A method of defining wire diameter by a number, with wire diameter increasing as the number gets smaller.

Working drawings The drawings used to obtain a permit for building a structure.

Work triangle The relationship between the work areas formed by drawing lines from the centers of the storage, preparation, and cleaning areas. This triangle outlines the main traffic area required to prepare a meal with food taken from the refrigerator, cleaned at the sink, and cooked at the microwave or stove, and finally, bringing leftovers to the refrigerator.

Wythe A single-unit thickness of a masonry wall.

Y

Yield point The measurement of stress in steel, which corresponds to the limiting value of the usefulness of the material. Once steel is stressed past its yield point, it will not return to its original shape or size.

Z

Zero-clearance fireplace A premanufactured fireplace unit that can be built with little or no clearance between the unit and wood framing.

Zoned heating system A zoned heating system that provides one heater and one thermostat per room, allowing the heater in an unoccupied room to be turned off.

Zoning regulations Regulations that limit the uses of property and the structures that may be built by controlling the use of land, lot sizes, types of structure permitted, building heights, setbacks, and density (the ratio of land area to improvement area).

Index